MEI STRUCTURED MATHEMATICS

RD
TION

A2

tics

Catherine I
Val Hanrah
Roger Pork
Peter Secke

Series Edit

Hodder Murray
A MEMBER OF THE HODDER HEADLINE GROUP

Acknowledgements

We are grateful to the following companies, institutions and individuals who have given permission to reproduce photographs in this book. Every effort has been made to trace and acknowledge ownership of copyright. The publishers will be glad to make suitable arrangements with any copyright holders whom it has not been possible to contact.

OCR, AQA and Edexcel accept no responsibility whatsoever for the accuracy or method of working in the answers given.

Hodder Headline's Policy is to use papers that are natural, renewable and recyclable products and made from wood grown in sustainable forests. The logging and manufacturing processes are expected to conform to the environmental regulations of the country of origin.

Photos
Page 19, David Simson; page 63, Roddy Paine Photographer; page 156, Guinness Records; page 183: left, Mark Ferguson/Life File; right D. Boone/CORBIS; page 194, Phil Cole/Allsport; page 198, Robert Harding; page 209, Marc Garanger/CORBIS; page 224, Jeremy Hoare/Life File; page 253: top, Science Photo Library; bottom, J-C Cuillandre/Canada-France-Hawaii/ Science Photo Library; page 275, Robert Whistler/Life File; page 303, Robert Harding; page 315, Topham Picturepoint; page 332, Hodder Picture Library; page 335, Emma Lee/Life File

Orders: please contact Bookpoint Ltd, 130 Milton Park, Abingdon, Oxon OX14 4TD. Telephone: (44) 01235 827720, Fax: (44) 01235 400454. Lines are open from 9 am to 5 pm, Monday to Saturday, with a 24 hour message answering service. You can also order through our website at *www.hodderheadline.co.uk*

British Library Cataloguing in Publication Data
A catalogue record for this title is available from the The British Library

ISBN-10: 0 340-88851-2
ISBN-13: 978-0-340-88851-3

First Edition Published 1995
Second Edition Published 2000
Third Edition Published 2004
Impression number 10 9 8 7 6 5 4
Year 2010 2009 2008 2007 2006

Typeset by Pantek Arts Ltd, *Maidstone, Kent.*
Printed in Great Britain for Hodder Murray, a member of the Hodder Headline Group, 338 Euston Road, London NW1 3BH by Martins the Printers Ltd, Berwick upon Tweed.

MEI Structured Mathematics

Mathematics is not only a beautiful and exciting subject in its own right but also one that underpins many other branches of learning. It is consequently fundamental to the success of a modern economy.

MEI Structured Mathematics is designed to increase substantially the number of people taking the subject post-GCSE, by making it accessible, interesting and relevant to a wide range of students.

It is a credit accumulation scheme based on 45 hour modules which may be taken individually or aggregated to give Advanced Subsidiary (AS) and Advanced GCE (A Level) qualifications in Mathematics, Further Mathematics and related subjects (like Statistics). The modules may also be used to obtain credit towards other types of qualification.

The course is examined by OCR (previously the Oxford and Cambridge Schools Examination Board) with examinations held in January and June each year.

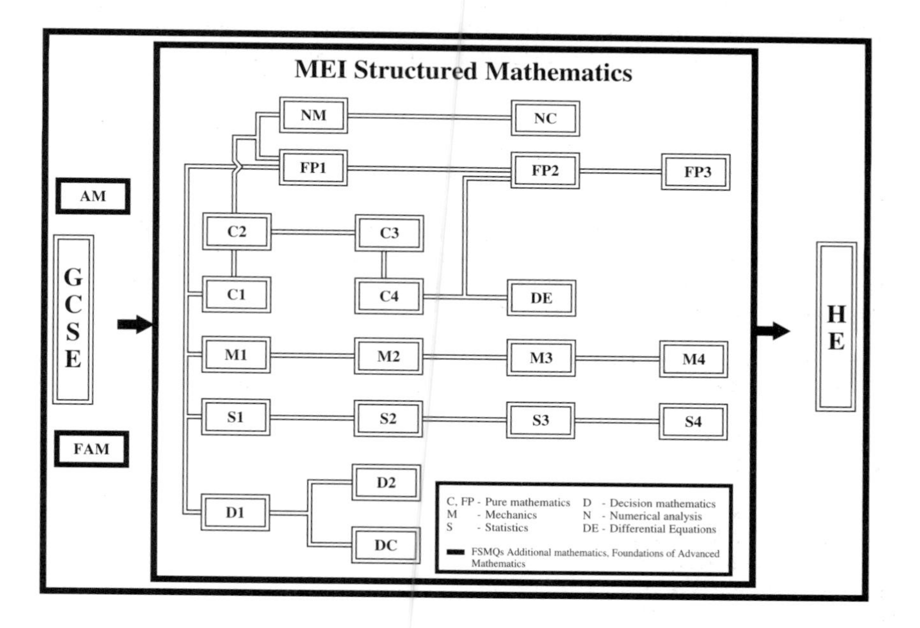

This is one of the series of books written to support the course. Its position within the whole scheme can be seen in the diagram above.

Mathematics in Education and Industry (MEI) is an independent curriculum development body which aims to promote links between education and industry in mathematics. MEI produce relevant examination specifications at GCSE, AS and A Level (including Further Mathematics) and for Free Standing Mathematics Qualifications (FSMQs); these are examined by OCR.

In partnership with Hodder Murray, MEI are responsible for three major series of textbooks: Formula One Maths for Key Stage 3, Hodder Mathematics for GCSE and the MEI Structured Mathematics series, including this book, for AS and A Level.

As well as textbooks, MEI take a leading role in the development of on-line resources to support mathematics. The books in this series are complemented by a major MEI website providing full solutions to the exercises, extra questions including on-line multiple choice tests, interactive demonstrations of the mathematics, schemes of work, and much more.

In recent years MEI have worked hard to promote Further Mathematics and, in conjunction with the DfES, they are now establishing the national network of Further Mathematics Centres.

MEI are committed to supporting the professional development of teachers. In addition to a programme of Continual Professional Development, MEI, in partnership with several universities, co-ordinate the Teaching Advanced Mathematics programme, a course designed to give teachers the skills and confidence to teach A Level mathematics successfully.

Much of the work of MEI is supported by the Gatsby Charitable Foundation.

MEI is a registered charity and a charitable company.

MEI's website and email addresses are www.mei.org.uk *and* office@mei.org.uk.

Introduction

The twelve chapters of this book cover the pure mathematics required for the A2 subject criteria. The material is divided into the two units (or modules) for MEI Structured Mathematics: C3, *Methods for Advanced Mathematics* and C4, *Applications of Advanced Mathematics*. It is the second in a series of pure mathematics books for AS and A Levels in Mathematics and Further Mathematics.

Since their total content is the same, this book also covers the requirements of all the other specifications for A2 Mathematics, and it is also suitable for other courses at this level.

Throughout the series the emphasis is on understanding rather than mere routine calculations, but the varied exercises do nonetheless provide plenty of scope for practising basic techniques. Extensive on-line support is available via the MEI site, *www.mei.org.uk.*

This book is part of the third edition of this series and is written on the assumption that you have already studied AS Mathematics. Much of its content was previously in *Pure Mathematics 2* and *3* but it has now been reorganised to meet the requirements of the new specification being first taught in September 2004. Thanks are due to Val Hanrahan for her work in preparing the new edition and for her original contributions. Thanks are also due to the various examination boards who have given permission for their past questions to be included in the exercises.

Roger Porkess
Series Editor

Key to symbols in this book

This symbol means that you may want to discuss a point with your teacher. If you are working on your own there are answers in the back of the book. It is important, however, that you have a go at answering the questions before looking up the answers if you are to understand the mathematics fully.

This is a warning sign. It is used where a common mistake, misunderstanding or tricky point is being described.

This is the ICT icon. It indicates where you should use a graphic calculator or a computer.

This symbol invites you to join in a discussion about proof. The answers to these questions are given in the back of the book.

This symbol and a dotted line down the right-hand side of the page indicates material which is beyond the criteria for the unit but which is included for completeness.

Harder questions are indicated with stars. Many of these go beyond the usual examination standard.

Contents

Methods for Advanced Mathematics

1 Proof

Mathematics teaches us to solve puzzles. You can claim to be a mathematician if, and only if, you feel that you will be able to solve a puzzle that neither you, nor anyone else, has studied before. That is the test of reasoning.

W W Sawyer

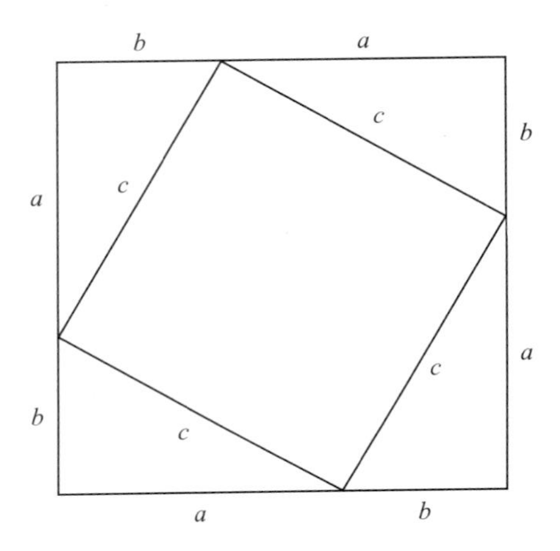

Figure 1.1

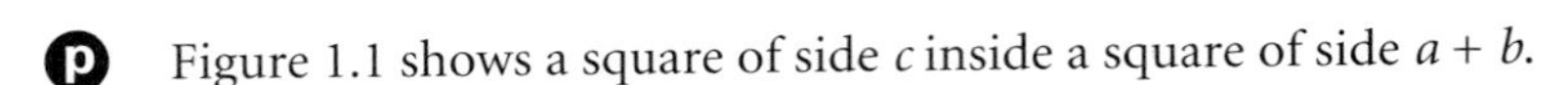

Figure 1.1 shows a square of side c inside a square of side $a + b$.

How can you deduce Pythagoras' theorem ($c^2 = a^2 + b^2$) by finding two ways of expressing the area of the central square?

You have now reached the stage where it is no longer always satisfactory to assume that a fact is true without proving it, since one fact is often used to deduce another. A proof deals with a general case and there are a number of different techniques that you can use. You are invited to participate in discussions about proof at points throughout the rest of the book. They are indicated by the icon **p**.

Proof by direct argument

EXAMPLE 1.1

Prove that the product of an even number and an odd number is always even.

SOLUTION

Here are two examples of 'an even number × an odd number'.

$2 \times 3 = 6 \qquad 8 \times 5 = 40$

In both cases it is true that the right-hand side is even but, however many examples you take, this is still not a proof.

To construct a proof, you need to go back to the definition of an even number; a number that is divisible by 2.

Let m and n represent any two numbers, so $2m$ will be even and $2n + 1$ will be odd.

$$2m \times (2n + 1) = 2[m(2n + 1)]$$

This is a multiple of 2 and so must be even.

Direct proof is often used to prove geometrical theorems, as in Example 1.2.

EXAMPLE 1.2

Prove that the opposite angles of a cyclic quadrilateral are supplementary (add up to 180°).
You may assume the result that the angle subtended by an arc at the centre of a circle is twice the angle subtended by the same arc at the circumference.

SOLUTION

Figure 1.2 shows a circle centre O and a cyclic quadrilateral ABCD.
$\angle ABC = x$ and $\angle ADC = y$.

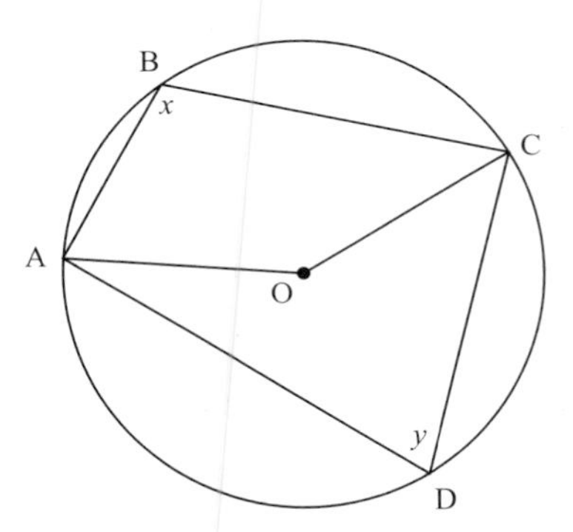

Figure 1.2

Reflex $\angle AOC = 2x$ and obtuse $\angle AOC = 2y$.

Adding the two angles at O gives $2x + 2y = 360°$

$\Rightarrow \quad x + y = 180°$.

The sum of the four angles of any quadrilateral is 360°, so the sum of each pair of opposite angles of a cyclic quadrilateral is 180°.

Proof by exhaustion

For some conjectures it is possible to test all possible cases, as in Example 1.3.

EXAMPLE 1.3

Prove that when a two-digit number is divisible by 3, reversing its digits will also give a number that is divisible by 3.

SOLUTION

There are only 30 two-digit numbers divisible by 3.

12, 15, 18, 21, …, 93, 96, 99

Reversing each of these give the following.

21, 51, 81, 12, …, 39, 69, 99

These numbers are also divisible by 3, so the conjecture has been proved.

Note

There is a well-known result on divisibility that includes the conjecture above.

A number is divisible by 3 if and only if the sum of its digits is divisible by 3.

Similarly:

A number is divisible by 9 if and only if the sum of its digits is divisible by 9.

Proof by contradiction

In some cases it is possible to deduce a result by showing that the converse is impossible, as in the following examples.

EXAMPLE 1.4

Prove that the sum of the interior angles x and y for a pair of parallel lines, as shown in figure 1.3, is 180°.

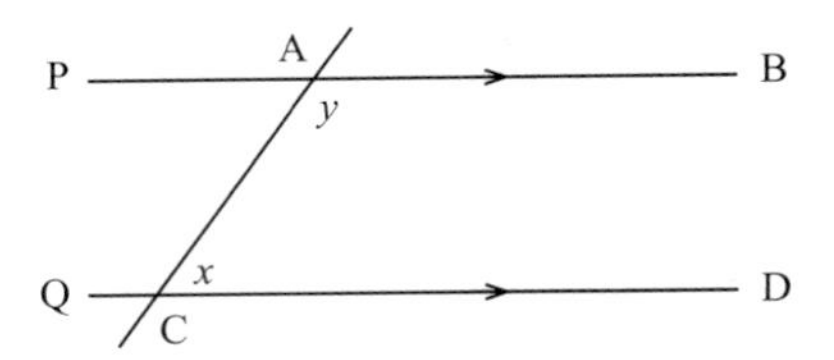

Figure 1.3

SOLUTION

Assume that $x + y < 180°$ as in figure 1.4.

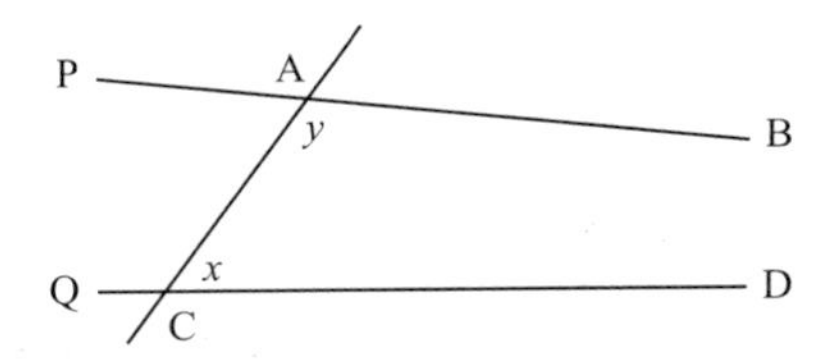

Figure 1.4

In this case the lines AB and CD, when extended, will meet at a point E, where $\angle BED = 180° - x - y$.

This means that AB and CD are not parallel.

Similarly, assuming that $x + y > 180°$, as in figure 1.5, will give angles $(180° - x)$ and $(180° - y)$ with a sum of $(360° - (x + y))$.

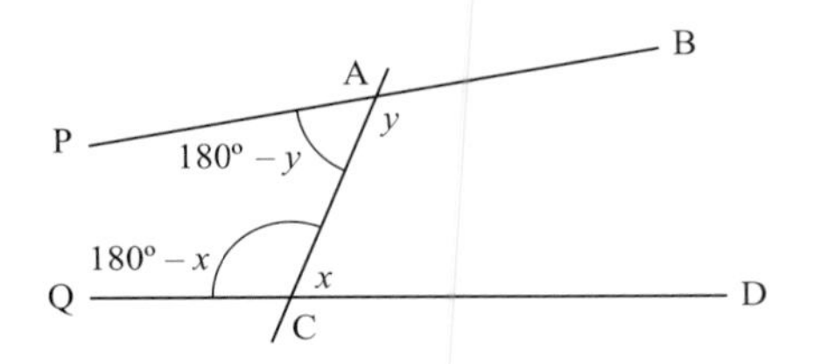

Figure 1.5

$360° - (x + y) < 180°$, so now AP and CQ when extended will meet at a point R, showing that AP and CQ are not parallel.

Consequently, $x + y = 180°$.

EXAMPLE 1.5

Prove that $\sqrt{2}$ is irrational.

SOLUTION

Assume that $\sqrt{2}$ is rational, so $\sqrt{2} = \frac{m}{n}$ where m and n have no common factor.

Squaring $\Rightarrow \quad 2 = \frac{m^2}{n^2}$

$\Rightarrow \quad 2n^2 = m^2 \qquad ①$

Since $2n^2$ is a multiple of 2, it is even, so m^2 is even.

Since m^2 is even, so is m.

Let $m = 2p$.

In equation ① this gives

$$2n^2 = (2p)^2 = 4p^2,$$

so

$$n^2 = 2p^2.$$

Continuing with the same argument as before, $2p^2$ is a multiple of 2, and therefore even, so n^2 and therefore n are even.

You have now shown that both m and n are even numbers, which contradicts the assumption that m and n had no common factor.

Consequently, $\sqrt{2}$ is not rational, so must be irrational.

Disproof by the use of a counter-example

Sometimes you may come across a conjecture that looks as if it might be true, but is in fact false. Always start by checking the result for a few particular values, to try and get a 'feel' for what is happening. Next, if you think that it is true, you could try to prove it using any of the methods discussed earlier. If you seem to be getting nowhere, then finding just one case, a *counter-example*, when it fails is sufficient to disprove it.

EXAMPLE 1.6

Is it true that any number whose square is the sum of two squares is itself the sum of two squares?
Either prove it or find a counter-example.

SOLUTION

Pythagorean triples, such as (3, 4, 5), (5, 12, 13) and (8, 15, 17) form the basis of this conjecture.

Checking a few of these:

$$5 = 1^2 + 2^2$$
$$13 = 2^2 + 3^2$$
$$17 = 1^2 + 4^2$$

So it seems possible that this could be true.

However, looking at multiples of some of the basic triples gives you a counter-example. One of these is (9, 12, 15).

$$15^2 = 9^2 + 12^2$$

15 can be written as $1 + 14$ or $2 + 13$ or $3 + 12$ or $4 + 11$ or $5 + 10$ or $6 + 9$ or $7 + 8$ showing that 15 cannot be written as the sum of two squares.

Historical note

This is one of a number of results proposed by Charles Dodgson who, under the nom-de-plume of Lewis Carroll, wrote *Alice in Wonderland*.

EXERCISE 1A

In each question a conjecture is given. Decide whether it is true or false.
If it is true, prove it using a suitable method and name the method.
If it is false, give a counter-example.

1 $(a + b)^2 - (a - b)^2 = 4ab$

2 The triangle with sides of length $\sqrt{2n+1}$, n and $(n + 1)$ is right-angled.

3 No square number ends in a 8.

4 The sum of the squares of any two consecutive integers is an odd number.

5 $\sqrt{3}$ is irrational.

6 If T is a triangular number (given by $T = \frac{1}{2}n(n+1)$ where n is an integer), then
 (i) $9T + 1$ is a triangular number
 (ii) $8T + 1$ is a square number.

7 **(i)** A four-digit number formed by writing down two digits and then repeating them is divisible by 101.
 (ii) A four-digit number formed by writing down two digits and then reversing them is divisible by 11.

8 The value of $(n^2 + n + 11)$ is a prime number for all positive integer values of n.

9 **(i)** The sum of the squares of any five consecutive integers is divisible by 5.
 (ii) The sum of the squares of any four consecutive integers is divisible by 4.

10 For any pair of numbers x and y, $2(x^2 + y^2)$ is the sum of two squares.

KEY POINTS

The methods of proof are

1 proof by direct argument

2 proof by exhaustion

3 proof by contradiction.

The methods of disproof are

4 disproof by direct argument

5 disproof by the use of a counter-example.

2 Natural logarithms and exponentials

Normally speaking it may be said that the forces of a capitalist society, if left unchecked, tend to make the rich richer and the poor poorer and thus increase the gap between them.

Jawaharlal Nehru

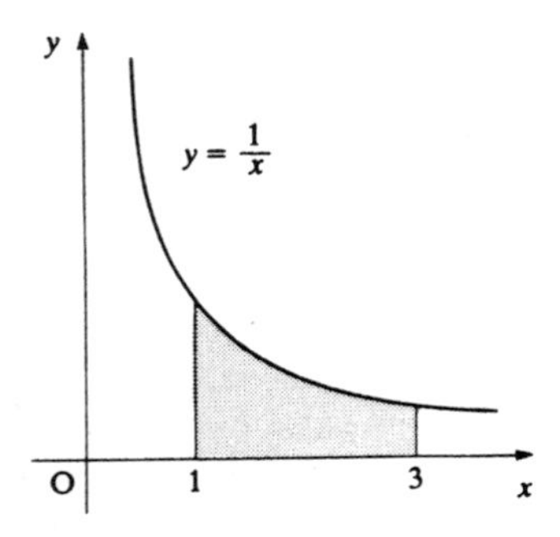

Figure 2.1

The shaded region in figure 2.1 is bounded by the x axis, the lines $x = 1$ and $x = 3$, and the curve $y = \frac{1}{x}$. The area of this region may be represented by $\int_1^3 \frac{1}{x} \mathrm{d}x$.

❓ Explain why you cannot apply the rule

$$\int kx^n \, \mathrm{d}x = \frac{kx^{n+1}}{n+1} + c$$

to this integral.

However, the area in the diagram clearly has a definite value, and so we need to find ways to express and calculate it.

INVESTIGATION

Estimate, using numerical integration (for example the trapezium rule), the areas represented by these integrals.

(i) $\int_1^3 \frac{1}{x} \mathrm{d}x$ **(ii)** $\int_1^2 \frac{1}{x} \mathrm{d}x$ **(iii)** $\int_1^6 \frac{1}{x} \mathrm{d}x$

What relationship can you see between your answers?

A new function

The area under the curve $y = \frac{1}{x}$ between $x = 1$ and $x = a$, that is $\int_1^a \frac{1}{x}\,\mathrm{d}x$, depends on the value a. For every value of a (greater than 1) there is a definite value of the area. Consequently, the area is a function of a.

To investigate this function you need to give it a name, say L, so that $\mathrm{L}(a)$ is the area from 1 to a and $\mathrm{L}(x)$ is the area from 1 to x. Then look at the properties of $\mathrm{L}(x)$ to see if its behaviour is like that of any other function with which you are familiar.

The investigation you have just done should have suggested to you that

$$\int_1^3 \frac{1}{x}\,\mathrm{d}x + \int_1^2 \frac{1}{x}\,\mathrm{d}x = \int_1^6 \frac{1}{x}\,\mathrm{d}x.$$

This can now be written as

$$\mathrm{L}(3) + \mathrm{L}(2) = \mathrm{L}(6).$$

This suggests a possible law, that

$$\mathrm{L}(a) + \mathrm{L}(b) = \mathrm{L}(ab).$$

At this stage this is just a conjecture, based on one particular example. To prove it, you need to take the general case and this is done in the activity below. (At first reading you may prefer to leave the activity, accepting that the result can be proved.)

ACTIVITY 2.1 Prove that $\mathrm{L}(a) + \mathrm{L}(b) = \mathrm{L}(ab)$, by following the steps below.

p

(i) Explain, with the aid of a diagram, why

$$\mathrm{L}(a) + \int_a^{ab} \frac{1}{x}\,\mathrm{d}x = \mathrm{L}(ab).$$

(ii) Now call $x = az$, so that $\mathrm{d}x$ can be replaced by $a\mathrm{d}z$. Show that

$$\int_a^{ab} \frac{1}{x}\,\mathrm{d}x = \int_1^b \frac{1}{z}\,\mathrm{d}z.$$

Explain why $\int_1^b \frac{1}{z}\,\mathrm{d}z = \mathrm{L}(b)$.

(iii) Use the results from 1 and 2 to show that

$$\mathrm{L}(a) + \mathrm{L}(b) = \mathrm{L}(ab).$$

What function has this property? Look back to *AS Pure Mathematics*, Chapter 11, and you will see that for all logarithms

$$\log(a) + \log(b) = \log(ab).$$

Could it be that this is a logarithmic function?

ACTIVITY 2.2 Satisfy yourself that the function has the following properties of logarithms.

(i) $L(1) = 0$ **(ii)** $L(a) - L(b) = L\left(\frac{a}{b}\right)$ **(iii)** $L(a^n) = nL(a)$

The base of the logarithm function L(*x*)

Having accepted that L(x) is indeed a logarithmic function, the remaining problem is to find the base of the logarithm. By convention this is denoted by the letter e. A further property of logarithms is that for any base p

$$\log_p p = 1 \quad (p > 1).$$

So to find the base e, you need to find the point such that the area, L(e) under the graph, is 1. See figure 2.2.

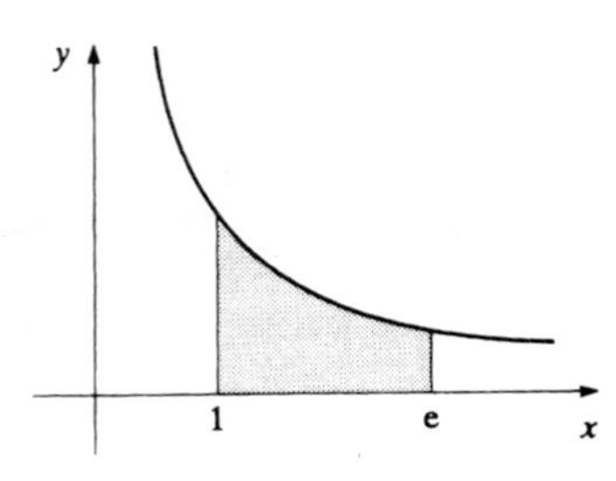

Figure 2.2

You have already estimated the value of L(2) to be about 0.7 and that of L(3) to be about 1.1 so clearly the value of e is between 2 and 3.

ACTIVITY 2.3 You will need a calculator with an area-finding facility, or other suitable technology, to do this. If you do not have this, read on.

Use the fact that $\int_1^e \frac{1}{x}\,dx = 1$ to find the value of e, knowing that it lies between 2 and 3, to 2 decimal places.

The value of e is given to 9 decimal places in the key points on page 18. Like π, e is a number which occurs naturally within mathematics. It is irrational: when written as a decimal, it never terminates and has no recurring pattern.

The function L(x) is thus the logarithm of x to the base e, $\log_e x$. This is often called the natural logarithm of x, and written as $\ln x$.

Values of *x* between 0 and 1

So far it has been assumed that the value of x within $\ln x$ is greater than 1. As an example of a value of x between 0 and 1, look at $\ln \frac{1}{2}$.

$$\text{Since} \quad \ln\left(\frac{a}{b}\right) = \ln a - \ln b$$

$$\Rightarrow \quad \ln\left(\frac{1}{2}\right) = \ln 1 - \ln 2$$

$$= -\ln 2 \quad (\text{since } \ln 1 = 0).$$

In the same way, you can show that for any value of x between 0 and 1, the value of $\ln x$ is negative.

When the value of x is very close to zero, the value of $\ln x$ is a large negative number.

$$\ln\left(\frac{1}{1000}\right) = -\ln 1000 = -6.9$$

$$\ln\left(\frac{1}{1\,000\,000}\right) = -\ln 1\,000\,000 = -13.8$$

So as $x \rightarrow 0$, $\ln x \rightarrow -\infty$ (for positive values of x).

The natural logarithm function

The graph of the natural logarithm function (shown in figure 2.3) has the characteristic shape of all logarithmic functions, and like other such functions it is only defined for $x > 0$. The value of $\ln x$ increases without limit, but ever more slowly: it has been described as 'the slowest way to get to infinity'.

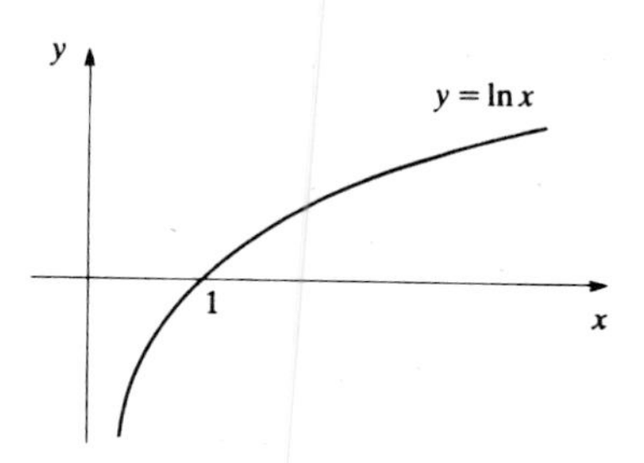

Figure 2.3

Historical note

Logarithms were discovered independently by John Napier (1550–1617), who lived at Merchiston Castle in Edinburgh, and Jolst Bürgi (1552–1632) from Switzerland. It is generally believed that Napier had the idea first, and so he is credited with their discovery. Natural logarithms are also called Naperian logarithms but there is no basis for this since Napier's logarithms were definitely not the same as natural logarithms. Napier was deeply involved in the political and religious events of his day and mathematics and science were little more than hobbies for him. He was a man of remarkable ingenuity and imagination and also drew plans for war chariots that look very like modern tanks, and for submarines.

The exponential function

Making x the subject of $y = \ln x$, using the theory of logarithms developed in *AS Pure Mathematics*, Chapter 11, you obtain $x = e^y$.

Interchanging x and y, which has the effect of reflecting the graph in the line $y = x$, gives the *exponential function* $y = e^x$.

The graphs of the logarithm function and its inverse are shown in figure 2.4.

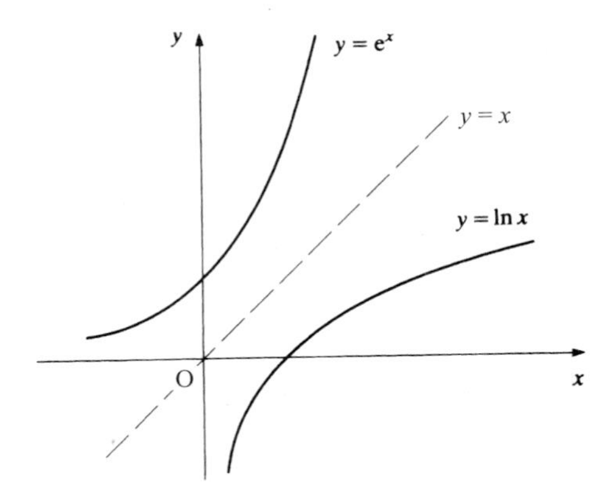

Figure 2.4

You will see in Chapter 3 that reflecting in the line $y = x$ gives an *inverse* function, so it follows that e^x and $\ln x$ are each the inverse of the other.

Notice that $e^{(\ln x)} = x$, using the definition of logarithms, and

$$\ln(e^x) = x \ln e = x.$$

Although the function e^x is called *the* exponential function, in fact any function of the form a^x is exponential. Figure 2.5 shows several exponential curves.

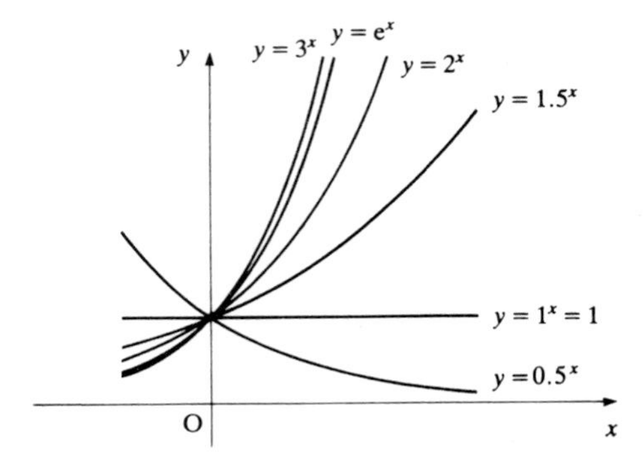

Figure 2.5

The exponential function $y = e^x$ increases at an ever-increasing rate. This is described as exponential growth.

By contrast, the graph of $y = e^{-x}$, shown in figure 2.6, approaches the x axis ever more slowly as x increases: this is called exponential decay.

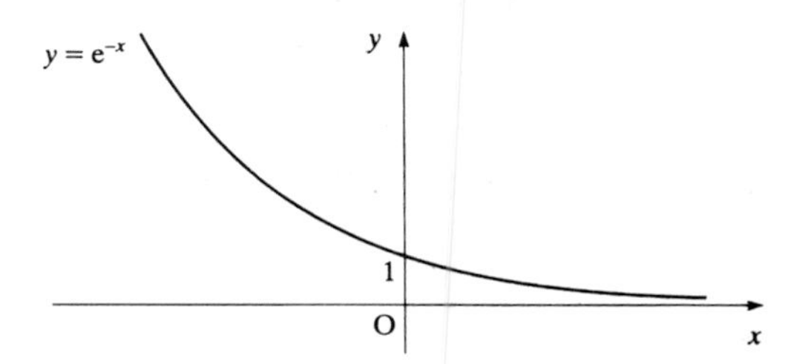

Figure 2.6

You will meet e^x and $\ln x$ again later in this book. In Chapter 4 you learn how to differentiate these functions and in Chapter 5 you learn how to integrate them. In this secion you focus on practical applications which require you to use the [ln] button on your calculator.

EXAMPLE 2.1

The number, N, of insects in a colony is given by $N = 2000e^{0.1t}$ where t is the number of days after observations have begun.

(i) Sketch the graph of N against t.

(ii) What is the population of the colony after 20 days?

(iii) How long does it take the colony to reach a population of 10 000?

SOLUTION

(i)

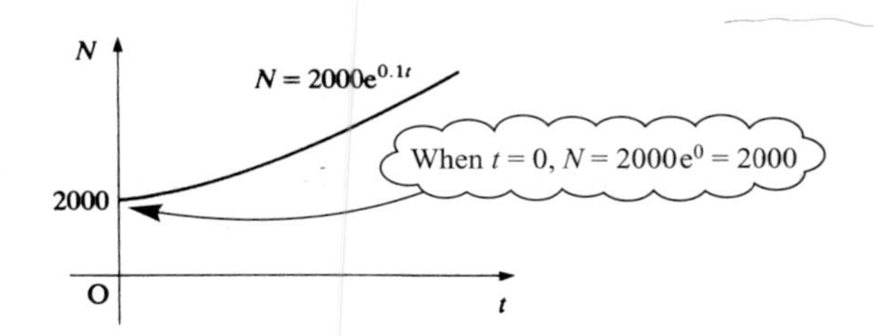

Figure 2.7

(ii) When $t = 20$, $\quad N = 2000e^{0.1 \times 20} = 14\,778$.

The population is 14 778 insects.

(iii) When $N = 10\,000$, $\quad 10\,000 = 2000\,e^{0.1t}$

$$5 = e^{0.1t}.$$

Taking natural logarithms of both sides,

$$\ln 5 = \ln(e^{0.1t}) = 0.1t$$

Remember $\ln(e^x) = x$.

and so $\quad t = 10 \ln 5 = 16.09\ldots$.

It takes just over 16 days for the population to reach 10 000.

EXAMPLE 2.2

The radioactive mass, Mg in a lump of material is given by $M = 25e^{-0.0012t}$ where t is the time in seconds since the first observation.

exponential decay (−)

(i) Sketch the graph of M against t.

(ii) What is the initial size of the mass?

(iii) What is the mass after 1 hour?

(iv) The half-life of a radioactive substance is the time it takes to decay to half of its mass. What is the half-life of this material?

SOLUTION

(i)

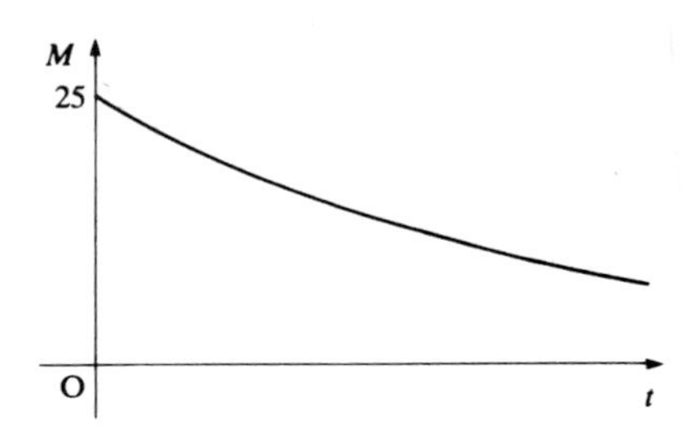

Figure 2.8

(ii) When $t = 0$, $M = 25e^0$
$= 25$.

The initial mass is 25 g.

(iii) After 1 hour, $t = 3600$
$M = 25e^{-0.0012 \times 3600}$.

The mass after 1 hour is 0.33 g (to 2 decimal places).

(iv) The initial mass is 25 g, so after one half-life,

$$M = \tfrac{1}{2} \times 25 = 12.5\,\text{g}.$$

At this point the value of t is given by

$$12.5 = 25e^{-0.0012t}.$$

Dividing both sides by 25 gives

$$0.5 = e^{-0.0012t}.$$

Taking logarithms of both sides:

$$\begin{aligned} \ln 0.5 &= \ln e^{-0.0012t} \\ &= -0.0012t \\ \Rightarrow \quad t &= \frac{\ln 0.5}{-0.0012} \\ &= 577.6 \text{ (to 1 decimal place).} \end{aligned}$$

The half-life is 577.6 seconds. (This is just under 10 minutes, so the substance is highly radioactive.)

EXAMPLE 2.3

Make p the subject of $\ln(p) - \ln(1-p) = t$.

SOLUTION

Using $\log a - \log b = \log\left(\frac{a}{b}\right)$

$$\ln\left(\frac{p}{1-p}\right) = t$$

Writing both sides as powers of e gives

Remember $e^{\ln x} = x$

$$e^{\ln\left(\frac{p}{1-p}\right)} = e^t$$

$$\Rightarrow \quad \frac{p}{1-p} = e^t$$

$$p = e^t(1-p)$$

$$p = e^t - pe^t$$

$$p + pe^t = e^t$$

$$p(1+e^t) = e^t$$

$$p = \frac{e^t}{1+e^t}.$$

EXERCISE 2A

1 Make x the subject of $\ln x - \ln x_0 = kt$.

2 Make t the subject of $s = s_0 e^{-kt}$.

3 Make p the subject of $\ln p = -0.02t$.

4 Make x the subject of $y - 5 = (y_0 - 5)e^x$.

5 A colony of humans settles on a previously uninhabited planet. After t years, their population, P, is given by

$$P = 100e^{0.05t}.$$

(i) Sketch the graph of P against t.
(ii) How many settlers land on the planet initially?
(iii) What is the population after 50 years?
(iv) How long does it take the population to reach 1 million?

6 Ela sits on a swing. Her father pulls it back and then releases it. The swing returns to its maximum backwards displacement once every 5 seconds, but the maximum displacement, $\theta°$, becomes progressively smaller because of friction. At time t seconds, θ is given by

$$\theta = 25e^{-0.03t} \quad (t = 0, 5, 10, 15, \ldots).$$

(i) Plot the values of θ for $0 \leqslant t \leqslant 30$ on graph paper.
(ii) To what angle did Ela's father pull the swing?
(iii) What is the value of θ after 1 minute?
(iv) After how many swings is the angle θ less than 1°?

7 Alexander lives 800 metres from school. One morning he sets out at 8.00 am and t minutes later the distance s m, which he has walked is given by

$$s = 800\,(1 - e^{-0.1t}).$$

(i) Sketch the graph of s against t.

(ii) How far has Alexander walked by 8.15 am?

(iii) What time is it when Alexander is half-way to school?

(iv) When does Alexander get to school?

8 A parachutist jumps out of an aircraft and some time later opens the parachute. His speed at time t seconds from when the parachute opens is $v\,\text{ms}^{-1}$. It is given by

$$v = 8 + 22\,e^{-0.07t}.$$

(i) Sketch the graph of v against t.

(ii) State the speed of the parachutist when the parachute opens, and the final speed that he would attain if he jumped from a very great height.

(iii) Find the value of v as the parachutist lands, 60 seconds later.

(iv) Find the value of t when the parachutist is travelling at $20\,\text{ms}^{-1}$.

9 The height h metres of a species of pine tree t years after planting is modelled by the equation

$$h = 20 - 19 \times 0.9^t.$$

(i) What is the height of the trees when they are planted?

(ii) Calculate the height of the trees after 2 years, and the time taken for the height to reach 10 metres.

The relationship between the market value £y of the timber from the tree and the height h metres of the tree is modelled by the equation

$$y = ah^b,$$

where a and b are constants. The diagram shows the graph of $\ln y$ plotted against $\ln h$.

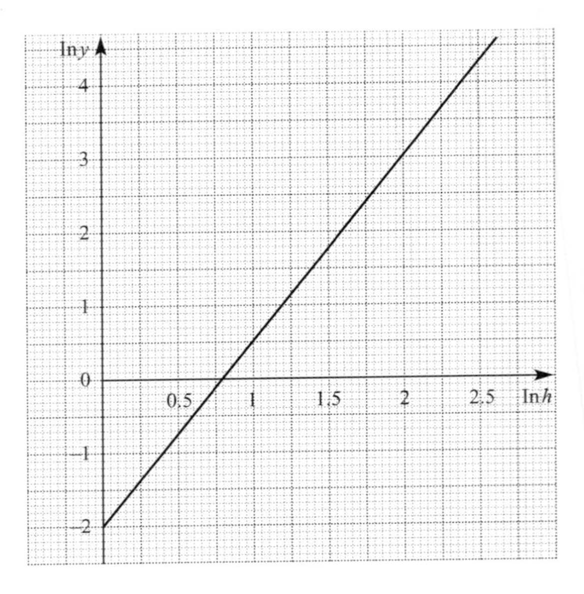

(iii) Use the graph to calculate the values of a and b.

(iv) Calculate how long it takes to grow trees worth £100.

[MEI]

10 A new car is tested for the amount of petrol it uses.
Suppose the rate of consumption at v miles per hour (mph) is p miles per gallon.

At a steady 49 mph, its rate of consumption is 45 miles per gallon.
At a steady 81 mph, its rate of consumption is 35 miles per gallon.

One model for the petrol consumption is

$$p = ab^v,$$

where a and b are positive constants.

(i) Show that plotting $\ln p$ against v gives a straight line graph if this model is appropriate.

(ii) The diagram shows a straight line drawn through the points $(49, \ln 45)$ and $(81, \ln 35)$.
Use the graph to find the petrol consumption of the car at 25 mph and at 64 mph according to this model.

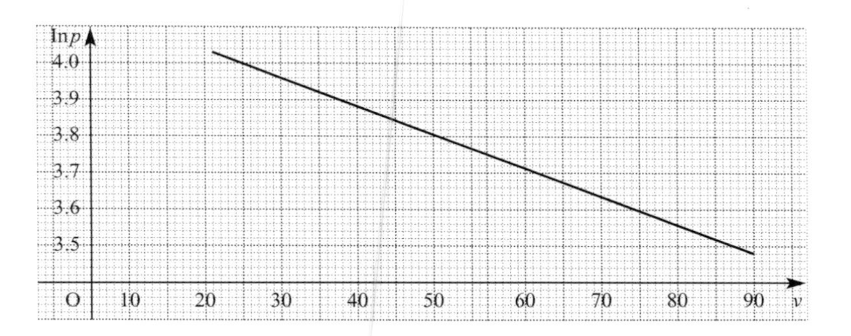

An alternative model for the petrol consumption is

$$p = cv^{-d},$$

where c and d are positive constants.

(iii) Show that, using this model,

$$d = \frac{\ln 45 - \ln 35}{\ln 81 - \ln 49}.$$

Use the laws of logarithms to simplify this expression, and hence show that $d = \frac{1}{2}$.
Show also that $c = 315$.

Find the petrol consumption of the car at 25 mph and at 64 mph according to this model.

(iv) Further testing of the car yields the results $v = 25$, $p = 55$ and $v = 64$, $p = 40$.
Comment on the suitability of the two models.

[MEI]

KEY POINTS

1. $\int \frac{1}{x}\,\mathrm{d}x = \log_e |x| + c.$
2. $\log_e x$ is called the natural logarithm of x and denoted by $\ln x$.
3. $\mathrm{e} = 2.718\,281\,828\,4 \ldots$ is the base of natural logarithms.
4. e^x and $\ln x$ are inverse functions: $\mathrm{e}^{\ln x} = x$; $\ln(\mathrm{e}^x) = x$.

3 Functions

Still glides the stream and shall forever glide;
The form remains, the function never dies.

William Wordsworth

Why fly to Geneva in January?

Several people arriving at Geneva airport from London were asked the main purpose of their visit. Their answers were recorded.

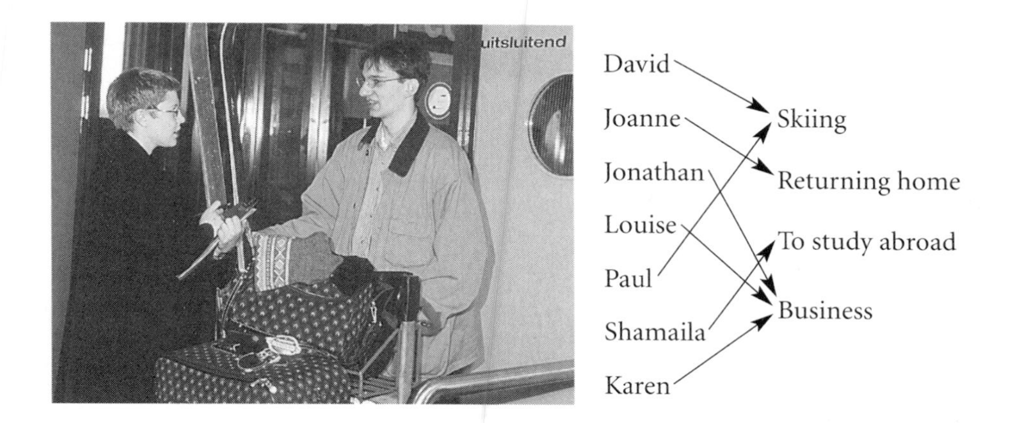

This is an example of a *mapping*.

The language of functions

A mapping is any rule which associates two sets of items. In this example, each of the names on the left is an *object*, or *input*, and each of the reasons on the right is an *image*, or *output*.

For a mapping to make sense or to have any practical application, the inputs and outputs must each form a natural collection or set. The set of possible inputs (in this case, all of the people who flew to Geneva from London in January) is called the *domain* of the mapping. The set of possible outputs (in this case, the set of all possible reasons for flying to Geneva) is called the *co-domain* of the mapping.

The seven people questioned in this example gave a set of four reasons, or outputs. These form the *range* of the mapping for this particular set of inputs. The range of any mapping forms part or all of its co-domain.

Notice that Jonathan, Louise and Karen are all visiting Geneva on business: each person gave only one reason for the trip, but the same reason was given by several people. This mapping is said to be *many-to-one*. A mapping can also be *one-to-one*, *one-to-many* or *many-to-many*. The relationship between the people and their UK passport numbers will be one-to-one. The relationship between the people and their items of luggage is likely to be one-to-many, and that between the people and the countries they have visited in the last 10 years will be many-to-many.

Mappings

In mathematics, many (but not all) mappings can be expressed using algebra. Here are some examples of mathematical mappings.

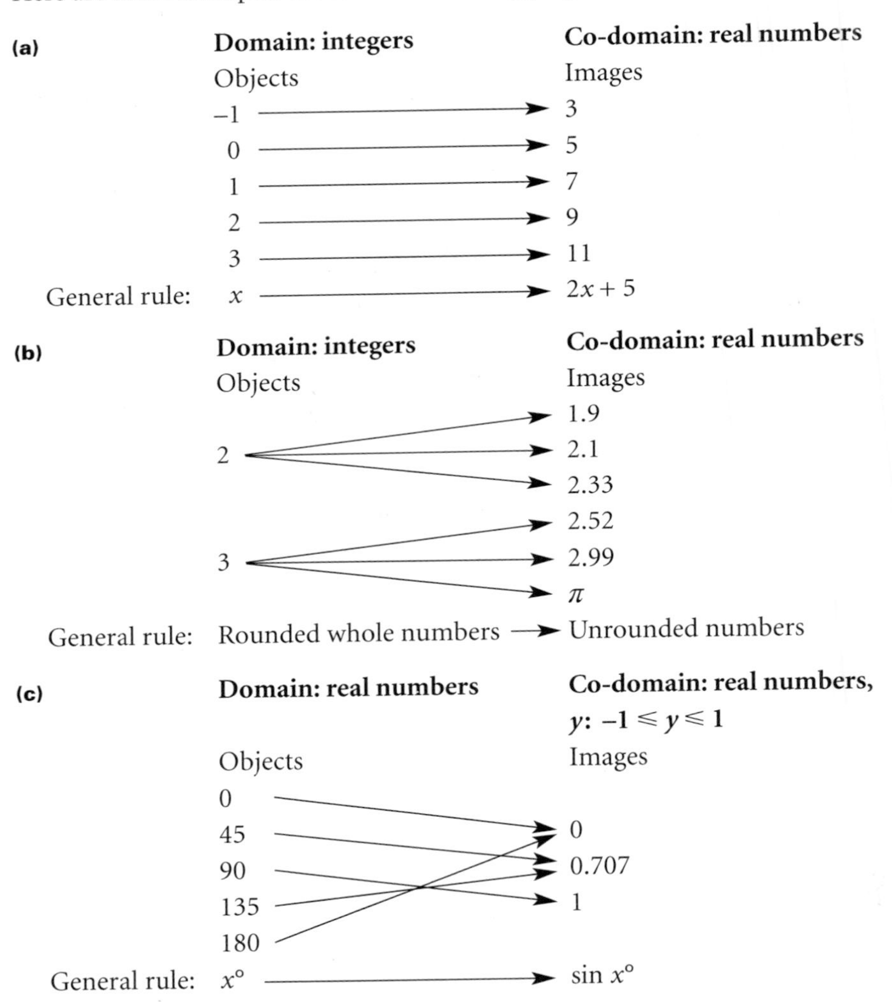

(d) **Domain: quadratic equations with real roots** — **Co-domain: real numbers**

Objects	Images
$x^2 - 4x + 3 = 0$	0
$x^2 - x = 0$	1
$x^2 - 3x + 2 = 0$	2
	3

($x^2 - 4x + 3 = 0 \to 1, 3$; $x^2 - x = 0 \to 0, 1$; $x^2 - 3x + 2 = 0 \to 1, 2$)

General rule: $ax^2 + bx + c = 0 \to x = \dfrac{-b - \sqrt{b^2 - 4ac}}{2a}$, $x = \dfrac{-b + \sqrt{b^2 - 4ac}}{2a}$

? For each of the examples above:

(i) decide whether the mapping is one-to-one, many-to-many, one-to-many or many-to-one

(ii) take a different set of inputs and identify the corresponding range.

Functions

Mappings which are one-to-one or many-to-one are of particular importance, since in these cases there is only one possible image for any object. Mappings of these types are called *functions*. For example, $x \to x^2$ and $x \to \cos x°$ are both functions, because in each case for any value of x there is only one possible answer. The mapping of rounded whole numbers on to unrounded numbers is not a function, since, for example, the rounded number 5 could be the image of any unrounded number between 4.5 and 5.5.

There are several different but equivalent ways of writing a function. For example, the function which maps x on to x^2 can be written in any of the following ways.

- $y = x^2$
- $f(x) = x^2$
- $f{:}x \to x^2$

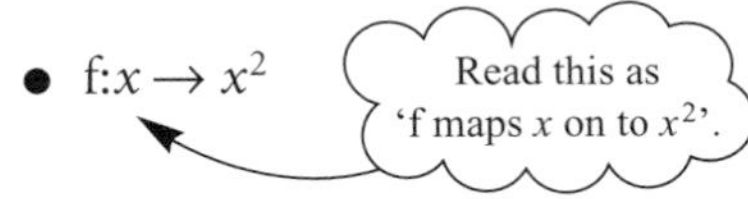

It is often helpful to represent a function graphically, as in the following example, which also illustrates the importance of knowing the domain.

EXAMPLE 3.1

Sketch the graph of $y = 3x + 2$ when the domain of x is

(i) $x \in \mathbb{R}$

(ii) $x \in \mathbb{R}^+$ (i.e. positive real numbers)

(iii) $x \in \mathbb{N}$.

SOLUTION

(i) When the domain is $\mathbb{R}$, all values of y are possible. The range is therefore $\mathbb{R}$, also.

(ii) When x is restricted to positive values, all the values of y are greater than 2, so the range is $y > 2$.

(iii) In this case the range is the set of points $\{2, 5, 8, \ldots\}$. These are clearly all of the form $3x + 2$ where x is a natural number $(0, 1, 2, \ldots)$. This set can be written neatly as $\{3x + 2 : x \in \mathbb{N}\}$.

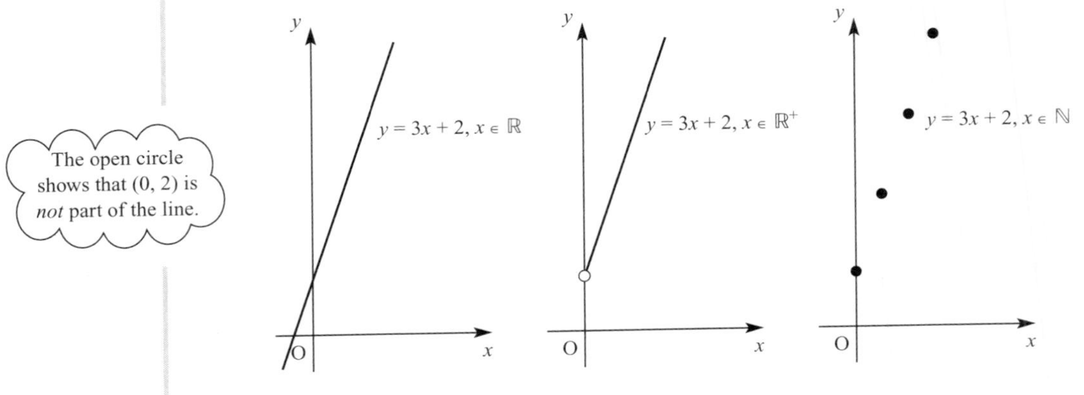

Figure 3.1

When you draw the graph of a mapping, the x co-ordinate of each point is an input value, the y co-ordinate is the corresponding output value. The table below shows this for the mapping $x \rightarrow x^2$, or $y = x^2$, and figure 3.2 shows the resulting points on a graph.

Input (x)	Output (y)	Point plotted
−2	4	(−2, 4)
−1	1	(−1, 1)
0	0	(0, 0)
1	1	(1, 1)
2	4	(2, 4)

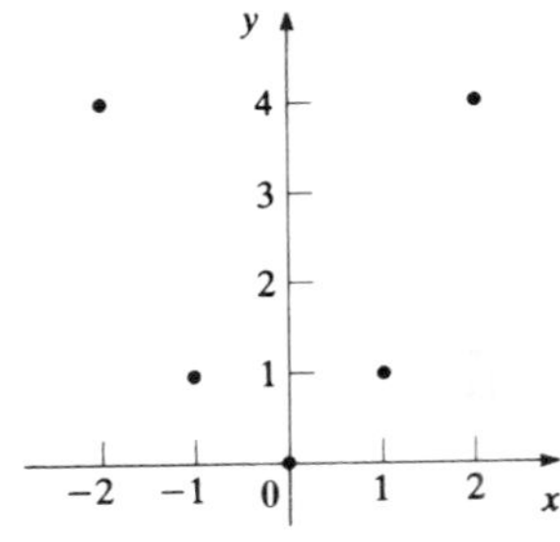

Figure 3.2

If the mapping is a function, there is one and only one value of y for every value of x in the domain. Consequently the graph of a function is a simple curve or line going from left to right, with no doubling back.

Figure 3.3 illustrates some different types of mapping. The graphs in **(a)** and **(b)** illustrate functions, those in **(c)** and **(d)** do not.

(a) One-to-one

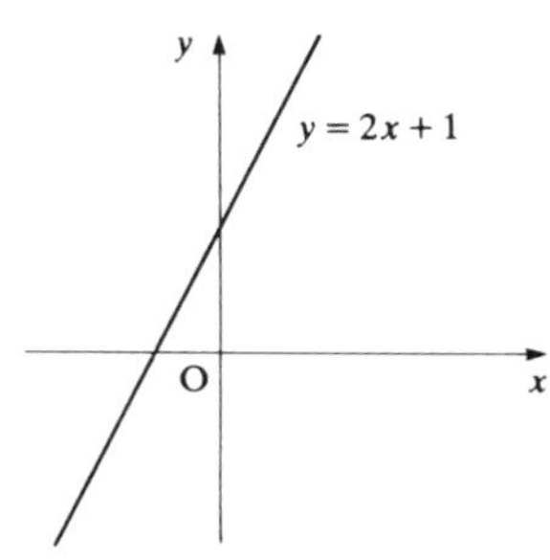

(b) Many-to-one

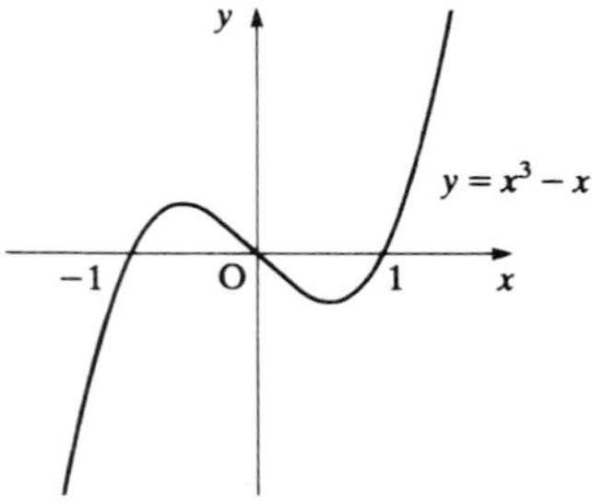

(c) One-to-many

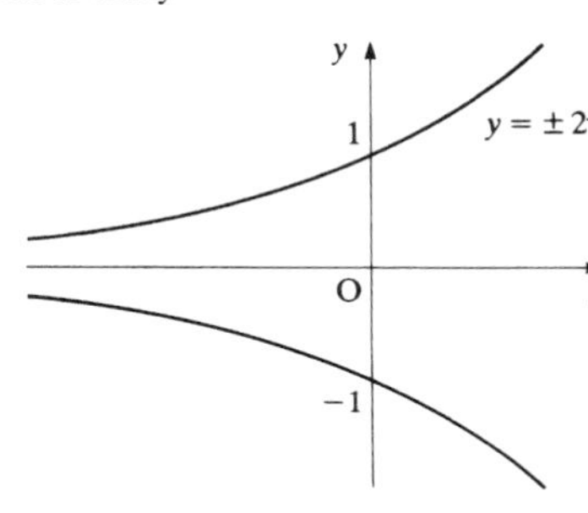

(d) Many-to-many

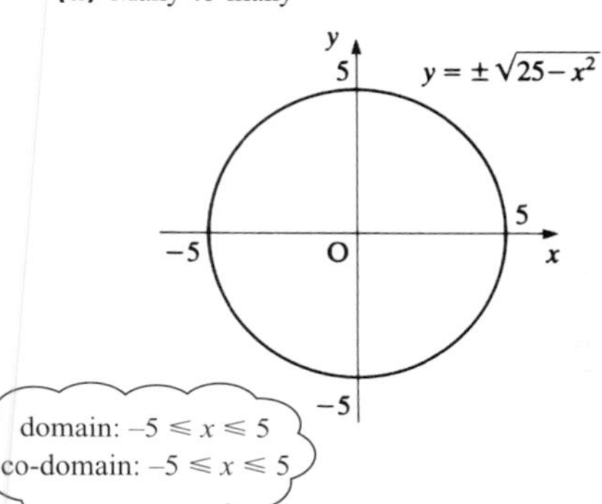

Figure 3.3

EXERCISE 3A

1 Describe each of the following mappings as either one-to-one, many-to-one, one-to-many or many-to-many, and say whether it represents a function. In each case state whether the co-domain and range are equal.

(i)

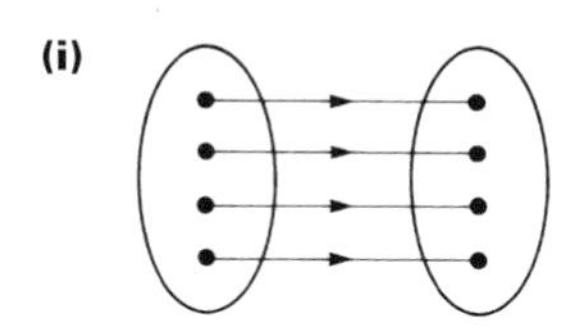

(ii)

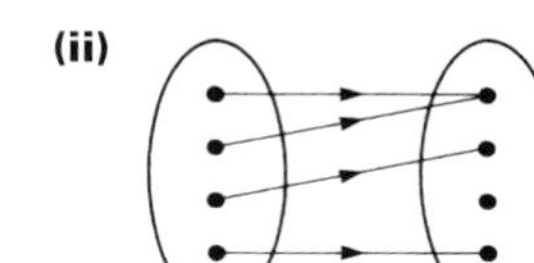

(iii)

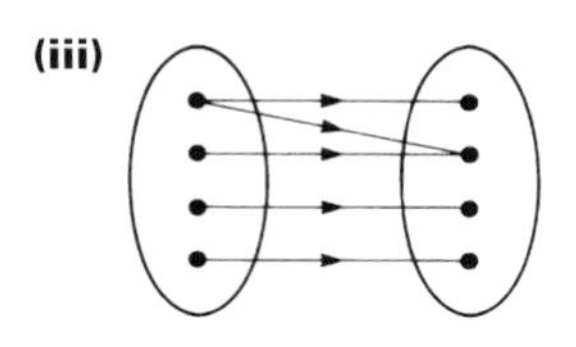

(iv)

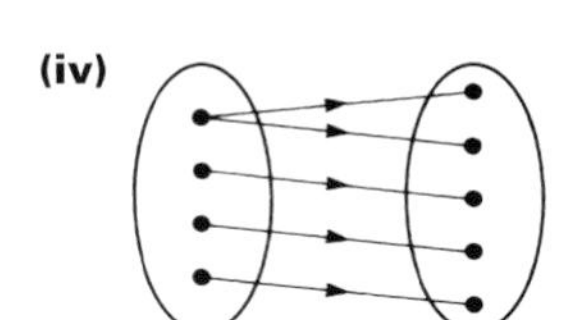

(v)

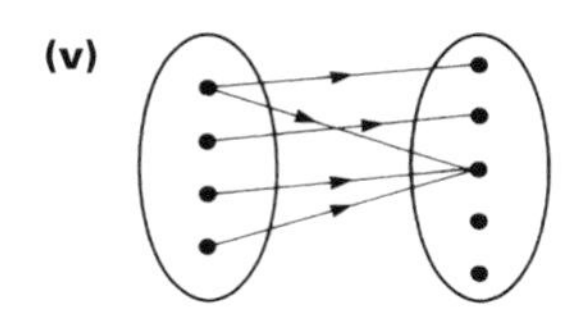

(vi)

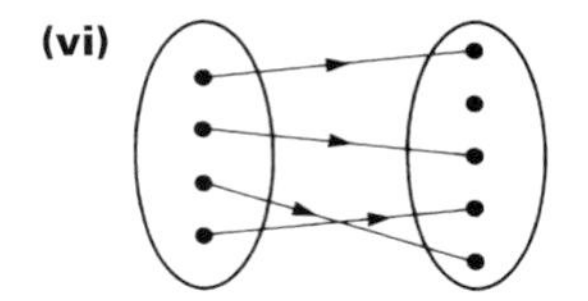

(vii)

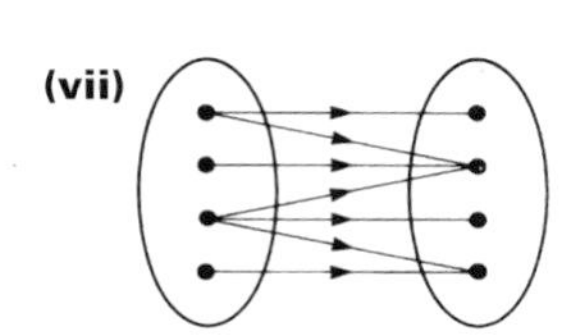

(viii)

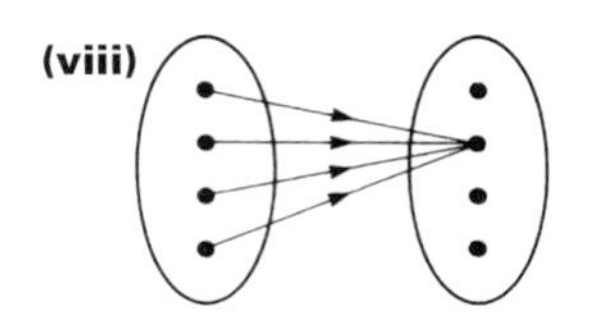

2 For each of the following mappings:

(a) write down a few examples of inputs and corresponding outputs
(b) state the type of mapping (one-to-one, many-to-one, etc.)
(c) suggest suitable domains and co-domains.

(i) Words $\longrightarrow$ number of letters they contain
(ii) Side of a square in cm $\longrightarrow$ its perimeter in cm
(iii) Natural numbers $\longrightarrow$ the number of factors (including 1 and the number itself)
(iv) $x \longrightarrow 2x - 5$
(v) $x \longrightarrow \sqrt{x}$
(vi) The volume of a sphere in $\text{cm}^3 \longrightarrow$ its radius in cm
(vii) The volume of a cylinder in $\text{cm}^3 \longrightarrow$ its height in cm
(viii) The length of a side of a regular hexagon in cm $\longrightarrow$ its area in cm^2
(ix) $x \longrightarrow x^2$

3 **(i)** A function is defined by $\text{f}(x) = 2x - 5$. Write down the values of
(a) $\text{f}(0)$ **(b)** $\text{f}(7)$ **(c)** $\text{f}(-3)$.

(ii) A function is defined by g:(polygons) $\longrightarrow$ (number of sides). What are
(a) g(triangle) **(b)** g(pentagon) **(c)** g(decagon)?

(iii) The function t maps Celsius temperatures on to Fahrenheit temperatures. It is defined by t: $C \longrightarrow \frac{9C}{5} + 32$. Find
(a) $\text{t}(0)$ **(b)** $\text{t}(28)$ **(c)** $\text{t}(-10)$ **(d)** the value of C when $\text{t}(C) = C$.

4 Find the range of each of the following functions.
(You may find it helpful to draw the graph first.)

(i) $\text{f}(x) = 2 - 3x$ $\quad x \geqslant 0$
(ii) $\text{f}(\theta) = \sin\theta$ $\quad 0° \leqslant \theta \leqslant 180°$
(iii) $y = x^2 + 2$ $\quad x \in \{0, 1, 2, 3, 4\}$
(iv) $y = \tan\theta$ $\quad 0° < \theta < 90°$
(v) $\text{f}: x \longrightarrow 3x - 5$ $\quad x \in \mathbb{R}$
(vi) $\text{f}: x \longrightarrow 2^x$ $\quad x \in \{-1, 0, 1, 2\}$
(vii) $y = \cos x$ $\quad -\frac{\pi}{2} \leqslant x \leqslant \frac{\pi}{2}$
(viii) $\text{f}: x \longrightarrow x^3 - 4$ $\quad x \in \mathbb{R}$
(ix) $\text{f}(x) = \frac{1}{1 + x^2}$ $\quad x \in \mathbb{R}$
(x) $\text{f}(x) = \sqrt{x - 3} + 3$ $\quad x \geqslant 3$

5 The mapping f is defined by
$$\text{f}(x) = x^2 \quad 0 \leqslant x \leqslant 3$$
$$\text{f}(x) = 3x \quad 3 \leqslant x \leqslant 10.$$

The mapping g is defined by
$$\text{g}(x) = x^2 \quad 0 \leqslant x \leqslant 2$$
$$\text{g}(x) = 3x \quad 2 \leqslant x \leqslant 10.$$

Explain why f is a function and g is not.

Using transformations to sketch the curves of functions

In *AS Pure Mathematics* you used translations and one-way stretches to relate the equation of a function to that of a standard function of the same form. This then allowed you to obtain a sketch of the curve of your function.

It is possible to combine translations and stretches, but care must be taken over the order in which these are applied, as shown in Activity 3.1.

ACTIVITY 3.1 Copy the triangle in figure 3.4 and, for each of parts **(i)** to **(v)**, perform the transformations in the order given.
In each case comment if the end results are the same or different.

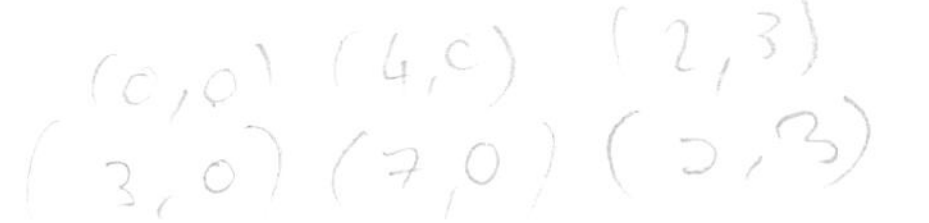

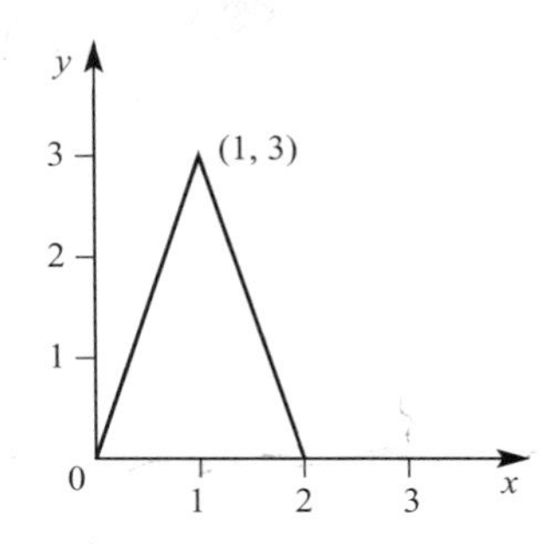

Figure 3.4

(i) **(a)** Translate the triangle through $\begin{pmatrix}3\\0\end{pmatrix}$ and then stretch the image with a scale factor of 2 parallel to the x axis.

(b) Stretch the triangle with a scale factor of 2 parallel to the x axis and then translate the image through $\begin{pmatrix}3\\0\end{pmatrix}$.

(ii) **(a)** Translate the triangle through $\begin{pmatrix}3\\0\end{pmatrix}$ and then stretch the image with a scale factor of 2 parallel to the y axis.

(b) Stretch the triangle with a scale factor of 2 parallel to the y axis and then translate the image through $\begin{pmatrix}3\\0\end{pmatrix}$.

(iii) **(a)** Translate the triangle through $\begin{pmatrix}0\\3\end{pmatrix}$ and then stretch the image with a scale factor of 2 parallel to the x axis.

(b) Stretch the triangle with a scale factor of 2 parallel to the x axis and then translate the image through $\begin{pmatrix}0\\3\end{pmatrix}$.

(iv) **(a)** Translate the triangle through $\begin{pmatrix}0\\3\end{pmatrix}$ and then stretch the image with a scale factor of 2 parallel to the y axis.

(b) Stretch the triangle with a scale factor of 2 parallel to the y axis and then translate the image through $\begin{pmatrix}0\\3\end{pmatrix}$.

(v) **(a)** Stretch the triangle with a scale factor of 2 parallel to the x axis and then stretch the image with a scale factor of 3 parallel to the y axis.

(b) Stretch the triangle with a scale factor of 3 parallel to the y axis and then stretch the image with a scale factor of 2 parallel to the x axis.

Activity 3.1 should have emphasised to you the importance of performing the transformations in the correct order. It is a good idea to check your results using a graphic calculator whenever possible.

EXAMPLE 3.2

(i) Find the values of a, p and q when $y = 2x^2 + 4x - 1$ is written in the form $y = a[(x + p)^2 + q]$.

(ii) Show how the graph can be obtained from the graph of $y = x^2$ by successive transformations, and list the transformations in the order in which they are applied.

SOLUTION

Expanding the equivalent expression

$$\begin{aligned} a[(x+p)^2 + q] &= a[x^2 + 2px + p^2 + q] \\ &= ax^2 + 2apx + a(p^2 + q). \end{aligned}$$

Comparing the coefficients in $y = 2x^2 + 4x - 1$ with those above gives

- coefficient of x^2: $a = 2$
- coefficient of x: $2ap = 4$, which gives $p = 1$
- constant term: $a(p^2 + q) = -1$, which gives $q = -1\frac{1}{2}$.

The equation of the curve can be written as $y = 2[(x + 1)^2 - 1\frac{1}{2}]$.

To sketch the graph, start with the curve $y = x^2$.

The curve $y = x^2$ becomes $y = (x + 1)^2 - 1\frac{1}{2}$ by applying the translation $\begin{pmatrix} -1 \\ -1\frac{1}{2} \end{pmatrix}$.

The curve $y = (x + 1)^2 - 1\frac{1}{2}$ becomes $y = 2[(x + 1)^2 - 1\frac{1}{2}]$ by applying a stretch of scale factor 2 parallel to the y axis.

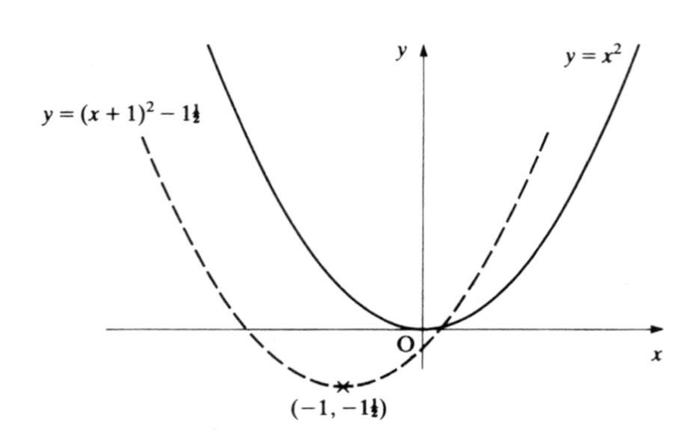

The translation $\begin{pmatrix} -1 \\ -1\frac{1}{2} \end{pmatrix}$

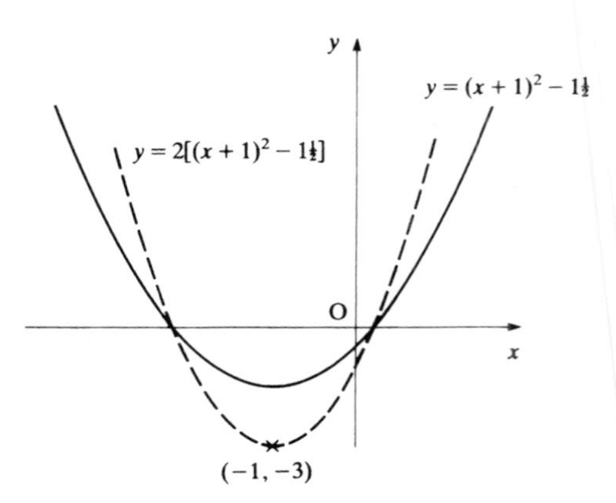

The stretch of scale factor 2 parallel to the y axis

Figure 3.5

Note

Notice in figure 3.5 how the stretch doubles the y co-ordinate of every point on the curve, including the turning point.

Points on the x axis have a zero y co-ordinate, so are unchanged.

P How would you prove that the equation $(x+a)^2 + b = 0$ has no real roots if $b > 0$?

EXAMPLE 3.3

Starting with the curve $y = \cos x$, show how transformations can be used to sketch the curves

(i) $y = 2\cos 3x$ **(ii)** $y = 3 + \cos \frac{x}{2}$ **(iii)** $y = \cos(2x - 60°)$.

SOLUTION

(i) The curve with equation $y = \cos 3x$ is obtained from the curve with equation $y = \cos x$ by a stretch of scale factor $\frac{1}{3}$ parallel to the x axis. There will therefore be one complete oscillation of the curve in 120° (instead of 360°).

The curve of $y = 2\cos 3x$ is obtained from that of $y = \cos 3x$ by a stretch of scale factor 2 parallel to the y axis. The curve therefore oscillates between $y = 2$ and $y = -2$ (instead of $y = 1$ and $y = -1$). This is shown in figure 3.6.

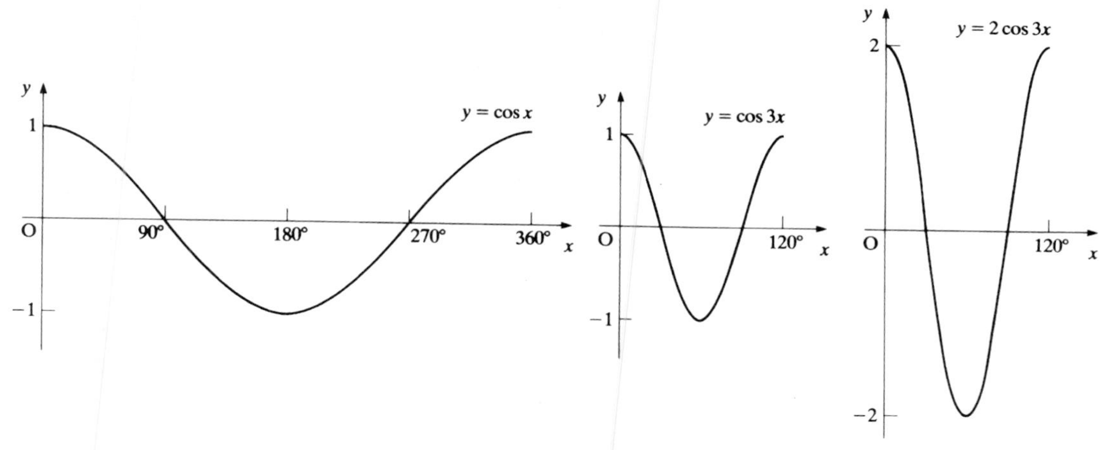

Figure 3.6

(ii) The curve of $y = \cos \frac{x}{2}$ is obtained from that of $y = \cos x$ by a stretch of scale factor 2 in the x direction. There will therefore be one complete oscillation of the curve in 720° (instead of 360°).

The curve of $y = 3 + \cos \frac{x}{2}$ is obtained from that of $y = \cos \frac{x}{2}$ by a translation $\begin{pmatrix} 0 \\ 3 \end{pmatrix}$.

The curve therefore oscillates between $y = 4$ and $y = 2$ (see figure 3.7).

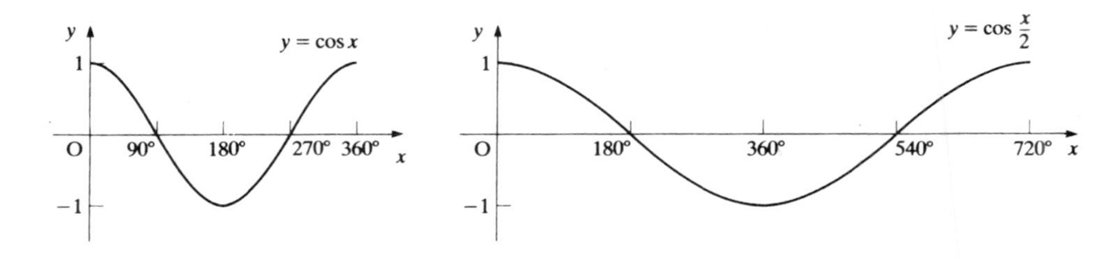

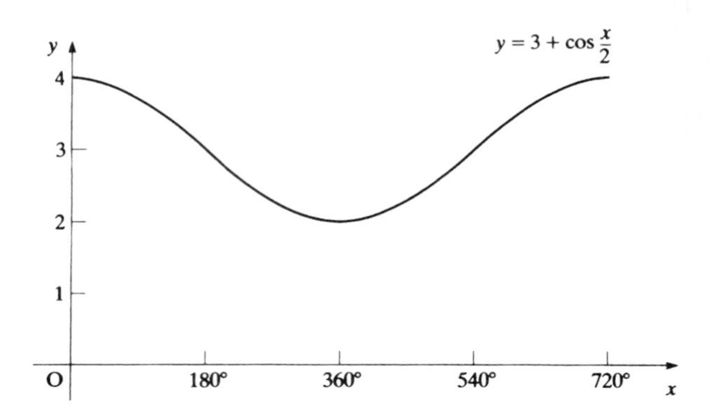

Figure 3.7

(iii) The curve of $y = \cos(x - 60°)$ is obtained from that of $y = \cos x$ by a translation of $\begin{pmatrix} 60° \\ 0 \end{pmatrix}$.

The curve of $y = \cos(2x - 60°)$ is obtained from that of $y = \cos(x - 60°)$ by a stretch of scale factor $\frac{1}{2}$ parallel to the x axis (see figure 3.8).

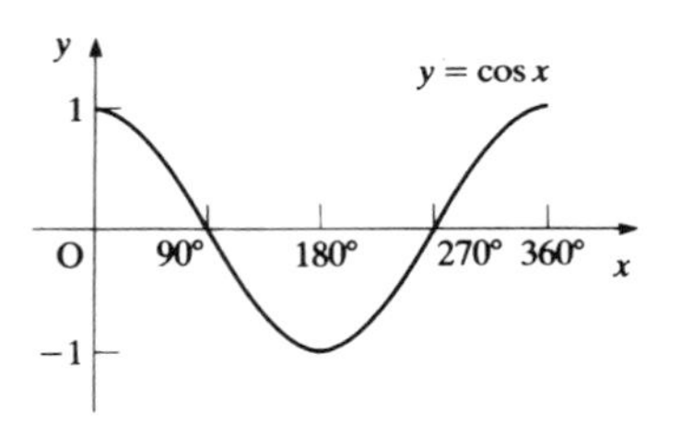

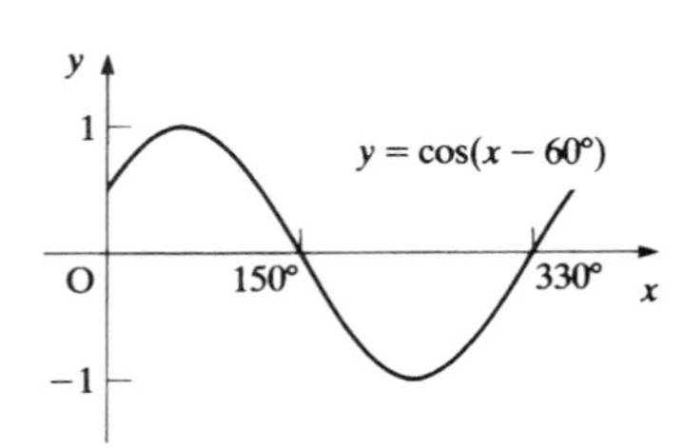

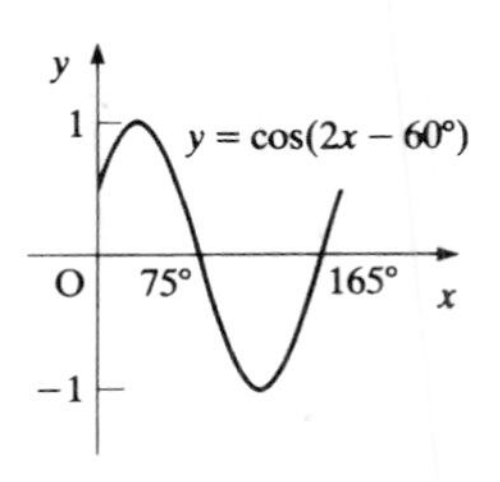

Figure 3.8

EXERCISE 3B

1 Starting with the graph of $y = x^2$, state the transformations which can be used to sketch each of the following curves.
Specify the transformations in the order in which they are used and, where there is more than one stage in the sketching of the curve, state each stage.
State the equation of the line of symmetry.

(i) $y = x^2 - 2$
(ii) $y = 3x^2$
(iii) $y = (x - 2)^2$
(iv) $y = 3(x - 2)^2$
(v) $y = (3x - 2)^2$
(vi) $y = x^2 - 4x$
(vii) $y = 2x^2 + 4x - 1$
(viii) $y = 3x^2 - 6x - 2$

2 The diagram shows a sketch of the graph of $y = f(x)$, where $f(x) = x^2 + 4x$.

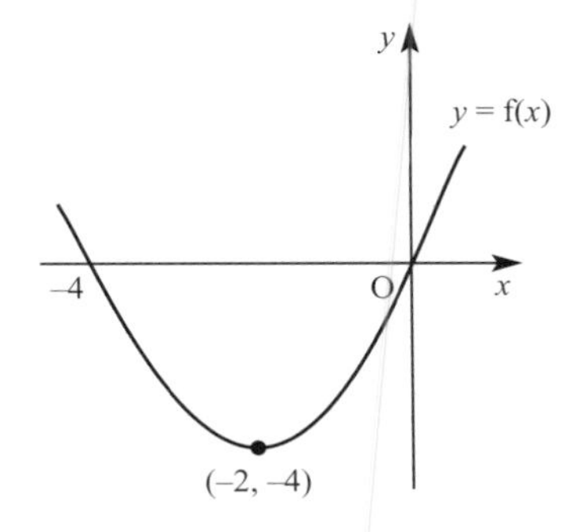

For each of the following

(i) $y = f(x) + 7$
(ii) $y = f(x - 2)$
(iii) $y = 2f(x) + 3$
(iv) $y = f(2x) + 3$
(v) $y = 3f(x - 2)$

(a) explain how the graph of $y = f(x)$ could be used to sketch the graph
(b) draw a separate sketch of the graph.

3 The diagram shows a sketch of the graph of $y = f(x)$, where $f(x) = 6x - x^2$.

Use this graph to sketch

(i) $y = f(x - 2)$
(ii) $y = \frac{1}{2}f(x)$
(iii) $y = 2f(x - 1)$

indicating clearly where these graphs cross the x axis and the co-ordinates of the highest point.

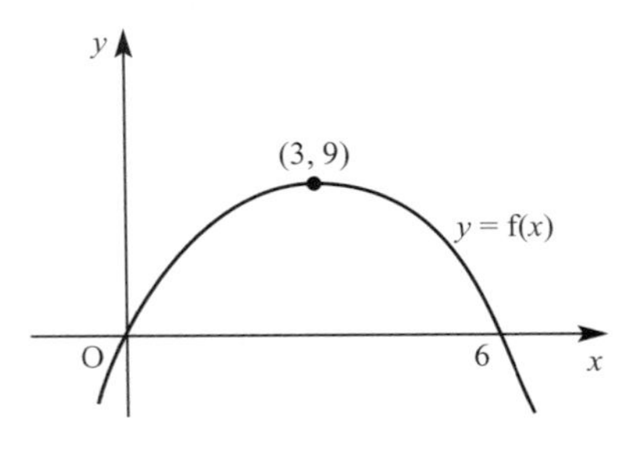

4 The diagram shows the graph of $y = f(x)$.

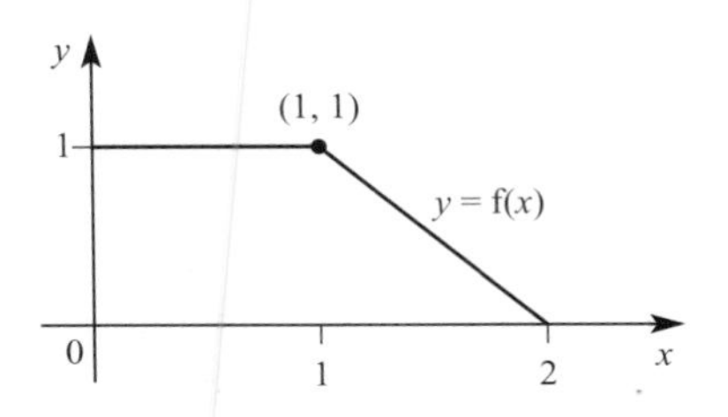

Sketch the graph of each of these functions.

(i) $y = f(2x)$
(ii) $y = f(x + 2)$
(iii) $y = 2f(x - 1)$
(iv) $y = 3f(x)$
(v) $y = f\left(\frac{x}{2} - 1\right)$
(vi) $y = f(3x + 1)$

5 Starting with the curve $y = \cos x$, show how transformations can be used to sketch these curves.

(i) $y = 3\cos 2x$

(ii) $y = \cos\dfrac{x}{3} - 1$

(iii) $y = \cos(2x + 30°)$

6 (i) Each diagram shows the graph of $y = \sin x$ (where x is measured in degrees) together with the graph of another sine function. These are labelled $y = \mathrm{f}(x)$, $y = \mathrm{g}(x)$ and $y = \mathrm{h}(x)$ respectively.

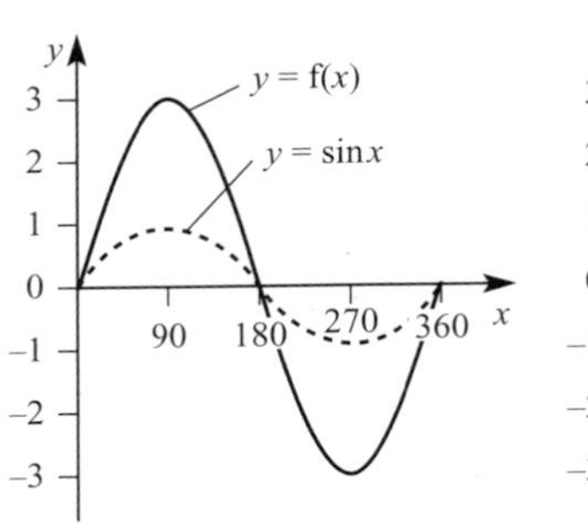

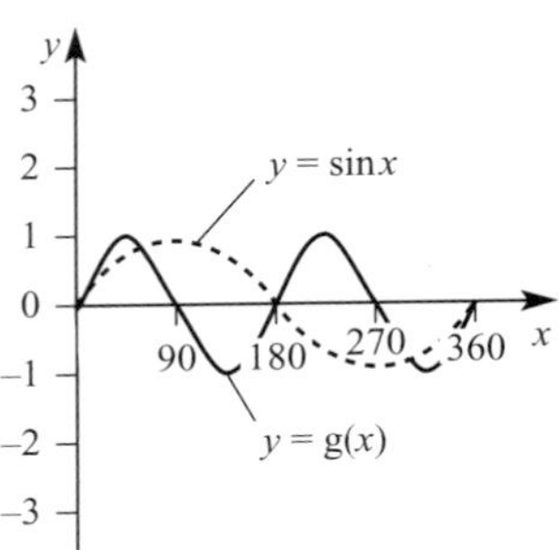

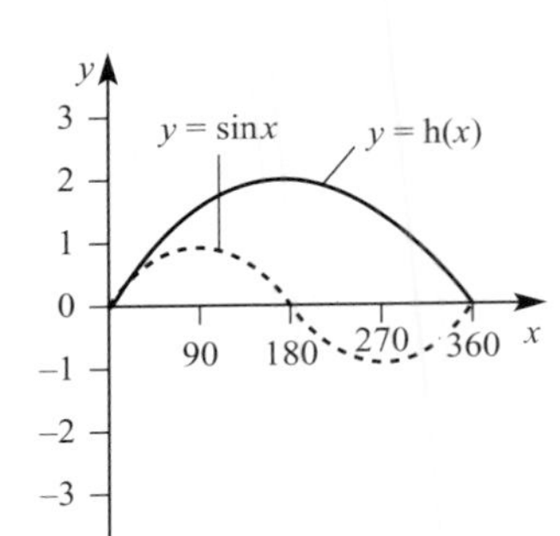

(a) Write down expressions for $\mathrm{f}(x)$, $\mathrm{g}(x)$ and $\mathrm{h}(x)$.

(b) Write down equations for the graphs which result from the following transformations of the graph of $y = \sin x$.

(A) A translation of 2 units in the positive y direction

(B) A translation of 90 units in the positive x direction

(c) Write down a value for a such that $\sin(x + a) = -\sin x$.

(ii) The function $\mathrm{F}(x)$ is defined by

$$\mathrm{F}(x) = b - c\sin x, \qquad 0° \leqslant x \leqslant 360°,$$

where b and c are constants, with $c > 0$.

(a) Find the range of $\mathrm{F}(x)$ in terms of b and c.

(b) Show that the graph of $y = \mathrm{F}(x)$ crosses the x axis if $-c < b < c$.
Given that $b = \frac{1}{2}c$, find the co-ordinates of the points where the graph crosses the x axis, and sketch the graph.

[MEI]

Reflections

ACTIVITY 3.2

Sketch the curves of $y = \mathrm{f}(x)$ and $y = -\mathrm{f}(x)$ for each of the following functions.

(i) x^2 **(ii)** $\sin x$ **(iii)** $x^3 - 6x^2 + 11x - 6$

Describe the relationship between the graphs of $y = \mathrm{f}(x)$ and $y = -\mathrm{f}(x)$ in these cases. Would you be confident to generalise this result?

Figure 3.9 shows the graphs of $y = \cos x$ and $y = -\cos x$ for $0° \leqslant x \leqslant 180°$. For any particular value of x, the y co-ordinates of the two graphs have the same magnitude but opposite signs. The graphs are reflections of each other in the x axis.

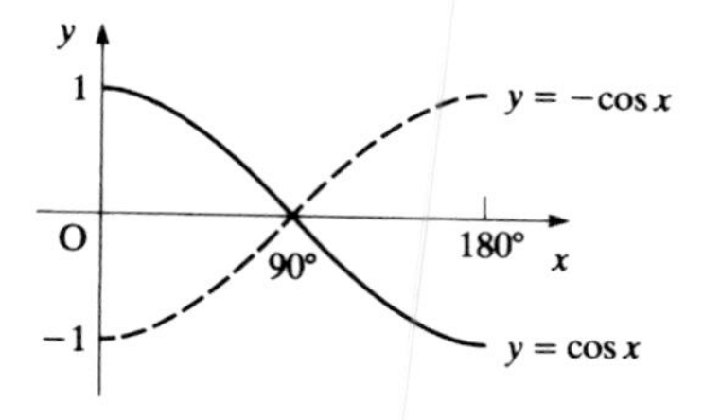

Figure 3.9

In general, starting with the graph of $y = f(x)$ and replacing $f(x)$ by $-f(x)$ gives a reflection in the x axis. This is the equivalent of replacing y by $-y$ in the equation.

In the next activity you investigate the effect of replacing x by $-x$.

ACTIVITY 3.3

Sketch the curves of $y = f(x)$ and $y = f(-x)$ for each of the following functions.

(i) x^2 **(ii)** $\sin x$ **(iii)** $x^3 - 6x^2 + 11x - 6$

Describe the relationship between the graphs of $y = f(x)$ and $y = f(-x)$ in these cases. Would you be confident to generalise this result?

Figure 3.10 shows the graph of $y = 2x + 1$, a straight line with gradient 2 passing through (0, 1). The graph of $y = 2(-x) + 1$ (which can be written as $y = -2x + 1$) is a straight line with gradient -2, and as you can see it is a reflection of the line $y = 2x + 1$ in the y axis.

In general, starting with the graph of $y = f(x)$ and replacing x by $(-x)$ gives a reflection in the y axis.

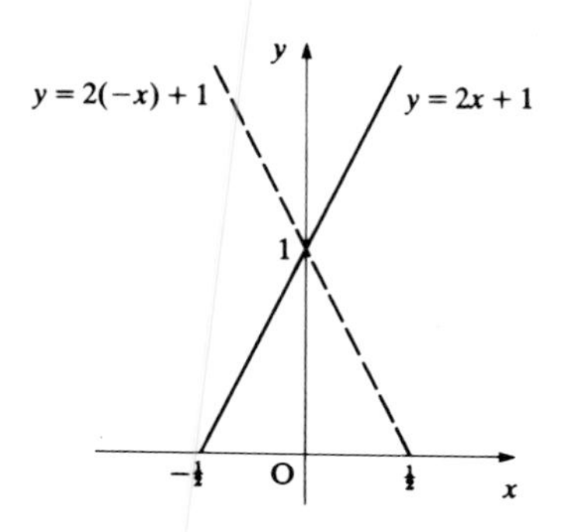

Figure 3.10

EXAMPLE 3.4

Figure 3.11 shows the graph of $y = 2^x$. The curve passes through the point (0, 1).

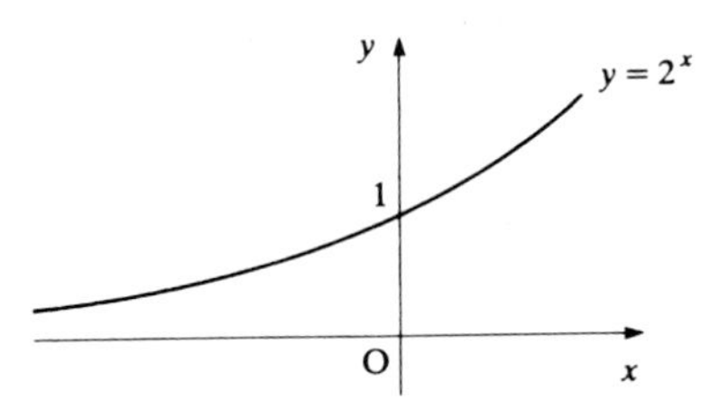

Figure 3.11

Sketch, on separate diagrams, the graphs of

(i) $y = 2^{-x}$ **(ii)** $y = -(2^x)$.

SOLUTION

(i) Replacing x by $-x$ reflects the curve in the y axis (see figure 3.12).

(ii) The equation $y = -2^x$ can be written as $-y = 2^x$. Replacing y by $-y$ reflects the curve in the x axis (see figure 3.13).

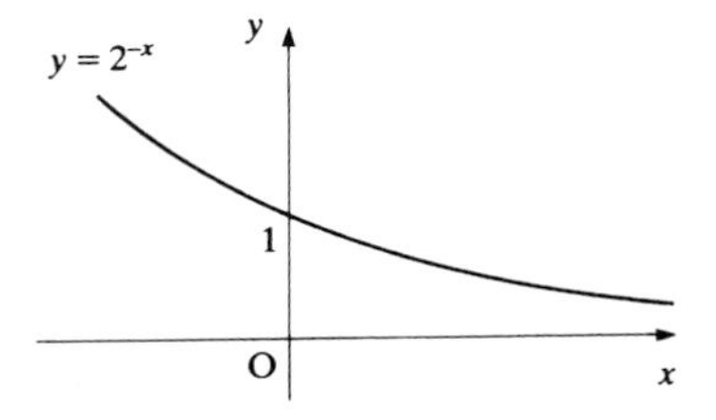

Figure 3.12

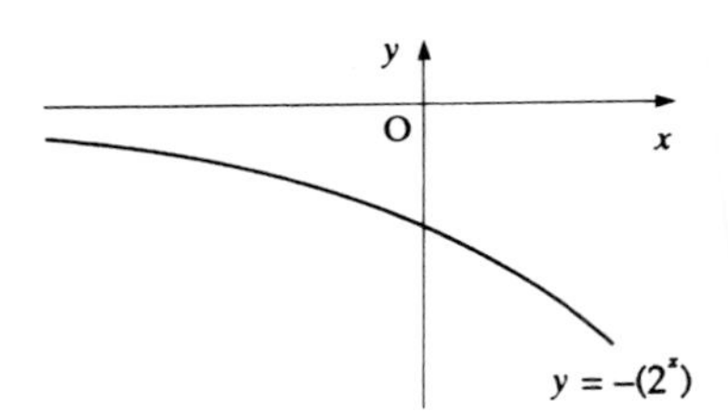

Figure 3.13

The general quadratic curve

You are now able to relate any quadratic curve to that of $y = x^2$.

EXAMPLE 3.5

(i) Write the equation $y = 1 + 4x - x^2$ in the form $y = a[(x + p)^2 + q]$.

(ii) Show how the graph of $y = 1 + 4x - x^2$ can be obtained from the graph of $y = x^2$ by a succession of transformations, and list the transformations in the order in which they are applied.

(iii) Sketch the graph.

SOLUTION

(i) If $\quad 1 + 4x - x^2 \equiv a[(x + p)^2 + q]$

then $\quad -x^2 + 4x + 1 \equiv ax^2 + 2apx + a(p^2 + q)$

Comparing coefficients of x^2: $a = -1$.

Comparing coefficients of x: $2ap = 4$, giving $p = -2$.

Comparing constant terms: $a(p^2 + q) = 1$, giving $q = -5$.

The equation is $y = -[(x-2)^2 - 5]$.

(ii) The curve $y = x^2$ becomes the curve $y = (x-2)^2 - 5$ by applying the translation $\begin{pmatrix} 2 \\ -5 \end{pmatrix}$ as shown in figure 3.14.

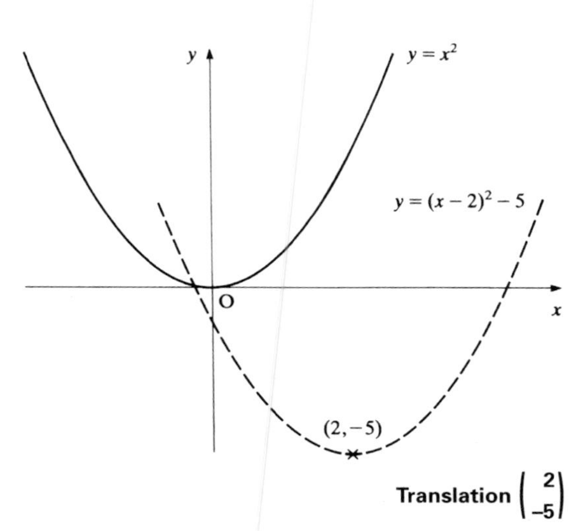

Figure 3.14

The curve $y = (x-2)^2 - 5$ becomes the curve $y = -[(x-2)^2 - 5]$ by applying a reflection in the x axis (see figure 3.15).

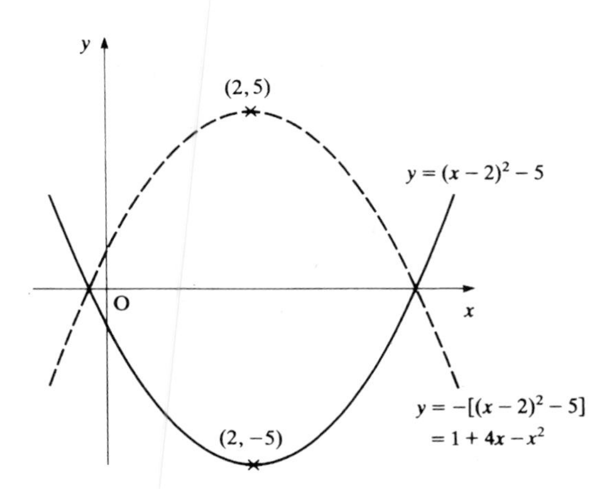

Figure 3.15

EXERCISE 3C

1 Starting with the graph of $y = x^2$, state the transformations which can be used to sketch the following curves.
Specify the transformations in the order in which they are used and, where there is more than one stage in the sketching of the curve, state each stage.
State the equation of the line of symmetry.

(i) $y = -2x^2$ **(ii)** $y = 4 - x^2$ **(iii)** $y = 2x - 1 - x^2$

2 For each of the following curves

(a) sketch the curve

(b) identify the curve as being the same as one of the following.

$y = \pm\sin x$, $y = \pm\cos x$, or $y = \pm\tan x$

(i) $y = \cos(-x)$ **(ii)** $y = \tan(-x)$

(iii) $y = \sin(180° - x)$ **(iv)** $y = \tan(180° - x)$

(v) $y = \sin(-x)$

3 (i) Write the expression $x^2 - 6x + 14$ in the form $(x - a)^2 + b$ where a and b are numbers which you are to find.

(ii) Sketch the curves $y = x^2$ and $y = x^2 - 6x + 14$ and state the transformation which maps $y = x^2$ on to $y = x^2 - 6x + 14$.

(iii) The curve $y = x^2 - 6x + 14$ is reflected in the x axis.
Write down the equation of the image.

4 (i) Sketch the curve with equation $y = x^2$.

(ii) Given that $f(x) = (x - 2)^2 + 1$ sketch the curves with the following equations on separate diagrams. Label each curve and give the co-ordinates of its vertex and the equation of its axis of symmetry.

(a) $y = f(x)$ **(b)** $y = -f(x)$ **(c)** $y = f(x + 1) + 2$

[MEI]

5 Write the expression $2x^2 + 4x + 5$ in the form $a(x + b)^2 + c$ where a, b and c are numbers to be found.

Use your answer to *write down* the co-ordinates of the minimum point on the graph of $y = 2x^2 + 4x + 5$.

[O & C]

6 The circle with equation $x^2 + y^2 = 1$ is stretched with scale factor 3 parallel to the x axis and with scale factor 2 parallel to the y axis. Sketch both curves on the same graph, and write down the equation of the new curve. (It is an ellipse.)

7 In each of the diagrams opposite, the curve drawn with a dashed line is obtained as a mapping of the curve $y = f(x)$ using a single transformation. It could be a translation, a one-way stretch or a reflection.
In each case, write down the equation of the image (dashed) in terms of $f(x)$.

(i)

(ii)

(iii)

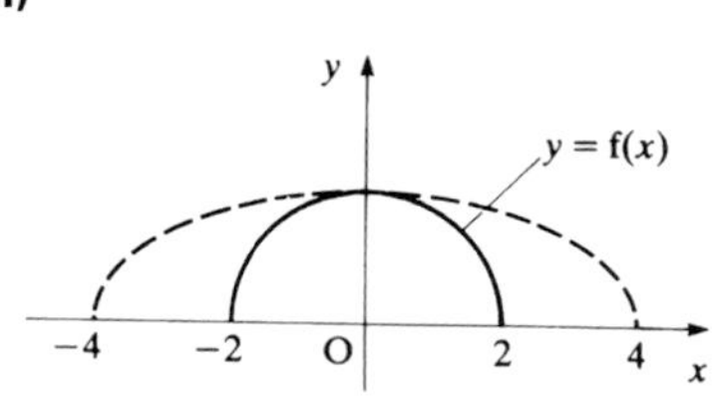

(iv)

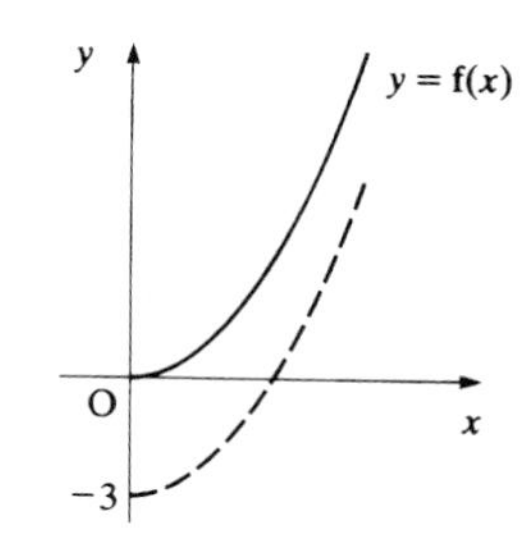

(v)

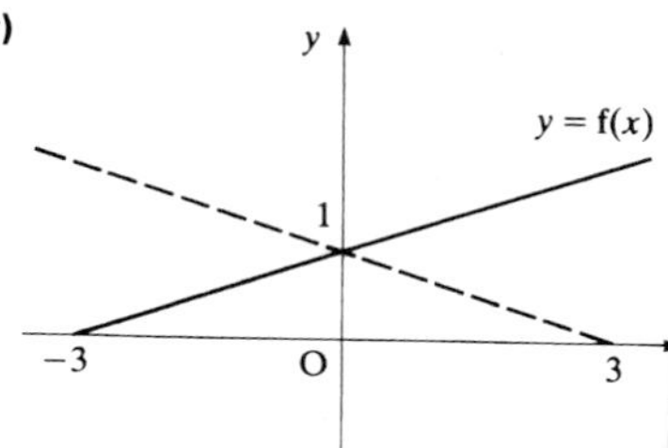

(vi)

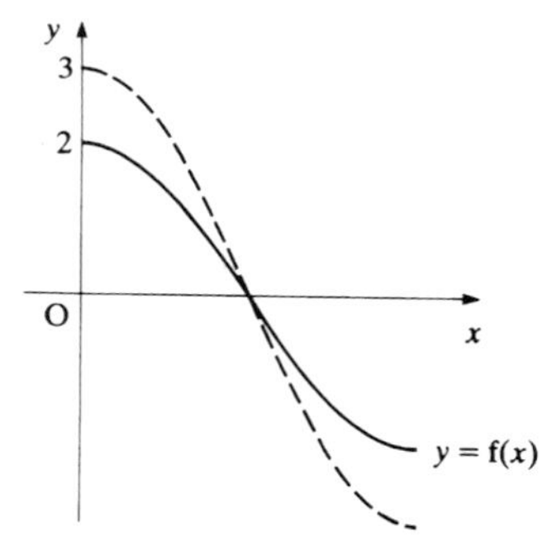

8 The sketch shows the curve with equation $y = 2 - 6x - 3x^2$ and its axis of symmetry $x = -1$.

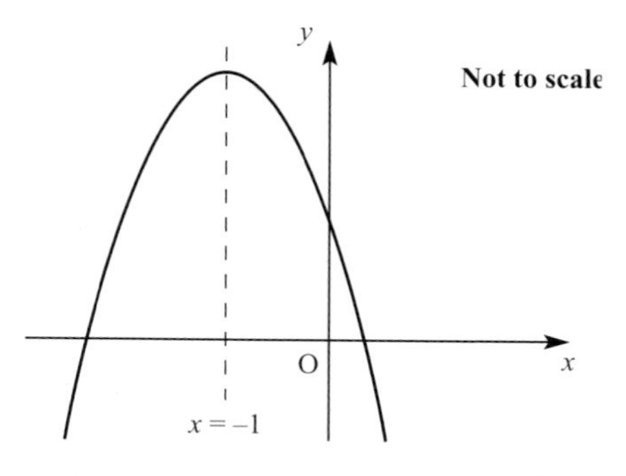

(i) Give the co-ordinates of the vertex and the value of y when $x = 0$.

(ii) Find the values of the constants a, b such that $2 - 6x - 3x^2 = a(x + 1)^2 + b$.

(iii) Copy the sketch and draw in the reflection of the curve with equation $y = 2 - 6x - 3x^2$ in the line $y = 2$.

(iv) Write down the equation of the new curve and give the co-ordinates of its vertex.

[MEI]

9 The diagram shows the graph of $y = f(x)$. The curve passes through the origin and has a maximum point at $(1, 1)$.

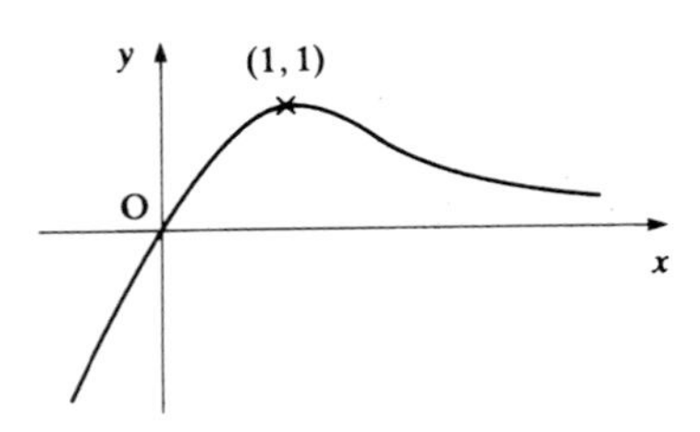

Sketch, on separate diagrams, the graphs of

(i) $y = f(x) + 2$ **(ii)** $y = f(x + 2)$ **(iii)** $y = f(2x)$

giving the co-ordinates of the maximum point in each case.

[UCLES]

Composite functions

It is possible to combine functions in several different ways, and you have already met some of these. For example, if $f(x) = x^2$ and $g(x) = 2x$, then you could write

$$f(x) + g(x) = x^2 + 2x.$$

In this example, two functions are added.

Similarly if $f(x) = x$ and $g(x) = \sin x$, then

$$f(x).g(x) = x\sin x.$$

In this example, two functions are multiplied.

Sometimes you need to apply one function and then apply another to the answer. You are then creating a *composite function* or a *function of a function.*

EXAMPLE 3.6

A new mother is bathing her baby for the first time. She takes the temperature of the bath water with a thermometer which reads in Celsius, but then has to convert the temperature to degrees Fahrenheit to apply the rule that her own mother taught her:

At one o five
He'll cook alive
But ninety four
is rather raw.

Write down the two functions that are involved, and apply them to readings of

(i) 30°C **(ii)** 38°C **(iii)** 45°C.

SOLUTION

The first function converts the Celsius temperature C into a Fahrenheit temperature, F.

$$F = \frac{9C}{5} + 32$$

The second function maps Fahrenheit temperatures on to the state of the bath.

$F \leqslant 94$	Too cold
$94 < F < 105$	All right
$F \geqslant 105$	Too hot

This gives

(i) 30°C $\longrightarrow$ 86°F $\longrightarrow$ too cold
(ii) 38°C $\longrightarrow$ 100.4°F $\longrightarrow$ all right
(iii) 45°C $\longrightarrow$ 113°C $\longrightarrow$ too hot.

In this case the composite function would be (to the nearest degree)

$C \leqslant 34°\text{C}$	too cold
$35°\text{C} \leqslant C \leqslant 40°\text{C}$	all right
$C \geqslant 41°\text{C}$	too hot.

In algebraic terms, a composite function is constructed as

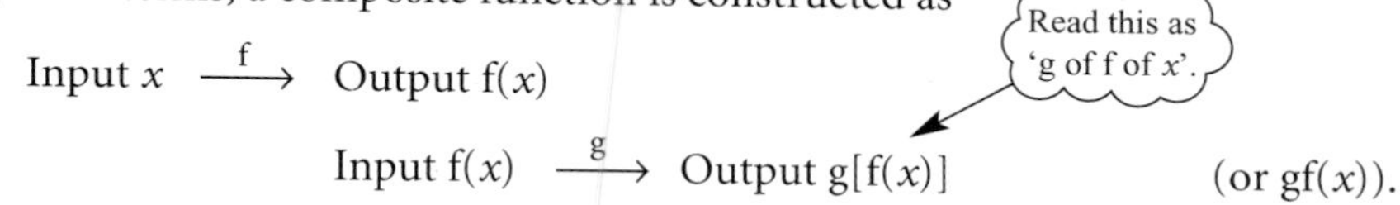

Thus the composite function $gf(x)$ should be performed from right to left: start with x then apply f and then g.

Notation

To indicate that f is being applied twice in succession, you could write $ff(x)$ but you would usually use $f^2(x)$ instead. Similarly $g^3(x)$ means three applications of g.

In order to apply a function repeatedly its domain and co-domain must be the same.

Order of functions

If f is the rule 'square the input value' and g is the rule 'add 1', then

$$x \xrightarrow[\text{square}]{f} x^2 \xrightarrow[\text{add 1}]{g} x^2 + 1.$$

So $\quad gf(x) = x^2 + 1.$

Notice that $gf(x)$ is not the same as $fg(x)$, since for $fg(x)$ you must apply g first. In the example above, this would give:

$$x \xrightarrow[\text{add 1}]{g} (x+1) \xrightarrow[\text{square}]{f} (x+1)^2$$

and so $fg(x) = (x+1)^2$.

Clearly this is *not* the same result.

Figure 3.16 illustrates the relationship between the domains and co-domains of the functions f and g, and the co-domain of the composite function gf.

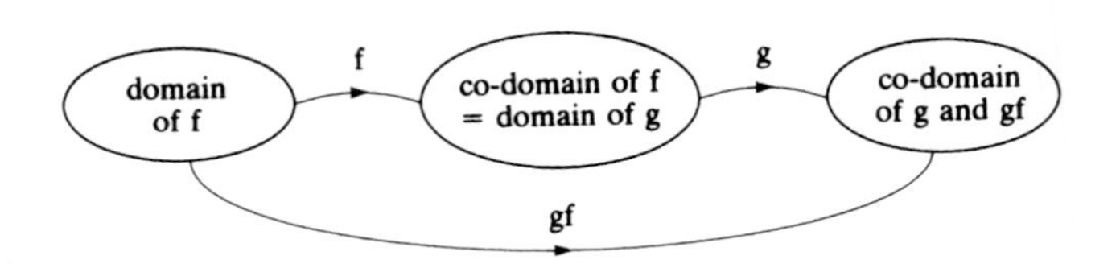

Figure 3.16

EXAMPLE 3.7

Given that $f(x) = 2x$, $g(x) = x^2$, and $h(x) = \frac{1}{x}$, find the following.

(i) $fg(x)$ **(ii)** $gf(x)$ **(iii)** $gh(x)$
(iv) $f^2(x)$ **(v)** $fgh(x)$ **(vi)** $hfg(x)$

SOLUTION

(i) $fg(x) = f[g(x)]$
$= f(x^2)$
$= 2x^2$

(ii) $gf(x) = g[f(x)]$
$= g(2x)$
$= (2x)^2$
$= 4x^2$

(iii) $gh(x) = g[h(x)]$
$= g\left(\frac{1}{x}\right)$
$= \frac{1}{x^2}$

(iv) $f^2(x) = f[f(x)]$
$= f(2x)$
$= 2(2x)$
$= 4x$

(v) $fgh(x) = f[gh(x)]$
$= f\left(\frac{2}{x^2}\right)$ using **(iii)**
$= \frac{2}{x^2}$

(vi) $hfg(x) = h[fg(x)]$
$= h(2x^2)$ using **(i)**
$= \frac{1}{2x^2}$

Inverse functions

Look at the mapping $x \rightarrow x + 2$ with domain and co-domain the set of integers.

Domain	Co-domain
...	...
...	...
-1 →	-1
0 →	0
1 →	1
2 →	2
...	3
...	4
x →	$x + 2$

The mapping is clearly a function, since for every input there is one and only one output, the number that is two greater than that input.

This mapping can also be seen in reverse. In that case, each number maps on to the number two less than itself: $x \rightarrow x - 2$. The reverse mapping is also a function because for any input there is one and only one output. The reverse mapping is called the *inverse function*, f^{-1}.

Function: $\mathrm{f}: x \rightarrow x + 2 \quad x \in \mathbb{Z}$.

Inverse function: $\mathrm{f}^{-1}: x \rightarrow x - 2 \quad x \in \mathbb{Z}$.

For a mapping to be a function which also has an inverse function, every object in the domain must have one and only one image in the co-domain, and vice versa. This can only be the case if the mapping is one-to-one.

So the condition for a function f to have an inverse function is that, over the given domain and co-domain, f represents a one-to-one mapping. This is a common situation, and many inverse functions are self-evident as in the following examples, for all of which the domain and co-domain are the real numbers.

$\mathrm{f}: x \rightarrow x - 1; \qquad \mathrm{f}^{-1}: x \rightarrow x + 1$

$\mathrm{g}: x \rightarrow 2x; \qquad \mathrm{g}^{-1}: x \rightarrow \frac{1}{2}x$

$\mathrm{h}: x \rightarrow x^3; \qquad \mathrm{h}^{-1}: x \rightarrow \sqrt[3]{x}$

? Some of the following mappings are functions which have inverse functions, and others are not.

(a) Decide which mappings fall into each category, and for those which do not have inverse functions, explain why.

(b) For those which have inverse functions, how can the functions and their inverses be written down algebraically?

(i) Temperature measured in Celsius → temperature measured in Fahrenheit.

(ii) Marks in an examination → grade awarded.

(iii) Distance measured in light years → distance measured in metres.

(iv) Number of stops travelled on the London Underground → fare.

You can decide whether an algebraic mapping is a function, and whether it has an inverse function, by looking at its graph. The curve or line representing a one-to-one mapping does not double back on itself, has no turning points and covers the full domain and co-domain. Figure 3.17 illustrates the functions f, g and h given on the previous page.

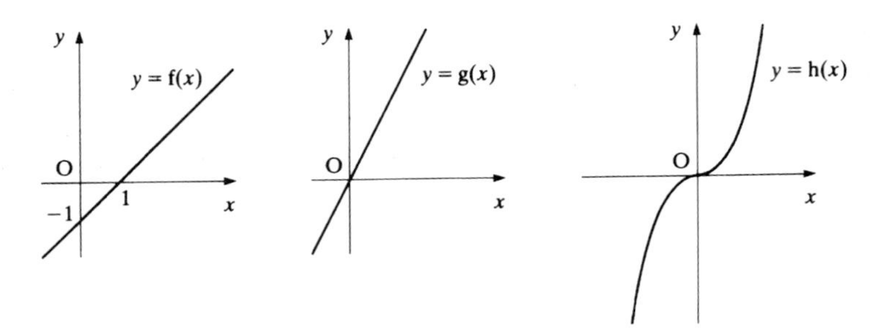

Figure 3.17

Now look at $f(x) = x^2$ for $x \in \mathbb{R}$ (figure 3.18). You can see that there are two distinct input values giving the same output: for example $f(2) = f(-2) = 4$. When you want to reverse the effect of the function, you have a mapping which for a single input of 4 gives two outputs, -2 and $+2$. Such a mapping is not a function.

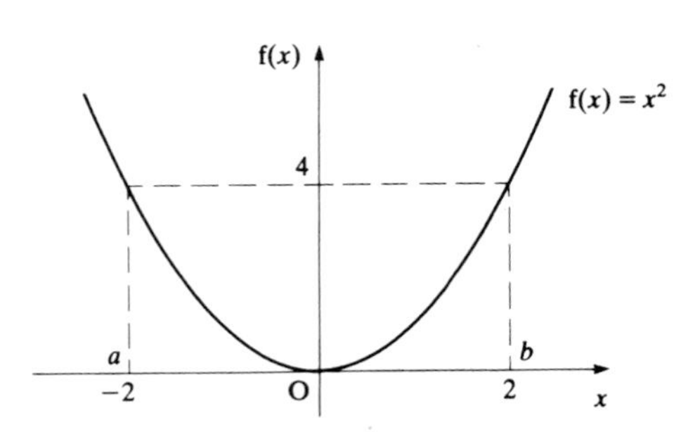

Figure 3.18

If the domain of $f(x) = x^2$ is restricted to $\mathbb{R}^+$ (the set of positive real numbers), you have the situation shown in figure 3.19. This shows that the function which is now defined is one-to-one. The inverse function is given by $f^{-1}(x) = \sqrt{x}$, since the sign $\sqrt{}$ means 'the positive square root of'.

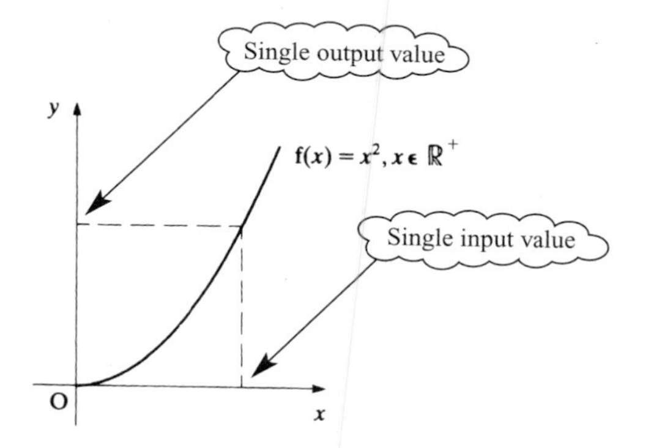

Figure 3.19

It is often helpful to restrict the domain of a function so that its inverse is also a function. When you use the inv sin (i.e. $\sin^{-1}$ or arcsin) key on your calculator the answer is restricted to the range $-90°$ to $90°$, and is described as the *principal value.* Although there are infinitely many roots of the equation $\sin x = 0.5$ $(\ldots, -330°, -210°, 30°, 150°, \ldots)$, only one of these, $30°$, lies in the restricted range and this is the value your calculator will give you.

The graph of a function and its inverse

ACTIVITY 3.4

For each of the following functions, work out the inverse function, and draw the graphs of both the original and the inverse on the same axes, using the same scale on both axes.

(i) $f(x) = x^2 \quad x \in \mathbb{R}^+$ **(ii)** $f(x) = 2x$
(iii) $f(x) = x + 2$ **(iv)** $f(x) = x^3 + 2$

Look at your graphs and see if there is any pattern emerging.

Try out a few more functions of your own to check your ideas.

Make a conjecture about the relationship between the graph of a function and its inverse.

You have probably realised by now that the graph of the inverse function is the same shape as that of the function, but reflected in the line $y = x$. To see why this is so, think of a function $f(x)$ mapping a on to b; (a, b) is clearly a point on the graph of $f(x)$. The inverse function $f^{-1}(x)$, maps b on to a and so (b, a) is a point on the graph of $f^{-1}(x)$.

The point (b, a) is the reflection of the point (a, b) in the line $y = x$. This is shown for a number of points in figure 3.20.

This result can be used to obtain a sketch of the inverse function without having to find its equation, provided that the sketch of the original function uses the same scale on both axes.

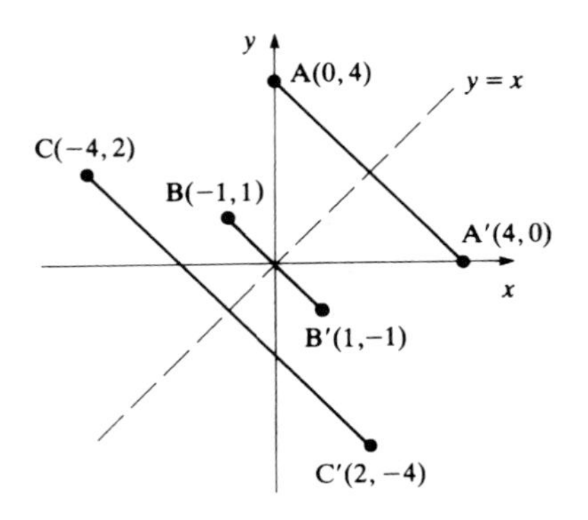

Figure 3.20

Finding the algebraic form of the inverse function

To find the algebraic form of the inverse of a function $f(x)$, you should start by changing notation and writing it in the form $y = \dots$.

Since the graph of the inverse function is the reflection of the graph of the original function in the line $y = x$, it follows that you may find its equation by interchanging y and x in the equation of the original function. You will then need to make y the subject of your new equation. This procedure is illustrated in Example 3.8.

EXAMPLE 3.8

Find $f^{-1}(x)$ when $f(x) = 2x + 1$.

SOLUTION

The function $f(x)$ is given by $\quad y = 2x + 1$

Interchanging x and y gives $\quad x = 2y + 1$

Rearranging to make y the subject: $\quad y = \dfrac{x-1}{2}$

So $f^{-1}(x) = \dfrac{x-1}{2}$.

Sometimes the domain of the function f will not include the whole of $\mathbb{R}$. When any real numbers are excluded from the domain of f, it follows that they will be excluded from the co-domain of f^{-1}, and vice versa.

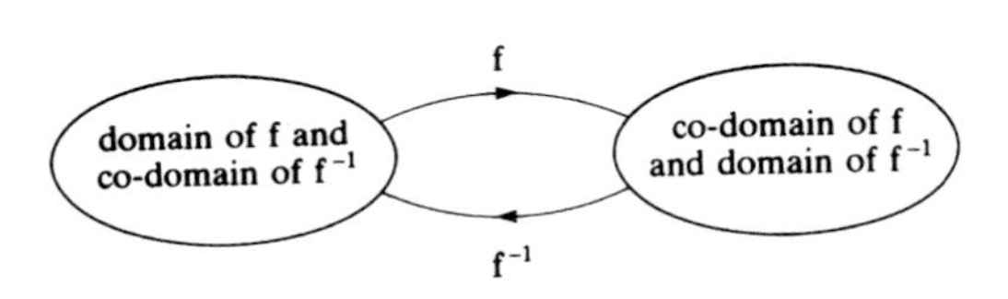

Figure 3.21

EXAMPLE 3.9

Find $f^{-1}(x)$ when $f(x) = 2x - 3$ and the domain of f is $x \geqslant 4$.

SOLUTION

	Domain	Co-domain
Function: $y = 2x - 3$	$x \geqslant 4$	$y \geqslant 5$
Inverse function: $x = 2y - 3$	$x \geqslant 5$	$y \geqslant 4$

Rearranging the inverse function to make y the subject,

$$y = \frac{x + 3}{2}.$$

The full definition of the inverse function is therefore

$$f^{-1}(x) = \frac{x + 3}{2} \text{ for } x \geqslant 5.$$

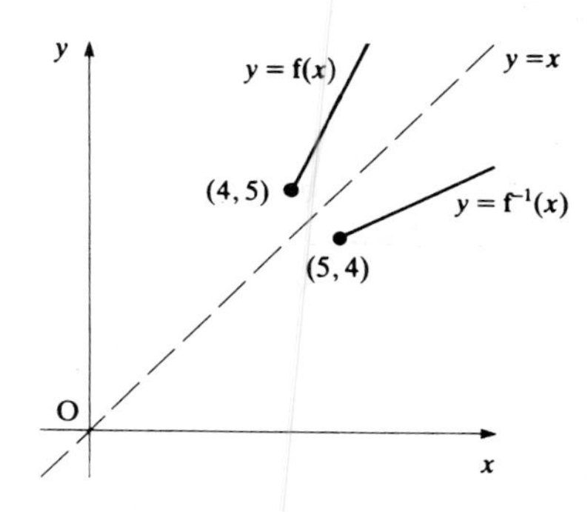

Figure 3.22

You can see in figure 3.22 that the inverse function is the reflection of a restricted part of the line $y = 2x - 3$.

EXAMPLE 3.10

(i) Find $f^{-1}(x)$ when $f(x) = x^2 + 2,\ x \geqslant 0$.

(ii) Find f(7) and f^{-1} f(7). What do you notice?

SOLUTION

(i)

	Domain	Co-domain
Function: $y = x^2 + 2$	$x \geqslant 0$	$y \geqslant 2$
Inverse function: $x = y^2 + 2$	$x \geqslant 2$	$y \geqslant 0$

Rearranging the inverse function to make y its subject:

$$y^2 = x - 2.$$

This gives $y = \pm\sqrt{x - 2}$, but since you know the co-domain of the inverse function to be $y \geqslant 0$ you can write:

$$y = +\sqrt{x-2} \qquad \text{or just} \qquad y = \sqrt{x-2}.$$

The full definition of the inverse function is therefore:

$$f^{-1}(x) = \sqrt{x-2} \text{ for } x \geqslant 2.$$

The function and its inverse function are shown in figure 3.23.

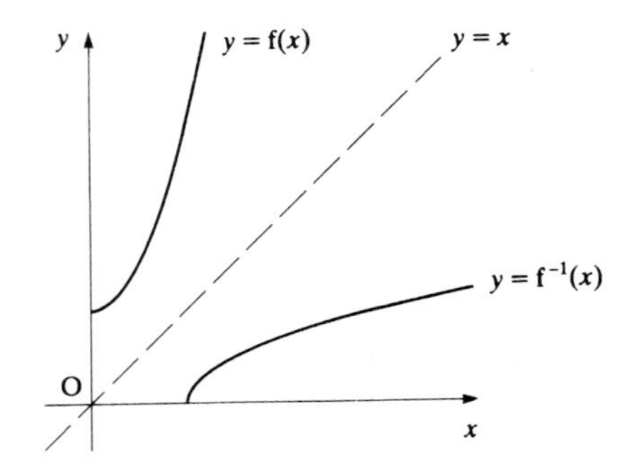

Figure 3.23

(ii) $f(7) = 7^2 + 2 = 51$

$f^{-1}\,f(7) = f^{-1}\,(51) = \sqrt{51-2} = 7$

Applying the function followed by its inverse brings you back to the original input value.

Note

Part **(ii)** of Example 3.10 illustrates an important general result. For any function $f(x)$ with an inverse $f^{-1}(x)$, $f^{-1}f(x) = x$. Similarly $ff^{-1}(x) = x$. The effects of a function and its inverse can be thought of as cancelling each other out.

EXAMPLE 3.11

Find the inverse of the function $f(x) = 10^x$, and sketch $f(x)$ and $f^{-1}(x)$ on the same diagram.

SOLUTION

The function $f(x)$ is given by $y = 10^x$.

Interchanging x and y, the inverse function is given by

$$x = 10^y.$$

This can be written as $\log_{10} x = y$, so the inverse function is

$$f^{-1}(x) = \log_{10} x.$$

The function and its inverse function are shown in figure 3.24.

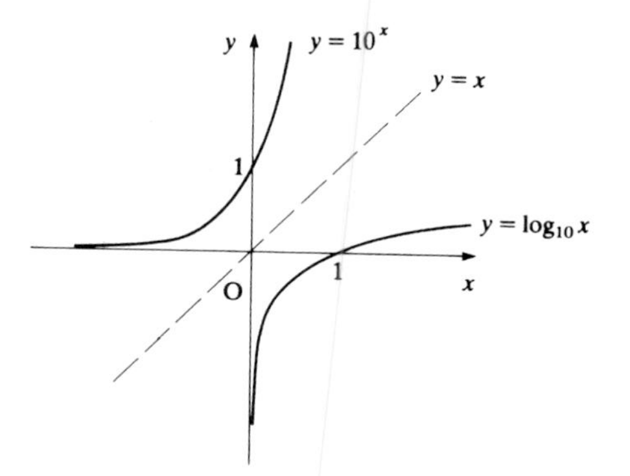

Figure 3.24

Many calculators have a function and its inverse on the same key, for example log and 10^x, $\sqrt{\ }$ and x^2, sin and arcsin, ln and e^x.

(i) With some calculators you can enter a number, apply x^2 and then $\sqrt{\ }$, and come out with a slightly different number. How is this possible?

(ii) Explain what happens if you find sin 199° and then the arcsin of the answer.

Inverse trigonometrical functions

The functions sine, cosine and tangent are all many-to-one mappings, so their inverse mappings are one-to-many. Thus the problem 'find sin 30°' has only one solution, 0.5, whilst 'find θ such that $\sin\theta = 0.5$' has infinitely many solutions. You can see this from the graph of $y = \sin\theta$ (figure 3.25).

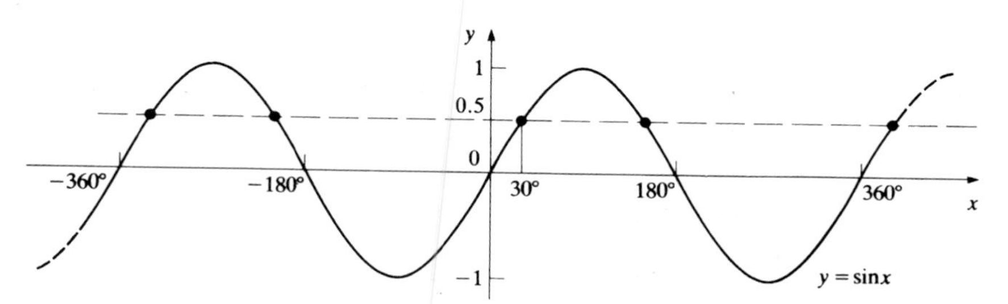

Figure 3.25

In order to define inverse functions for sine, cosine and tangent, a restriction has to be placed on the domain of each so that it becomes a one-to-one mapping.

The restriction of the domain determines the principal values for that trigonometrical function. The restricted domains are not all the same. They are listed below.

Function	Domain (degrees)	Domain (radians)
$y = \sin\theta$	$-90° \leqslant \theta \leqslant 90°$	$-\frac{\pi}{2} \leqslant \theta \leqslant \frac{\pi}{2}$
$y = \cos\theta$	$0° \leqslant \theta \leqslant 180°$	$0 \leqslant \theta \leqslant \pi$
$y = \tan\theta$	$-90° < \theta < 90°$	$-\frac{\pi}{2} < \theta < \frac{\pi}{2}$

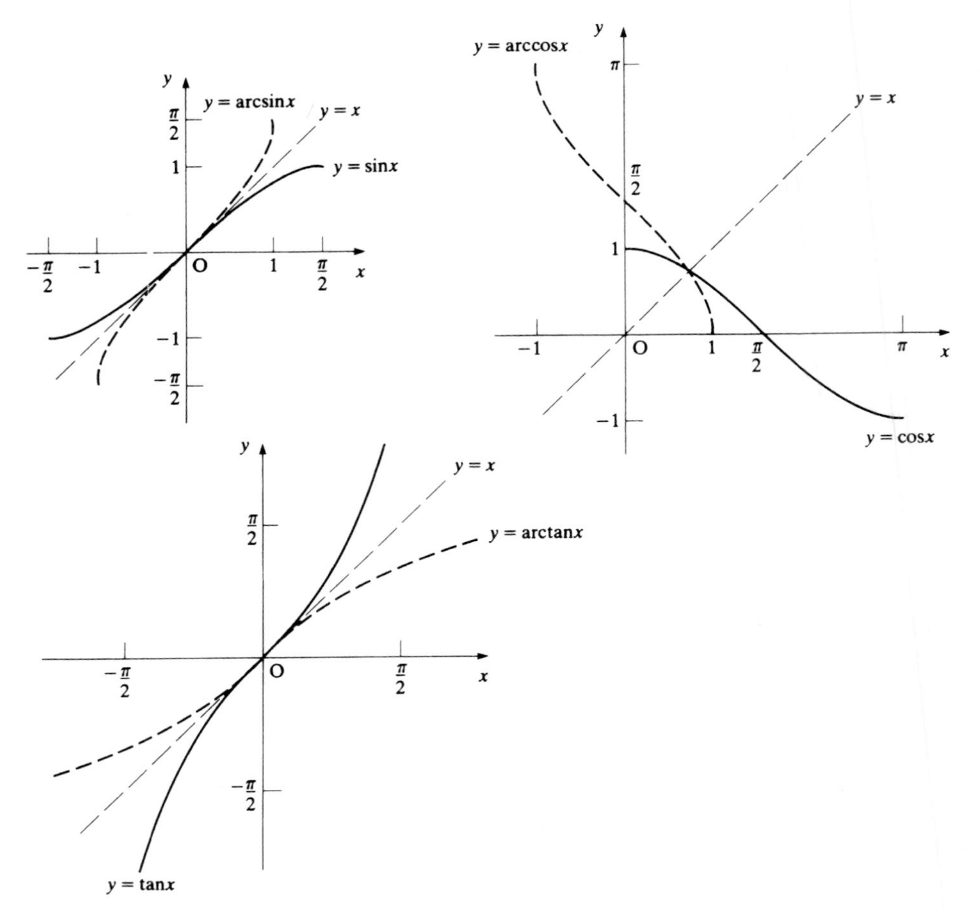

Figure 3.26

Figure 3.26 shows the graph of each trigonometrical function over its restricted domain, and that of its corresponding inverse function. The inverse functions have been drawn using the reflection property and, since this requires that the same scale is used on both axes, the angle must be plotted in radians rather than degrees.

In Chapter 8 you will meet the reciprocal trigonometrical functions,
$y = \operatorname{cosec}\theta = \frac{1}{\sin\theta}$, $y = \sec\theta = \frac{1}{\cos\theta}$ and $y = \cot\theta = \frac{1}{\tan\theta}$,
each have the same restricted domain as their parent function.

---

p How can you prove that the equation $\sec\theta = 0.5$ has no solution

(i) for $0 \leqslant \theta \leqslant \frac{\pi}{2}$ **(ii)** for any value of θ?

EXERCISE 3D

1 The functions f, g and h are defined by $f(x) = x^3$, $g(x) = 2x$ and $h(x) = x + 2$. Find each of the following, in terms of x.

(i) fg **(ii)** gf **(iii)** fh
(iv) hf **(v)** fgh **(vi)** ghf
(vii) g^2 **(viii)** $(fh)^2$ **(ix)** h^2

2 Find the inverses of the following functions.

(i) $f(x) = 2x + 7$ **(ii)** $f(x) = 4 - x$
(iii) $f(x) = \dfrac{4}{2 - x}$ **(iv)** $f(x) = x^2 - 3 \quad x \geqslant 0$

3 The function f is defined by $f(x) = (x - 2)^2 + 3$ for $x \geqslant 2$.

(i) Sketch the graph of $f(x)$.
(ii) On the same axes, sketch the graph of $f^{-1}(x)$ without finding its equation.

4 Express the following in terms of the functions $f: x \rightarrow \sqrt{x}$ and $g: x \rightarrow x + 4$.

(i) $x \rightarrow \sqrt{x + 4}$ **(ii)** $x \rightarrow x + 8$
(iii) $x \rightarrow \sqrt{x + 8}$ **(iv)** $x \rightarrow \sqrt{x} + 4$

5 The functions f, g and h are defined by

$$f(x) = \frac{3}{x - 4} \qquad g(x) = x^2 \qquad h(x) = \sqrt{2 - x}.$$

(i) For each function, state any real values of x for which it is not defined.
(ii) Find the inverse functions f^{-1} and h^{-1}.
(iii) Explain why g^{-1} does not exist when the domain of g is $\mathbb{R}$.
(iv) Suggest a suitable domain for g so that g^{-1} does exist.
(v) Is the domain for the composite function fg the same as for the composite function gf? Give reasons for your answer.

6 A function f is defined by:

$$f: x \rightarrow \frac{1}{x} \qquad x \in \mathbb{R},\ x \neq 0.$$

Find **(i)** $f^2(x)$ **(ii)** $f^3(x)$ **(iii)** $f^{-1}(x)$ **(iv)** $f^{999}(x)$.

7 (i) Show that $x^2 + 4x + 7 = (x + 2)^2 + a$, where a is to be determined.

(ii) Sketch the graph of $y = x^2 + 4x + 7$, giving the equation of its axis of symmetry and the co-ordinates of its vertex.

The function f is defined by $f: x \rightarrow x^2 + 4x + 7$ and has as its domain the set of all real numbers.

(iii) Find the range of f.
(iv) Explain, with reference to your sketch, why f has no inverse with its given domain. Suggest a domain for f for which it has an inverse.

[MEI]

8 The function f is defined by f: $x \rightarrow 4x^3 + 3 \quad x \in \mathbb{R}$.
Give the corresponding definition of f^{-1}.
State the relationship between the graphs of f and f^{-1}.

[UCLES]

9 Two functions are defined as $f(x) = x^2$ and $g(x) = x^2 + 4x - 1$.

(i) Find a and b so that $g(x) = f(x + a) + b$.

(ii) Show how the graph of $y = g(x)$ is related to the graph of $y = f(x)$ and sketch the graph of $y = g(x)$.

(iii) State the range of the function $g(x)$.

(iv) State the least value of c so that $g(x)$ is one-to-one for $x \geqslant c$.

(v) With this restriction, sketch $g(x)$ and $g^{-1}(x)$ on the same axes.

10 You are given that the function $f(x)$ is defined by

$$f(x) = \frac{ax - b}{x - c} \; (x \neq c),$$

where a, b and c are positive. The sketch shows the graph of $y = f(x)$.

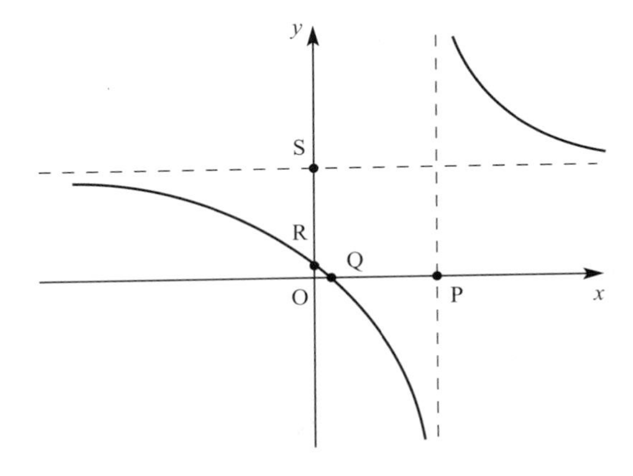

(i) Write down (in terms of a, b, c) the co-ordinates of the points P, Q, R and S.

(ii) If $y = \dfrac{ax - b}{x - c}$, express x in terms of y, a, b, and c. Hence show that the inverse function is given by

$$f^{-1}(x) = \frac{cx - b}{x - a}.$$

(iii) Find the values of a, b and c for which the function has all the following properties:
– it is self-inverse;
– its range is the set of all real numbers except 3;
– its graph passes through $(2, -2)$.

(iv) Find the values of a, b and c for which the graph of $y = f(x)$ can be obtained from that of $y = \dfrac{1}{x}$ by a translation of 1 unit parallel to the x axis followed by a translation of 3 units parallel to the y axis.

[MEI]

11 (i) A curve has equation $y = 12 \times 4^x$. Find the value of x for which $y = 20\,000$.

(ii) The graph of $y = 12 \times 4^x$ is translated by 1 unit parallel to the positive x axis. Given that the new graph has equation $y = cd^x$, write down the values of c and d.

(iii) The graph of $y = 12 \times 4^x$ is transformed by a stretch of scale factor 2 parallel to the x axis followed by a stretch of scale factor $\frac{1}{3}$ parallel to the y axis. Given that the new graph has equation $y = gh^x$, find the values of g and h.

[MEI]

Even, odd and periodic functions

Several of the curves with which you are familiar have symmetry of one form or another. For example

- the curve of any quadratic in x has a line of symmetry parallel to the y axis
- the curve of $y = \cos x$ has the y axis as a line of symmetry
- the curves of $y = \sin x$ and $y = \tan x$ have rotational symmetry of order 2 about the origin
- all the trigonometrical graphs have a repeating pattern (translational symmetry).

In this section you will be looking at particular types of symmetry.

Even functions

A function is *even* if its graph has the y axis as a line of symmetry. This is true for all three of the functions in figure 3.27.

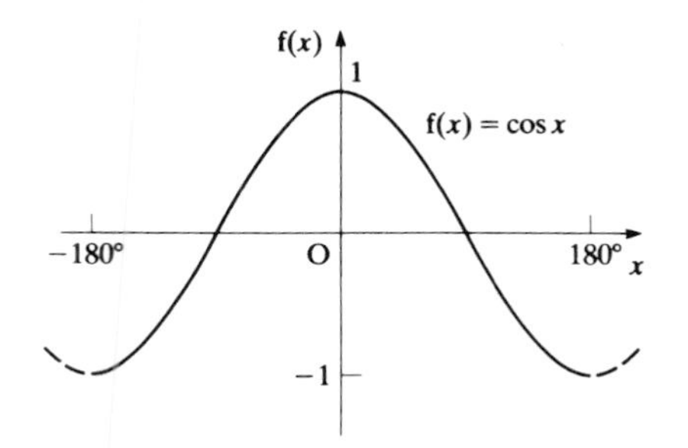

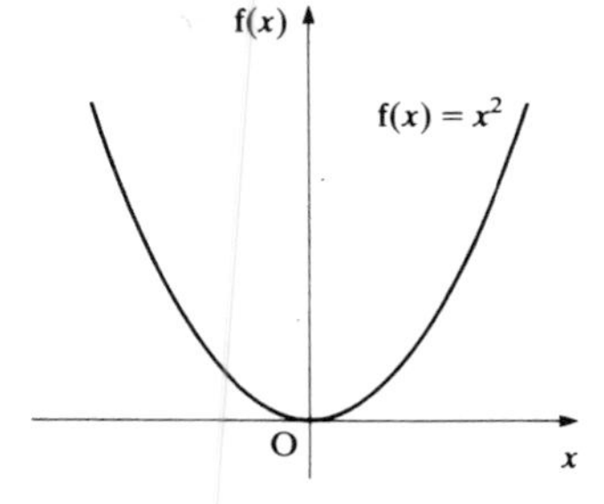

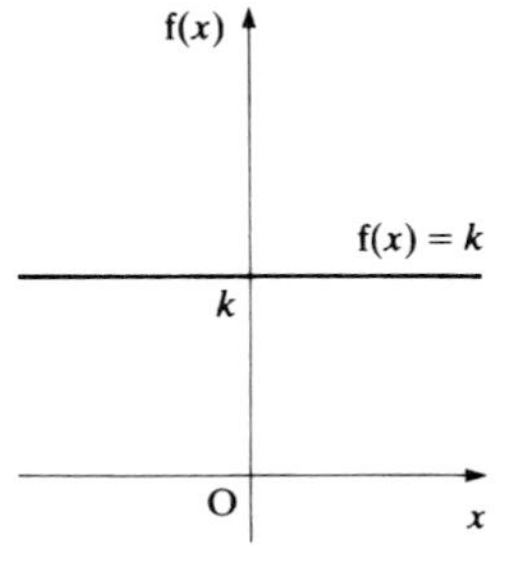

Figure 3.27

Reflecting a curve $y = f(x)$ in the y axis gives the curve $y = f(-x)$, so a curve which has the y axis as a line of symmetry satisfies the condition

$$f(-x) = f(x).$$

This relationship can be used to check whether a function is even, without drawing its graph.

EXAMPLE 3.12

Show that the function $f(x) = x^4 - 2x^2 + 3$ is an even function.

SOLUTION

$$\begin{aligned} f(-x) &= (-x)^4 - 2(-x)^2 + 3 \\ &= x^4 - 2x^2 + 3 \\ &= f(x), \end{aligned}$$

so the function is even.

Note

In general, if $f(x)$ is any polynomial function containing only even powers of x, and possibly a constant term, then $f(x)$ is an even function.

Odd functions

A function whose curve has rotational symmetry of order 2 about the origin, like the curves shown in figure 3.28, is called an *odd function.*

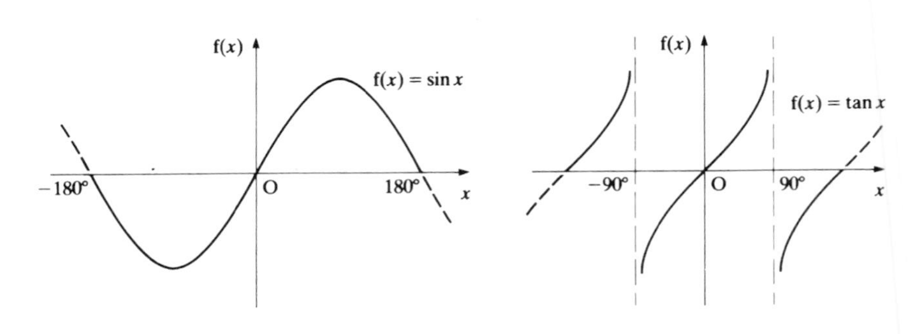

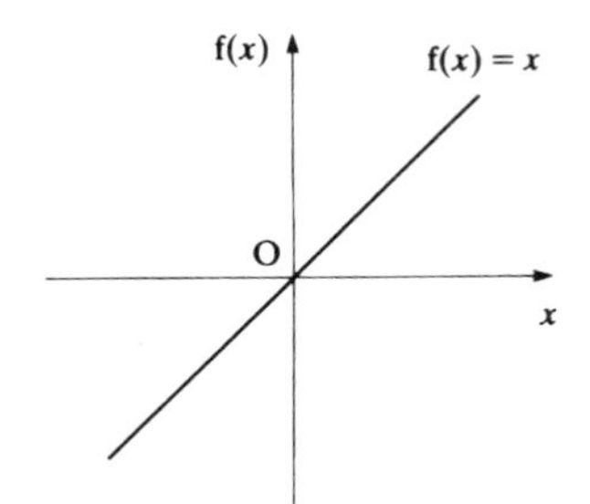

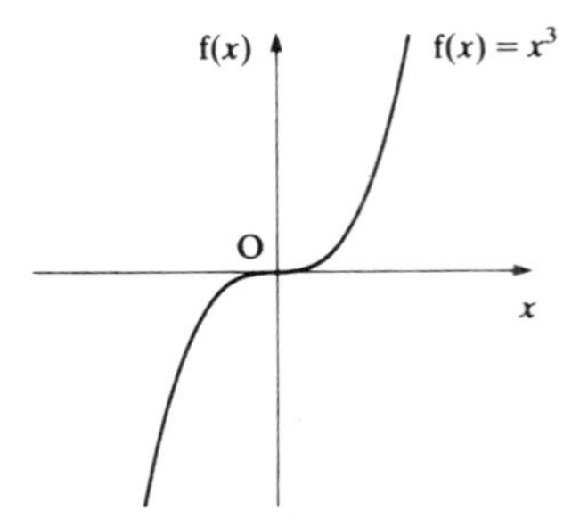

Figure 3.28

In all of these, the left-hand side of the graph is obtained from the right-hand side by rotating it through 180° around the origin.

In such cases,

$$f(-x) = -f(x).$$

EXAMPLE 3.13

Show that the function $f(x) = 3x^5 - 2x^3 + x$ is an odd function.

SOLUTION

$$\begin{aligned} f(-x) &= 3(-x)^5 - 2(-x)^3 + (-x) \\ &= -3x^5 + 2x^3 - x \\ &= -(3x^5 - 2x^3 + x) \\ &= -f(x), \end{aligned}$$

so the function is an odd function.

Note

Any polynomial function $f(x)$ containing only odd powers of x is an odd function.

Not all functions can be classified as even or odd – in fact the majority are neither.

EXAMPLE 3.14

For each of the graphs in figure 3.29, say whether the function is odd, even or neither.

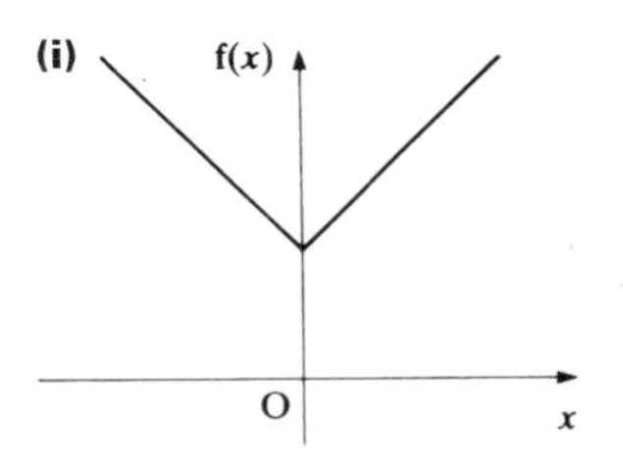

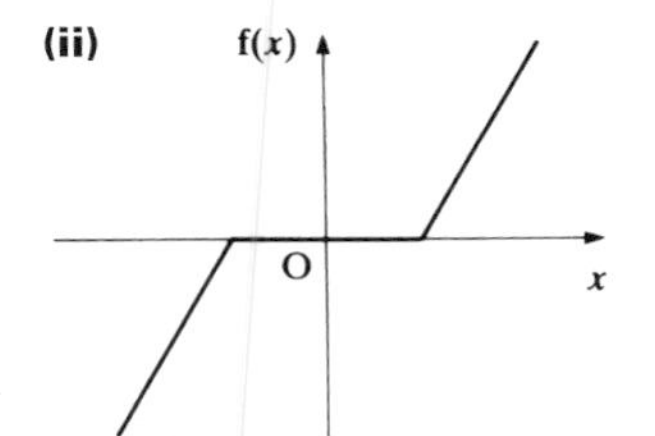

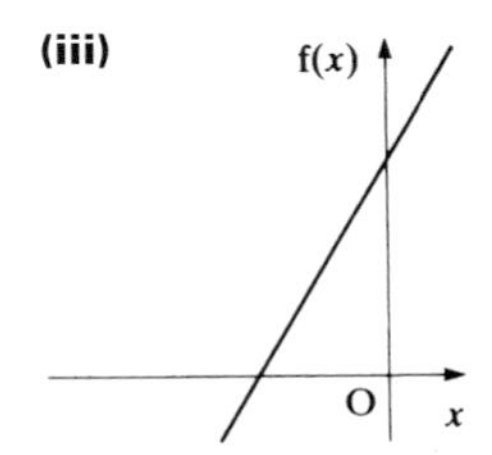

Figure 3.29

SOLUTION

(i) The graph is symmetrical about the y axis, therefore the function is even.

(ii) A rotation of 180° about the origin leaves the graph unchanged, therefore the function is odd.

(iii) The graph is changed by a rotation of 180° about the origin, and the y axis is not a line of symmetry, therefore the function is neither odd nor even.

---

p Prove that the function $f(x) = x^2 - 2x$ is neither even nor odd.

Periodic functions

A *periodic function* is one whose graph has a repeating pattern, just as a periodic sequence is a sequence which repeats itself at regular intervals. You have already met the most common periodic functions – the trigonometrical functions such as $f(x) = \sin x$ (shown in figure 3.30).

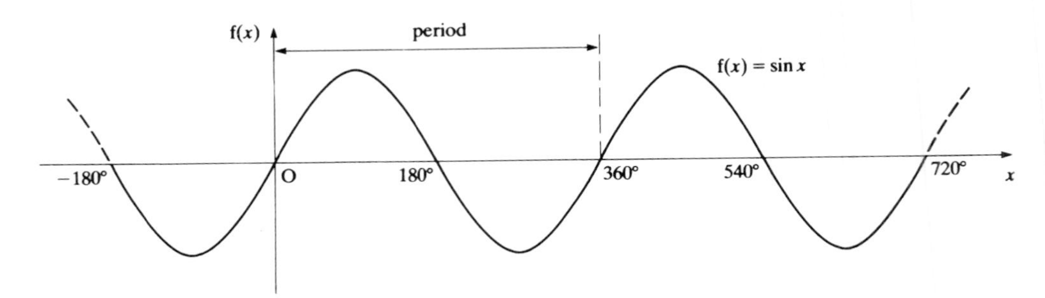

Figure 3.30

A periodic function $f(x)$ is such that there is some value of k for which

$$f(x + k) = f(x) \text{ for all values of } x.$$

The smallest value of k for which this is true is called the *period* of the function.

The functions $f(x) = \sin x$ and $f(x) = \cos x$ both have a period of $360°$ (or 2π), and $f(x) = \tan x$ has a period of $180°$ (or π).

EXAMPLE 3.15

(i) Sketch the curve of the function $f(x) = 3\sin(2x - 30°)$.

(ii) State the period of this function.

SOLUTION

(i)

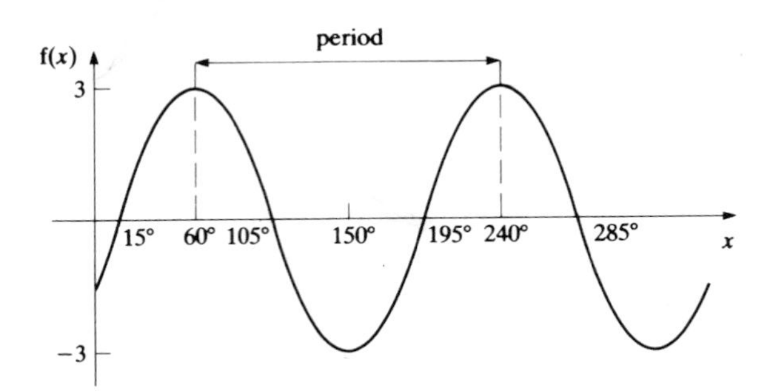

Figure 3.31

(ii) Period $= 180°$

You can draw the graph of a periodic function if you know its behaviour over one period.

EXAMPLE 3.16

The function f(x) is periodic with period 2. Given that

$$f(x) = x^2 \qquad 0 \leqslant x < 1$$
$$f(x) = 2 - x \qquad 1 \leqslant x < 2,$$

sketch the graph of f(x) for $-2 \leqslant x < 4$.

SOLUTION

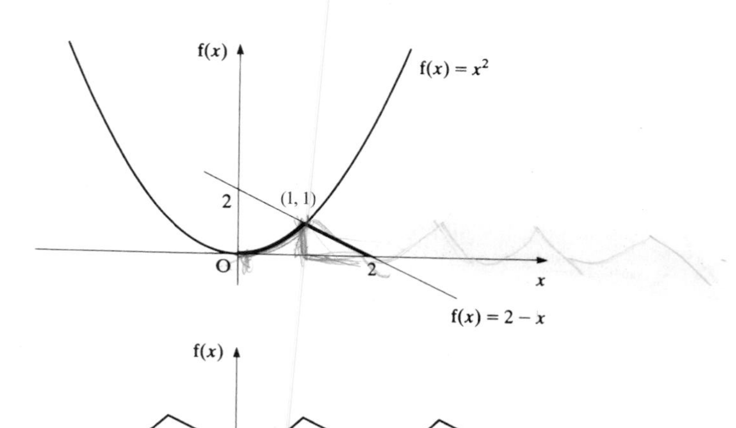

Figure 3.32

The first part of figure 3.32 shows the parts of the line and the curve which define f(x). These parts span an interval of length 2 (the period of the function) and thus form the basic repeating pattern. The second diagram shows this pattern repeated three times in the interval $-2 \leqslant x < 4$.

EXERCISE 3E

1 For each of the following curves, say whether the function is odd, even or neither.

(i)

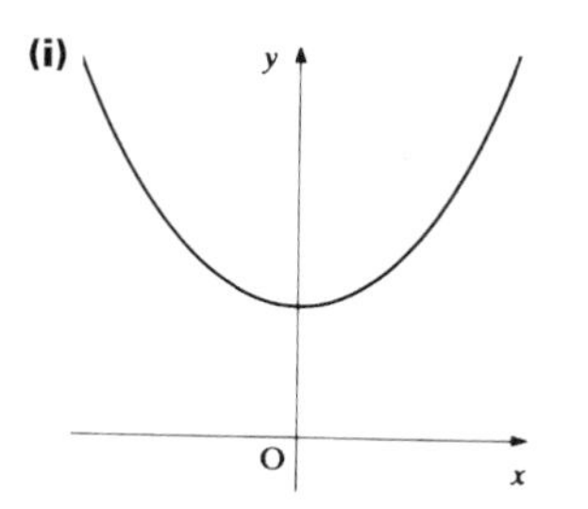

(ii)

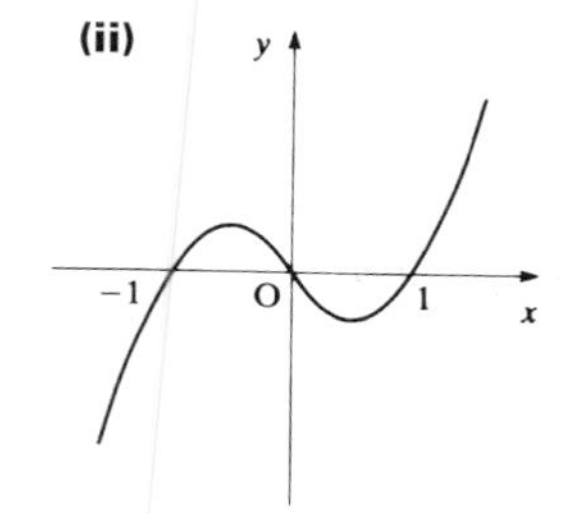

(iii)

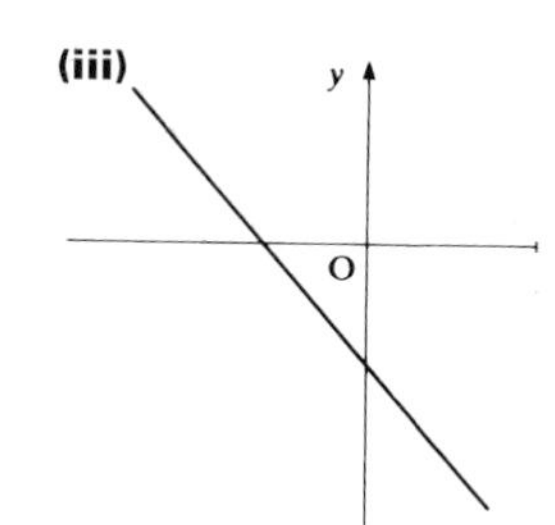

(iv)
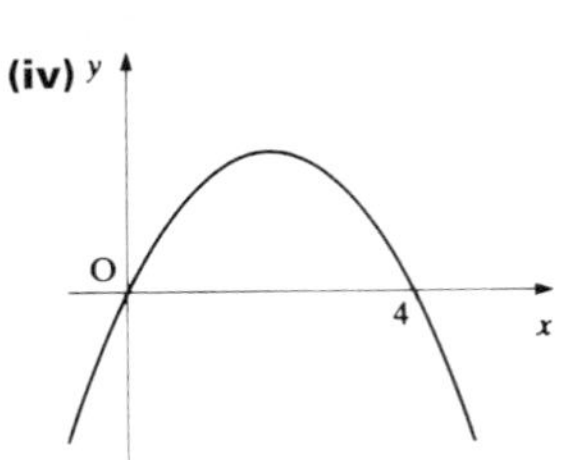

(v)
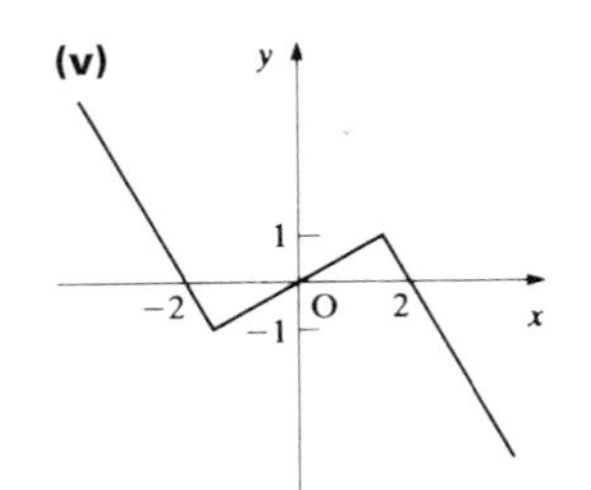

(vi)
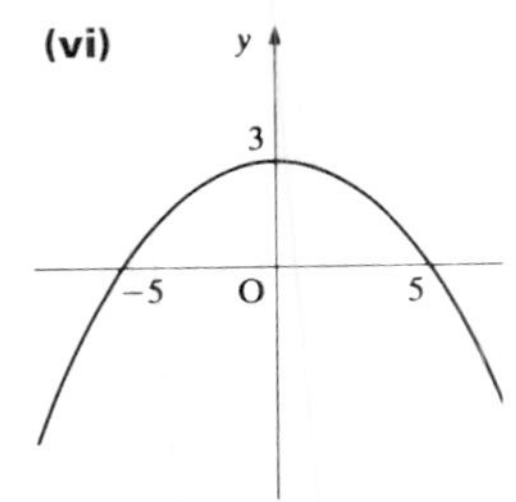

2 For each of the following functions, say whether it is odd, even, periodic, or any combination of these. For any function that is periodic, find its period.

(i) $f(x) = 2 - x^2$ **(ii)** $f(x) = \sin 3x$

(iii) $f(x) = x^2 + 2x - 3$ **(iv)** $f(x) = 2x^3 - 3x$

(v) $f(x) = \sin x + \cos x$ **(vi)** $f(x) = \sin x \cos x$

3 **(i)** Sketch the function $f(x) = \sin 2x$ for $0° \leqslant x \leqslant 360°$ and hence state its period.

(ii) Say how the period of this function is related to the period of $\sin x$.

(iii) What are the periods of the following functions?

(a) $f(x) = \sin 4x$ **(b)** $f(x) = \sin 3x$ **(c)** $f(x) = \sin \frac{x}{2}$

4 The function f is even, periodic with period 2 and, for $0 \leqslant x \leqslant 1$, $f(x) = x$. Sketch the graph of $f(x)$ for $-4 \leqslant x \leqslant 4$.

5 A function f has as its domain the set of real numbers. For $0 \leqslant x \leqslant 1$, it is given by the equation

$$f(x) = 1 - x.$$

Given also that f is an even function with period 2, draw its graph over the interval $-3 \leqslant x \leqslant 3$.

Write down equations of the function for

(i) $-1 \leqslant x \leqslant 0$ **(ii)** $2 \leqslant x \leqslant 3$.

[SMP]

6 A function $g(x)$ of period 2 is defined by

$$g(x) = x^2 \quad \text{for } 0 \leqslant x \leqslant \tfrac{1}{2}$$

$$g(x) = \tfrac{1}{4} \quad \text{for } \tfrac{1}{2} \leqslant x \leqslant 1.$$

Given also that $g(x) = g(-x)$ for all x, sketch the graph of $g(x)$ for $-2 \leqslant x \leqslant 2$.

7 The sketch shows part of the graph of $y = f(x)$. The points A, B, C and D have co-ordinates (0, 1), (1, 0), (2, 1) and (3, 0) respectively.

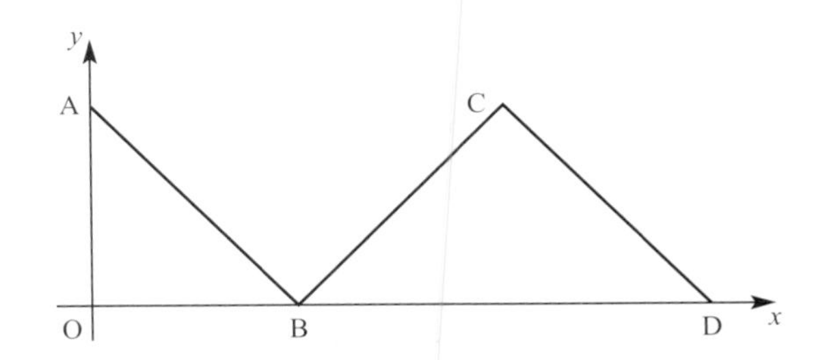

(i) Given that $f(x)$ is a periodic function with the shape of section BCD repeated

(a) state its period

(b) give its equation for $-1 \leq x \leq 1$.

(ii) Sketch separately the graphs of

(a) $y = f(2x)$

(b) $y = f(x + 3)$,

stating in each case the co-ordinates of the points corresponding to A, B, C and D.

8 A light elastic string is stretched between two points A and B which are 3 m apart on a smooth horizontal surface. A heavy object attached to the mid-point of the string is pulled 50 cm towards A and then released.

During the subsequent motion the string remains taut, and the object oscillates along part of the line AB in such a way that its displacement x cm from the centre of AB at a time t seconds after the motion commences is given by

$$x = 0.5 \cos 2.5t \text{ where the angle is in radians.}$$

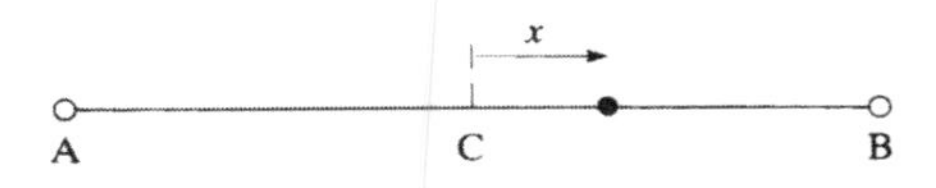

Sketch the graph of x against t for $0 \leq t \leq 2\pi$.

Hence show that the motion is periodic, and state its period.

9 The functions $f(x)$ and $g(x)$ are defined by

$$f(x) = x^2 + 18, \quad g(x) = 2x - 1,$$

for all real values of x.

(i) State the ranges of $f(x)$ and $g(x)$. Explain why $g(x)$ has an inverse function and $f(x)$ does not.
Find an expression for the inverse function $g^{-1}(x)$ in terms of x.

(ii) Find expressions for gf(x) and fg(x).

(iii) Solve the equation gf(x) = fg(x).

A function $y = \mathrm{h}(x)$ is defined for all real values of x.
The diagram shows a sketch of part of the graph of this function for $0 \leqslant x \leqslant 1$.
The function h(x) is an odd function and is periodic with period 2.

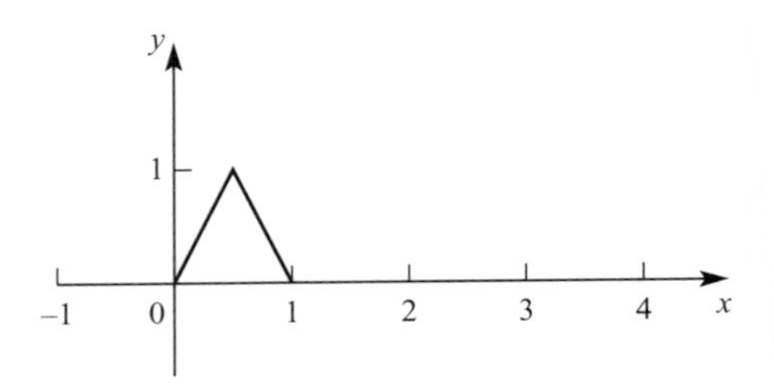

Sketch the graphs of the following functions for $-4 \leqslant x \leqslant 4$.

(iv) $y = \mathrm{h}(x)$ **(v)** $y = \mathrm{h}\left(\frac{1}{2}x\right)$ **(vi)** $y = \frac{1}{2}\mathrm{h}(x)$

[MEI]

The modulus function

Look at the graph of $y = \mathrm{f}(x)$, where $\mathrm{f}(x) = x$.

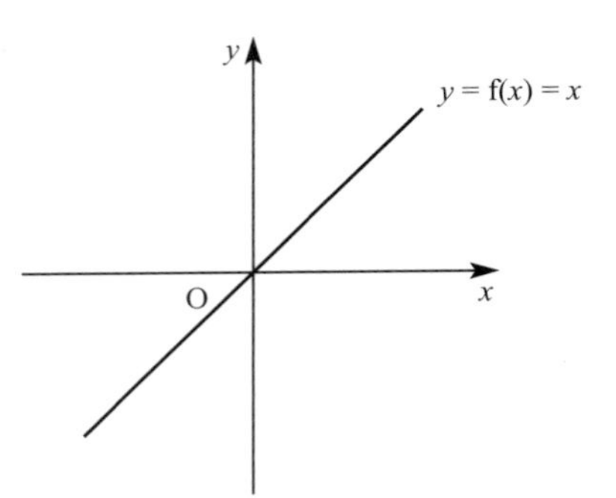

Figure 3.33

The function f(x) is positive when x is positive and negative when x is negative.

Now look at the graph of $y = \mathrm{g}(x)$, where $\mathrm{g}(x) = |x|$.

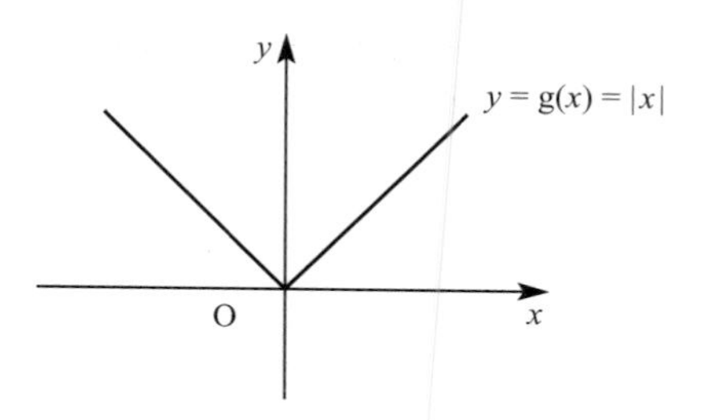

Figure 3.34

The function $g(x)$ is called the *modulus* of x. $g(x)$ always takes the positive numerical value of x. For example, when $x = -2$, $g(x) = 2$, so $g(x)$ is always positive. The modulus is also called the *magnitude* of the quantity.

Another way of writing the modulus function $g(x)$ is

$$g(x) = x \qquad \text{for } x \geqslant 0$$
$$g(x) = -x \qquad \text{for } x < 0.$$

What is the value of $g(3)$ and $g(-3)$?

What is the value of $|3 + 3|$, $|3 - 3|$, $|3| + |3|$ and $|3| + |-3|$?

The graph of $y = g(x)$ can be obtained from the graph of $y = f(x)$ by replacing values where $f(x)$ is negative by the equivalent positive values. This is the equivalent of reflecting that part of the line in the x axis.

EXAMPLE 3.17

Sketch the graphs of the following on separate axes.

(i) $y = 1 - x$
(ii) $y = |1 - x|$
(iii) $y = 2 + |1 - x|$

SOLUTION

(i) $y = 1 - x$ is the straight line through $(0, 1)$ and $(1, 0)$.

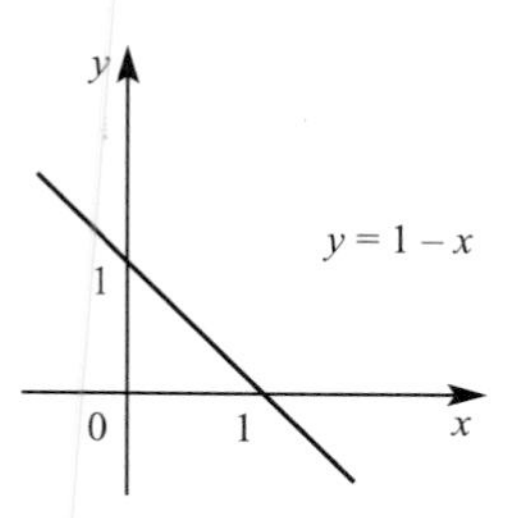

Figure 3.35

(ii) $y = |1 - x|$ is obtained by reflecting the part of the line for $x > 1$ in the x axis.

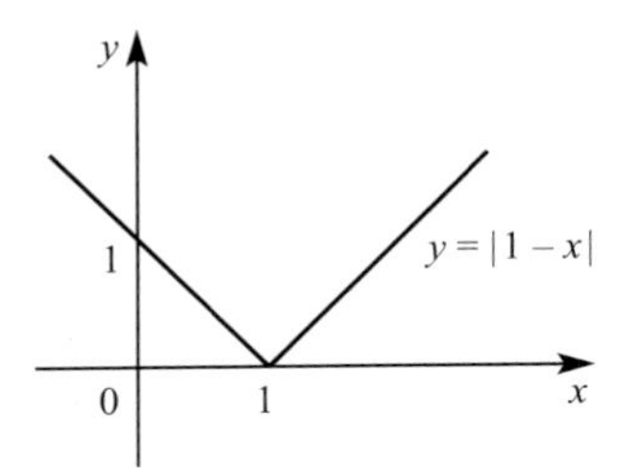

Figure 3.36

(iii) $y = 2 + |1 - x|$ is obtained from the previous graph by applying the translation $\begin{pmatrix} 0 \\ 2 \end{pmatrix}$.

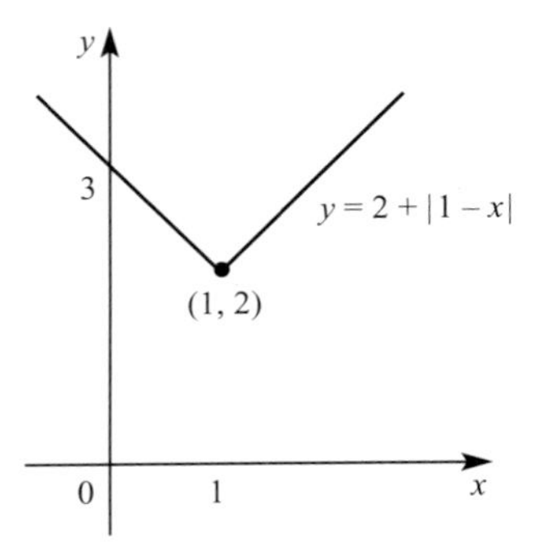

Figure 3.37

Inequalities involving the modulus sign

You will often meet inequalities involving the modulus sign.

Look back at the graph of $y = |x|$ in figure 3.34.

How does this show that $|x| < 2$ is equivalent to $-2 < x < 2$?

EXAMPLE 3.18

Solve the following.

(i) $|x + 3| \leqslant 4$
(ii) $|2x - 1| > 9$
(iii) $5 - |x - 2| > 1$

SOLUTION

(i) $|x + 3| \leqslant 4 \quad \Leftrightarrow \quad -4 \leqslant x + 3 \leqslant 4$
$\Leftrightarrow \quad -7 \leqslant x \leqslant 1$

(ii) $|2x-1| > 9 \iff 2x-1 < -9$ or $2x-1 > 9$
$\iff 2x < -8$ or $2x > 10$
$\iff x < -4$ or $x > 5$

(iii) $5-|x-2| > 1 \iff 4 > |x-2|$
$\iff |x-2| < 4$
$\iff -4 < x-2 < 4$
$\iff -2 < x < 6$

Note

The solution to part **(ii)** represents two separate intervals on the number line, so cannot be written as a single inequality.

EXAMPLE 3.19

Express the inequality $-2 < x < 6$ in the form $|x-a| < b$, where a and b are to be found.

SOLUTION

$|x-a| < b \iff -b < x-a < b$
$\iff a-b < x < a+b$

Comparing this with $-2 < x < 6$ gives

$$a-b=-2$$
$$a+b=6.$$

Solving these simultaneously gives $a=2$, $b=4$, so $|x-2| < 4$.

EXERCISE 3F

1 Solve the following inequalities.

(i) $|x+3| < 5$
(ii) $|x-2| \leqslant 2$
(iii) $|x-5| > 6$
(iv) $|x+1| \geqslant 2$
(v) $|2x-3| < 7$
(vi) $|3x-2| \leqslant 4$

2 Express each of the following inequalities in the form $|x-a| < b$, where a and b are to be found.

(i) $-1 < x < 3$
(ii) $2 < x < 8$
(iii) $-2 < x < 4$
(iv) $-1 < x < 6$
(v) $9.9 < x < 10.1$
(vi) $0.5 < x < 7.5$

3 Sketch each of the following graphs on a separate set of axes.

(i) $y = |x + 2|$
(ii) $y = |2x - 3|$
(iii) $y = |x + 2| - 2$
(iv) $y = |x| + 1$
(v) $y = |2x + 5| - 4$
(vi) $y = 3 + |x - 2|$

Curve sketching

You have already had some experience of curve sketching, and have probably realised that it is of fundamental importance in mathematics. Throughout this course, the curve sketching techniques available to you will be progressively extended. This section reviews the techniques you have met so far.

When sketching a curve you need to mark points in approximately the right positions and join them up in the right general shape. You should also indicate the co-ordinates of any important points, such as points of intersection with the axes and turning points. Your sketch should show up any symmetry which the curve possesses, any asymptotes, and should indicate the behaviour of the curve for large values of x or y.

A graphic calculator or suitable computer graph-drawing package is often useful, but you must be careful that important features of a graph are not missed. This happens most often when either a turning point is off the screen with the range which is being used, or two or more turning points are so close together that they cannot be distinguished. The following activity shows how this can happen, and suggests some questions which you should ask yourself before you accept the graph that is displayed.

ACTIVITY 3.5

Use a graphic calculator or computer graph-drawing package with the range set at x min: –2, x max: 2, y min: –10, y max: 20.

1 Sketch the graph of $f(x) = x^3 - 15x^2 + 27x + 1$.

(i) How many turning points are there in the display?
(ii) The function is a cubic function. How many turning points might you expect?
(iii) The function has a positive x^3 term. What would you expect for the general shape of the curve?
(iv) Use your answers to parts **(ii)** and **(iii)** to alter the range so that you obtain a true picture of the function.

2 Sketch the graph of $f(x) = 10x^4 - x^2 + 1$.

(i) How many turning points seem to be in the display?

(ii) The function is a quartic (fourth degree) function. How many turning points might you expect?

(iii) The function has a positive x^4 term. What would you expect for the general shape of the curve?

(iv) Use your answers to parts **(ii)** and **(iii)** to alter the range (or zoom in) so that you obtain a more detailed picture of the function.

3 Sketch the graph of $f(x) = \frac{8x + 3}{x - 5}$.

(i) The display obviously shows only part of the curve. The function has the term $x - 5$ in the denominator: which value of x must therefore be excluded from the domain?

(ii) Alter the range setting so that this value is visible. You will find that altering it just to include this value tells you very little more about the curve – you need to make quite considerable alterations to get a good idea of the correct graph. Possible settings are x min: –10, x max: 20, y min: –20, y max: 40.

INVESTIGATION

Investigate the relationship between the graphs of $y = f(x)$ and $y = \frac{1}{f(x)}$ for different functions $f(x)$.

KEY POINTS

Mappings and functions

1 A mapping is any rule connecting input values (objects) and output values (images). It can be many-to-one, one-to-many, one-to-one or many-to-many.

2 A many-to-one or one-to-one mapping is called a function. It is a mapping for which each input value gives exactly one output value.

3 The domain of a mapping or function is the set of possible input values (values of x).

4 The co-domain of a mapping or function is the set of possible output values (values of y).

5 The range of a mapping or function is the set of output values which are actually achieved.

Transformations of the graphs of the function $y = \mathrm{f}(x)$

Function	Transformation
$\mathrm{f}(x - t) + s$	Translation $\begin{pmatrix} t \\ s \end{pmatrix}$
$a\,\mathrm{f}(x)$	One-way stretch, parallel to y axis, scale factor a
$\mathrm{f}(ax)$	One-way stretch, parallel to x axis, scale factor $\frac{1}{a}$
$-\mathrm{f}(x)$	Reflection in x axis
$\mathrm{f}(-x)$	Reflection in y axis

Composite functions

6 A composite function is obtained when one function (say g) is applied after another (say f). The notation used is $\mathrm{g}[\mathrm{f}(x)]$ or $\mathrm{gf}(x)$.

Inverse functions

7 For any one-to-one function $\mathrm{f}(x)$, there is an inverse function $\mathrm{f}^{-1}(x)$.

8 The curves of a function and its inverse are reflections of each other in the line $y = x$.

Special functions

9 For an even function $\mathrm{f}(x) = \mathrm{f}(-x)$: the y axis is a line of symmetry.

10 For an odd function $\mathrm{f}(-x) = -\mathrm{f}(x)$: it has rotation symmetry about the origin.

11 For a periodic function $\mathrm{f}(x + k) = \mathrm{f}(x)$: it has a repeating pattern of length k.

12 The modulus of x, written $|x|$, means the positive value of x.

13 The modulus function is

$$|x| = x, \quad \text{for } x \geqslant 0$$
$$|x| = -x, \quad \text{for } x < 0.$$

4 Techniques for differentiation

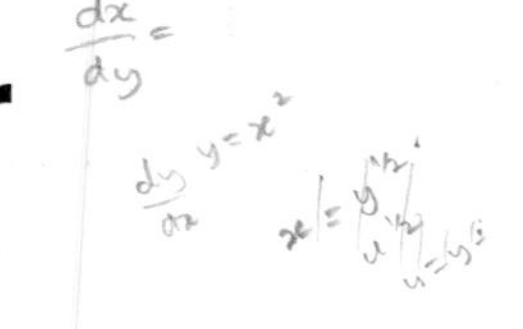

Almost everything that distinguishes the modern world from earlier centuries is attributable to science, which achieved its most spectacular triumphs in the seventeenth century.

A W Bertrand Russell (1872–1970)

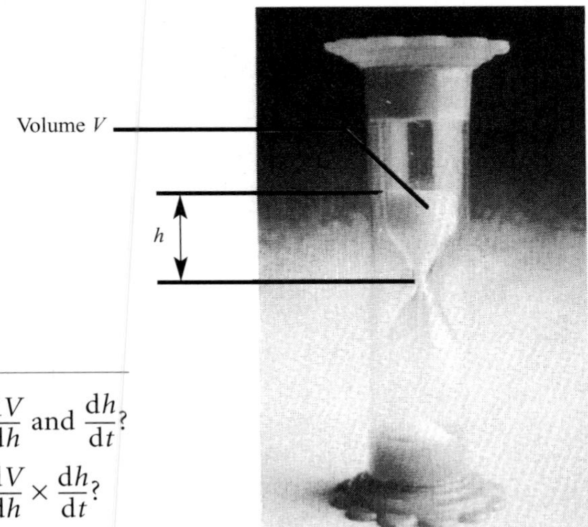

? What information is given by $\frac{\mathrm{d}V}{\mathrm{d}h}$ and $\frac{\mathrm{d}h}{\mathrm{d}t}$?

What information is given by $\frac{\mathrm{d}V}{\mathrm{d}h} \times \frac{\mathrm{d}h}{\mathrm{d}t}$?

The chain rule

How would you differentiate an expression like

$$y = \sqrt{x^2 + 1}?$$

Your first thought may be to write it as $y = (x^2 + 1)^{\frac{1}{2}}$ and then get rid of the brackets, but that is not possible in this case because the power $\frac{1}{2}$ is not a positive integer. Instead you need to think of the expression as a composite function, a 'function of a function'.

You have already met composite functions in Chapter 3, using the notation $\mathrm{g}[\mathrm{f}(x)]$ or $\mathrm{gf}(x)$.

In this chapter we call the first function to be applied $\mathrm{u}(x)$, or just u, rather than $\mathrm{f}(x)$.

In this case, $\quad u = x^2 + 1$

and $\quad y = \sqrt{u} = u^{\frac{1}{2}}$.

This is now in a form which you can differentiate using the *chain rule.*

Differentiating a composite function

To find $\frac{dy}{dx}$ for a function of a function, you consider the effect of a small change in x on the two variables, y and u, as follows. A small change δx in x leads to a small change δu in u and a corresponding small change δy in y, and by simple algebra,

$$\frac{\delta y}{\delta x} = \frac{\delta y}{\delta u} \times \frac{\delta u}{\delta x}.$$

In the limit, as $\delta x \to 0$,

$$\frac{\delta y}{\delta x} \to \frac{dy}{dx}, \frac{\delta y}{\delta u} \to \frac{dy}{du} \text{ and } \frac{\delta u}{\delta x} \to \frac{du}{dx}$$

and so the relationship above becomes

$$\frac{dy}{dx} = \frac{dy}{du} \times \frac{du}{dx}.$$

This is known as the chain rule.

EXAMPLE 4.1

Differentiate $y = (x^2 + 1)^{\frac{1}{2}}$.

SOLUTION

As you saw earlier, you can break down this expression as follows.

$$y = u^{\frac{1}{2}}, \quad u = x^2 + 1$$

Differentiating these gives

$$\frac{dy}{du} = \frac{1}{2}u^{-\frac{1}{2}} = \frac{1}{2\sqrt{x^2 + 1}}$$

and

$$\frac{du}{dx} = 2x.$$

By the chain rule

$$\frac{dy}{dx} = \frac{dy}{du} \times \frac{du}{dx}$$

$$= \frac{1}{2\sqrt{x^2 + 1}} \times 2x$$

$$= \frac{x}{\sqrt{x^2 + 1}}$$

Notice that the answer must be given in terms of the same variables as the question, in this case x and y. The variable u was your invention and so should not appear in the answer.

You can see that effectively you have made a substitution, in this case $u = x^2 + 1$. This transformed the problem into one that could easily be solved.

Note

Notice that the substitution gave you two functions that you could differentiate. Some substitutions would not have worked. For example, the substitution $u = x^2$, would give you

$$y = (u + 1)^{\frac{1}{2}} \text{ and } u = x^2.$$

You would still not be able to differentiate y, so you would have gained nothing.

EXAMPLE 4.2

Use the chain rule to find $\frac{dy}{dx}$ when $y = (x^2 - 2)^4$.

SOLUTION

Let $u = x^2 - 2$, then $y = u^4$.

$$\frac{du}{dx} = 2x$$

and

$$\begin{aligned}\frac{dy}{du} &= 4u^3 \\ &= 4(x^2 - 2)^3\end{aligned}$$

$$\begin{aligned}\frac{dy}{dx} &= \frac{dy}{du} \times \frac{du}{dx} \\ &= 4(x^2 - 2)^3 \times 2x \\ &= 8x\,(x^2 - 2)^3.\end{aligned}$$

---

p A student does this question by first multiplying out $(x^2 - 2)^4$ to get a polynomial of order 8. Prove that this heavy-handed method gives the same result.

With practice you may find that you can do some stages of questions like this in your head, and just write down the answer. If you have any doubt, however, you should write down the full method.

Differentiation with respect to different variables

The chain rule makes it possible to differentiate with respect to a variable which does not feature in the original expression. For example, the volume V of a sphere of radius r is given by $V = \frac{4}{3}\pi r^3$. Differentiating this with respect to r gives the rate of change of volume with radius, $\frac{dV}{dr} = 4\pi r^2$. However you might be more interested in finding $\frac{\mathrm{d}V}{\mathrm{d}t}$, the rate of change of volume with time, t.

To find this, you would use the chain rule:

$$\frac{\mathrm{d}V}{\mathrm{d}t} = \frac{\mathrm{d}V}{\mathrm{d}r} \times \frac{\mathrm{d}r}{\mathrm{d}t}$$

$$\frac{\mathrm{d}V}{\mathrm{d}t} = 4\pi r^2 \frac{\mathrm{d}r}{\mathrm{d}t}$$

Notice that the expression for $\frac{\mathrm{d}V}{\mathrm{d}t}$ includes $\frac{\mathrm{d}r}{\mathrm{d}t}$, the rate of increase of radius with time.

You have now differentiated V with respect to t.

The use of the chain rule in this way widens the scope of differentiation and this means that you have to be careful how you describe the process.

'Differentiate $y = x^2$' could mean differentiation with respect to x, or t, or any other variable. In this book, and others in this series, we have adopted the convention that, unless otherwise stated, differentiation is with respect to the variable on the right-hand side of the expression. So when we write 'differentiate $y = x^2$' or simply 'differentiate x^2', it is to be understood that the differentiation is with respect to x.

The expression 'increasing at a rate of' is generally understood to imply differentation with respect to time, t.

EXAMPLE 4.3

The radius r cm of a circular ripple made by dropping a stone into a pond is increasing at a rate of $8\,\text{cm s}^{-1}$. At what rate is the area $A\,\text{cm}^2$ enclosed by the ripple increasing when the radius is 25 cm?

SOLUTION

$$A = \pi r^2$$

$$\frac{\mathrm{d}A}{\mathrm{d}r} = 2\pi r$$

The question is asking for $\frac{\mathrm{d}A}{\mathrm{d}t}$, the rate of change of area with respect to time.

Now $\frac{\mathrm{d}A}{\mathrm{d}t} = \frac{\mathrm{d}A}{\mathrm{d}r} \times \frac{\mathrm{d}r}{\mathrm{d}t}$

$$= 2\pi r \frac{\mathrm{d}r}{\mathrm{d}t}.$$

When $r = 25$ and $\frac{\mathrm{d}r}{\mathrm{d}t} = 8$

$$\frac{\mathrm{d}A}{\mathrm{d}t} = 2\pi \times 25 \times 8$$

$$\approx 1260\,\text{cm}^2\,\text{s}^{-1}.$$

EXERCISE 4A

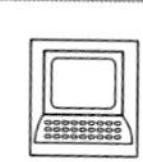

In some of these questions you are asked to find the stationary points of a curve and then to use them as a guide for sketching it. You will find it helpful to use a graphic calculator to check your answers in these cases.

1 Use the chain rule to differentiate the following functions.

(i) $y = (x + 2)^3$ **(ii)** $y = (2x + 3)^4$ **(iii)** $y = (x^2 - 5)^3$

(iv) $y = (x^3 + 4)^5$ **(v)** $y = (3x + 2)^{-1}$ **(vi)** $y = \dfrac{1}{(x^2 - 3)^3}$

(vii) $y = (x^2 - 1)^{\frac{3}{2}}$ **(viii)** $y = \left(\dfrac{1}{x} + x\right)^3$ **(ix)** $y = (\sqrt{x} - 1)^4$

2 Given that $y = (3x - 5)^3$

(i) find $\dfrac{dy}{dx}$

(ii) find the equation of the tangent to the curve at (2, 1)

(iii) show that the equation of the normal to the curve at (1, –8) can be written in the form

$$36y + x + 287 = 0.$$

3 Given that $y = (2x - 1)^4$

(i) find $\dfrac{dy}{dx}$

(ii) find the co-ordinates of any stationary points and determine their nature

(iii) sketch the curve.

4 Given that $y = (x^2 - 4)^3$

(i) find $\dfrac{dy}{dx}$

(ii) find the co-ordinates of any stationary points and determine their nature

(iii) sketch the curve.

5 Given that $y = (x^2 - x - 2)^4$

(i) find $\dfrac{dy}{dx}$

(ii) find the co-ordinates of any stationary points and determine their nature

(iii) sketch the curve.

6 The length of a side of a square is increasing at a rate of $0.2\,\text{cm s}^{-1}$.
At what rate is the area increasing when the length of the side is 10 cm?

7 The force F newtons between two magnetic poles is given by the formula
$F = \dfrac{1}{500r^2}$, where r m is their distance apart.
Find the rate of change of the force when the poles are 0.2 m apart and the distance between them is increasing at a rate of $0.03\,\text{ms}^{-1}$.

8 The radius of a circular fungus is increasing at a uniform rate of 5 cm per day.
At what rate is the area increasing when the radius is 1 m?

9 The graph of $y = (x^3 - x^2 + 2)^3$, is shown in the diagram.

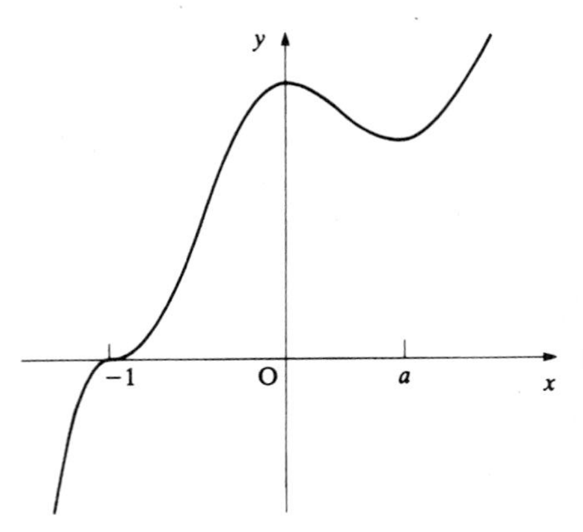

(i) Find the gradient function $\frac{dy}{dx}$.

(ii) Verify, showing your working clearly, that when $x = -1$ the curve has a point of inflection and when $x = 0$ the curve has a maximum.

(iii) The curve has a minimum when $x = a$.
Find a and verify that this corresponds to a minimum.

(iv) Find the gradient at $(1, 8)$ and the equation of the tangent to the curve at this point.

10 ☆☆☆☆☆☆☆ Some students on an expedition reach the corner of a very muddy field. They need to reach the opposite corner as quickly as possible as they are behind schedule. They estimate that they could walk along the edge of the field at $5\,\text{km h}^{-1}$ and across the field at $3\,\text{km h}^{-1}$. They know from their map that the field is a square of side 0.5 km.

How far should they walk along the edge of the field before cutting across?

The product rule

Figure 4.1 shows a sketch of the curve of $y = 20x(x - 1)^6$.

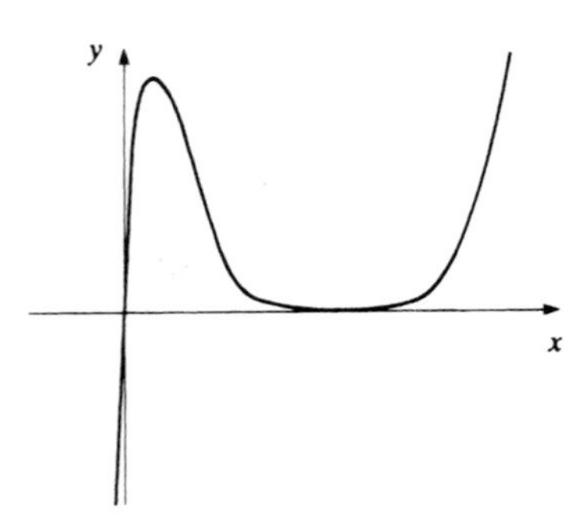

Figure 4.1

If you wanted to find the gradient function, $\frac{dy}{dx}$, for the curve, you could expand the right-hand side then differentiate it term by term – a long and cumbersome process!

There are other functions like this, made up of the product of two or more simpler functions, which are not just time-consuming to expand – they are *impossible* to expand. One such function is

$$y = (x - 1)^{\frac{1}{2}}(x + 1)^6.$$

Clearly you need a technique for differentiating functions that are products of simpler ones, and a suitable notation with which to express it.

The most commonly used notation involves writing

$$y = uv,$$

where the variables u and v are both functions of x. Using this notation, $\frac{dy}{dx}$ is given by

$$\frac{dy}{dx} = u\frac{dv}{dx} + v\frac{du}{dx}.$$

This is called the *product rule* and it is derived from first principles in the next section.

The product rule from first principles

A small increase δx in x leads to corresponding small increases δu, δv and δy in u, v and y. And so

$$\begin{aligned} y + \delta y &= (u + \delta u)(v + \delta v) \\ &= uv + v\delta u + u\delta v + \delta u\delta v. \end{aligned}$$

Since $y = uv$, the increase in y is given by

$$\delta y = v\delta u + u\delta v + \delta u\delta v.$$

Dividing both sides by δx, $\frac{\delta y}{\delta x} = v\,\frac{\delta u}{\delta x} + u\,\frac{\delta v}{\delta x} + \delta u\,\frac{\delta v}{\delta x}$.

In the limit, as $\delta x \to 0$, so do δu, δv and δy, and

$$\frac{\delta u}{\delta x} \to \frac{du}{dx}, \quad \frac{\delta v}{\delta x} \to \frac{dv}{dx} \quad \text{and} \quad \frac{\delta y}{\delta x} \to \frac{dy}{dx}.$$

The expression becomes $\frac{dy}{dx} = v\frac{du}{dx} + u\frac{dv}{dx}$.

Notice that since $\delta u \to 0$ the last term on the right-hand side has disappeared.

EXAMPLE 4.4

Given that $y = (2x+3)(x^2-5)$, find $\frac{dy}{dx}$ using the product rule.

SOLUTION

$y = (2x+3)(x^2-5)$

Let $u = 2x+3$ and $v = x^2-5$.

Then $\frac{du}{dx} = 2$ and $\frac{dv}{dx} = 2x$.

Using the product rule,
$$\begin{aligned}\frac{dy}{dx} &= v\frac{du}{dx} + u\frac{dv}{dx}\\ &= (x^2-5)\times 2 + (2x+3)\times 2x\\ &= 2(x^2-5+2x^2+3x)\\ &= 2(3x^2+3x-5).\end{aligned}$$

Note

In this case you could have multiplied out the expression for y.

$$\begin{aligned}y &= 2x^3+3x^2-10x-15\\ \frac{dy}{dx} &= 6x^2+6x-10\\ &= 2(3x^2+3x-5)\end{aligned}$$

EXAMPLE 4.5

Differentiate $y = 20x(x-1)^6$.

SOLUTION

Let $u = 20x$ and $v = (x-1)^6$.

Then $\frac{du}{dx} = 20$, and $\frac{dv}{dx} = 6(x-1)^5$ (using the chain rule).

Using the product rule,
$$\begin{aligned}\frac{dy}{dx} &= v\frac{du}{dx} + u\frac{dv}{dx}\\ &= (x-1)^6\times 20 + 20x\times 6(x-1)^5\\ &= 20(x-1)^5\times(x-1) + 20(x-1)^5\times 6x\\ &= 20(x-1)^5[(x-1)+6x]\\ &= 20(x-1)^5(7x-1)\end{aligned}$$

$20(x-1)^5$ is a common factor.

The factorised result is the most useful form for the solution, as it allows you to find stationary points easily. You should always try to factorise your answer as much as possible. Once you have used the product rule, look for factors straight away and do not be tempted to multiply out.

The quotient rule

In the last section, you met a technique for differentiating the product of two functions. In this section you will see how to differentiate a function which is the quotient of two simpler functions.

As before, you start by identifying the simpler functions. For example, the function

$$y = \frac{3x+1}{x-2},$$

can be written as $y = \frac{u}{v}$ where $u = 3x + 1$ and $v = x - 2$. Using this notation, $\frac{dy}{dx}$ is given by

$$\frac{dy}{dx} = \frac{v\frac{du}{dx} - u\frac{dv}{dx}}{v^2}$$

This is called the *quotient rule*, and it is derived from first principles below.

The quotient rule from first principles

A small increase, δx in x results in corresponding small increases δu, δv and δy in u, v and y. The new value of y is given by

$$y + \delta y = \frac{u + \delta u}{v + \delta v},$$

and since $y = \frac{u}{v}$, you can rearrange this to obtain an expression for δy in terms of u and v.

$$\begin{aligned}\delta y &= \frac{u+\delta u}{v+\delta v} - \frac{u}{v} \\ &= \frac{v(u+\delta u) - u(v+\delta v)}{v(v+\delta v)} \\ &= \frac{uv + v\delta u - uv - u\delta v}{v(v+\delta v)} \\ &= \frac{v\delta u - u\delta v}{v(v+\delta v)}\end{aligned}$$

Dividing both sides by δx gives

$$\frac{\delta y}{\delta x} = \frac{v\frac{\delta u}{\delta x} - u\frac{\delta v}{\delta x}}{v(v+\delta v)}.$$

To divide the right-hand side by δx you only divide the numerator by δx.

In the limit as $\delta x \to 0$, this is written in the form you met on the previous page.

$$\frac{dy}{dx} = \frac{v\frac{du}{dx} - u\frac{dv}{dx}}{v^2}$$

ACTIVITY 4.1 Verify that the quotient rule gives $\frac{dy}{dx}$ correctly when $u = x^{10}$ and $v = x^7$.

EXAMPLE 4.6

Given that $y = \frac{3x+1}{x-2}$, find $\frac{dy}{dx}$ using the quotient rule.

SOLUTION

Letting $u = 3x + 1$ and $v = x - 2$ gives

$$\frac{du}{dx} = 3 \quad \text{and} \quad \frac{dv}{dx} = 1.$$

Using the quotient rule,
$$\frac{dy}{dx} = \frac{v\frac{du}{dx} - u\frac{dv}{dx}}{v^2}$$
$$= \frac{(x-2) \times 3 - (3x+1) \times 1}{(x-2)^2}$$
$$= \frac{3x - 6 - 3x - 1}{(x-2)^2}$$
$$= \frac{-7}{(x-2)^2}.$$

EXAMPLE 4.7

Given that $y = \frac{x^2+1}{3x-1}$, find $\frac{dy}{dx}$ using the quotient rule.

SOLUTION

Letting $u = x^2 + 1$ and $v = 3x - 1$ gives

$$\frac{du}{dx} = 2x \quad \text{and} \quad \frac{dv}{dx} = 3.$$

Using the quotient rule,
$$\frac{dy}{dx} = \frac{v\frac{du}{dx} - u\frac{dv}{dx}}{v^2}$$
$$= \frac{(3x-1) \times 2x - (x^2+1) \times 3}{(3x-1)^2}$$
$$= \frac{6x^2 - 2x - 3x^2 - 3}{(3x-1)^2}$$
$$= \frac{3x^2 - 2x - 3}{(3x-1)^2}.$$

EXERCISE 4B

1 Differentiate the following functions using the product rule or the quotient rule.

(i) $y = (x^2 - 1)(x^3 + 3)$

(ii) $y = x^5(3x^2 + 4x - 7)$

(iii) $y = x^2(2x + 1)^4$

(iv) $y = \dfrac{2x}{3x - 1}$

(v) $y = \dfrac{x^3}{x^2 + 1}$

(vi) $y = (2x + 1)^2(3x^2 - 4)$

(vii) $y = \dfrac{2x - 3}{2x^2 + 1}$

(viii) $y = \dfrac{x - 2}{(x + 3)^2}$

(ix) $y = (x + 1)\sqrt{x - 1}$

2 The graph of $y = \dfrac{x}{x - 1}$ is shown below.

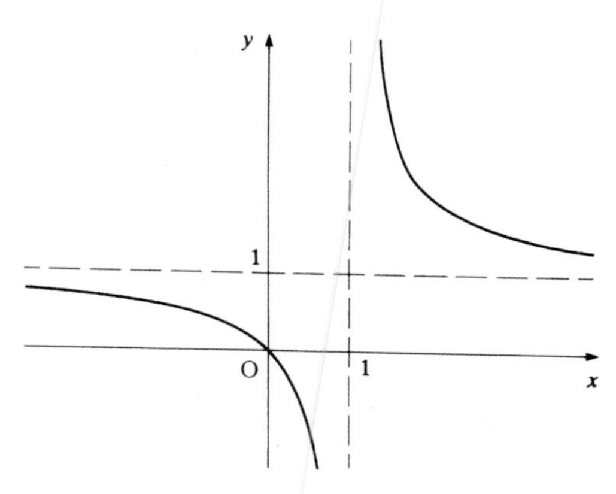

(i) Find $\dfrac{dy}{dx}$.

(ii) Find the gradient of the curve at (0, 0), and the equation of the tangent at (0, 0).

(iii) Find the gradient of the curve at (2, 2), and the equation of the tangent at (2, 2).

(iv) What can you deduce about the two tangents?

3 Given that $y = (x + 1)(x - 2)^2$

(i) find $\dfrac{dy}{dx}$

(ii) find any stationary points and determine their nature

(iii) sketch the curve.

4 Given that $y = \dfrac{x - 3}{x - 4}$

(i) find $\dfrac{dy}{dx}$

(ii) find the equation of the tangent to the curve at the point (6, 1.5)

(iii) find the equation of the normal to the curve at the point (5, 2)

(iv) use your answer from **(i)** to deduce that the curve has no turning points, and sketch the graph.

5 Given that $y = (2x - 1)^3(x + 1)^3$

(i) find $\dfrac{dy}{dx}$ and factorise the expression you obtain

(ii) find the values of x for which $\dfrac{dy}{dx} = 0$, and determine the nature of the corresponding stationary points.

The graph of $y = (2x - 1)^3(x + 1)^3$ is shown below.

(iii) Write down the co-ordinates of P, Q and R.

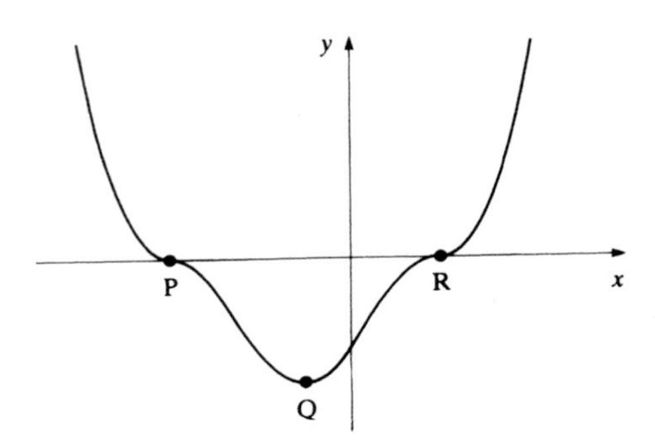

6 The graph of $y = \dfrac{2x}{\sqrt{x} - 1}$, which is undefined for $x < 0$ and $x = 1$, is shown below. P is a minimum point.

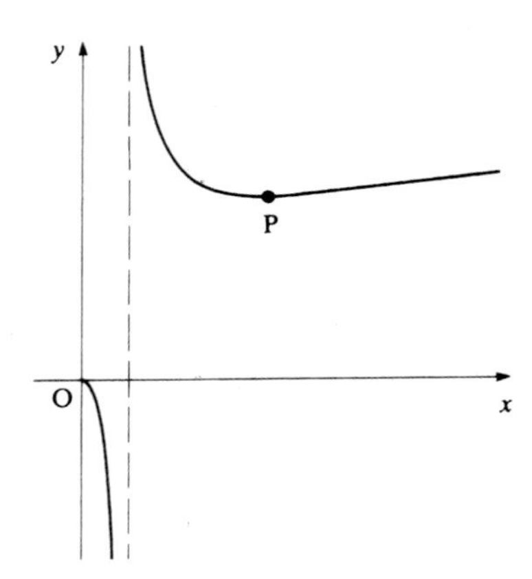

(i) Find $\dfrac{dy}{dx}$.

(ii) Find the gradient of the curve at (9, 9), and show that the equation of the normal at (9, 9) is $y = -4x + 45$.

(iii) Find the co-ordinates of P and verify that it is a minimum point.

(iv) Write down the equation of the tangent and the normal to the curve at P.

(v) Write down the point of intersection of

(a) the normal found in **(ii)** and the tangent found in **(iv)**, call it Q

(b) the normal found in **(ii)** and the normal found in **(iv)**, call it R.

(vi) Show that the area of the triangle PQR is $\frac{441}{8}$.

7 The graph of $y = \dfrac{x^2 - 2x - 5}{2x + 3}$ is shown below.

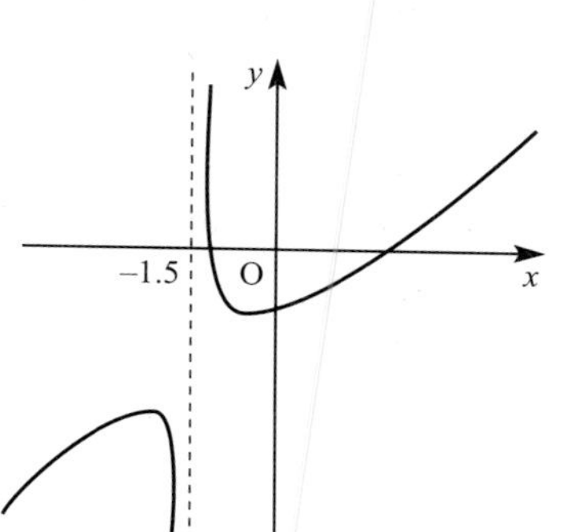

(i) Find $\dfrac{dy}{dx}$.

(ii) Use your answer from part **(i)** to find any stationary points of the curve.

(iii) Classify each of the stationary points and use calculus to justify your answer.

8 A curve has the equation $y = \dfrac{x^2}{2x + 1}$.

(i) Find $\dfrac{dy}{dx}$.

Hence find the co-ordinates of the stationary points on the curve.

(ii) You are given that $\dfrac{d^2y}{dx^2} = \dfrac{2}{(2x + 1)^3}$.

Use this information to determine the nature of the stationary points in **(i)**.

[MEI]

9 You are given that $x = y^2 + 4$.

(i) Find $\dfrac{dx}{dy}$ in terms of y.

(ii) Rearrange $x = y^2 + 4$ in the form $y = g(x)$.

(iii) Differentiate $y = g(x)$ to find $\dfrac{dy}{dx}$ in terms of x.

(iv) Show that $\dfrac{dy}{dx} \times \dfrac{dx}{dy} = 1$.

(v) For what values of x are your answers valid?

[MEI]

10 You are given that $f(x) = \dfrac{4x}{x^2 + 1}$.

(i) Find f(0), f(1), f(2).

(ii) Show that $f'(x) = \dfrac{4(1 - x^2)}{(x^2 + 1)^2}$.

Hence show that there is only one stationary point for $x \geqslant 0$ and state its co-ordinates.

(iii) State what happens to $f(x)$ as $x \to \infty$.

(iv) Using the information gained so far, sketch the graph of $y = f(x)$ for $x \geqslant 0$.

(v) Show that $f(x)$ is an odd function and hence complete the sketch graph for all values of x.

(vi) Given that $g(x) = \dfrac{1}{x} (x \neq 0)$, prove that: $fg(x) = f(x)$.

[MEI]

11 The diagram shows a sketch of the graph of $y = f(x)$, where

$$f(x) = \frac{1 - x^2}{1 + x^2}.$$

The graph cuts the x axis at points P and Q, and the y axis at R.

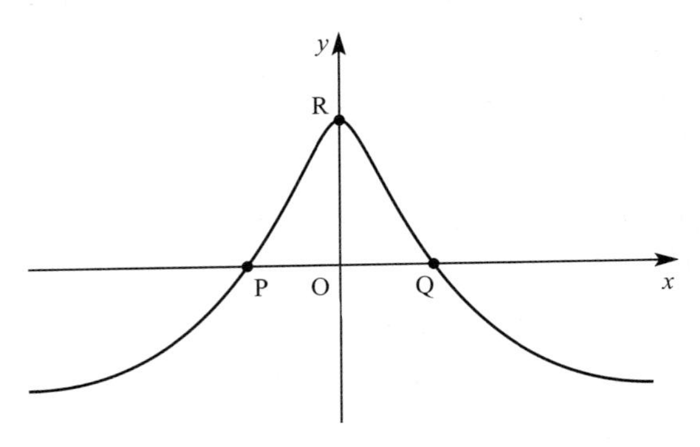

(i) Find the co-ordinates of the points, P, Q and R.
Find also the limiting value of the function $f(x)$ as $x \to \infty$.

(ii) Verify algebraically that $f(-x) = f(x)$.
Explain what this result tells you about the graph.

(iii) Show that the derivative $f'(x)$ is given by

$$\frac{-4x}{(1 + x^2)^2}.$$

Hence show that $f'(x)$ is an odd function.
Interpret this result by relating it to the graph in the diagram.

(iv) Find the co-ordinates of the two points on the graph of $y = f(x)$ where the second derivative $f''(x)$ is zero.
What can you say about the shape of the graph at these points?

[MEI]

12 The diagram shows part of the graph with the equation $y = x\sqrt{9 - 2x^2}$.
It crosses the x axis at $(a, 0)$.

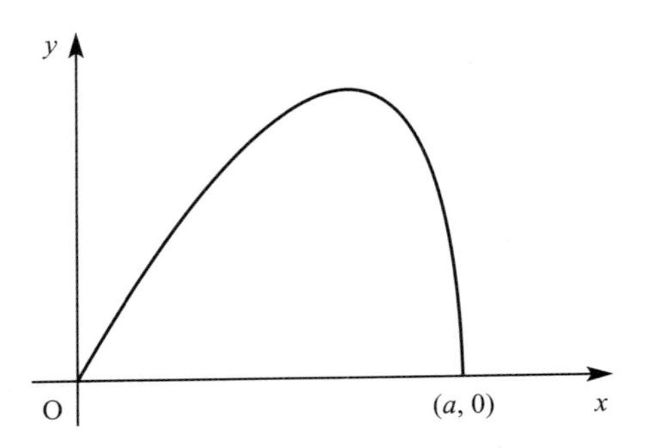

(i) Find the value of a, giving your answer as a multiple of $\sqrt{2}$.

(ii) Show that the result of differentiating $\sqrt{9 - 2x^2}$ is $\dfrac{-2x}{\sqrt{9 - 2x^2}}$.

Hence show that if $y = x\sqrt{9-2x^2}$ then

$$\frac{dy}{dx} = \frac{9-4x^2}{\sqrt{9-2x^2}}.$$

(iii) Find the x co-ordinate of the maximum point on the graph of $y = x\sqrt{9-2x^2}$.

Write down the gradient of the curve at the origin.
What can you say about the gradient at the point $(a, 0)$?

Differentiating an inverse function

ACTIVITY 4.2 What is the relationship between $\frac{dy}{dx}$ and $\frac{dx}{dy}$?
Follow the steps below to help you to answer this question.

1 Differentiate $y = x^3$.

2 Rearrange $y = x^3$ in the form $x = f(y)$, and hence find $\frac{dx}{dy}$ as a function of y.

3 Write $\frac{dx}{dy}$ as a function of x.

4 Write down a relationship between $\frac{dy}{dx}$ and $\frac{dx}{dy}$.

5 Repeat steps 1–4 for other functions such as $y = 2x$, $y = x^2$ and $y = x^4$.

6 Use your results to propose a general rule relating $\frac{dy}{dx}$ and $\frac{dx}{dy}$.

For part 6 of the activity you may have proposed the general result $\frac{dy}{dx} = \frac{1}{\frac{dx}{dy}}$.

If so, well done! The result looks algebraically obvious, but remember that $\frac{dy}{dx}$ and $\frac{dx}{dy}$ are not fractions. The function $\frac{dy}{dx}$ is the rate of change of y with x, and $\frac{dx}{dy}$ is the rate of change of x with y.

The geometrical interpretation of this result can be seen in figure 4.2 where, as an example, the line $y = \frac{1}{2}x$ is drawn first with the axes the normal way round, and then with them interchanged.

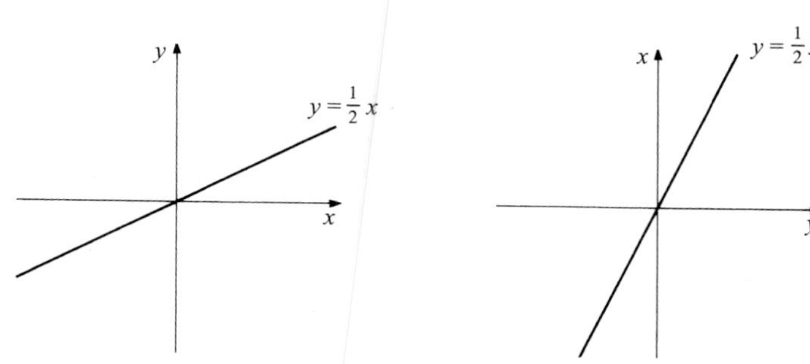

Figure 4.2

p How does this demonstrate that $\dfrac{dy}{dx} = \dfrac{1}{\frac{dx}{dy}}$?

Does it prove it?

EXAMPLE 4.8

Given that $x = y^{\frac{1}{5}}$, find $\dfrac{dy}{dx}$

(i) by first finding $\dfrac{dx}{dy}$

(ii) by first making y the subject.

SOLUTION

(i) $x = y^{\frac{1}{5}} \Rightarrow \dfrac{dx}{dy} = \dfrac{1}{5} \times y^{\frac{1}{5}-1}$

$$= \frac{1}{5}y^{-\frac{4}{5}}$$

$$= \frac{1}{5(y^{\frac{1}{5}})^4}$$

$$= \frac{1}{5x^4}$$

Since $\dfrac{dy}{dx} = \dfrac{1}{\frac{dx}{dy}}$ it follows that $\dfrac{dy}{dx} = \dfrac{1}{\frac{1}{5x^4}}$

$$= 5x^4.$$

(ii) $x = y^{\frac{1}{5}} \Rightarrow y = x^5 \Rightarrow \dfrac{dy}{dx} = 5x^4.$

Note

The result $\dfrac{dy}{dx} = \dfrac{1}{\frac{dx}{dy}}$ has applications in two areas which you have met earlier: inverse functions and their gradients, and differentation with respect to different variables.

EXAMPLE 4.9

(i) Sketch the graphs of $y = x^2 + 1$ for $x \in \mathbb{R}$ and its inverse function $y = \sqrt{x-1}$.

(ii) Find the gradient of $y = \sqrt{x-1}$ at the point (5, 2) by

(a) direct differentiation

(b) relating it to the gradient of $y = x^2 + 1$ at the point (2, 5).

SOLUTION

(i)

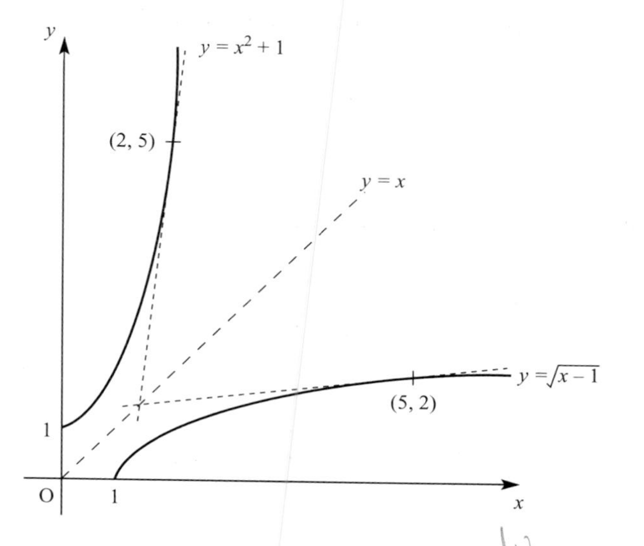

Figure 4.3

(ii) (a)

$$y = \sqrt{x-1}$$
$$= (x-1)^{\frac{1}{2}}$$
$$\frac{dy}{dx} = \tfrac{1}{2}(x-1)^{-\frac{1}{2}} \times 1 \quad \text{(chain rule)}$$
$$= \frac{1}{2\sqrt{x-1}}$$

At (5, 2) the gradient is $\dfrac{1}{2\sqrt{5-1}} = \tfrac{1}{4}$.

(b) Since any function and its inverse are reflections of each other in the line $y = x$, the two tangents shown in the sketch will meet on the line $y = x$.

So the gradient of $y = \sqrt{x-1}$ at $(5, 2) = \dfrac{1}{\text{gradient of } y = x^2 + 1 \text{ at } (2, 5)}$

$$= \frac{1}{2x \text{ when } x = 2}$$

$$= \frac{1}{4}.$$

Note

This is an illustration of the general result

$$\text{gradient of } f^{-1}(x) \text{ at } (a, b) = \frac{1}{\text{gradient of } f(x) \text{ at } (b, a)}$$

and this is particularly useful when the equation of the inverse function cannot be found easily.

EXAMPLE 4.10

The area of a circular patch of mould is increasing at a rate of $0.4\,\text{cm}^2\,\text{h}^{-1}$. Calculate the rate at which the radius is increasing when the radius is 5 cm.

SOLUTION

You are required to find $\dfrac{dr}{dt}$

$$= \frac{dr}{dA} \times \frac{dA}{dt}.$$

But $A = \pi r^2$, so $\dfrac{dA}{dr} = 2\pi r$

$$\frac{dr}{dA} = \frac{1}{\frac{dA}{dr}} = \frac{1}{2\pi r},$$

$$\text{so } \frac{dr}{dt} = \frac{1}{2\pi r} \times \frac{dA}{dt}.$$

When $r = 5$ and $\dfrac{dA}{dt} = 0.4$

$$\frac{dr}{dt} = \frac{1}{2\pi \times 5} \times 0.4$$

$$= \frac{1}{25\pi}$$

$$= 0.0127\ \text{cm}\,\text{h}^{-1}.$$

EXERCISE 4C

1 The area of a circle is increasing at the uniform rate of $8\,\text{cm}^2\,\text{min}^{-1}$. Calculate the rate at which the radius is increasing when the circumference is 50 cm.

2 **(i)** Sketch $f(x) = x(x+1)(x+2)$ for $x \in \mathbb{R}$.

(ii) The function $g(x) = x(x+1)(x+2)$ for $x \in \mathbb{R}^+$.
Sketch $g(x)$ and $g^{-1}(x)$ on the same axes.

(iii) Find the gradient of $g(x)$ at the point (2, 24) and hence find the gradient of $g^{-1}(x)$ at (24, 2).

3 Sand is poured on to a horizontal floor at a rate of $4\,\text{cm}^3\,\text{s}^{-1}$ and forms a pile in the shape of a right circular cone, of which the height is three-quarters of the radius.
Calculate the rate of change of the radius when the radius is 4 cm, leaving your answer in terms of π.

(The formula for the volume of a cone is $V = \frac{1}{3}\pi r^2 h$.)

4 A filter funnel is in the shape of a cone (vertex downwards) of vertical angle 90° with a small tube leaving at the vertex as shown in the diagram on the next page.

(i) When the depth of liquid in the funnel is 4 cm, the level is falling at $0.2\,\text{cm}\,\text{s}^{-1}$. At what rate is the volume decreasing?

(ii) If the rate found in part **(i)** is steady, how fast is the level falling when the depth is 2 cm?

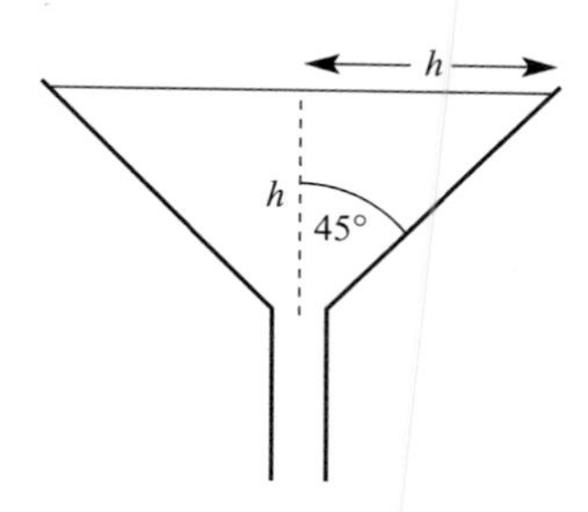

5 You are given a curve with the equation $y = x^2(4 - x)$.

(i) Find the values of x for which $\frac{dy}{dx} = 0$.

(ii) Denoting the values of x which you have just calculated by a and b, where $a < b$, show that $\frac{dy}{dx}$ is positive when $a < x < b$.

(iii) Sketch the graph of y in the interval $a < x < b$, using the same scale on each axis.

(iv) A function $f(x) = x^2(4 - x)$ is defined over the domain $a \leqslant x \leqslant b$ and has inverse function $f^{-1}(x)$. Find the gradient of $f^{-1}(x)$ at the point $\left(\frac{7}{8}, \frac{1}{2}\right)$.

[MEI]

6 The sketch below shows the graph of $y = f(x)$.

(i) Sketch the graphs of

(a) $y = 2f(x)$ **(b)** $y = f(-x)$ **(c)** $y = f(x + 2)$

in each case superimposing them on a copy of the graph of $y = f(x)$.

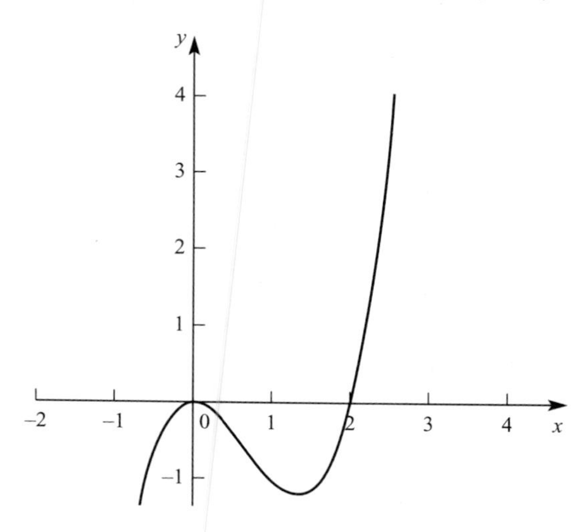

(ii) Explain why the function $f(x)$ does not have an inverse function.

(iii) The function $f(x)$ restricted to the domain $x > 2$ is called $g(x)$.
The inverse function of $g(x)$ is $g^{-1}(x)$.
Sketch the graphs of $y = g^{-1}(x)$ and $y = g(x)$ on the same axes.

(iv) Given that $g(x) = x^2(x - 2)$, for $x > 2$, calculate the gradient of the graph of $y = g(x)$ at the point $(3, 9)$.
Deduce the gradient of the graph $y = g^{-1}(x)$ at the point $(9, 3)$.

[MEI]

ACTIVITY 4.3 Follow the steps below to *prove* that the rule

$$y = x^n \Rightarrow \frac{dy}{dx} = nx^{n-1},$$

is true for all positive rational numbers n. You use the fact that it is true for all positive integers.

Since n is a positive rational number it can be written as $n = \frac{p}{q}$ where p and q are positive integers.

Therefore $y = x^n = x^{\frac{p}{q}}$.

Raising to the power q gives $y^q = x^p = z$ (say).

(i) Find $\frac{dz}{dx}$ and $\frac{dz}{dy}$.

(ii) Use these results together with the chain rule and the relationship $\frac{dy}{dz} = \frac{1}{\frac{dz}{dy}}$ to show that $\frac{dy}{dx} = \frac{p}{q}x^{\left(\frac{p}{q}-1\right)}$.

Since $n = \frac{p}{q}$, this proves the result.

---

p How would you describe this proof: direct argument, exhaustion or contradiction?

Differentiating natural logarithms and exponentials

In chapter 2 you learnt that the integral of $\frac{1}{x}$ is $\ln x$. It follows, therefore, that the differential of $\ln x$ is $\frac{1}{x}$.

So $\quad y = \ln x \quad \Rightarrow \quad \frac{dy}{dx} = \frac{1}{x}.$

The differential of the inverse function, $y = e^x$, may be found by interchanging y and x.

$$x = \ln y \quad \Rightarrow \quad \frac{dx}{dy} = \frac{1}{y}$$

$$\Rightarrow \quad \frac{dy}{dx} = \frac{1}{\frac{dx}{dy}} = y = e^x.$$

Therefore $\frac{d}{dx}e^x = e^x$.

The differential of e^x is itself e^x. This may at first seem rather surprising.

P The function $f(x)$ is a polynomial in x of order n.
So

$$f(x) = a_n x^n + a_{n-1} x^{n-1} + \dots + a_1 x + a_0$$

where $a_n, a_{n-1}, \dots, a_0$ are all constants and at least a_n is not zero.
How can you prove that $\frac{d}{dx}f(x)$ cannot equal $f(x)$?

Since the differential of e^x is e^x, it follows that the integral of e^x is also e^x.

$$\int e^x dx = e^x + c.$$

This may be summarised as in the following table.

Differentiation	Integration
$y \longrightarrow \frac{dy}{dx}$	$y \longrightarrow \int y\,dx$
$\ln x \longrightarrow \frac{1}{x}$	$\frac{1}{x} \longrightarrow \ln x + c$
$e^x \longrightarrow e^x$	$e^x \longrightarrow e^x + c$

These results allow you to extend very considerably the range of functions which you are able to differentiate and integrate.

EXAMPLE 4.11

Differentiate $y = e^{5x}$.

SOLUTION

Make the substitution $u = 5x$ to give $y = e^u$.

$$\text{Now } \frac{dy}{du} = e^u = e^{5x} \quad \text{and} \quad \frac{du}{dx} = 5.$$

By the chain rule,

$$\begin{aligned}\frac{dy}{dx} &= \frac{dy}{du} \times \frac{du}{dx} \\ &= e^{5x} \times 5 \\ &= 5e^{5x}.\end{aligned}$$

This result can be generalised as follows.

$$y = e^{ax} \quad \Rightarrow \quad \frac{dy}{dx} = ae^{ax} \quad \text{where } a \text{ is any constant.}$$

This is an important standard result, and you would normally use it automatically, without recourse to the chain rule.

EXAMPLE 4.12

Differentiate $y = \frac{4}{e^{2x}}$.

SOLUTION

$$y = \frac{4}{e^{2x}} = 4e^{-2x}$$

$$\Rightarrow \quad \frac{dy}{dx} = 4 \times (-2e^{-2x})$$

$$= -8e^{-2x}$$

EXAMPLE 4.13

Differentiate $y = 3e^{(x^2+1)}$.

SOLUTION

Let $u = x^2 + 1$, then $y = 3e^u$.

$$\Rightarrow \quad \frac{dy}{du} = 3e^u = 3e^{(x^2+1)} \quad \text{and} \quad \frac{du}{dx} = 2x$$

By the chain rule,

$$\frac{dy}{dx} = \frac{dy}{du} \times \frac{du}{dx}$$

$$= 3e^{(x^2+1)} \times 2x$$

$$= 6xe^{(x^2+1)}.$$

EXAMPLE 4.14

Differentiate the following functions.

(i) $y = 2 \ln x$ **(ii)** $y = \ln(3x)$

SOLUTION

(i) $$\frac{dy}{dx} = 2 \times \frac{1}{x}$$

$$= \frac{2}{x}$$

(ii) Let $u = 3x$, then $y = \ln u$

$$\Rightarrow \quad \frac{dy}{du} = \frac{1}{u} = \frac{1}{3x} \quad \text{and} \quad \frac{du}{dx} = 3.$$

By the chain rule,

$$\frac{dy}{dx} = \frac{dy}{du} \times \frac{du}{dx}$$

$$= \frac{1}{3x} \times 3$$

$$= \frac{1}{x}.$$

Note

An alternative solution to part **(ii)** is

$$y = \ln(3x) = \ln 3 + \ln x \quad \Rightarrow \quad \frac{dy}{dx} = 0 + \frac{1}{x} = \frac{1}{x}.$$

❓ The gradient function found in part **(ii)** above for $y = \ln(3x)$ is the same as that for $y = \ln(x)$. What does this tell you about the shapes of the two curves?

EXAMPLE 4.15

Differentiate the following functions.

(i) $y = \ln(x^4)$ **(ii)** $y = \ln(x^2 + 1)$

SOLUTION

(i) By the properties of logarithms

$$y = \ln(x^4)$$
$$= 4\ln(x)$$
$$\Rightarrow \frac{dy}{dx} = \frac{4}{x}.$$

(ii) Let $u = x^2 + 1$, then $y = \ln u$

$$\Rightarrow \frac{dy}{du} = \frac{1}{u} = \frac{1}{x^2 + 1} \quad \text{and} \quad \frac{du}{dx} = 2x.$$

By the chain rule,

$$\frac{dy}{dx} = \frac{dy}{du} \times \frac{du}{dx}$$
$$= \frac{1}{x^2 + 1} \times 2x$$
$$= \frac{2x}{x^2 + 1}.$$

If you need to differentiate functions similar to those in the examples above, follow exactly the same steps. The results can be generalised as follows.

$y = a\ln x \Rightarrow \frac{dy}{dx} = \frac{a}{x}$	$y = ae^x \Rightarrow \frac{dy}{dx} = ae^x$
$y = \ln(ax) \Rightarrow \frac{dy}{dx} = \frac{1}{x}$	$y = e^{ax} \Rightarrow \frac{dy}{dx} = ae^{ax}$
$y = \ln(f(x)) \Rightarrow \frac{dy}{dx} = \frac{f'(x)}{f(x)}$	$y = e^{f(x)} \Rightarrow \frac{dy}{dx} = f'(x)e^{f(x)}$

EXAMPLE 4.16

Differentiate $y = \frac{\ln x}{x}$.

SOLUTION

Here y is of the form $\frac{u}{v}$ where $u = \ln x$ and $v = x$

$$\Rightarrow \quad \frac{du}{dx} = \frac{1}{x} \quad \text{and} \quad \frac{du}{dx} = 1.$$

By the quotient rule,

$$\frac{dy}{dx} = \frac{v\frac{du}{dx} - u\frac{dv}{dx}}{v^2}$$

$$= \frac{x \times \frac{1}{x} - 1 \times \ln x}{x^2}$$

$$= \frac{1 - \ln x}{x^2}.$$

EXERCISE 4D

1 Differentiate the following functions.

(i) $y = 3\ln x$

(ii) $y = \ln(4x)$

(iii) $y = \ln(x^2)$

(iv) $y = \ln(x^2 + 1)$

(v) $y = \ln\left(\frac{1}{x}\right)$

(vi) $y = x\ln x$

(vii) $y = x^2 \ln(4x)$

(viii) $y = \ln\left(\frac{x+1}{x}\right)$

(ix) $y = \ln\sqrt{x^2 - 1}$

(x) $y = \frac{\ln x}{x^2}$

2 Differentiate the following functions.

(i) $y = 3e^x$

(ii) $y = e^{2x}$

(iii) $y = e^{x^2}$

(iv) $y = e^{(x+1)^2}$

(v) $y = xe^{4x}$

(vi) $y = 2x^3e^{-x}$

(vii) $y = \frac{x}{e^x}$

(viii) $y = (e^{2x} + 1)^3$

3 Knowing how much rain has fallen in a river basin, hydrologists are often able to give forecasts of what will happen to a river level over the next few hours. In one case it is predicted that the height h, in metres, of a river above its normal level during the next 3 hours will be $0.12e^{0.9t}$, where t is the time elapsed, in hours, after the prediction.

(i) Find $\frac{dh}{dt}$, the rate at which the river is rising.

(ii) At what rate will the river be rising after 0, 1, 2 and 3 hours?

4 The graph of $y = xe^x$ is shown below.

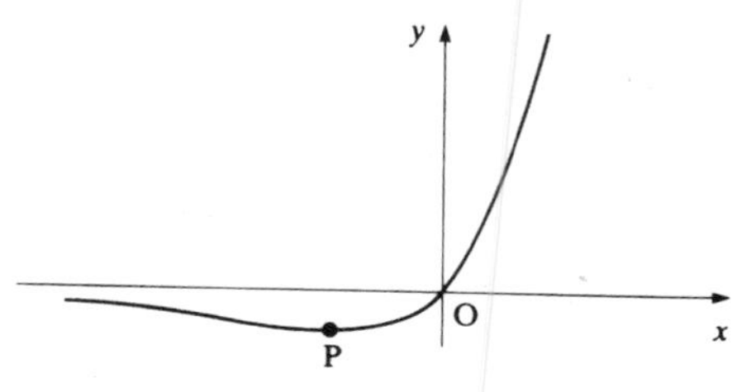

(i) Find $\frac{dy}{dx}$ and $\frac{d^2y}{dx^2}$.

(ii) Find the co-ordinates of the minimum point P.

5 The graph of $f(x) = x\ln(x^2)$ is shown below.

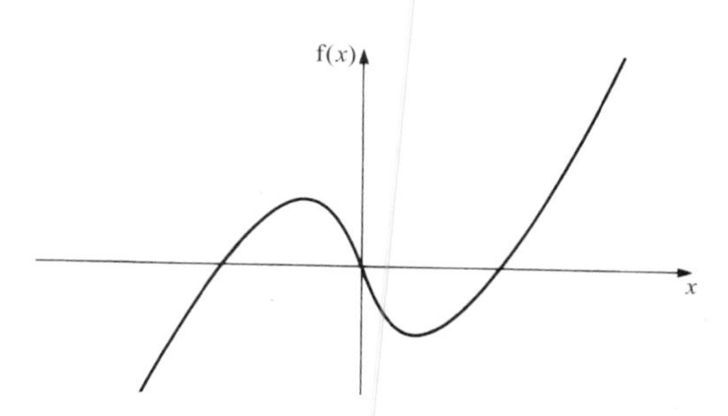

(i) Describe, giving a reason, any symmetries of the graph.

(ii) Find $f'(x)$ and $f''(x)$.

(iii) Find the co-ordinates of any stationary points.

6 Given that $y = \frac{e^x}{x}$

(i) find $\frac{dy}{dx}$

(ii) find the co-ordinates of any stationary points on the curve of the function

(iii) sketch the curve.

7 **(i)** Differentiate $\ln x$ and $x\ln x$ with respect to x.

The sketch shows the graph of $y = x\ln x$ for $0 \leqslant x \leqslant 3$.

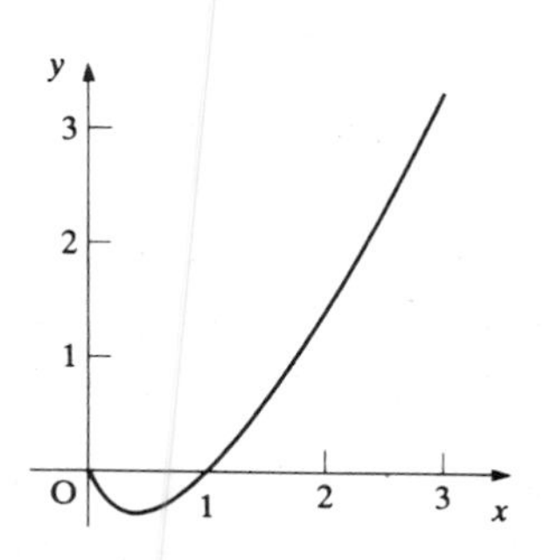

(ii) Show that the curve has a stationary point $\left(\frac{1}{e}, -\frac{1}{e}\right)$.

[MEI]

8 The diagram shows the graph of $y = xe^{-x}$.

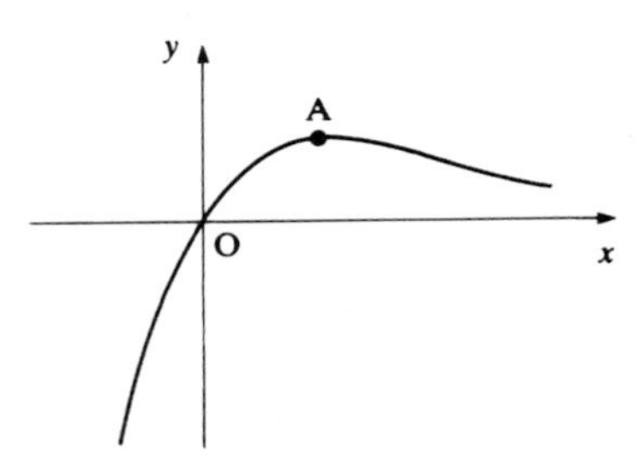

(i) Differentiate xe^{-x}.

(ii) Find the co-ordinates of the point A, the maximum point on the curve.

[MEI]

9 In a biological experiment, bacteria are being grown in a culture. The mass of the bacteria at time t hours is P milligrams. At time $t = 0$, $P = 3$ and $\frac{dP}{dt} = 6$.

(i) A standard model for this situation is given by $P = Ae^{kt}$, where A and k are constants.

(a) Write down $\frac{dP}{dt}$ in terms of A, k and t. Find the values of A and k.

(b) Find the value of t for which $P = 12$.

(c) According to this model, what happens to the mass of the bacteria after a long time?

(ii) As the experiment progresses it is found that the value of P increases to a maximum at time $t = 10$ and then begins to decrease. A new model is proposed in which $P = 3e^{at-bt^2}$, where a and b are constants.

(a) Express $\frac{dP}{dt}$ in terms of a, b and t. Find the values of a and b.

(b) According to this new model, what happens to the mass of the bacteria after a long time?

[MEI]

10 A sample of a radioactive substance has a mass m at time t, where $m = ae^{-bt}$ (where a and b are positive constants), in appropriate units.

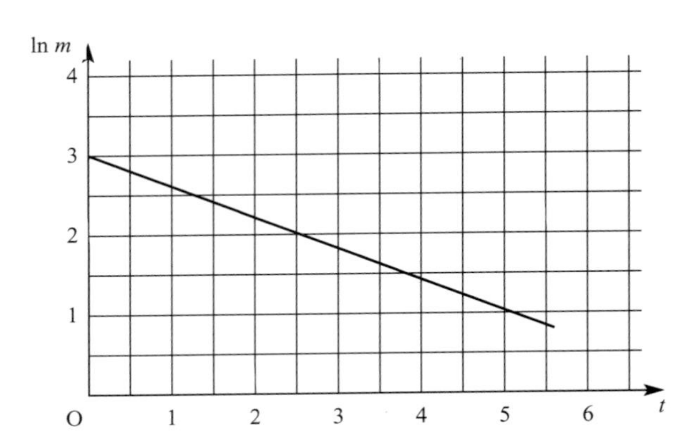

EXAMPLE 4.18

Differentiate $y = x^2 \sin x$.

SOLUTION

$x^2 \sin x$ is of the form uv, so the product rule can be used with $u = x^2$ and $v = \sin x$.

$$\frac{du}{dx} = 2x \qquad \frac{dv}{dx} = \cos x$$

Using the product rule

$$\frac{dy}{dx} = v\frac{du}{dx} + u\frac{dv}{dx}$$

$$\Rightarrow \quad \frac{dy}{dx} = 2x \sin x + x^2 \cos x.$$

EXAMPLE 4.19

Differentiate $y = e^{\tan x}$.

SOLUTION

$e^{\tan x}$ is a function of a function, so the chain rule may be used.

$$\text{Let} \quad u = \tan x \quad \Rightarrow \quad \frac{du}{dx} = \frac{1}{\cos^2 x}$$

$$y = e^u \quad \Rightarrow \quad \frac{dy}{du} = e^u.$$

Using the chain rule

$$\frac{dy}{dx} = \frac{dy}{du} \times \frac{du}{dx}$$

$$= \frac{e^u}{\cos^2 x}$$

$$= \frac{e^{\tan x}}{\cos^2 x}.$$

EXAMPLE 4.20

Differentiate $y = \dfrac{1 + \sin x}{\cos x}$.

SOLUTION

$\dfrac{1 + \sin x}{\cos x}$ is of the form $\dfrac{u}{v}$ so the quotient rule can be used, with

$$u = 1 + \sin x \quad \text{and} \quad v = \cos x$$

$$\Rightarrow \quad \frac{du}{dx} = \cos x \quad \text{and} \quad \frac{dv}{dx} = -\sin x.$$

The quotient rule is

$$\frac{dy}{dx} = \frac{v\dfrac{du}{dx} - u\dfrac{dv}{dx}}{v^2}.$$

Summary of results

$$\frac{\mathrm{d}}{\mathrm{d}x}(\sin x) = \cos x \qquad\qquad \frac{\mathrm{d}}{\mathrm{d}x}(\cos x) = -\sin x$$

Remember that these results are only valid when the angle is measured in radians, so when you are using any of the derivatives of trigonometrical functions you need to work in radians.

ACTIVITY 4.5

By writing $\tan x = \dfrac{\sin x}{\cos x}$, use the quotient rule to show that

$$\frac{\mathrm{d}}{\mathrm{d}x}(\tan x) = \frac{1}{\cos^2 x} \quad \text{where } x \text{ is measured in radians.}$$

$\left(\dfrac{1}{\cos x}\right.$ is the reciprocal function $\left.\sec x.\right)$

You can use the three results met so far to differentiate a variety of functions involving trigonometrical functions, by using the chain rule, product rule or quotient rule, as in the following examples.

EXAMPLE 4.17

Differentiate $y = \cos 2x$.

SOLUTION

As $\cos 2x$ is a function of a function, you may use the chain rule.

Let $\quad u = 2x \quad \Rightarrow \quad \dfrac{\mathrm{d}u}{\mathrm{d}x} = 2$

$\quad\quad y = \cos u \Rightarrow \quad \dfrac{\mathrm{d}y}{\mathrm{d}u} = -\sin u$

$$\frac{\mathrm{d}y}{\mathrm{d}x} = \frac{\mathrm{d}y}{\mathrm{d}u} \times \frac{\mathrm{d}u}{\mathrm{d}x}$$
$$= -\sin u \times 2$$
$$= -2\sin 2x.$$

With practice it should be possible to do this in your head, without needing to write down the substitution.

This result may be generalised.

$$y = \cos kx \quad \Rightarrow \quad \frac{\mathrm{d}y}{\mathrm{d}x} = -k\sin kx.$$

Similarly

$$y = \sin kx \quad \Rightarrow \quad \frac{\mathrm{d}y}{\mathrm{d}x} = k\cos kx.$$

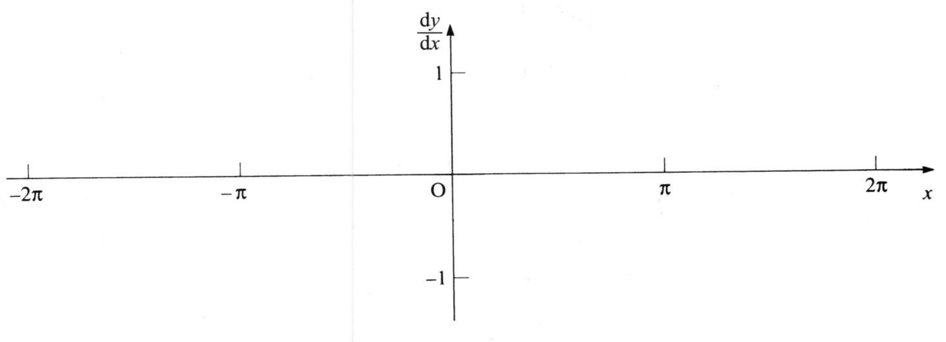

Figure 4.5

First, look for the angles for which the gradient of $y = \sin x$ is zero. Mark zeros at these angles on your gradient graph.

Decide which parts of $y = \sin x$ have a positive gradient and which have a negative gradient. This will tell you whether your gradient graph should be above or below the y axis at any point.

Look at the part of the graph of $y = \sin x$ near $x = 0$ and compare it with the graph of $y = x$. What do you think the gradient of $y = \sin x$ is at this point? Mark this point on your gradient graph. Also mark on any other points with plus or minus the same gradient.

Now, by considering whether the gradient of $y = \sin x$ is increasing or decreasing at any particular point, sketch in the rest of the gradient graph.

The gradient graph that you have drawn should look like a familiar graph. What graph do you think it is?

Sketch the graph of $y = \cos x$, with x measured in radians, and use it as above to obtain a sketch of the graph of the gradient function of $y = \cos x$.

? Is $y = x$ still a tangent of $y = \sin x$ if x is measured in degrees?

Activity 4.4 showed you that the graph of the gradient function of $y = \sin x$ resembled the graph of $y = \cos x$. You will also have found that the graph of the gradient function of $y = \cos x$ looks like the graph of $y = \sin x$ reflected in the x axis to become $y = -\sin x$.

---

p Both of these results are in fact true but the work above does not amount to a proof. Explain why.

(They are proved on page 214, once the necessary trigonometry has been covered.)

---

14 The diagram shows a sketch of the graph of $y = (x^2 - 3)e^{-x}$.
The graph crosses the x axis at points A and D and the y axis at C.
Points B and E are stationary points on the curve.

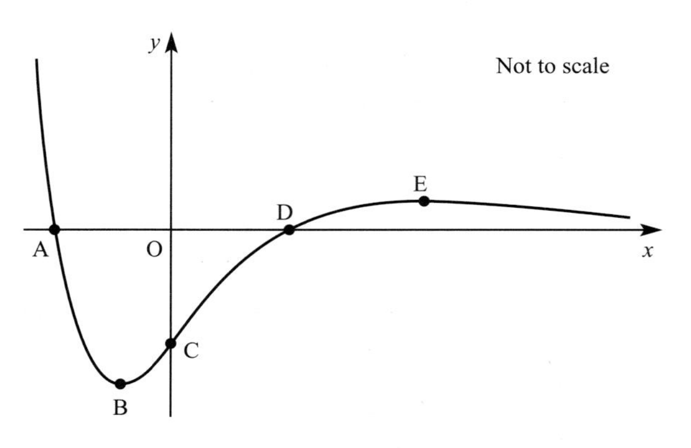

(i) Find the co-ordinates of the points A, C and D.

(ii) Show that $\dfrac{dy}{dx} = -(x^2 - 2x - 3)e^{-x}$.

(iii) Deduce that the x co-ordinates of the points B and E are -1 and 3 respectively, and find the corresponding y co-ordinates.

(iv) Copy the diagram and mark clearly the positions of two points of inflection.
You are given that $\dfrac{d^2y}{dx^2} = (x^2 - 4x - 1)e^{-x}$.
Deduce from this result that there are exactly two points of inflection.

[MEI]

Differentiating sin *x* and cos *x*

ACTIVITY 4.4 Figure 4.4 shows the graph of $y = \sin x$, with x measured in radians together with the graph of $y = x$. You are going to sketch the graph of the gradient function for the graph of $y = \sin x$.

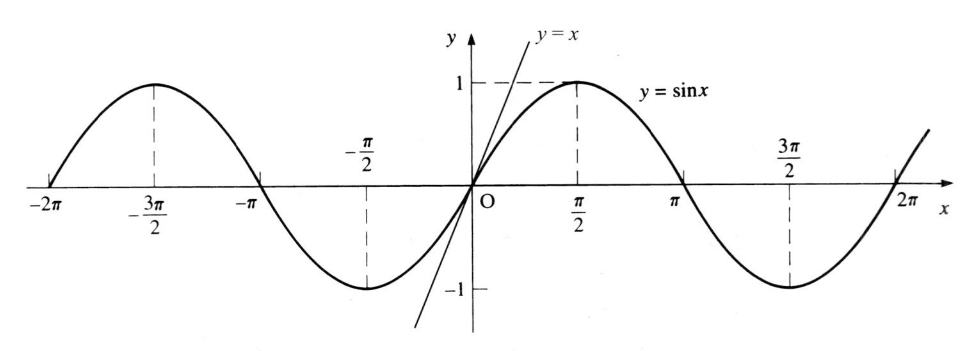

Figure 4.4

Draw a horizontal axis for the angles, marked from -2π to 2π, and a vertical axis for the gradient, marked from -1 to 1.

12 The diagram shows the graph of $y = \dfrac{e^{2x}}{x^2}$.

(i) Show that $\dfrac{dy}{dx} = \dfrac{2(x-1)e^{2x}}{x^3}$.

Hence find the co-ordinates of the minimum point P.

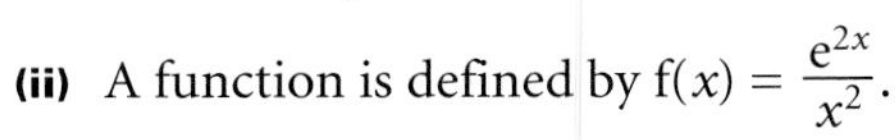

(ii) A function is defined by $f(x) = \dfrac{e^{2x}}{x^2}$.

Three different transformations are applied to the graph of $y = f(x)$ in the diagram producing the graphs with equations

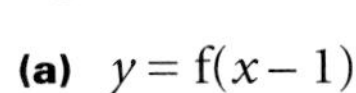

(a) $y = f(x-1)$

(b) $y = f(-x)$

(c) $y = f(2x)$.

In each case, describe the transformation and state the co-ordinates of the point corresponding to P.

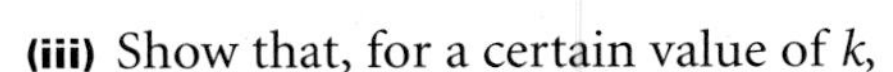

(iii) Show that, for a certain value of k,

$$f(x-1) = k\left(\frac{x}{x-1}\right)^2 f(x).$$

State the value of k.

[MEI]

13 The diagram shows a sketch of the graph of $y = f(x)$, where

$$f(x) = \frac{\ln x}{x} \qquad (x > 0).$$

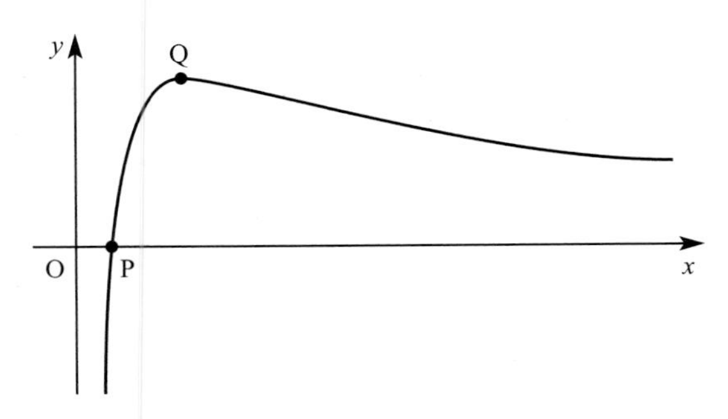

The graph crosses the x axis at the point P and has a turning point at Q.

(i) Write down the x co-ordinate of P.

(ii) Find the first and second derivaties, $f'(x)$ and $f''(x)$, simplifying your answers as far as possible.

(iii) Hence show that the x co-ordinate of Q is e.

Find the y co-ordinate of Q in terms of e.

Find $f''(e)$, and use this result to verify that Q is a maximum point.

[MEI, *part*]

(i) Explain why a graph of $\ln m$ against t will be a straight line.

(ii) The graph of $\ln m$ against t (shown) passes through (0, 3) and (5, 1). Find the values of a and b.

(iii) At what time will m have reduced to 0.01?

(iv) A second radioactive sample is known to consist of a mixture of two substances. The total mass $m = m_1 + m_2$, where $m_1 = pe^{-0.3t}$ and $m_2 = qe^{-0.2t}$ (where p and q are positive constants).

Express $\dfrac{dm}{dt}$ in terms of p, q and t.

The diagram shows a sketch of the graph of m against t. The tangent to this curve at the point (0, 17) passes through the point (4.25, 0).

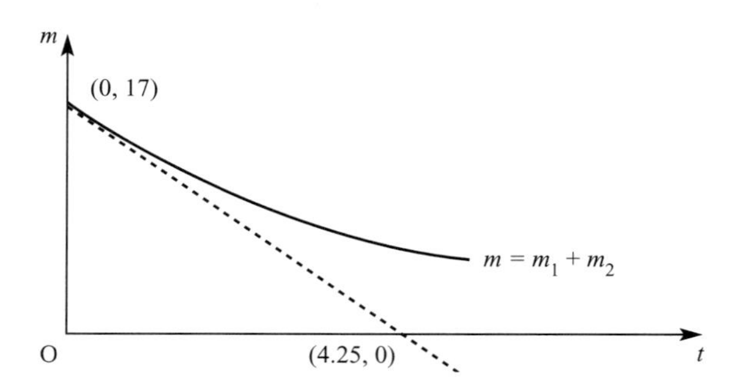

(v) Form two simultaneous equations for p and q and solve them.

[MEI]

11 For $x > 0$ the function f(x) is given by

$$f(x) = 2x - x\ln x.$$

The diagram shows part of the graph of this function.

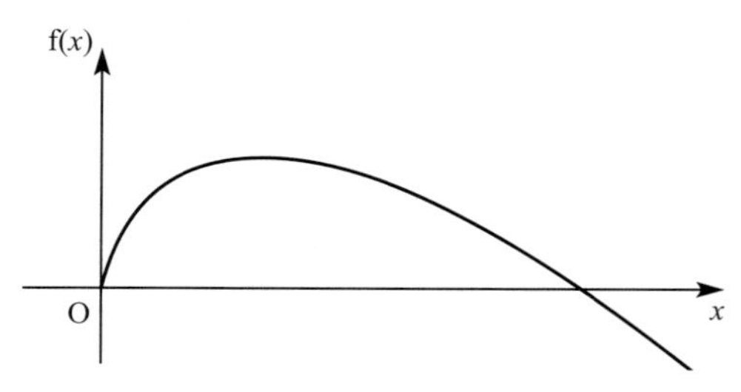

(i) Show that $f(e^3) = -e^3$.

(ii) Find $f'(x)$ and $f''(x)$.

(iii) Show that the curve $y = f(x)$ has just one stationary point and find its co-ordinates. Verify that $f''(x) < 0$ at this point.

The function g(x) is defined for the domain $x \geqslant e$. In this domain $g(x) = f(x)$.

(iv) Write down the range of g(x).

(v) Explain why g(x) has an inverse, $g^{-1}(x)$.
Sketch, on the same axes, graphs of $y = g(x)$ and $y = g^{-1}(x)$.
Calculate the gradient of the graph of $y = g^{-1}(x)$ at the point where $x = -e^3$.

[MEI]

Substituting for u and v and their derivatives gives

$$\frac{dy}{dx} = \frac{(\cos x)(\cos x) - (1 + \sin x)(-\sin x)}{(\cos x)^2}$$

$$= \frac{\cos^2 x + \sin x + \sin^2 x}{\cos^2 x}$$

$$= \frac{1 + \sin x}{\cos^2 x} \qquad \text{(using } \sin^2 x + \cos^2 x = 1\text{)}.$$

EXERCISE 4E

1 Differentiate each of the following functions.

(i) $2\cos x + \sin x$ **(ii)** $\tan x + 5$ **(iii)** $\sin x - \cos x$

2 Use the product rule to differentiate each of the following functions.

(i) $x \tan x$ **(ii)** $\sin x \cos x$ **(iii)** $e^x \sin x$

3 Use the quotient rule to differentiate each of the following functions.

(i) $\dfrac{\sin x}{x}$ **(ii)** $\dfrac{e^x}{\cos x}$ **(iii)** $\dfrac{x + \cos x}{\sin x}$

4 Use the chain rule to differentiate each of the following functions.

(i) $\tan(x^2 + 1)$ **(ii)** $\cos^2 x$ **(iii)** $\ln(\sin x)$

5 Use an appropriate method to differentiate each of the following functions.

(i) $\sqrt{\cos x}$ **(ii)** $e^x \tan x$ **(iii)** $\sin 4x^2$

(iv) $e^{\cos 2x}$ **(v)** $\dfrac{\sin x}{1 + \cos x}$ **(vi)** $\ln(\tan x)$

6 **(i)** Differentiate $y = x\cos x$.

(ii) Find the gradient of the curve $y = x\cos x$ at the point where $x = \pi$.

(iii) Find the equation of the tangent to the curve $y = x\cos x$ at the point where $x = \pi$.

(iv) Find the equation of the normal to the curve $y = x\cos x$ at the point where $x = \pi$.

7 The function $y = \sin^3 x$ has five stationary points in $-\pi \leqslant x \leqslant \pi$.

(i) Find $\dfrac{dy}{dx}$ for this function.

(ii) Find the co-ordinates of the five stationary points.

(iii) Determine whether each of the five points is a maximum, minimum or point of inflection.

(iv) Use this information to sketch the graph of $y = \sin^3 x$ for values of x in $-\pi \leqslant x \leqslant \pi$.

8 If $y = e^x \cos 3x$, find $\dfrac{dy}{dx}$ and $\dfrac{d^2y}{dx^2}$ and hence show that

$$\frac{d^2y}{dx^2} - 2\frac{dy}{dx} + 10y = 0.$$

[MEI]

9 Consider the function $y = e^{-x}\sin x$, where $-\pi \leqslant x \leqslant \pi$.

(i) Find $\frac{dy}{dx}$.

(ii) Show that, at stationary points, $\tan x = 1$.

(iii) Determine the co-ordinates of the stationary points, correct to 2 significant figures.

(iv) Explain how you could determine whether your stationary points are maxima or minima. You are not required to do any calculations.

[MEI]

Differentiating functions defined implicitly

All the functions you have differentiated so far have been of the form $y = f(x)$. However, many functions cannot be arranged in this way at all, for example $x^3 + y^3 = xy$, and others can look clumsy when you try to make y the subject.

An example of this is the semi-circle $x^2 + y^2 = 4$, $y \geqslant 0$, illustrated in figure 4.6.

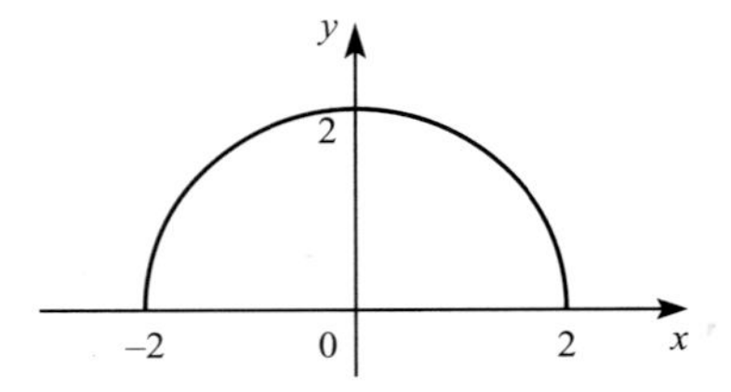

Figure 4.6

The curve is much more easily recognised in this form than in the equivalent $y = \sqrt{4 - x^2}$.

When a function is specified by an equation connecting x and y which does not have y as the subject it is called an *implicit function*.

⚠ Although restrictions on x or y are often necessary to make the function unambiguous, these are frequently assumed and not mentioned.

The chain rule $\frac{dy}{dx} = \frac{dy}{du} \times \frac{du}{dx}$ and the product rule $\frac{d}{dx}(uv) = u\frac{dv}{dx} + v\frac{du}{dx}$ are used extensively to help in the differentiation of implicit functions.

EXAMPLE 4.21

Differentiate each of the following with respect to x.

(i) y^2 **(ii)** xy **(iii)** $3x^2y^3$ **(iv)** $\sin y$

SOLUTION

(i)
$$\frac{d}{dx}(y^2) = \frac{d}{dy}(y^2) \times \frac{dy}{dx} \text{(chain rule)}$$
$$= 2y\frac{dy}{dx}$$

(ii)
$$\frac{d}{dx}(xy) = x\frac{dy}{dx} + y \quad \text{(product rule)}$$

(iii)
$$\frac{d}{dx}(3x^2y^3) = 3\left(x^2\frac{d}{dx}(y^3) + y^3\frac{d}{dx}(x^2)\right) \quad \text{(product rule)}$$
$$= 3\left(x^2 \times 3y^2\frac{dy}{dx} + y^3 \times 2x\right) \quad \text{(chain rule)}$$
$$= 3xy^2\left(3x\frac{dy}{dx} + 2y\right)$$

(iv)
$$\frac{d}{dx}(\sin y) = \frac{d}{dy}(\sin y) \times \frac{dy}{dx} \quad \text{(chain rule)}$$
$$= (\cos y)\frac{dy}{dx}$$

EXAMPLE 4.22

The equation of a curve is given by $y^3 + xy = 2$.

(i) Find an expression for $\frac{dy}{dx}$ in terms of x and y.

(ii) Hence find the gradient of the curve at $(1, 1)$ and the equation of the tangent to the curve at that point.

SOLUTION

(i) $y^3 + xy = 2$

$$\Rightarrow \quad 3y^2\frac{dy}{dx} + (x\frac{dy}{dx} + y) = 0$$
$$\Rightarrow \quad (3y^2 + x)\frac{dy}{dx} = -y$$
$$\Rightarrow \quad \frac{dy}{dx} = \frac{-y}{3y^2 + x}$$

(ii) At $(1, 1)$, $\frac{dy}{dx} = -\frac{1}{4}$

$\Rightarrow$ using $y - y_1 = m(x - x_1)$ the equation of the tangent is $(y - 1) = -\frac{1}{4}(x - 1)$

$\Rightarrow$ $x + 4y - 5 = 0$.

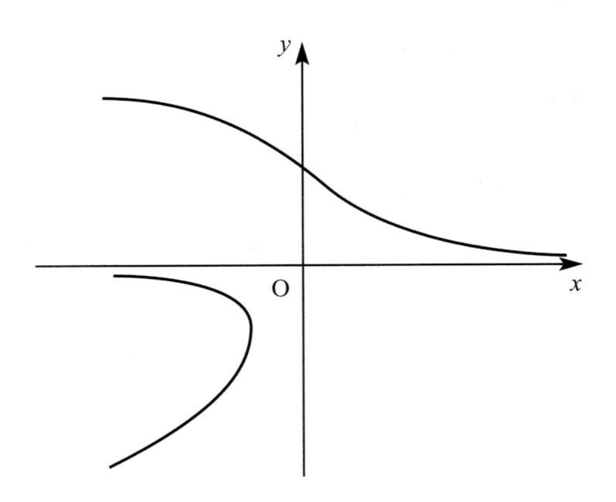

Figure 4.7

Figure 4.7 shows the graph of the curve with the equation $y^3 + xy = 2$.

(i) How can you use your graphic calculator to sketch this?
(**Hint:** What effect does interchanging x and y have on a graph?)

(ii) Why is this not a function?

Stationary points

As before these occur where $\frac{dy}{dx} = 0$.

Putting $\frac{dy}{dx} = 0$ will not usually give values of x directly, but will give a relationship between x and y. This needs to be solved simultaneously with the equation of the curve to find the co-ordinates.

EXAMPLE 4.23

(i) Differentiate $x^3 + y^3 = 3xy$ with respect to x.

(ii) Hence find the co-ordinates of any stationary points.

SOLUTION

(i) $\frac{d}{dx}(x^3) + \frac{d}{dx}(y^3) = \frac{d}{dx}(3xy)$

$$\Rightarrow \quad 3x^2 + 3y^2\frac{dy}{dx} = 3\left[x\frac{dy}{dx} + y\right].$$

(ii) At stationary points, $\frac{dy}{dx} = 0$

$$\Rightarrow \quad 3x^2 = 3y$$

$$\Rightarrow \quad x^2 = y$$

Notice how it is not necessary to find an expression for $\frac{dy}{dx}$ unless you are told to.

To find the co-ordinates of the stationary points, solve

$$\left.\begin{array}{l} x^2 = y \\ x^3 + y^3 = 3xy \end{array}\right\} \quad \text{simultaneously}$$

Substituting for y gives

$$x^3 + (x^2)^3 = 3x(x^2)$$

$$\Rightarrow \quad x^3 + x^6 = 3x^3$$

$$\Rightarrow \quad x^6 = 2x^3$$

$$\Rightarrow \quad x^3(x^3 - 2) = 0$$

$$\Rightarrow \quad x = 0 \quad \text{or} \quad x = \sqrt[3]{2}$$

$y = x^2$ so the stationary points are $(0, 0)$ and $(\sqrt[3]{2}, \sqrt[3]{4})$.

The stationary points are A and B in figure 4.8.

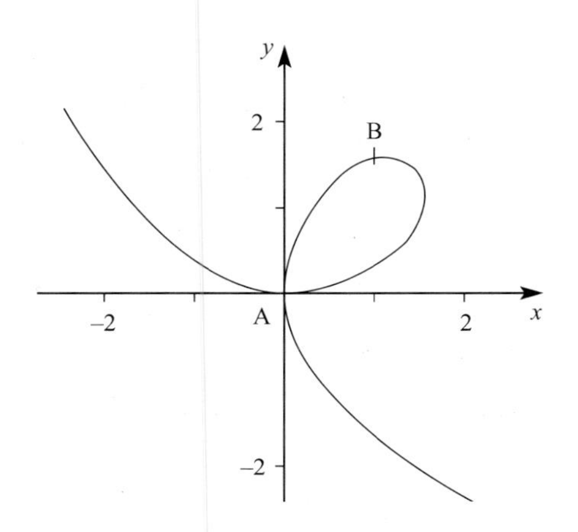

Figure 4.8

Types of stationary points

As with explicit functions, the nature of a stationary point can usually be determined by considering the sign of the second derivative $\frac{d^2y}{dx^2}$ at the stationary point.

EXAMPLE 4.24

The curve with equation $\sin x + \sin y = 1$ for $0 \leqslant x \leqslant \pi$, $0 \leqslant y \leqslant \pi$ is shown in figure 4.9.

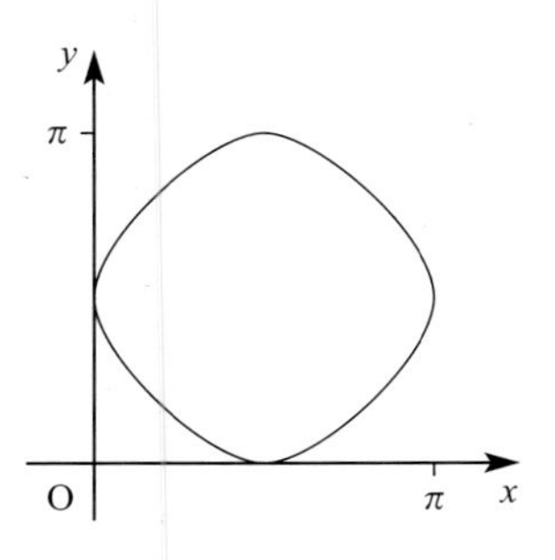

Figure 4.9

(i) Differentiate the equation of the curve with respect to x and hence find the co-ordinates of any stationary points.

(ii) Differentiate the equation again with respect to x to determine the nature of the stationary points.

SOLUTION

(i)
$$\sin x + \sin y = 1$$

$$\Rightarrow \quad \cos x + (\cos y)\frac{dy}{dx} = 0 \qquad ①$$

$$\Rightarrow \quad \frac{dy}{dx} = -\frac{\cos x}{\cos y}.$$

At any stationary point $\frac{dy}{dx} = 0 \Rightarrow \cos x = 0$

$$\Rightarrow \quad x = \frac{\pi}{2}\text{(only solution in range)}$$

Substitute in $\sin x + \sin y = 1$.

When $x = \frac{\pi}{2}$, $\sin x = 1 \Rightarrow \sin y = 0$

$$\Rightarrow \quad y = 0 \text{ or } y = \pi$$

$\Rightarrow$ turning points at $\left(\frac{\pi}{2}, 0\right)$ and $\left(\frac{\pi}{2}, \pi\right)$.

(ii) Differentiating equation ① again with respect to x.

$$\cos x + (\cos y)\frac{dy}{dx} = 0$$

$$\Rightarrow \quad -\sin x + \left[(\cos y)\frac{d^2y}{dx^2} + \frac{dy}{dx}\left((-\sin y)\frac{dy}{dx}\right)\right] = 0$$

At $\left(\frac{\pi}{2}, 0\right)$, $\frac{dy}{dx} = 0$

$$\Rightarrow \quad -\sin\frac{\pi}{2} + (\cos 0)\frac{d^2y}{dx^2} = 0$$

$\Rightarrow \quad \frac{d^2y}{dx^2} = 1 \Rightarrow$ minimum turning point at $\left(\frac{\pi}{2}, 0\right)$.

At $\left(\frac{\pi}{2}, \pi\right)$, $\frac{dy}{dx} = 0$

$$\Rightarrow \quad -\sin\frac{\pi}{2} + (\cos \pi)\frac{d^2y}{dx^2} = 0$$

$$\Rightarrow \quad -1 - \frac{d^2y}{dx^2} = 0$$

$\Rightarrow \quad \frac{d^2y}{dx^2} = -1 \Rightarrow$ maximum turning point at $\left(\frac{\pi}{2}, \pi\right)$.

These points are confirmed by considering the sketch in figure 4.9.

EXERCISE 4F

1 Differentiate each of the following with respect to x.

(i) y^4 **(ii)** $x^2 + y^3 - 5$ **(iii)** $xy + x + y$

(iv) $\cos y$ **(v)** $e^{(y+2)}$ **(vi)** xy^3

(vii) $2x^2y^5$ **(viii)** $x + \ln y - 3$ **(ix)** $xe^y - \cos y$

(x) $x^2 \ln y$ **(xi)** $xe^{\sin y}$ **(xii)** $x \tan y - y \tan x$

2 Find the gradient of the curve $xy^3 = 5\ln y$ at the point $(0, 1)$.

3 Find the gradient of the curve $e^{\sin x} + e^{\cos y} = e + 1$ at the point $\left(\frac{\pi}{2}, \frac{\pi}{2}\right)$.

4 (i) Find the gradient of the curve $x^2 + 3xy + y^2 = x + 3y$ at the point $(2, -1)$.

(ii) Hence find the equation of the tangent to the curve at this point.

5 Find the co-ordinates of all the stationary points on the curve $x^2 + y^2 + xy = 3$.

6 A curve has the equation $(x - 6)(y + 4) = 2$.

(i) Find an expression for $\frac{dy}{dx}$ in terms of x and y.

(ii) Find the equation of the normal to the curve at the point $(7, -2)$.

(iii) Find the co-ordinates of the point where the normal meets the curve again.

(iv) By rewriting the equation in the form $y - a = \frac{b}{x - c}$ identify any asymptotes and sketch the curve.

7 A curve has the equation $y = x^x$ for $x > 0$.

(i) Take logarithms to base e of both sides of the equation.

(ii) Differentiate the resulting equation with respect to x.

(iii) Find the co-ordinates of the stationary point, giving your answer to 3 decimal places.

(iv) Sketch the curve for $x > 0$.

8 ☆☆☆☆ **(i)** Show that the graph of $xy + 48 = x^2 + y^2$ has stationary points at $(4, 8)$ and $(-4, -8)$.

(ii) By differentiating with respect to x a second time determine the nature of these stationary points.

KEY POINTS

1. $y = kx^n \Rightarrow \dfrac{dy}{dx} = knx^{n-1}$ where k and n are real constants.

2. Chain rule: $\dfrac{dy}{dx} = \dfrac{dy}{du} \times \dfrac{du}{dx}$.

3. Product rule (for $y = uv$): $\dfrac{dy}{dx} = v\dfrac{du}{dx} + u\dfrac{dv}{dx}$.

4. Quotient rule $\left(\text{for } y = \dfrac{u}{v}\right)$: $\dfrac{dy}{dx} = \dfrac{v\dfrac{du}{dx} - u\dfrac{dv}{dx}}{v^2}$.

5. $\dfrac{dy}{dx} = \dfrac{1}{\dfrac{dx}{dy}}$.

6. $\dfrac{d}{dx}(\ln x) = \dfrac{1}{x}$

7. $\dfrac{d}{dx}(e^x) = e^x$

8. $\dfrac{d}{dx}(\sin kx) = k\cos kx$

   $\dfrac{d}{dx}(\cos kx) = -k\sin kx$

   $\dfrac{d}{dx}(\tan kx) = \dfrac{k}{\cos^2 kx}$

5 Techniques for integration

The mathematical process has a reality and virtue in itself, and once discovered it constitutes a new and independent factor.

Winston Churchill (1876–1965)

Figure 5.1 shows the graph of $y = \sqrt{x}$.

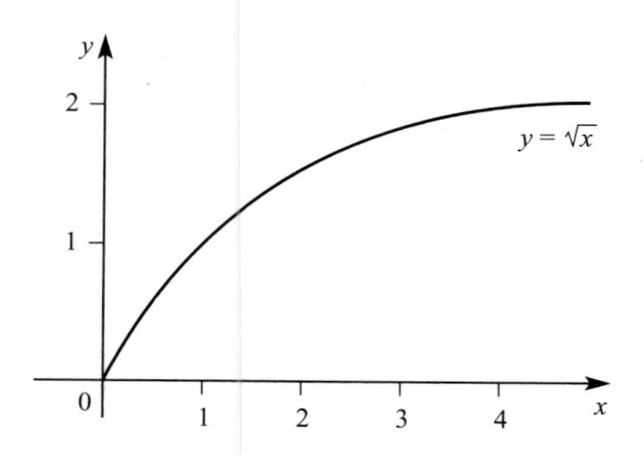

Figure 5.1

? How does it allow you to find the area shaded in the graph in figure 5.2?

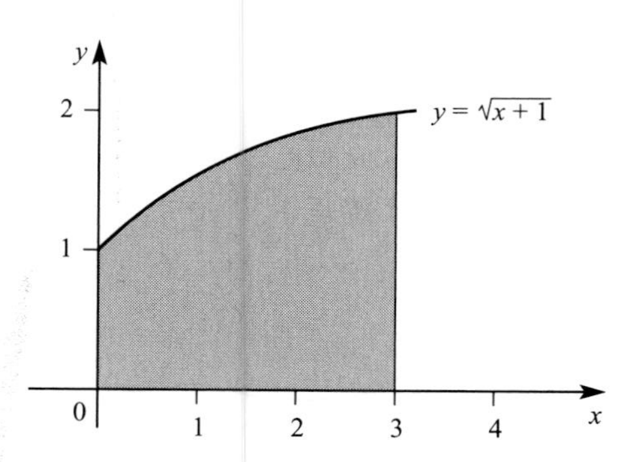

Figure 5.2

Integration by substitution

The graph of $y = \sqrt{x-1}$ is shown in figure 5.3.

The shaded area is given by

$$\int_1^5 \sqrt{x-1}\,\mathrm{d}x = \int_1^5 (x-1)^{\frac{1}{2}}\,\mathrm{d}x.$$

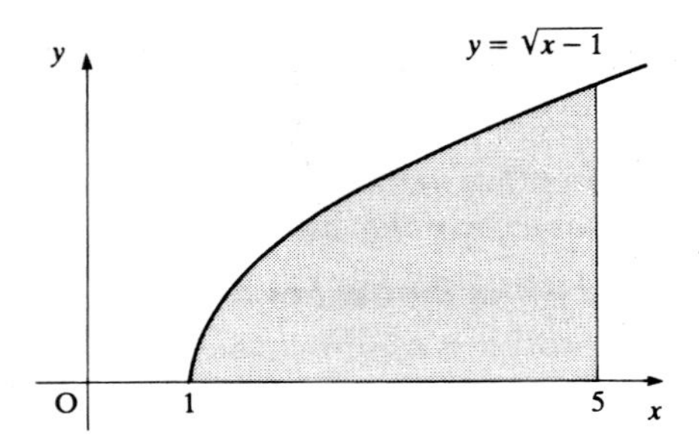

Figure 5.3

You have not needed to find such an integral before, but you do know how to evaluate $\int_a^b u^{\frac{1}{2}}\,\mathrm{d}u$, so making the substitution $u = x - 1$ will transform the integral into one that you can do.

When you make this substitution it means that you are now integrating with respect to a new variable, namely u. The limits of the integral, and the 'dx', must be written in terms of u.

The new limits are given by $\quad x = 1 \quad \Rightarrow \quad u = 1 - 1 = 0$

and $\quad x = 5 \quad \Rightarrow \quad u = 5 - 1 = 4.$

Since $u = x - 1$, $\frac{\mathrm{d}u}{\mathrm{d}x} = 1$.

Even though $\frac{\mathrm{d}u}{\mathrm{d}x}$ is not a fraction, it is usual to treat it as one in this situation (see the warning below), and to write the next step as '$\mathrm{d}u = \mathrm{d}x$'.

The integral now becomes:

$$\int_{u=0}^{u=4} u^{\frac{1}{2}}\,\mathrm{d}u = \left[\frac{u^{\frac{3}{2}}}{\frac{3}{2}}\right]_0^4$$

$$= \left[\frac{2u^{\frac{3}{2}}}{3}\right]_0^4$$

$$= 5\tfrac{1}{3}.$$

This method by integration is known as *integration by substitution*. It is a very powerful method which allows you to integrate many more functions. Since you are changing the variable from x to u, the method is also referred to as *integration by change of variable*.

⚠ The last example included the statement '$\mathrm{d}u = \mathrm{d}x$'. Some mathematicians are reluctant to write such statements on the grounds that $\mathrm{d}u$ and $\mathrm{d}x$ may only be used in the form $\frac{\mathrm{d}u}{\mathrm{d}x}$, i.e. as a gradient. This is not in fact true; there is a well defined branch of mathematics which justifies such statements but it is well beyond the scope of this book. In the meantime it may help you to think of it as shorthand for 'in the limit as $\delta x \to 0$, $\frac{\delta u}{\delta x} \to 1$, and so $\delta u = \delta x$'.

EXAMPLE 5.1

Evaluate $\int_1^3 (x+1)^3\,dx$ by making a suitable substitution.

SOLUTION

Let $u = x + 1$.

Converting the limits: $x = 1 \Rightarrow u = 1 + 1 = 2$
$x = 3 \Rightarrow u = 3 + 1 = 4.$

Converting dx to du:

$$\frac{du}{dx} = 1 \Rightarrow du = dx.$$

$$\int_1^3 (x+1)^3\,dx = \int_2^4 u^3\,du$$
$$= \left[\frac{u^4}{4}\right]_2^4$$
$$= \frac{4^4}{4} - \frac{2^4}{4}$$
$$= 60$$

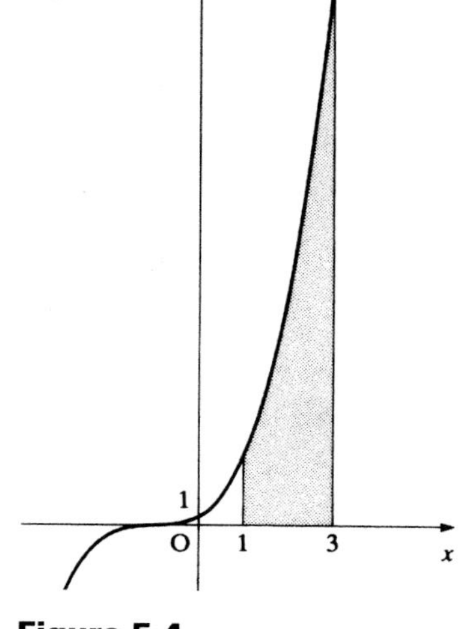

Figure 5.4

? Can integration by substitution be described as the reverse of the chain rule?

EXAMPLE 5.2

Evaluate $\int_3^4 2x(x^2-4)^{\frac{1}{2}}\,dx$ by making a suitable substitution.

SOLUTION

Notice that $2x$ is the derivative of the function in the brackets, $x^2 - 4$, and so $u = x^2 - 4$ is a natural substitution to try.

This gives $\frac{du}{dx} = 2x \Rightarrow du = 2x\,dx.$

Converting the limits: $x = 3 \Rightarrow u = 9 - 4 = 5$
$x = 4 \Rightarrow u = 16 - 4 = 12.$

So the integral becomes:

$$\int_3^4 (x^2-4)^{\frac{1}{2}} 2x\,dx = \int_5^{12} u^{\frac{1}{2}}\,du$$
$$= \left[\frac{2u^{\frac{3}{2}}}{3}\right]_5^{12}$$
$$= 20.3 \text{ (to 3 significant figures).}$$

Note

In the last example there were two functions of x multiplied together, the second function being an expression in brackets raised to a power. The two functions are in this case related, since the first function, $2x$, is the derivative of the expression in brackets, $x^2 - 4$. It was this relationship that made the integration possible.

EXAMPLE 5.3

Find $\int x(x^2 + 2)^3 \, dx$ by making an appropriate substitution.

SOLUTION

Since this is an indefinite integral there are no limits to change, and the final answer will be a function of x.

Let $u = x^2 + 2$, then:

$$\frac{du}{dx} = 2x \Rightarrow \tfrac{1}{2}du = x dx.$$

You only have $x dx$ in the integral, not $2x dx$.

$$\text{So } \int x(x^2+2)^3 \, dx = \int (x^2+2)^3 x dx$$
$$= \int u^3 \times \tfrac{1}{2} du$$
$$= \frac{u^4}{8} + c$$
$$= \frac{(x^2+2)^4}{8} + c.$$

Always remember, when finding an indefinite integral by substitution, to substitute back at the end. The original integral was in terms of x, so your final answer must be too.

EXAMPLE 5.4

By making a suitable substitution, find $\int x\sqrt{x-2} \, dx$.

SOLUTION

This question is not of the same type as the previous ones since x is not the derivative of $(x - 2)$. However, by making the substitution $u = x - 2$ you can still make the integral into one you can do.

Let $u = x - 2$, then:

$$\frac{du}{dx} = 1 \quad \Rightarrow \quad du = dx.$$

There is also an x in the integral so you need to write down an expression for x in terms of u. Since $u = x - 2$ it follows that $x = u + 2$.

In the original integral you can now replace $\sqrt{x-2}$ by $u^{\frac{1}{2}}$, $\mathrm{d}x$ by $\mathrm{d}u$, and x by $u + 2$.

$$\int x\sqrt{x-2}\,\mathrm{d}x = \int (u+2)u^{\frac{1}{2}}\,\mathrm{d}u$$

$$= \int \left(u^{\frac{3}{2}} + 2u^{\frac{1}{2}}\right)\mathrm{d}u$$

$$= \tfrac{2}{5}u^{\frac{5}{2}} + \tfrac{4}{3}u^{\frac{3}{2}} + c$$

Replacing u by $x - 2$ and tidying up gives $\frac{2}{15}(3x+4)(x-2)^{\frac{3}{2}} + c$.

ACTIVITY 5.1 Complete the algebraic steps involved in tidying up the previous answer.

EXERCISE 5A

1 Find the following indefinite integrals by making the suggested substitution. Remember to give your final answer in terms of x.

(i) $\int (x+1)^3\,\mathrm{d}x$, $u = x+1$

(ii) $\int 2\sqrt{2x-1}\,\mathrm{d}x$, $u = 2x-1$

(iii) $\int 3x^2(x^3+1)^7\,\mathrm{d}x$, $u = x^3+1$

(iv) $\int 2x(x^2+1)^5\,\mathrm{d}x$, $u = x^2+1$

(v) $\int 3x^2(x^3-2)^4\,\mathrm{d}x$, $u = x^3-2$

(vi) $\int x\sqrt{2x^2-5}\,\mathrm{d}x$, $u = 2x^2-5$

(vii) $\int x\sqrt{2x+1}\,\mathrm{d}x$, $u = 2x+1$

(viii) $\int \frac{x}{\sqrt{x+9}}\,\mathrm{d}x$, $u = x+9$

2 Evaluate each of the following definite integrals by using a suitable substitution. Give your answer to 3 significant figures where appropriate.

(i) $\int_{-1}^{4} (x-3)^4\,\mathrm{d}x$

(ii) $\int_{0}^{3} (3x+2)^6\,\mathrm{d}x$

(iii) $\int_{5}^{9} \sqrt{x-5}\,\mathrm{d}x$

(iv) $\int_{2}^{15} \sqrt[3]{2x-3}\,\mathrm{d}x$

(v) $\int_{1}^{5} x^2(x^3+1)^2\,\mathrm{d}x$

(vi) $\int_{-1}^{2} 2x(x-3)^5\,\mathrm{d}x$

(vii) $\int_{1}^{5} x\sqrt{x-1}\,\mathrm{d}x$

3 The graph of $y = (x-2)^3$ is shown here.

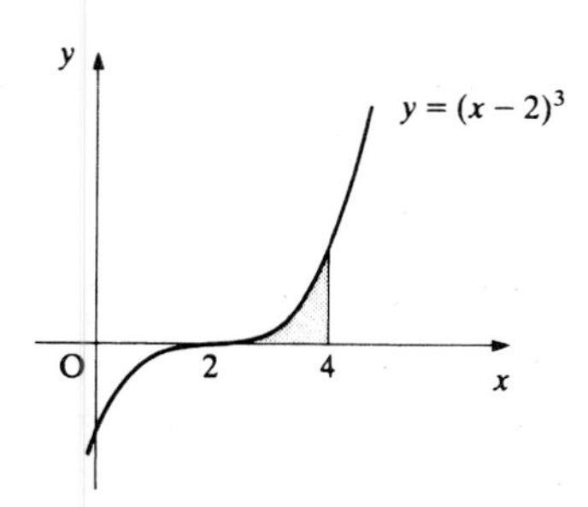

(i) Evaluate $\int_{2}^{4} (x-2)^3\,\mathrm{d}x$.

(ii) Without doing any calculations, state what you think the value of $\int_{0}^{2} (x-2)^3\,\mathrm{d}x$ would be. Give reasons.

(iii) Confirm your answer by carrying out the integration.

4 The graph of $y = (x-1)^4 - 1$ is shown below.

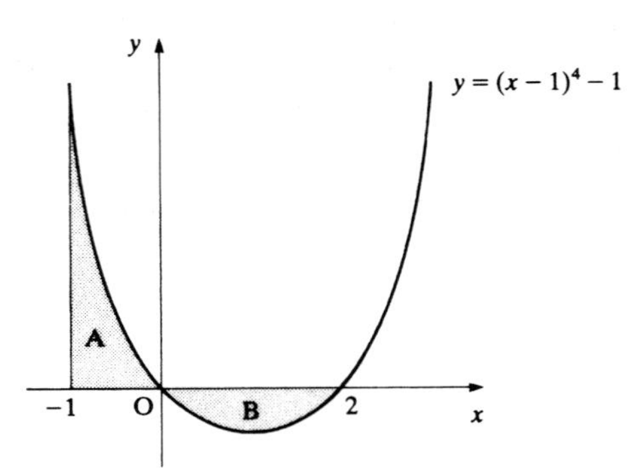

(i) Find the area of the shaded region A by evaluating $\int_{-1}^{0}((x-1)^4 - 1)\,dx$.

(ii) Find the area of the shaded region B by evaluating an appropriate integral.

(iii) Write down the area of the total shaded region.

(iv) Why could you not just evaluate $\int_{-1}^{2}((x-1)^4 - 1)\,dx$ to find the total area?

5 Find the area of the shaded region for each of the following graphs.

(i)

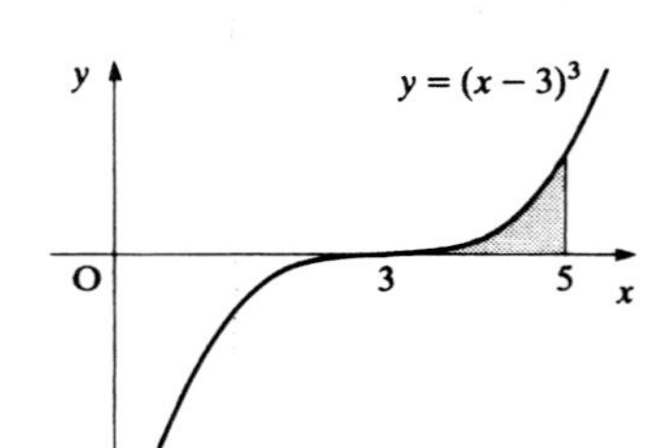

(ii)

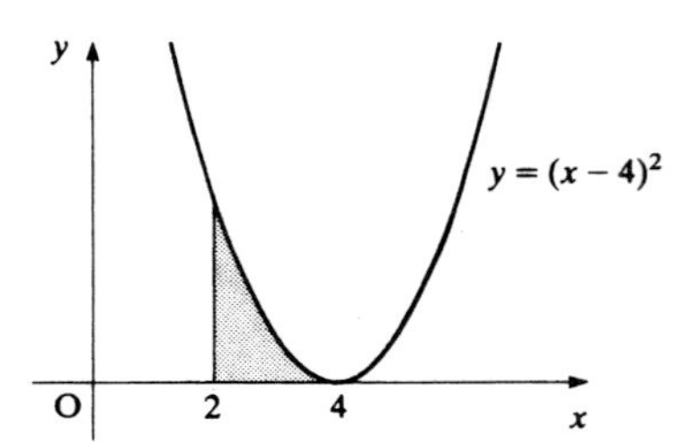

(iii)

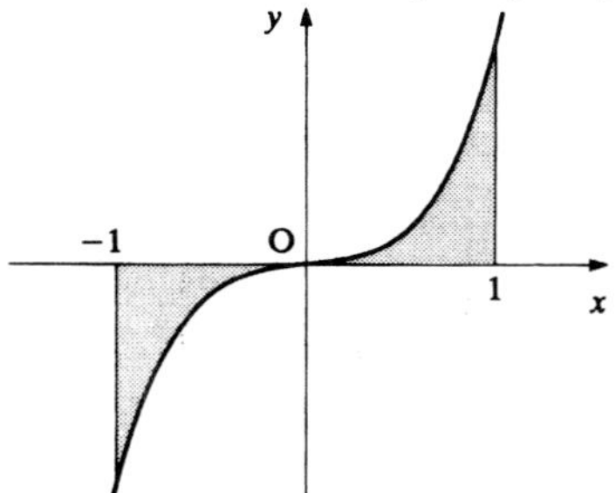

(iv)

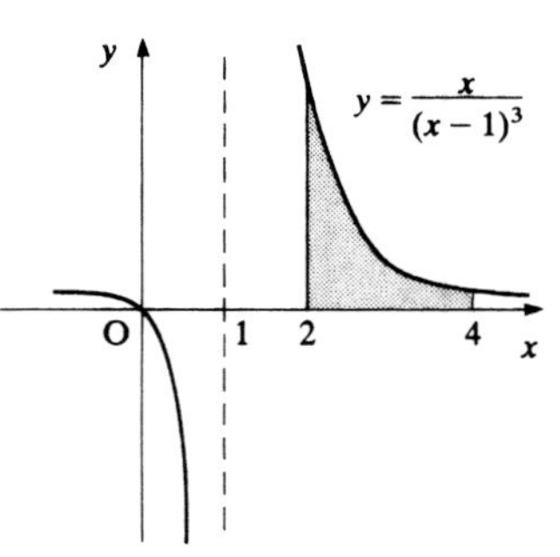

6 The sketch shows part of the graph of $y = x\sqrt{1+x}$.

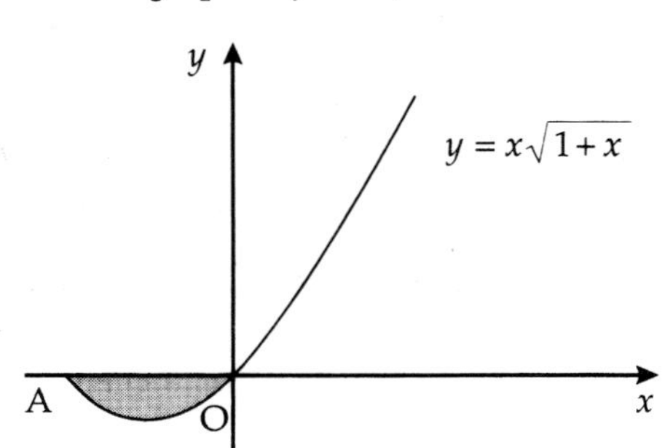

(i) Find the co-ordinates of point A and the range of values of x for which the function is defined.

(ii) Show that the area of the shaded region is $\frac{4}{15}$.
You may find the substitution $u = 1 + x$ useful.

[MEI]

7 (i) By substituting $u = 1 + x$ or otherwise, find

(a) $\int (1 + x)^3 \, dx$

(b) $\int_{-1}^{1} x(1 + x)^3 \, dx$.

(ii) By substituting $t = 1 + x^2$ or otherwise, evaluate $\int_0^1 x\sqrt{1 + x^2} \, dx$.

[MEI]

8 Sketch the graph of $y = \dfrac{x}{\sqrt{4 + x^2}}$ showing any asymptotes.

Find the area contained between the curve and the x axis for $0 \leqslant x \leqslant 2$.

[MEI]

9 (i) Differentiate $(2x - 1)^7$ with respect to x.

The diagram shows a sketch of the curve with equation $y = 4x(2x - 1)^7$.

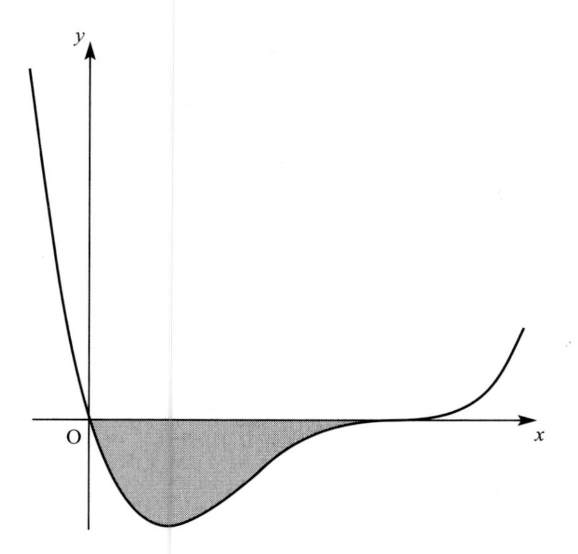

(ii) Show that $\dfrac{dy}{dx} = 4(2x - 1)^6(16x - 1)$.
Hence find the x co-ordinate of the minimum point on the curve.

(iii) Using the substitution $2x - 1 = u$, find the area of the shaded region enclosed between the curve and the x axis.

(iv) The function f with domain $x \geqslant \frac{1}{2}$ is defined by $f(x) = 4x(2x - 1)^7$.
Given that $f(1) = 4$, find the value of $\dfrac{d}{dx}\{f^{-1}(x)\}$ when $x = 4$.

[MEI]

10 **(i)** Integrate with respect to x the following functions.

(a) $\dfrac{4}{\sqrt{x}} + \dfrac{3}{x^3}$ **(b)** $6x(1 + x^2)^{\frac{1}{2}}$

(ii) Show that the substitution $x = u^2$ transforms $\displaystyle\int_1^4 \frac{(1+\sqrt{x})^3}{\sqrt{x}}\,dx$ into an integral of the form $\displaystyle\int_a^b k(1 + u)^3\,du$.

State the values of k, a and b.

Evaluate this integral. [MEI]

Integrals involving the exponential function

Since you know that

$$\frac{d}{dx}(e^{ax}) = ae^{ax},$$

you can see that

$$\int e^{ax}\,dx = \frac{1}{a}e^{ax} + c.$$

This increases the number of functions which you are able to integrate, as in the following example.

EXAMPLE 5.5

Find the following integrals.

(i) $\displaystyle\int e^{2x}\,dx$ **(ii)** $\displaystyle\int_1^5 6e^{3x}\,dx$

SOLUTION

(i) $\displaystyle\int e^{2x}\,dx = \frac{1}{2}e^{2x} + c$

(ii)
$$\begin{aligned}\int_1^5 6e^{3x}\,dx &= \left[\frac{6e^{3x}}{3}\right]_1^5\\ &= \left[2e^{3x}\right]_1^5\\ &= 2(e^{15} - e^3)\\ &= 6.54 \times 10^6 \quad \text{(to 3 significant figures)}\end{aligned}$$

EXAMPLE 5.6

By making a suitable substitution, find $\displaystyle\int_0^4 2xe^{x^2}\,dx$.

SOLUTION

$$\int_0^4 2xe^{x^2}\,dx = \int_0^4 e^{x^2}\,2x\,dx.$$

Since $2x$ is the derivative of x^2, let $u = x^2$.

$$\frac{du}{dx} = 2x \quad\Rightarrow\quad du = 2x\,dx$$

The new limits are given by $x = 0 \Rightarrow u = 0$

and $x = 4 \Rightarrow u = 16$.

The integral can now be written as

$$\int_0^{16} e^u \, du = \left[e^u\right]_0^{16}$$
$$= e^{16} - e^0$$
$$= 8.89 \times 10^6 \quad \text{to 3 significant figures.}$$

Integrals involving the natural logarithm function

You have already seen that

$$\int \frac{1}{x} dx = \ln x + c.$$

There are many other integrals that can be reduced to this form either by rearrangement or by substitution.

EXAMPLE 5.7

Evaluate $\int_2^5 \frac{1}{2x} dx$.

SOLUTION

$$\frac{1}{2}\int_2^5 \frac{1}{x} dx = \frac{1}{2}\left[\ln x\right]_2^5$$
$$= \frac{1}{2}(\ln 5 - \ln 2)$$
$$= 0.458 \quad \text{(to 3 significant figures)}$$

In this example the $\frac{1}{2}$ was taken outside the integral, allowing the standard result for $\frac{1}{x}$ to be used. It is not always possible to do this, and in the following example a substitution is necessary.

EXAMPLE 5.8

Evaluate $\int_1^5 \frac{2x}{x^2 + 3} dx$.

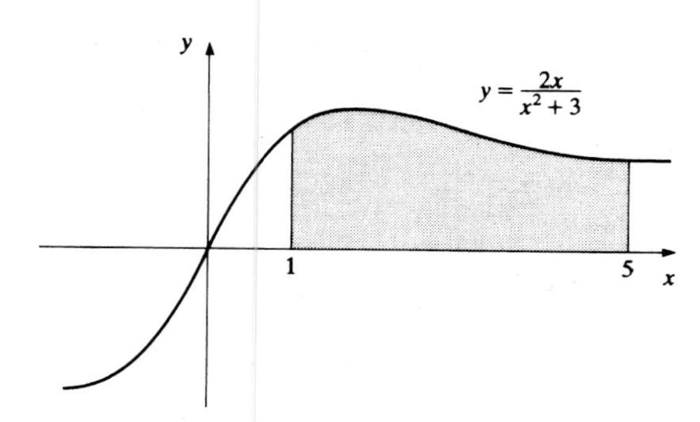

Figure 5.5

SOLUTION

In this case, substitute $u = x^2 + 3$, so that

$$\frac{du}{dx} = 2x \quad \Rightarrow \quad du = 2x\,dx$$

The new limits are given by $\quad x = 1 \quad \Rightarrow \quad u = 4$

and $\quad x = 5 \quad \Rightarrow \quad u = 28.$

$$\begin{aligned}\int_1^5 \frac{2x}{x^2+3}\,dx &= \int_4^{28} \frac{1}{u}\,du \\ &= \Big[\ln u\Big]_4^{28} \\ &= \ln 28 - \ln 4 \\ &= 1.95 \qquad \text{(to 3 significant figures)}\end{aligned}$$

The last example is of the form $\int \frac{f'(x)}{f(x)}\,dx$, where $f(x) = x^2 + 3$. In such cases the substitution $u = f(x)$ transforms the integral into $\int \frac{1}{u}\,du$. The answer is then $\ln u + c$ or $\ln(f(x)) + c$ (assuming that $u = f(x)$ is positive). This result may be stated as the working rule below.

If you obtain the top line when you differentiate the bottom line, the integral is the natural logarithm of the bottom line. So,

$$\int \frac{f'(x)}{f(x)}\,dx = \ln(f(x)) + c.$$

EXAMPLE 5.9

Evaluate $\int_1^2 \frac{5x^4 + 2x}{x^5 + x^2 + 4}\,dx$.

SOLUTION

You can work this out by substituting $u = x^5 + x^2 + 4$ but, since differentiating the bottom line gives the top line, you could apply the rule above and just write:

$$\begin{aligned}\int_1^2 \frac{5x^4 + 2x}{x^5 + x^2 + 4}\,dx &= \Big[\ln(x^5 + x^2 + 4)\Big]_1^2 \\ &= \ln 40 - \ln 6 = 1.90 \qquad \text{(to 2 significant figures).}\end{aligned}$$

In the next example some adjustment is needed to get the top line into the required form.

EXAMPLE 5.10

Evaluate $\int_0^1 \frac{x^5}{x^6 + 7}\,dx$.

SOLUTION

The differential of $x^6 + 7$ is $6x^5$, so the integral is rewritten as $\frac{1}{6}\int_0^1 \frac{6x^5}{x^6 + 7}\,dx$.

Integrating this gives $\frac{1}{6}\Big[\ln(x^6 + 7)\Big]_0^1$ or 0.022 (to 2 significant figures).

Extending the domain for logarithmic integrals

The use of $\int \frac{1}{x} dx = \ln x + c$ has so far been restricted to cases where $x > 0$, since logarithms are undefined for negative numbers.

Similarly, for $\int \frac{f'(x)}{f(x)} dx = \ln(f(x)) + c$ it has been required that $f(x) > 0$.

Look, however, at the area between $-b$ and $-a$ on the left-hand branch of the curve $y = \frac{1}{x}$ in figure 5.6. You can see that it is a real area, and that it must be possible to evaluate it.

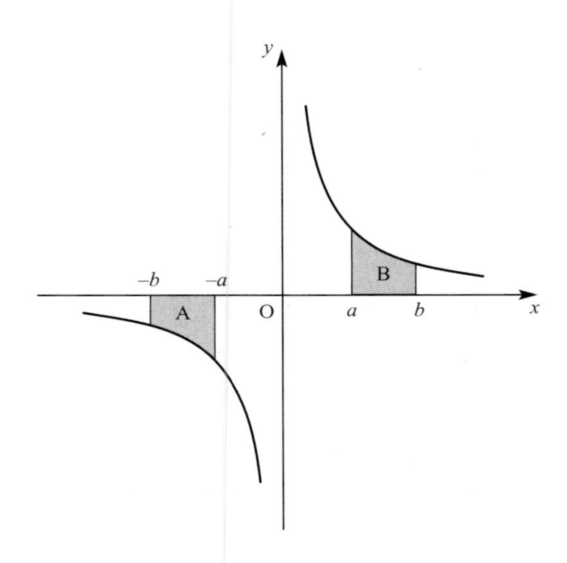

Figure 5.6

ACTIVITY 5.2

1 What can you say about the areas of the two shaded regions?

2 Try to prove your answer to part 1 before reading on.

Proof

Let $A = \int_{-b}^{-a} \frac{1}{x} dx$.

Substituting $u = -x$ gives new limits: $x = -b \Rightarrow u = b$

$x = -a \Rightarrow u = a$.

$$\frac{du}{dx} = -1 \Rightarrow dx = -du.$$

So the integral becomes

$$\begin{aligned} A &= \int_b^a \frac{1}{-u}(-du) \\ &= \int_b^a \frac{1}{u} du \\ &= [\ln a - \ln b] \\ &= -[\ln b - \ln a] = -\text{area B}. \end{aligned}$$

So the area has the same size as that obtained if no notice is taken of the fact that the limits a and b have minus signs. However it has the opposite sign, as you would expect because the area is below the axis.

Consequently the restriction that $x > 0$ may be dropped, and the integral is written

$$\int \frac{1}{x} \mathrm{d}x = \ln|x| + c.$$

Similarly, $\displaystyle\int \frac{f'(x)}{f(x)} \mathrm{d}x = \ln|f(x)| + c.$

EXAMPLE 5.11

Find the value of $\displaystyle\int_5^7 \frac{1}{4-x} \mathrm{d}x.$

SOLUTION

To make the top line into the differential of the bottom line, you write the integral as

$$\begin{aligned} -\int_5^7 \frac{-1}{4-x} \mathrm{d}x &= -[\ln|4-x|]_5^7 \\ &= -[(\ln|-3|) - (\ln|-1|)] \\ &= -[\ln 3 - \ln 1] \\ &= -1.10 \qquad \text{(to 3 significant figures).} \end{aligned}$$

Since the curve $y = \dfrac{1}{x}$ is not defined at the the discontinuity at $x = 0$ (see figure 5.7), it is not possible to integrate across this point.

Consequently in the integral $\displaystyle\int_p^q \frac{1}{x} \mathrm{d}x$ both the limits p and q must have the same sign, either + or –. The integral is invalid otherwise.

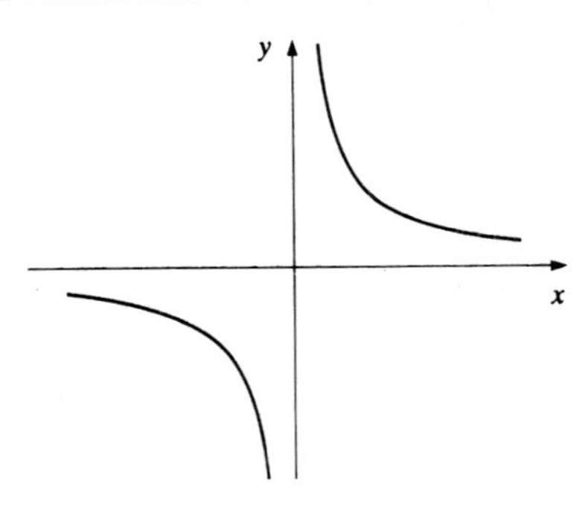

Figure 5.7

For non-trigometrical functions, how can you tell from the equation of a curve whether it has a discontinuity?

How can you prove $y = x^2 - 2x + 3$ has no discontinuities?

EXERCISE 5B

1 Find the following indefinite integrals.

(i) $\displaystyle\int \frac{3}{x} \mathrm{d}x$ **(ii)** $\displaystyle\int \frac{1}{4x} \mathrm{d}x$ **(iii)** $\displaystyle\int \frac{1}{x-5} \mathrm{d}x$

(iv) $\displaystyle\int \frac{1}{2x-9} \mathrm{d}x$ **(v)** $\displaystyle\int \frac{2x}{x^2+1} \mathrm{d}x$ **(vi)** $\displaystyle\int \frac{2x+3}{3x^2+9x-1} \mathrm{d}x$

2 Find the following indefinite integrals.

(i) $\int e^{3x}\,dx$ **(ii)** $\int e^{-4x}\,dx$ **(iii)** $\int e^{-\frac{x}{3}}\,dx$

(iv) $\int 12x^2 e^{x^3}\,dx$ **(v)** $\int \frac{10}{e^{5x}}\,dx$ **(vi)** $\int \frac{e^{3x}+4}{e^{2x}}\,dx$

3 Find the following definite integrals.
Where appropriate give your answers to 3 significant figures.

(i) $\int_0^4 4e^{2x}\,dx$ **(ii)** $\int_1^3 \frac{4}{2x+1}\,dx$ **(iii)** $\int_2^3 2xe^{-x^2}\,dx$

(iv) $\int_{-1}^1 (e^x + e^{-x})\,dx$ **(v)** $\int_{-2}^1 e^{3x-2}\,dx$ **(vi)** $\int_2^4 \frac{x+2}{x^2+4x-3}\,dx$

4 The sketch shows the graph of $y = xe^{x^2}$.

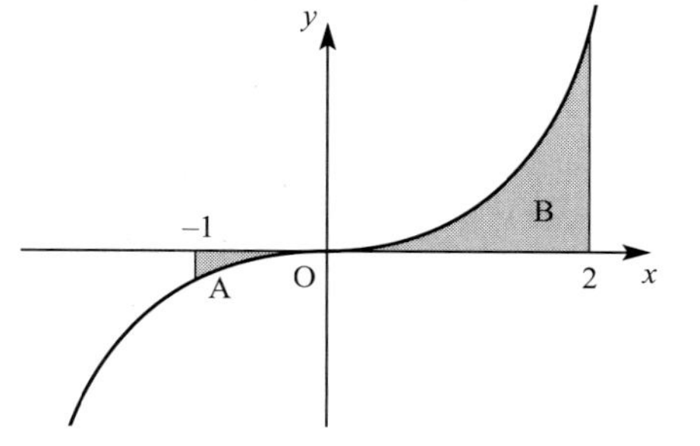

(i) Find the area of region A.
(ii) Find the area of region B.
(iii) Hence write down the total area of the shaded region.

5 The graph of $y = xe^{-x^2}$ is shown here.

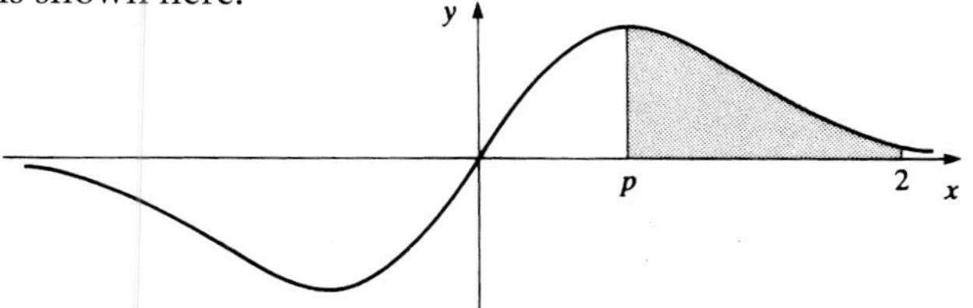

(i) Find $\frac{dy}{dx}$ using the product rule.
(ii) Find the x co-ordinate, p, of the maximum point.
(You do not need to prove that it corresponds to a maximum.)
(iii) Use your answer from part **(ii)** to find the area of the shaded region.

6 The graph of $y = \frac{x+2}{x^2+4x+3}$ is shown below.

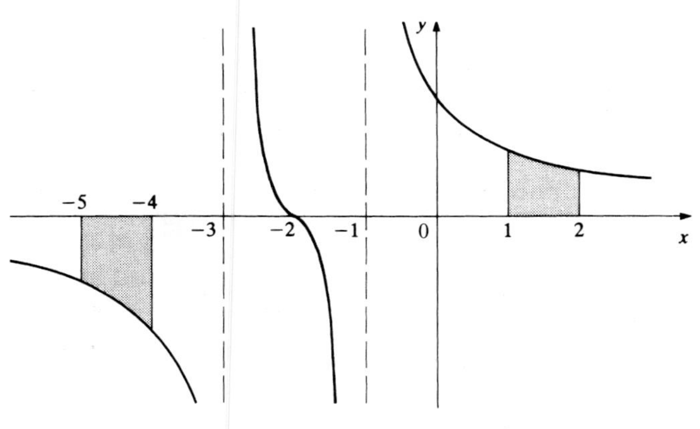

Find the area of each shaded region.

7 The graph of $y = x + \dfrac{4}{x}$ is shown below.

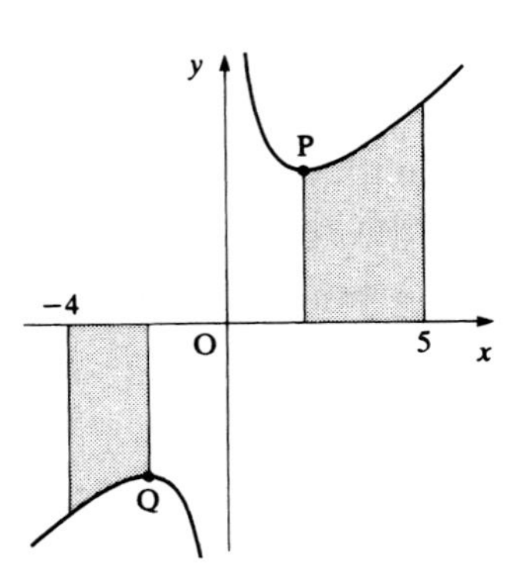

(i) Find the co-ordinates of the minimum point, P, and the maximum point, Q.

(ii) Find the area of each shaded region.

8 (i) Find $\int_0^X xe^{-x^2}\,dx$ in terms of X.

(ii) Evaluate $\int_0^X xe^{-x^2}\,dx$ for $X = 1, 2, 3$ and 4.
(Give your answers to 4 significant figures.)

(iii) As X gets bigger (i.e. as $X \to \infty$), towards what value does $\int_0^X xe^{-x^2}\,dx$ tend?

[MEI]

9 A curve has the equation $y = (x + 3)e^{-x}$.

(i) Find $\dfrac{dy}{dx}$.

(ii) Find the x and y co-ordinates of the stationary point S on the curve.

(iii) Calculate $\dfrac{d^2y}{dx^2}$ at the point S.
What does its value indicate about the stationary point?

(iv) Show that the substitution $u = e^x$ converts $\displaystyle\int \frac{2 + \ln u}{u^2}\,du$ into $\displaystyle\int \frac{2 + x}{e^x}\,dx$.

(v) Hence evaluate $\displaystyle\int_1^e \frac{2 + \ln u}{u^2}\,du$.

[MEI]

10 (i) Use a substitution, such as $u^2 = 2x - 3$, to find $\int 2x\sqrt{2x - 3}\,dx$.

(ii) Differentiate $x^{\frac{1}{2}} \ln x$ with respect to x. Hence find $\displaystyle\int \frac{2 + \ln x}{\sqrt{x}}\,dx$.

(iii) The function f(x) has the property $f'(x) = e^{-x^2}$.

(a) Find $f''(x)$.

(b) Differentiate $f(x^3)$ with respect to x.

[MEI]

11 (i) Find the following integrals.

(a) $\displaystyle\int_1^6 \frac{1}{2x + 3}\,dx$

(b) $\displaystyle\int \frac{x}{\sqrt{9 + x^2}}\,dx$ (Use the substitution $v = \sqrt{9 + x^2}$, or otherwise.)

(ii) (a) Show that $\dfrac{d}{dx}(e^{-x^2}) = -2xe^{-x^2}$.

The sketch below shows the curve with equation $y = xe^{-x^2}$.

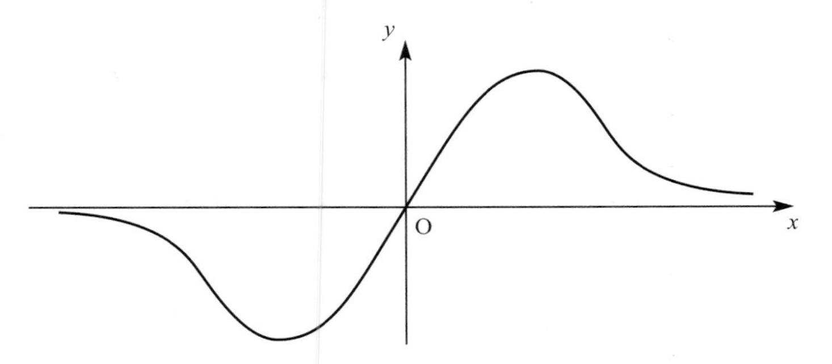

(b) Differentiate xe^{-x^2} and find the co-ordinates of the two stationary points on the curve.

(c) Find the area of the region between the curve and the x axis for $0 \leqslant x \leqslant 0.4$.

[MEI]

12 (i) Sketch the curve with equation $y = \dfrac{e^x}{e^x + 1}$ for values of x between 0 and 2.

(ii) Find the area of the region enclosed by this curve, the axes and the line $x = 2$.

(iii) Find the value of $\displaystyle\int_1^e \frac{2t}{t^2 + 1}\,dt$.

(iv) Compare your answers to parts **(ii)** and **(iii)**. Explain this result.

13 (i) Show that $\displaystyle\int_5^{10} \frac{1}{u}\,du = \ln 2$.

The function f(x) is defined by $f(x) = \dfrac{x}{x^2 + 1}$.

The graph of $y = f(x)$ for positive values of x is shown below.

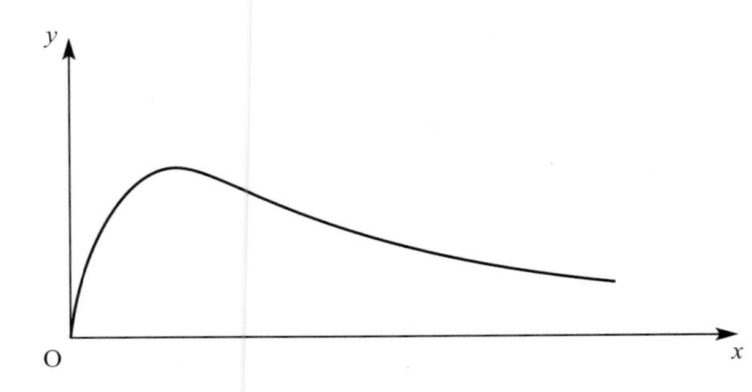

(ii) Calculate $\displaystyle\int_2^3 f(x)\,dx$. (You may wish to use the substitution $u = x^2 + 1$.)

(iii) Show that f(x) is an odd function.

Write down the value of $\displaystyle\int_{-3}^{-2} f(x)\,dx$.

(iv) State a transformation which will transform the graph of $y = f(x)$ into the graph of $y = f(x + 1)$.

(v) Using parts **(iii)** and **(iv)**, or otherwise, calculate the value of

$$\int_{-4}^{-3} \frac{x + 1}{x^2 + 2x + 2}\,dx.$$

[MEI]

14 (i) Differentiate with respect to x

(a) e^{-2x^2} **(b)** xe^{-2x^2}.

You are given that $f(x) = xe^{-2x^2}$.

(ii) Find $\int_0^k f(x)\,dx$ in terms of k.

(iii) Show that $f''(x) = 4xe^{-2x^2}(4x^2 - 3)$.

Show that there is just one stationary point on the curve $y = f(x)$ for positive x. State its co-ordinates and determine its nature.

[MEI]

15 The diagram illustrates the graph of $y = e^x$. The point A has co-ordinates $(\ln 5, 0)$, B has co-ordinates $(\ln 5, 5)$ and C has co-ordinates $(0, 5)$.

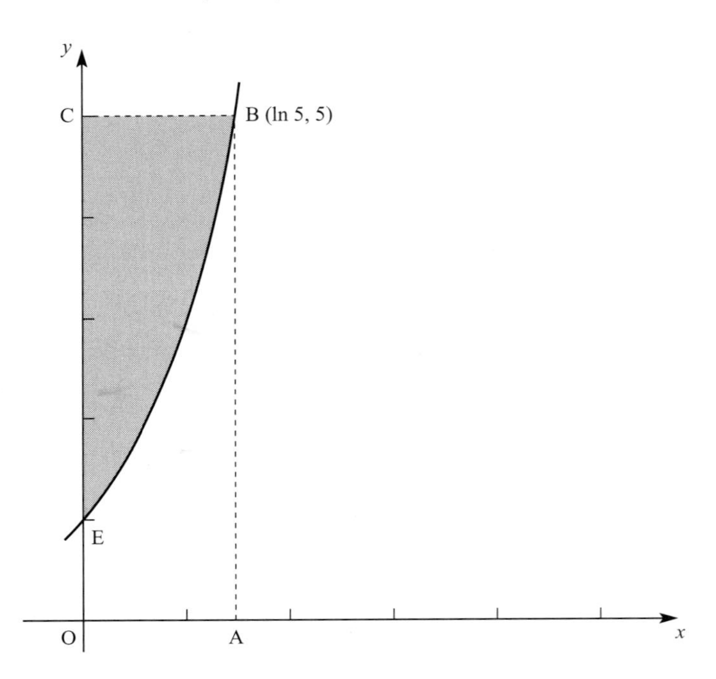

(i) Find the area of the region OABE enclosed by the curve $y = e^x$, the x axis, the y axis and the line AB. Hence find the area of the shaded region EBC.

(ii) (a) The graph of $y = e^x$ is transformed into the graph of $y = \ln x$. Describe this transformation geometrically.

(b) What stretch will transform the graph of $y = \ln x$ to the graph of $y = \ln(x^3)$?

(iii) Using your answers to parts **(i)** and **(ii) (a)**, or otherwise, show that

$$\int_1^5 \ln x\,dx = 5\ln 5 - 4.$$

(iv) Deduce the values of

(a) $\int_1^5 \ln(x^3)\,dx$

(b) $\int_1^5 \ln(3x)\,dx$.

[MEI]

16 P and Q are two points on a hillside. P is 500 m above sea level and Q is 2000 m due east of P.

The graph below shows the height, y, of the hillside above sea level against the horizontal distance, x, from P. The units are 100 m on each axis.

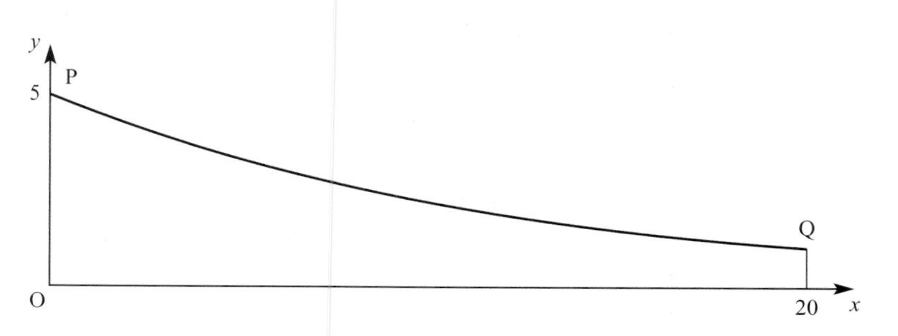

The equation of this graph is $y = 5e^{-0.08x}$.

(i) Calculate the height of Q above sea level to the nearest metre.

(ii) Find $\frac{dy}{dx}$. What is the gradient of the hillside at P?

(iii) Find by integration the area under the graph from $x = 0$ to $x = 20$, in units^2, correct to 2 decimal places.

A stream has its source at P and flows due east. It has cut a gorge down into the rock of the hillside, so that its present position is given by

$$y = \frac{25}{5 + x},$$

as illustrated below. The gorge is 5 m wide.

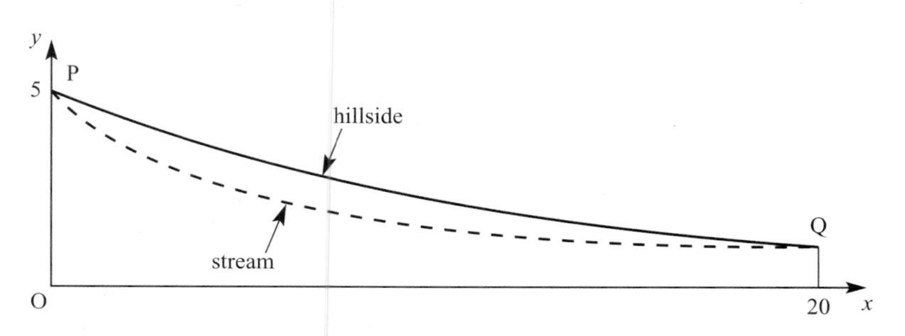

(iv) Use integration to calculate $\int_0^{20} \frac{25}{5 + x} dx$, giving your answer correct to 2 decimal places.
Hence estimate the volume of rock (in m^3) removed by the stream between P and Q, giving your answer to 2 significant figures.

[MEI]

17 The diagram shows a sketch of the curve $y = \dfrac{x}{x^2 + 1}$.

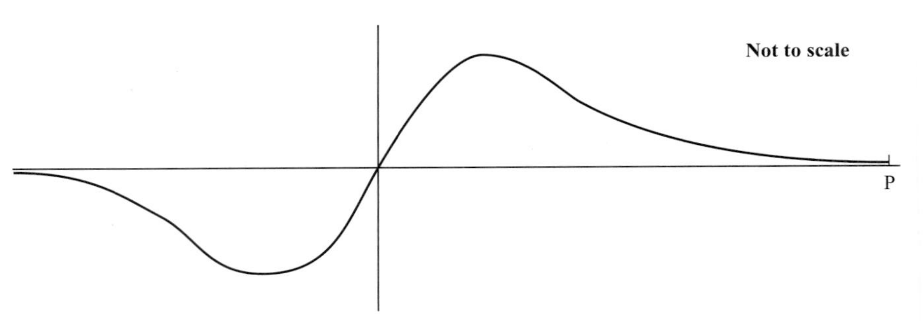

(i) Differentiate $y = \dfrac{x}{x^2 + 1}$.

(ii) Hence find the co-ordinates of the two turning points of the curve.

(iii) By substituting $t = x^2 + 1$, or otherwise, find $\displaystyle\int \frac{x}{x^2 + 1}\,dx$.

(iv) Hence find the x co-ordinate of the point P, given that the area of the region between the curve and the x axis, from the origin to P, is 10 units^2.

[MEI]

18 The diagram shows a sketch of the graph $y = f(x)$, where

$$f(x) = \frac{e^x}{1 + e^x}.$$

The graph crosses the y axis at the point P. It approaches the horizontal line l as $x \to \infty$.

The shaded region is bounded by the graph of $y = f(x)$, the x axis, the y axis and the line $x = 1$.

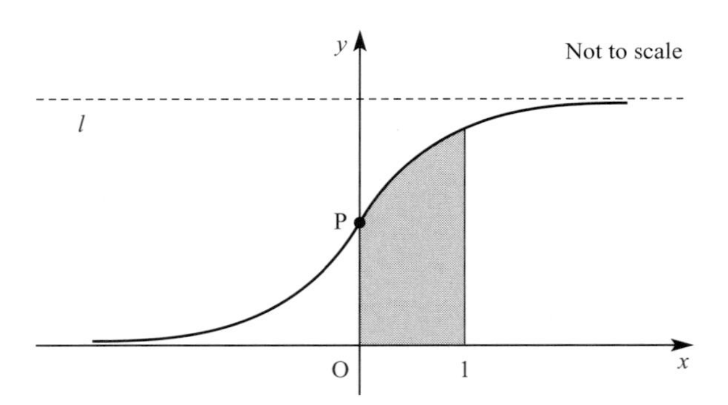

(i) Write down the co-ordinates of the point P, and the equation of the line l.

(ii) Find $f'(x)$, simplifying your answer as far as possible.
Hence calculate the gradient of the curve at the point P.

(iii) Find the exact area of the shaded region, using the substitution $u = 1 + e^x$, or otherwise.
Express your answer as a single logarithm.

(iv) Show that $f(x) + f(-x) = 1$, and interpret this result graphically.

[MEI]

19 The diagram shows the graph of $y = \mathrm{f}(x)$, where

$$\mathrm{f}(x) = \frac{x}{1 + x^2}.$$

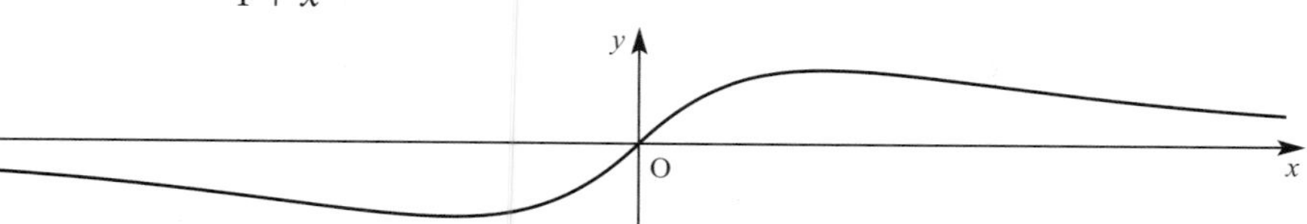

(i) Show algebraically that $\mathrm{f}(x)$ is an odd function.
State what feature of the graph corresponds to the fact that $\mathrm{f}(x)$ is an odd function.

(ii) Find, using calculus, the co-ordinates of the stationary points on the graph of $y = \mathrm{f}(x)$.
Verify that the maximum and minimum points are as shown in the diagram.

Justify the shape of the graph as $x \to \infty$ and as $x \to -\infty$.

(iii) Find the area of the finite region between the graph of $y = \mathrm{f}(x)$, the x axis and the line $x = 1$, giving your answer in terms of a logarithm.

[MEI]

20 The diagram shows a sketch of the graph of $y = \dfrac{x}{(2x-1)^2}$.

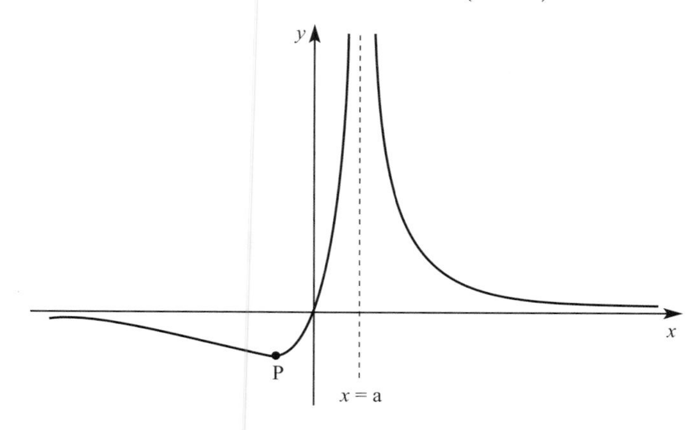

P is a stationary point on the curve. The line $x = a$ is an asymptote to the curve.

(i) Write down the value of a.

(ii) Show that $\dfrac{\mathrm{d}y}{\mathrm{d}x} = -\dfrac{2x+1}{(2x-1)^3}$.

Hence find the co-ordinates of P.

The area of the region enclosed by the graph of $y = \dfrac{x}{(2x-1)^2}$, the x axis, and the lines $x = 1$ and $x = 2$ is denoted by A.

(iii) Using a suitable substitution, show that $A = \displaystyle\int_1^3 \frac{u+1}{4u^2}\,\mathrm{d}u$.

Deduce that $A = \dfrac{3\ln 3 + 2}{12}$.

[MEI]

INVESTIGATION

e A series for e^x

The exponential function can be written as the infinite series

$$e^x = a_0 + a_1x + a_2x^2 + a_3x^3 + a_4x^4 + \dots$$

where $a_0, a_1, a_2, \dots$ are numbers.

You can find the value of a_0 by substituting the value zero for x.

Since $e^0 = 1$, it follows that $1 = a_0 + 0 + 0 + 0 + \dots$, and so $a_0 = 1$.

You can now write: $e^x = 1 + a_1x + a_2x^2 + a_3x^3 + a_4x^4 + \dots$.

Now differentiate both sides: $e^x = a_1 + 2a_2x + 3a_3x^2 + 4a_4x^3 + \dots$,

and substitute $x = 0$ again: $1 = a_1 + 0 + 0 + 0 + \dots$, and so $a_1 = 1$ also.

Now differentiate a second time, and again substitute $x = 0$. This time you find a_2. Continue this procedure until you can see the pattern in the values of $a_0, a_1, a_2, a_3, \dots$.

When you have the series for e^x, substitute $x = 1$. The left-hand side is e^1 or e, and so by adding the terms on the right-hand side you obtain the value of e. You will find that the terms become small quite quickly, so you will not need to use very many to obtain the value of e correct to several decimal places.

If you are also studying statistics you will meet this series expansion of e^x in connection with the Poisson distribution.

INVESTIGATION

e Compound interest

You win £100 000 in a prize draw and are offered two investment options.
A You are paid 100% interest at the end of 10 years, or
B You are paid 10% compound interest year by year for 10 years.
Under which scheme are you better off?

Clearly in scheme **A**, the ratio $R = \dfrac{\text{Final money}}{\text{Original money}}$ is $\dfrac{£200\,000}{£100\,000} = 2$.

What is the value of the ratio R in scheme **B**?

Suppose that you asked for the interest to be paid in 20 half-yearly instalments of 5% each (scheme **C**). What would be the value of R in this case?

Continue this process, investigating what happens to the ratio R when the interest is paid at increasingly frequent intervals.

Is there a limit to R as the time interval between interest payments tends to zero?

Integrating sin*x* and cos*x*

Since $\dfrac{d}{dx}(\sin x) = \cos x$

it follows that $\displaystyle\int \cos x \, dx = \sin x + c$

Similarly, since $\dfrac{d}{dx}(\cos x) = -\sin x$

it also follows that $\dfrac{d}{dx}(-\cos x) = \sin x$

and therefore $\displaystyle\int \sin x \, dx = -\cos x + c$

With this knowledge, you can now integrate not only the functions $\sin x$ and $\cos x$, but also many other functions by using substitution.

EXAMPLE 5.12

Find $\displaystyle\int \sin 7x \, dx$.

SOLUTION

Make the substitution $u = 7x$. Then differentiate.

$$\frac{du}{dx} = 7$$

$$\Rightarrow \quad dx = \tfrac{1}{7} du.$$

$$\int \sin 7x \, dx = \int \tfrac{1}{7} \sin u \, du$$

$$= -\tfrac{1}{7} \cos u + c$$

$$= -\tfrac{1}{7} \cos 7x + c$$

Note

You would not usually use a substitution for an integral like this but would quote the general result that

$$\int \sin kx \, dx = -\frac{1}{k} \cos kx + c.$$

Similarly $\displaystyle\int \cos kx \, dx = \frac{1}{k} \sin kx + c.$

EXAMPLE 5.13

Find $\int 2x\cos(x^2+1)\,dx$.

SOLUTION

Make the substitution $u = x^2 + 1$. Then differentiate.

$$\frac{du}{dx} = 2x$$

$$\Rightarrow \qquad 2x\,dx = du$$

$$\int 2x\cos(x^2+1)\,dx = \int \cos u\,du$$
$$= \sin u + c$$
$$= \sin(x^2+1) + c$$

Notice that the last example involves two functions of x multiplied together, namely $2x$ and $\cos(x^2+1)$. These two functions are related by the fact that $2x$ is the derivative of x^2+1. Because of this relationship, the substitution $u = x^2 + 1$ may be used to perform the integration. You can apply this method to other integrals involving trigonometrical functions, as in the next example.

EXAMPLE 5.14

Find $\int_0^{\frac{\pi}{2}} \cos x \sin^2 x\,dx$.

(Remember that $\sin^2 x$ means the same as $(\sin x)^2$.)

SOLUTION

This integral is the product of two functions, $\cos x$ and $(\sin x)^2$.

Now $(\sin x)^2$ is a function of $\sin x$, and $\cos x$ is the derivative of $\sin x$, so you should use the substitution $u = \sin x$.

Differentiating:

$$\frac{du}{dx} = \cos x \quad \Rightarrow \quad du = \cos x\,dx.$$

The limits of integration need to be changed as well:

$$x = 0 \quad \Rightarrow \quad u = 0$$

$$x = \frac{\pi}{2} \quad \Rightarrow \quad u = 1$$

Therefore $$\int_0^{\frac{\pi}{2}} \cos x \sin^2 x\,dx = \int_0^1 u^2 du$$
$$= \left[\frac{u^3}{3}\right]_0^1$$
$$= \frac{1}{3}.$$

Note

You may find that as you gain practice in this type of integration you become able to work out the integral without writing down the substitution. However, if you are unsure, it is best to write down the whole process.

EXERCISE 5C

1 Integrate the following functions with respect to x.

(i) $\sin x - 2\cos x$ **(ii)** $3\cos x + 2\sin x$ **(iii)** $5\sin x + 4\cos x$

2 Integrate the following functions by using the substitution given, or otherwise.

(i) $\cos 3x$ $u = 3x$

(ii) $\sin(1 - x)$ $u = 1 - x$

(iii) $\sin x \cos^3 x$ $u = \cos x$

(iv) $\dfrac{\sin x}{2 - \cos x}$ $u = 2 - \cos x$

(v) $\tan x$ $u = \cos x$ $\left(\text{write } \tan x \text{ as } \dfrac{\sin x}{\cos x}\right)$

(vi) $\sin 2x(1 + \cos 2x)^2$ $u = 1 + \cos 2x$

3 Use a suitable substitution to integrate the following functions.

(i) $2x\sin(x^2)$ **(ii)** $\cos x\, e^{\sin x}$

(iii) $\dfrac{\tan x}{\cos^2 x}$ **(iv)** $\dfrac{\cos x}{\sin^2 x}$

4 Evaluate the following definite integrals by using suitable substitutions.

(i) $\displaystyle\int_0^{\frac{\pi}{2}} \cos\left(2x - \frac{\pi}{2}\right) dx$ **(ii)** $\displaystyle\int_0^{\frac{\pi}{4}} \cos x \sin^3 x \, dx$

(iii) $\displaystyle\int_0^{\sqrt{\pi}} x\sin(x^2)\, dx$ **(iv)** $\displaystyle\int_0^{\frac{\pi}{4}} \frac{e^{\tan x}}{\cos^2 x}\, dx$

(v) $\displaystyle\int_0^{\frac{\pi}{4}} \frac{1}{\cos^2 x(1 + \tan x)}\, dx$

5 **(i)** Use a graphic calculator or computer to sketch the graph of the function $y = \sin x(\cos x - 1)^2$ for $0 \leqslant x \leqslant 4\pi$.

(ii) Use definite integration to find the area between the positive part of one cycle of the curve and the x axis.

Integration by parts

There are still many integrations which you cannot yet do. In fact, many functions cannot be integrated at all, although virtually all functions can be differentiated. However, some functions can be integrated by techniques which you have not yet met. Integration by parts is one of those techniques.

EXAMPLE 5.15

Find $\int x \cos x \, dx$.

SOLUTION

The function to be integrated is clearly a product of two simpler functions, x and $\cos x$, so your first thought may be to look for a substitution to enable you to perform the integration. However, there are some functions which are products but which cannot be integrated by substitution. This is one of them. You need a new technique to integrate such functions.

Take the function $x\sin x$ and differentiate it, using the product rule.

$$\frac{\mathrm{d}}{\mathrm{d}x}(x\sin x) = x\cos x + \sin x.$$

Now integrate both sides. This has the effect of 'undoing' the differentiation, so

$$x\sin x = \int x\cos x\,\mathrm{d}x + \int \sin x\,\mathrm{d}x.$$

Rearranging this gives

$$\begin{aligned}\int x\cos x\,\mathrm{d}x &= x\sin x - \int \sin x\,\mathrm{d}x \\ &= x\sin x - (-\cos x) + c \\ &= x\sin x + \cos x + c.\end{aligned}$$

This has enabled you to find the integral of $x\cos x$.

The work in this example can be generalised into the method of integration by parts. Before coming on to that, do the following activity.

ACTIVITY 5.3

For each of the following

(a) differentiate the given function $\mathrm{f}(x)$ using the product rule

(b) rearrange your expression to find an expression for the given integral I

(c) use this expression to find the given integral.

(i) $\mathrm{f}(x) = x\cos x \quad I = \int x\sin x\,\mathrm{d}x$

(ii) $\mathrm{f}(x) = x\mathrm{e}^{2x} \quad I = \int 2x\mathrm{e}^{2x}\,\mathrm{d}x$

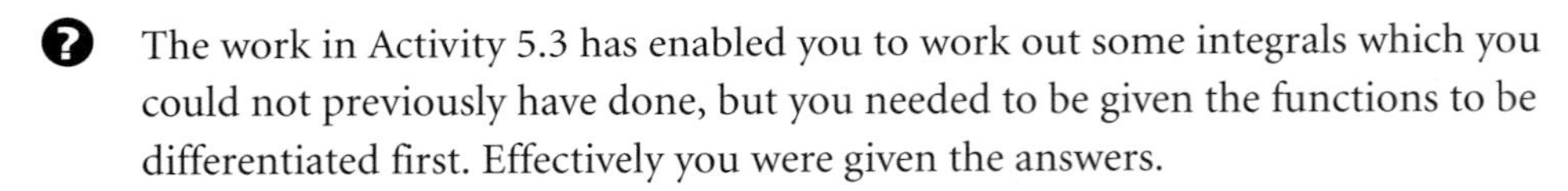

The work in Activity 5.3 has enabled you to work out some integrals which you could not previously have done, but you needed to be given the functions to be differentiated first. Effectively you were given the answers.

Look at the expressions you found in part **(b)** of Activity 5.3.
Can you see any way of working out these expressions without starting by differentiating a given product?

The general result for integration by parts

The method just investigated can be generalised.

Look back at Example 5.15. Use u to stand for the function x, and v to stand for the function $\sin x$.

Using the product rule to differentiate the function uv

$$\frac{\mathrm{d}}{\mathrm{d}x}(uv) = v\frac{\mathrm{d}u}{\mathrm{d}x} + u\frac{\mathrm{d}v}{\mathrm{d}x}.$$

Integrating gives

$$uv = \int v\frac{du}{dx}\,dx + \int u\frac{dv}{dx}\,dx.$$

Rearranging gives

$$\int u\frac{dv}{dx}\,dx = uv - \int v\frac{du}{dx}\,dx.$$

This is the formula you use when you need to integrate by parts.

In order to use it, you have to split the function you want to integrate into two simpler functions. In Example 5.15 you would split $x\cos x$ into the two functions x and $\cos x$. One of these functions will be called u, and the other $\frac{dv}{dx}$, to fit the left-hand side of the expression. You will need to decide which will be which. Two considerations will help you.

- As you want to use $\frac{du}{dx}$ on the right-hand side of the expression, u should be a function which becomes a simpler function after differentiation. So in this case, u will be the function x.
- As you need v to work out the right-hand side of the expression, it must be possible to integrate the function $\frac{dv}{dx}$ to obtain v. In this case, $\frac{dv}{dx}$ will be the function $\cos x$.

So now you can find $\int x\cos x\,dx$.

Put $\quad u = x \quad \Rightarrow \quad \frac{du}{dx} = 1$

and $\quad \frac{dv}{dx} = \cos x \quad \Rightarrow \quad v = \sin x$

Substituting in

$$\int u\frac{dv}{dx}\,dx = uv - \int v\frac{du}{dx}\,dx$$

gives

$$\begin{aligned}\int x\cos x\,dx &= x\sin x - \int 1 \times \sin x\,dx \\ &= x\sin x - (-\cos x) + c \\ &= x\sin x + \cos x + c.\end{aligned}$$

EXAMPLE 5.16

Find $\int 2xe^x\,dx$.

SOLUTION

First split $2xe^x$ into the two simpler functions, $2x$ and e^x. Both can be integrated easily, but as $2x$ becomes a simpler function after differentiation and e^x does not, take u to be $2x$.

$$u = 2x \quad \Rightarrow \quad \frac{du}{dx} = 2$$

$$\frac{dv}{dx} = e^x \quad \Rightarrow \quad v = e^x$$

Substituting in

$$\int u\frac{dv}{dx}\,dx = uv - \int v\frac{du}{dx}\,dx$$

gives

$$\int 2xe^x\,dx = 2xe^x - \int 2e^x\,dx$$
$$= 2xe^x - 2e^x + c.$$

In some cases, the choices of u and v may be less obvious.

EXAMPLE 5.17

Find $\int x \ln x\,dx$.

SOLUTION

It might seem at first that u should be taken as x, because it becomes a simpler function after differentiation.

$$u = x \quad \Rightarrow \quad \frac{du}{dx} = 1$$

$$\frac{dv}{dx} = \ln x$$

Now you need to integrate $\ln x$ to obtain v. Although it is possible to integrate $\ln x$, it has to be done by parts, as you will see in the next example. The wrong choice has been made for u and v, resulting in a more complicated integral.

So instead, let $u = \ln x$.

$$u = \ln x \quad \Rightarrow \quad \frac{du}{dx} = \frac{1}{x}$$

$$\frac{dv}{dx} = x \quad \Rightarrow \quad v = \tfrac{1}{2}x^2$$

Substituting in

$$\int u\frac{dv}{dx}\,dx = uv - \int v\frac{du}{dx}\,dx$$

gives

$$\int x\ln x\,dx = \tfrac{1}{2}x^2\ln x - \int \frac{\frac{1}{2}x^2}{x}\,dx$$
$$= \tfrac{1}{2}x^2\ln x - \int \tfrac{1}{2}x\,dx$$
$$= \tfrac{1}{2}x^2\ln x - \tfrac{1}{4}x^2 + c.$$

EXAMPLE 5.18

Find $\int \ln x \, dx$.

SOLUTION

You need to start by writing $\ln x$ as $1 \ln x$ and then use integration by parts.

As in the last example, let $u = \ln x$.

$$u = \ln x \quad \Rightarrow \quad \frac{du}{dx} = \frac{1}{x}$$

$$\frac{dv}{dx} = 1 \quad \Rightarrow \quad v = x$$

Substituting in

$$\int u\frac{dv}{dx}\,dx = uv - \int v\frac{du}{dx}\,dx$$

gives

$$\int 1 \ln x \, dx = x \ln x - \int \frac{x}{1} \times \frac{1}{x} \, dx$$

$$= x \ln x - x + c.$$

Using integration by parts twice

Sometimes it is necessary to use integration by parts twice or more to complete the integration successfully.

EXAMPLE 5.19

Find $\int x^2 \sin x \, dx$.

SOLUTION

First split $x^2 \sin x$ into two: x^2 and $\sin x$. As x^2 becomes a simpler function after differentiation, take u to be x^2.

$$u = x^2 \quad \Rightarrow \quad \frac{du}{dx} = 2x$$

$$\frac{dv}{dx} = \sin x \quad \Rightarrow \quad v = -\cos x.$$

Substituting in

$$\int u\frac{dv}{dx}\,dx = uv - \int v\frac{du}{dx}\,dx$$

gives

$$\int x^2 \sin x \, dx = -x^2 \cos x - \int -2x \cos x \, dx$$

$$= -x^2 \cos x + \int 2x \cos x \, dx. \qquad ①$$

Now the integral of $2x \cos x$ cannot be found without using integration by parts again. It has to be split into the functions $2x$ and $\cos x$, and as $2x$ becomes a simpler function after differentiation, take u to be $2x$.

$$u = 2x \quad \Rightarrow \quad \frac{du}{dx} = 2$$

$$\frac{dv}{dx} = \cos x \quad \Rightarrow \quad v = \sin x$$

Substituting in

$$\int u \frac{dv}{dx}\, dx = uv - \int v \frac{du}{dx}\, dx$$

gives

$$\begin{aligned}\int 2x \cos x\, dx &= 2x \sin x - \int 2 \sin x\, dx \\ &= 2x \sin x - (-2 \cos x) + c \\ &= 2x \sin x + 2 \cos x + c.\end{aligned}$$

So in ① $\int x^2 \sin x\, dx = -x^2 \cos x + 2x \sin x + 2 \cos x + c.$

The technique of integration by parts is usually used when the two functions are of different types: polynomials, trigonometrical functions, exponentials, logarithms. There are, however, some exceptions, as in questions 3 and 4 of Exercise 5D.

Integration by parts is a very important technique which is needed in many other branches of mathematics. For example, integrals of the form $\int x\, f(x)\, dx$ are used in statistics to find the mean of a probability density function, and in mechanics to find the centre of mass of a shape. Integrals of the form $\int x^2\, f(x)\, dx$ are used in statistics to find variance and in mechanics to find moments of inertia.

EXERCISE 5D

1 For each of these integrals

(a) write down the function to be taken as u and the function to be taken as $\frac{dv}{dx}$

(b) use the formula for integration by parts to complete the integration.

(i) $\int x e^x\, dx$ **(ii)** $\int x \cos 3x\, dx$

(iii) $\int (2x + 1) \cos x\, dx$ **(iv)** $\int x e^{-2x}\, dx$

(v) $\int x e^{-x}\, dx$ **(vi)** $\int x \sin 2x\, dx$

2 Use integraton by parts to integrate each of these functions.

(i) $x^3 \ln x$ **(ii)** $3x e^{3x}$

(iii) $2x \cos 2x$ **(iv)** $x^2 \ln 2x$

3 Find $\int x\sqrt{1+x}\,dx$

(i) by using integration by parts

(ii) by using the substitution $u = 1 + x$.

4 Find $\int 2x(x-2)^4\,dx$

(i) by using integration by parts

(ii) by using the substitution $u = x - 2$.

5 (i) By writing $\ln x$ as the product of $\ln x$ and 1, use integration by parts to find $\int \ln x\,dx$.

(ii) Use the same method to find $\int \ln 3x\,dx$.

(iii) Write down $\int \ln px\,dx$ where $p > 0$.

e *The remaining questions relate to enrichment material.*

6 Find $\int x^2 e^x\,dx$.

7 Find $\int (2-x)^2 \cos x\,dx$.

Definite integration by parts

When you use the method of integration by parts on a definite integral, it is important to remember that the term uv on the right-hand side of the expression has already been integrated and so should be written in square brackets with the limits indicated.

$$\int_a^b u\frac{dv}{dx}\,dx = \Big[uv\Big]_a^b - \int_a^b v\frac{du}{dx}\,dx.$$

EXAMPLE 5.20

Evaluate $\int_0^2 xe^x\,dx$.

SOLUTION

Put $u = x \quad \Rightarrow \quad \dfrac{du}{dx} = 1$

and $\dfrac{dv}{dx} = e^x \quad \Rightarrow \quad v = e^x.$

Substituting in

$$\int_a^b u\frac{dv}{dx}\,dx = \Big[uv\Big]_a^b - \int_a^b v\frac{du}{dx}\,dx$$

gives

$$\int_0^2 xe^x\,dx = \Big[xe^x\Big]_0^2 - \int_0^2 e^x\,dx$$

$$= \Big[xe^x\Big]_0^2 - \Big[e^x\Big]_0^2$$

$$= (2e^2 - 0) - (e^2 - e^0)$$

$$= 2e^2 - e^2 + 1$$

$$= e^2 + 1.$$

EXAMPLE 5.21

Find the area of the region between the curve $y = x\cos x$ and the x axis, between $x = 0$ and $x = \frac{\pi}{2}$.

SOLUTION

Figure 5.8 shows the region whose area is to be found.

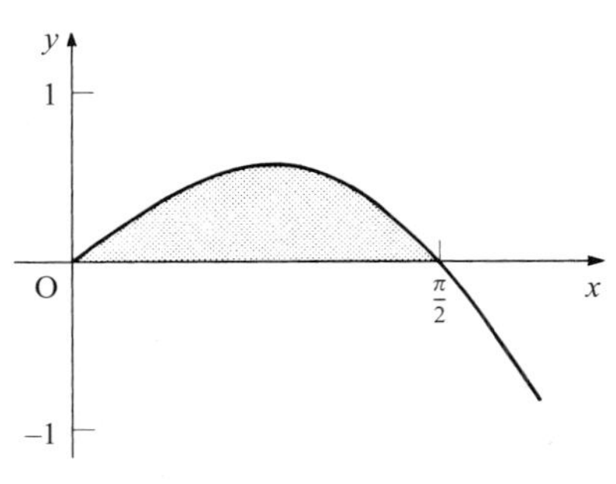

Figure 5.8

To find the required area, you need to integrate the function $x\cos x$ between the limits 0 and $\frac{\pi}{2}$. You therefore need to work out

$$\int_0^{\frac{\pi}{2}} x\cos x\,dx.$$

Put $\quad u = x \quad \Rightarrow \quad \frac{du}{dx} = 1$

and $\quad \frac{dv}{dx} = \cos x \quad \Rightarrow \quad v = \sin x$

Substituting in

$$\int_a^b u\frac{dv}{dx}\,dx = \Big[uv\Big]_a^b - \int_a^b v\frac{du}{dx}\,dx.$$

gives

$$\int_0^{\frac{\pi}{2}} x\cos x\,dx = \Big[x\sin x\Big]_0^{\frac{\pi}{2}} - \int_0^{\frac{\pi}{2}} \sin x\,dx$$

$$= \Big[x\sin x\Big]_0^{\frac{\pi}{2}} - \Big[-\cos x\Big]_0^{\frac{\pi}{2}}$$

$$= \Big[x\sin x + \cos x\Big]_0^{\frac{\pi}{2}}$$

$$= \left(\frac{\pi}{2} + 0\right) - \left(0 + 1\right)$$

$$= \frac{\pi}{2} - 1.$$

So the required area is $\frac{\pi}{2} - 1$ square units.

EXERCISE 5E

1 Evaluate these definite integrals.

(i) $\int_0^1 xe^{3x}\,dx$ **(ii)** $\int_0^{\pi} (x-1)\cos x\,dx$

(iii) $\int_0^2 (x+1)e^x\,dx$ **(iv)** $\int_1^2 \ln 2x\,dx$

(v) $\int_0^{\frac{\pi}{2}} x\sin 2x\,dx$ **(vi)** $\int_1^4 x^2 \ln x\,dx$

2 **(i)** Find the co-ordinates of the points where the graph of $y = (2-x)e^{-x}$ cuts the x and y axes.

(ii) Hence sketch the graph of $y = (2-x)e^{-x}$.

(iii) Use integration by parts to find the area of the region between the x axis, the y axis and the graph $y = (2-x)e^{-x}$.

3 **(i)** Sketch the graph of $y = x\sin x$ from $x = 0$ to $x = \pi$ and shade the region between the curve and the x axis.

(ii) Find the area of this region using integration by parts.

4 Find the area of the region between the x axis, the line $x = 5$ and the graph $y = \ln x$.

5 Find the area of the region between the x axis and the graph $y = x\sin x$ from $x = 0$ to $x = \frac{\pi}{2}$.

6 Find the area of the region between the negative x axis and the graph $y = x\sqrt{x+1}$

(i) using integration by parts

(ii) using the substitution $u = x + 1$.

7 The sketch shows the curve with equation $y = x^2 \ln 2x$.

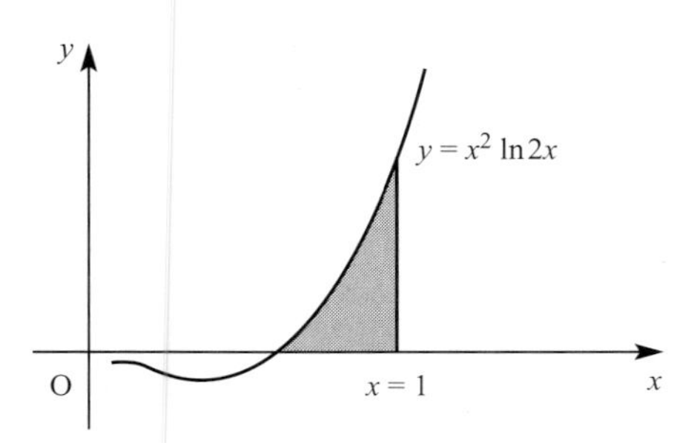

Find the x co-ordinate of the point where the curve cuts the x axis.
Hence calculate the area of the shaded region using the method of integration by parts applied to the product of $\ln 2x$ and x^2.
Give your answer correct to 3 decimal places.

[MEI]

The remaining questions relate to enrichment material.

8 Show that $\int_0^1 x^2 e^x \, dx = e - 2$.

Show that the use of the trapezium rule with five strips (six ordinates) gives an estimate that is about 3.8% too high.
Explain why approximate evaluation of this integral using the trapezium rule will always result in an overestimate, however many strips are used. [MEI]

9 If $I_n = \int_0^1 t^n e^{-t} \, dt$, where n is an integer, show that $I_0 = 1 - e^{-1}$.

By integrating by parts, show that $I_n = nI_{n-1} - e^{-1}$ for $n \geqslant 1$.
Hence evaluate I_3, leaving your answer in terms of e^{-1}. [MEI]

KEY POINTS

1 $\int kx^n \, dx = \frac{kx^{n+1}}{n+1} + c$ where k and n are constants but $n \neq -1$.

2 Substitution is often used to change a non-standard integral into a standard one.

3 $\int e^x \, dx = e^x + c$

4 $\int \frac{1}{x} \, dx = \ln|x| + c$

5 $\int \frac{f'(x)}{f(x)} \, dx = \ln|f(x)| + c$

6 $\int \sin kx \, dx = -\frac{1}{k}\cos kx + c$

$\int \cos kx \, dx = \frac{1}{k}\sin kx + c$

7 Some products may be integrated by parts using the formula

$$\int u\frac{dv}{dx} \, dx = uv - \int v\frac{du}{dx} \, dx.$$

6 Numerical solution of equations

It is the true nature of mankind to learn from his mistakes.

Fred Hoyle

Which of the following equations can be solved algebraically, and which cannot? For each equation find a solution, accurate or approximate.

(i) $x^2 - 4x + 3 = 0$ **(ii)** $x^2 + 10x + 8 = 0$ **(iii)** $x^5 - 5x + 3 = 0$

(iv) $x^3 - x = 0$ **(v)** $e^x = 4x$

You probably realised that the equations $x^5 - 5x + 3 = 0$ and $e^x = 4x$ cannot be solved algebraically. You may have decided to draw their graphs, either manually or using a graphic calculator or computer package, as in figure 6.1.

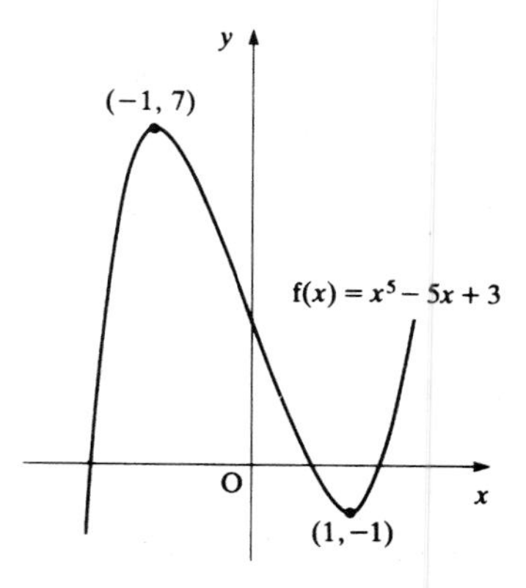

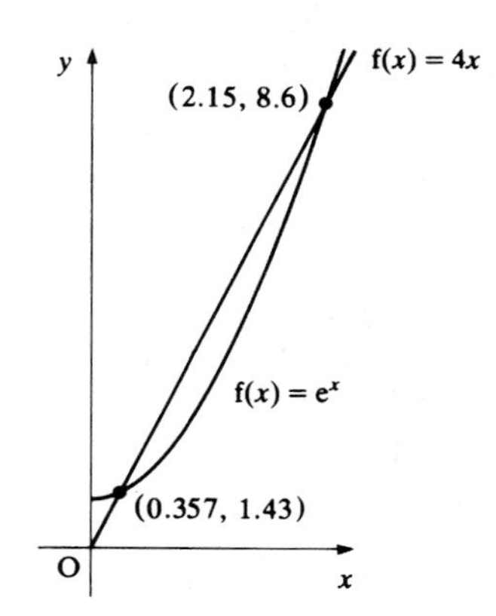

Figure 6.1

The graphs show you that

- $x^5 - 5x + 3 = 0$ has three roots, lying in the intervals $[-2, -1]$, $[0, 1]$ and $[1, 2]$.
- $e^x = 4x$ has two roots, lying in the intervals $[0, 1]$ and $[2, 3]$.

The problem now is how to find the roots to any required degree of accuracy, and as efficiently as possible.

In many real problems, equations are obtained for which solutions using algebraic or analytical methods are not possible, but for which you nonetheless want to know the answers. In this chapter you will be introduced to numerical methods for solving such equations. In applying these methods, keep the following points in mind.

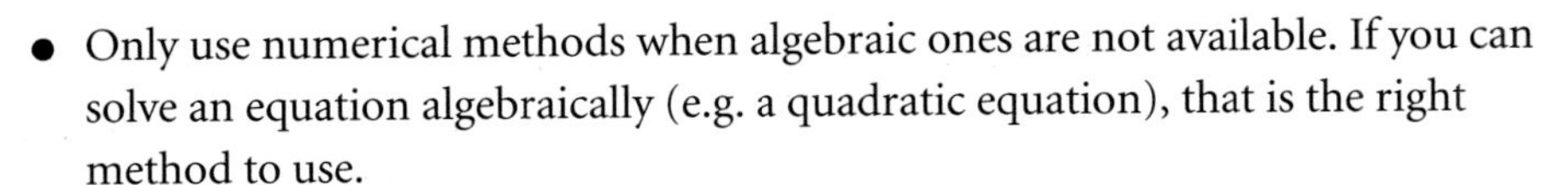

- Only use numerical methods when algebraic ones are not available. If you can solve an equation algebraically (e.g. a quadratic equation), that is the right method to use.
- Before starting to use a calculator or computer program, always start by drawing a sketch graph of the function whose equation you are trying to solve. This will show you how many roots the equation has and their approximate positions. It will also warn you of possible difficulties with particular methods. When using a graphic calculator or computer package ensure that the range of values of x is sufficiently large to, hopefully, find all the roots.
- Always give a statement about the accuracy of an answer (e.g. to 5 decimal places, or $\pm$ 0.000 005). An answer obtained by a numerical method is worthless without this; the fact that at some point your calculator display reads, say, 1.676 470 588 2 does not mean that all these figures are valid.
- Your statement about the accuracy must be obtained from within the numerical method itself. Usually you find a sequence of estimates of ever-increasing accuracy.
- Remember that the most suitable method for one equation may not be that for another.

Note

An interval written as $[a, b]$ means the interval between a and b, including a and b. This notation is used in this chapter. If a and b are not included, the interval is written (a, b). You may also elsewhere meet the notation $]a, b[$, indicating that a and b are *not* included.

Interval estimation – change of sign methods

Assume that you are looking for the roots of the equation $f(x) = 0$. This means that you want the values of x for which the graph of $y = f(x)$ crosses the x axis. As the curve crosses the x axis, $f(x)$ changes sign, so provided that $f(x)$ is a continuous function (its graph has no asymptotes or other breaks in it), once you have located an interval in which $f(x)$ changes sign, you know that that interval must contain a root. In both of the graphs in figure 6.2, there is a root lying between a and b.

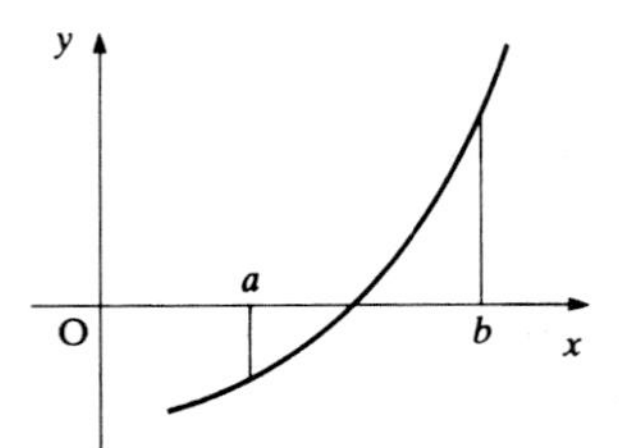

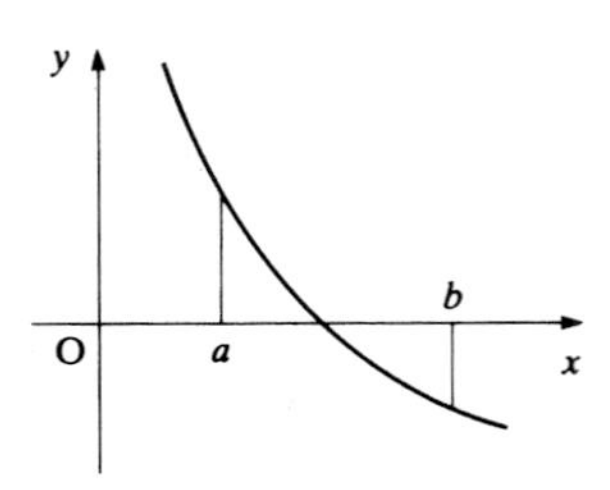

Figure 6.2

You have seen that $x^5 - 5x + 3 = 0$ has roots in the intervals [–2, –1], [0, 1] and [1, 2]. There are several ways of homing in on such roots systematically. Three of these are now described, using the search for the root in the interval [0, 1] as an example.

Decimal search

In this method you first take increments in x of size 0.1 within the interval [0, 1], working out the value of the function $f(x) = x^5 - 5x + 3$ for each one. You do this until you find a change of sign.

x	0.0	0.1	0.2	0.3	0.4	0.5	0.6	0.7
$f(x)$	3.00	2.50	2.00	1.50	1.01	0.53	0.08	–0.33

There is a sign change, and therefore a root, in the interval [0.6, 0.7] since the function is continuous. Having narrowed down the interval, you can now continue with increments of 0.01 within the interval [0.6, 0.7].

x	0.60	0.61	0.62
$f(x)$	0.08	0.03	–0.01

This shows that the root lies in the interval [0.61, 0.62].

Alternative ways of expressing this information are that the root can be taken as 0.615 with a maximum error of $\pm$ 0.005, or the root is 0.6 (to 1 decimal place).

This process can be continued by considering $x = 0.611$, $x = 0.612$, ... to obtain the root to any required number of decimal places.

How many steps of decimal search would be necessary to find each of the values 0.012, 0.385, and 0.989, using $x = 0$ as a starting point?

When you use this procedure on a computer or calculator you should be aware that the machine is working in base 2, and that the conversion of many simple numbers from base 10 to base 2 introduces small rounding errors. This can lead to simple roots such as 2.7 being missed and only being found as 2.699 999.

Interval bisection

This method is similar to the decimal search, but instead of dividing each interval into ten parts and looking for a sign change, in this case the interval is divided into two parts – it is bisected.

Looking as before for the root in the interval [0, 1], you start by taking the mid-point of the interval, 0.5.

$f(0.5) = 0.53$, so $f(0.5) > 0$. Since $f(1) < 0$, the root is in $[0.5, 1]$.

Now take the mid-point of this second interval, 0.75.

$f(0.75) = -0.51$, so $f(0.75) < 0$. Since $f(0.5) > 0$, the root is in $[0.5, 0.75]$.

The mid-point of this further reduced interval is 0.625.

$f(0.625) = -0.03$, so the root is in the interval $[0.5, 0.625]$.

The method continues in this manner until any required degree of accuracy is obtained. However, the interval bisection method is quite slow to converge to the root, and is cumbersome when performed manually.

ACTIVITY 6.1 Investigate how many steps of this method you need to achieve an accuracy of 1, 2, 3 and n decimal places, having started with an interval of length 1.

e Linear interpolation

A refinement of this type of method arises when you use not only the signs of the function at the end points of the interval, but its values there as well, to help you to define a reduced interval. As before, an interval (usually of unit length) containing the root is first located. The part of the curve in this interval is then approximated by the chord joining its end points, and the x co-ordinate of the point where the chord crosses the x axis is calculated.

Looking again at the function $f(x) = x^5 - 5x + 3$, you can see that $f(0) = 3$ and $f(1) = -1$. Figure 6.3 shows the chord of the curve between $(0, 3)$ and $(1, -1)$. It crosses the x axis at 0.75.

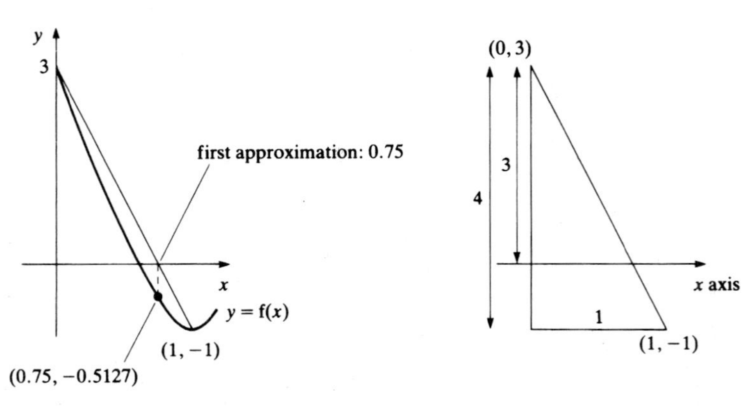

Figure 6.3

The value of $x^5 - 5x + 3$ at $x = 0.75$ is then calculated: $f(0.75) = -0.5127$.

Since $f(0) > 0$ and $f(0.75) < 0$, the root must lie in the interval $[0, 0.75]$.

The procedure is then repeated successively until the required level of accuracy is achieved. The second approximation is shown in figure 6.4.

For this example, the method of linear interpolation approaches the root more rapidly than the previous methods, the successive intervals being

[0, 1], [0, 0.75], [0, 0.6405],
[0, 0.6209], [0, 0.6184],
[0, 0.6181], [0, 0.6180].

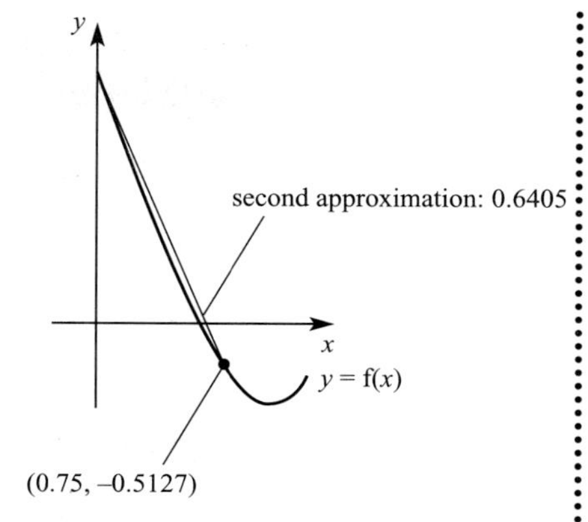

Figure 6.4

The sequence of numbers representing the right-hand end of the interval appears to be converging, so that you would suspect it to be getting close to the root. (It is not always the right-hand end of the interval that does this: in other examples, it may be the left-hand end.) The left-hand end of the interval is still far from the root, however, so you cannot be sure of your level of accuracy. You now need to see if you can move the left-hand end much closer to the suspected root without a change of sign. You might look at $x = 0.6179$, for example. It turns out that f(0.6179) is positive, so the interval for the root is now closed down to [0.6179, 0.6180].

This last step – finding a bound for the other end of the interval – is absolutely essential in order to justify the accuracy of any stated solution.

It is difficult to predict the number of steps of linear interpolation which would be needed to reach any required level of accuracy. The rate at which the root is found (the *rate of convergence*) is very variable for this method, as shown in figure 6.5.

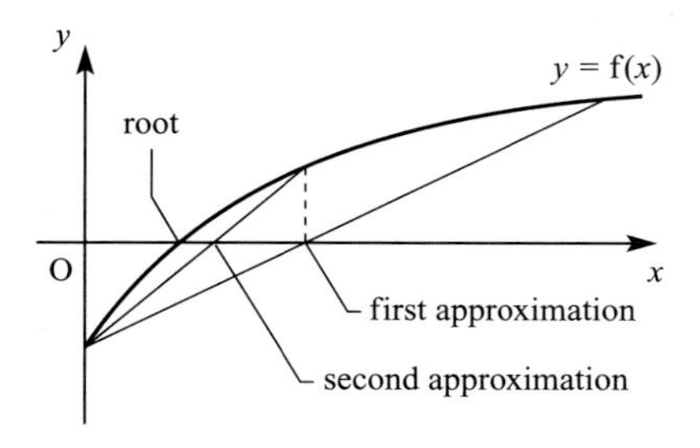

Rapid rate of convergence

y
root
y = f(x)
O
x
first approximation
second approximation
third approximation
fourth approximation

Slow rate of convergence

Figure 6.5

ACTIVITY 6.2 Given that the equation $f(x) = 0$ has a root between $x = a$ and $x = b$, show that linear interpolation would next lead you to investigate

$$x = \frac{bf(a) - af(b)}{f(a) - f(b)}.$$

Error (or solution) bounds

Change of sign methods have the great advantage that they automatically provide bounds (the two ends of the interval) within which a root lies, so the maximum possible error in a result is known. Knowing that a root lies in the interval [0.61, 0.62] means that you can take the root as 0.615 with a maximum error of ± 0.005.

Problems with change of sign methods

There are a number of situations which can cause problems for change of sign methods if they are applied blindly, for example by entering the equation into a computer program without prior thought. In all cases you can avoid problems by first drawing a sketch graph, provided that you know what dangers to look out for.

The curve touches the x axis

In this case there is no change of sign, so change of sign methods are doomed to failure (see figure 6.6).

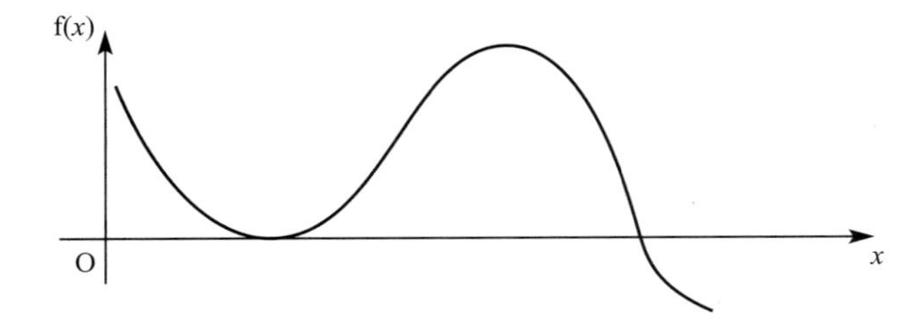

Figure 6.6

There are several roots close together

Where there are several roots close together, it is easy to miss a pair of them. The equation

$$f(x) = x^3 - 1.9x^2 + 1.11x - 0.189 = 0$$

has roots at 0.3, 0.7 and 0.9. A sketch of the curve of $f(x)$ is shown in figure 6.7.

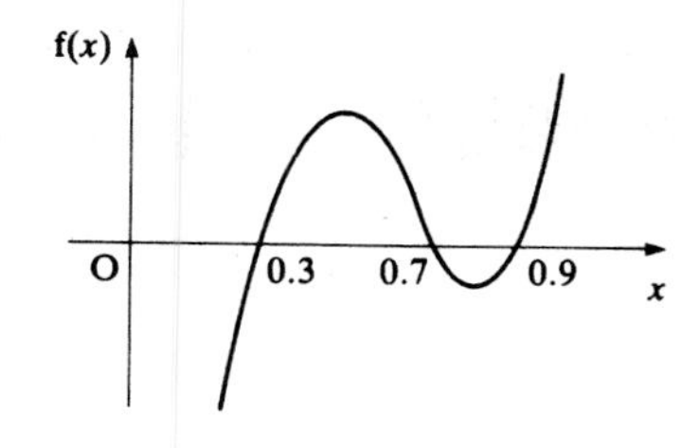

Figure 6.7

In this case $f(0) < 0$ and $f(1) > 0$, so you know there is a root between 0 and 1.

A decimal search would show that $f(0.3) = 0$, so that 0.3 is a root. You would be unlikely to search further in this interval.

Interval bisection gives $f(0.5) > 0$, so you would search the interval $[0, 0.5]$ and eventually arrive at the root 0.3, unaware of the existence of those at 0.7 and 0.9. Linear interpolation would give you 0.9 only.

There is a discontinuity in f(x)

The curve $y = \frac{1}{x - 2.7}$ has a discontinuity at $x = 2.7$, as shown by the asymptote in figure 6.8.

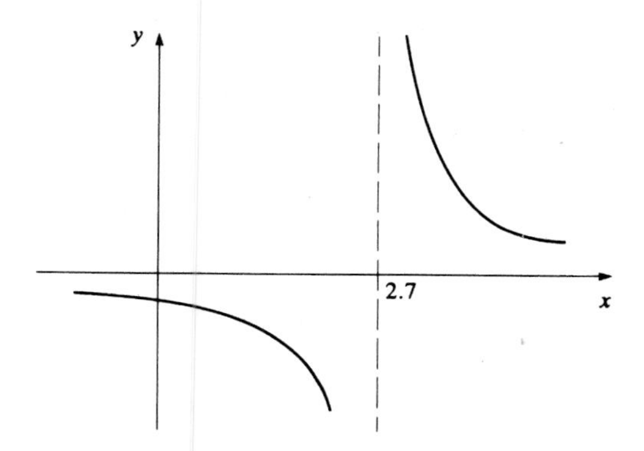

Figure 6.8

The equation $\frac{1}{x - 2.7} = 0$ has no root, but all change of sign methods will converge on a false root at $x = 2.7$.

None of these problems will arise if you start by drawing a sketch graph.

Note: Use of technology

It is important that you understand how each method works and are able, if necessary, to perform the calculations using only a scientific calculator. However, these repeated operations lend themselves to the use of a spreadsheet or a programmable calculator and you need to use a variety of approaches when working through the following exercises. Many packages, such as *Autograph*, will both perform the methods and illustrate them graphically.

EXERCISE 6A

1 Find the roots of $x^5 - 5x + 3 = 0$ in the intervals $[-2, -1]$ and $[1, 2]$, correct to 2 decimal places, using

(i) decimal search
(ii) interval bisection.

Comment on the ease and efficiency with which the roots are approached by each method.

2 (i) Use a systematic search for a change of sign, starting with $x = -2$, to locate intervals of unit length containing each of the three roots of

$$x^3 - 4x^2 - 3x + 8 = 0.$$

(ii) Sketch the graph of $f(x) = x^3 - 4x^2 - 3x + 8$.
(iii) Use the method of interval bisection to obtain each of the roots correct to 2 decimal places.
(iv) Use your last intervals in part **(iii)** to give each of the roots in the form $a \pm (0.5)^n$ where a and n are to be determined.

3 The diagram shows a sketch of the graph of $f(x) = e^x - x^3$ without scales.

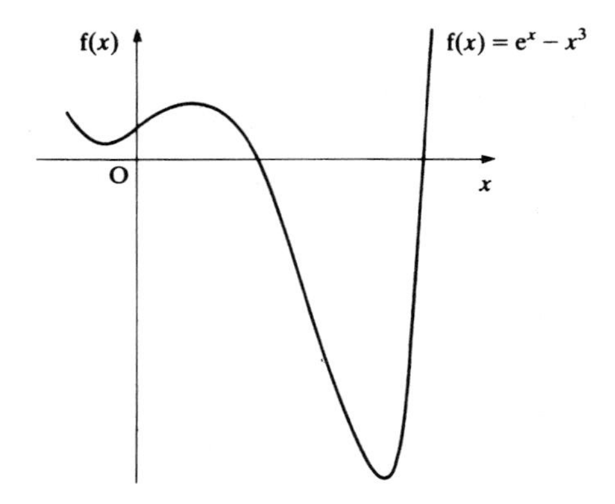

(i) Use a systematic search for a change of sign to locate intervals of unit length containing each of the roots.
(ii) Use a change of sign method to find each of the roots correct to 3 decimal places.

4 (i) Show that the equation $x^3 + 3x - 5 = 0$ has no turning points.
(ii) Show with the aid of a sketch that the equation can have only one root, and that this root must be positive.
(iii) Find the root, correct to 3 decimal places.

5 (i) How many roots has the equation $e^x - 3x = 0$?
(ii) Find an interval of unit length containing each of the roots.
(iii) Find each root correct to 2 decimal places.

6 (i) Sketch $y = 2^x$ and $y = x + 2$ on the same axes.
(ii) Use your sketch to deduce the number of roots of the equation $2^x = x + 2$.
(iii) Find each root, correct to 3 decimal places if appropriate.

7 Find all the roots of $x^3 - 3x + 1 = 0$, giving your answers correct to 2 decimal places.

8 For each of the equations below

(a) sketch the curve

(b) write down any roots

(c) investigate what happens when you use a change of sign method with a starting interval of $[-0.3, 0.7]$.

(i) $y = \frac{1}{x}$ **(ii)** $y = \frac{x}{x^2 + 1}$ **(iii)** $y = \frac{x^2}{x^2 + 1}$

Fixed point iteration

In fixed point iteration you find a single value or point as your estimate for the value of x, rather than establishing an interval within which it must lie. This involves an *iterative process*, a method of generating a sequence of numbers by continued repetition of the same procedure. If the numbers obtained in this manner approach some limiting value, then they are said to *converge* to this value.

INVESTIGATION

Notice what happens in each of the following cases, and try to find some explanation for it.

(i) Set your calculator to the radian mode, enter zero if not automatically displayed and apply the cosine function repeatedly.

(ii) Enter any positive number into your calculator and apply the square root function repeatedly. Try this for both large and small numbers.

(iii) Enter any positive number into your calculator and press the sequence [+] [1] [=] [√] repeatedly. Write down the number which appears each time you press [√]. The sequence generated appears to converge. You may recognise the number to which it appears to converge: it is called the Golden Ratio.

Two methods of fixed point iteration are introduced in this chapter: the first one involves rearranging the equation to be solved into the form $x = \mathrm{g}(x)$. The second is called the Newton–Raphson method; it is actually a special case of rearranging the equation, but it is treated as a separate method here.

Rearranging the equation $\mathrm{f}(x) = 0$ into the form $x = \mathrm{g}(x)$

The first step, with an equation $\mathrm{f}(x) = 0$, is to rearrange it into the form $x = \mathrm{g}(x)$. Any value of x for which $x = \mathrm{g}(x)$ is clearly a root of the original equation, as shown in figure 6.9.

When $f(x) = x^2 - x - 2$, $f(x) = 0$ is the same as $x = x^2 - 2$.

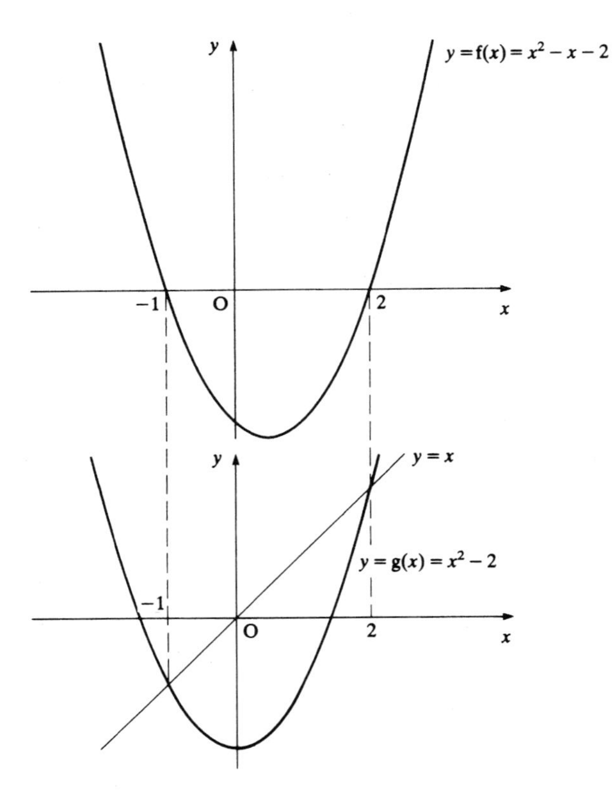

Figure 6.9

The equation $x^5 - 5x + 3 = 0$ which you met earlier can be rewritten in a number of ways. One of these is $5x = x^5 + 3$, giving

$$x = g(x) = \frac{x^5 + 3}{5}.$$

Figure 6.10 shows the graphs of $y = x$ and $y = g(x)$ in this case.

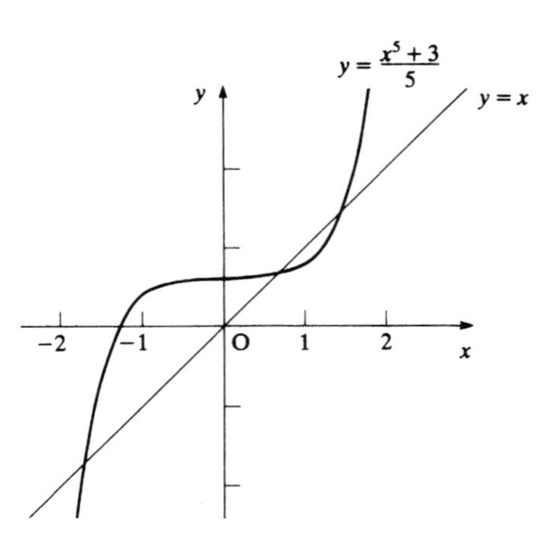

Figure 6.10

This provides the basis for the iterative formula

$$x_{r+1} = \frac{x_r^{\,5} + 3}{5}.$$

Taking $x = 1$ as a starting point to find the root in the interval $[0, 1]$, successive approximations are:

$$x_1 = 1, \quad x_2 = 0.8, \quad x_3 = 0.6655, \quad x_4 = 0.6261, \quad x_5 = 0.6192,$$

$$x_6 = 0.6182, \quad x_7 = 0.6181, \quad x_8 = 0.6180, \quad x_9 = 0.6180.$$

In this case the iteration has converged quite rapidly to the root for which you were looking.

? Another way of arranging $x^5 - 5x + 3 = 0$ is $x = \sqrt[5]{5x - 3}$. What other possible rearrangements can you find? How many are there altogether?

The iteration process is easiest to understand if you consider the graph. Rewriting the equation $f(x) = 0$ in the form $x = g(x)$ means that instead of looking for points where the graph of $y = f(x)$ crosses the x axis, you are now finding the points of intersection of the curve $y = g(x)$ and the line $y = x$.

What you do	**What it looks like on the graph**
• Choose a value, x_1, of x	Take a starting point on the x axis
• Find the corresponding value of $g(x_1)$	Move vertically to the curve $y = g(x)$
• Take this value $g(x_1)$ as the new value of x, i.e. $x_2 = g(x_1)$	Move horizontally to the line $y = x$
• Find the value of $g(x_2)$ and so on.	Move vertically to the curve

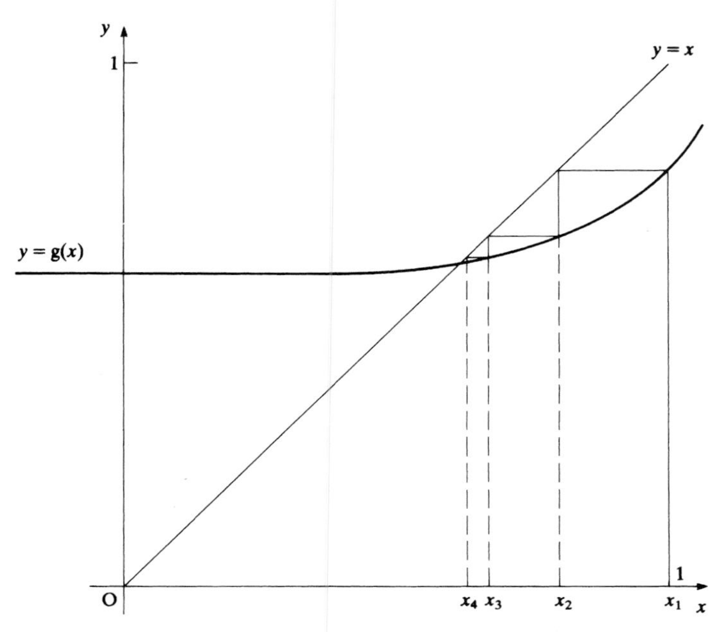

Figure 6.11

The effect of several repeats of this procedure is shown in figure 6.11. The successive steps look like a staircase approaching the root: this type of diagram is called a *staircase diagram*. In other examples, a *cobweb diagram* may be produced, as shown in figure 6.12.

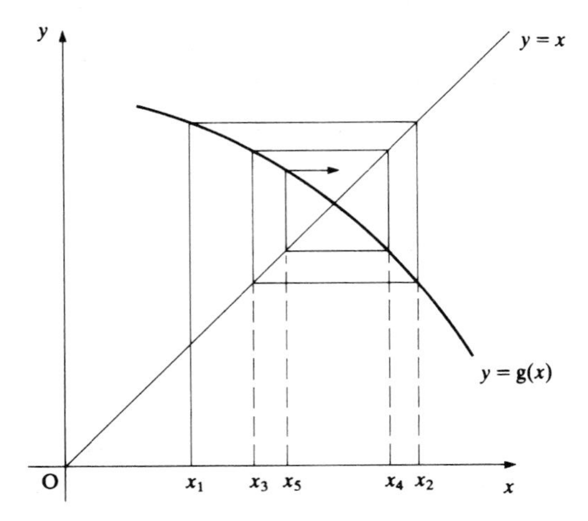

Figure 6.12

Successive approximations to the root are found by using the formula

$$x_{r+1} = g(x_r).$$

This is an example of an *iterative formula*. If the resulting values of x_r approach some limit, a, then $a = g(a)$, and so a is a *fixed point* of the iteration. It is also a root of the original equation $f(x) = 0$.

Note

In the staircase diagram, the values of x_r approach the root from one side, but in a cobweb diagram they oscillate about the root. From figures 6.11 and 6.12 it is clear that the error (the difference between a and x_r) is decreasing in both diagrams.

Using different arrangements of the equation

So far only one possible arrangement of the equation $x^5 - 5x + 3 = 0$ has been used. What happens when you use a different arrangement, for example $x = \sqrt[5]{5x - 3}$, which leads to the iterative formula

$$x_{r+1} = \sqrt[5]{5x_r - 3}?$$

The resulting sequence of approximations is:

$x_1 = 1$, $x_2 = 1.1486...$, $x_3 = 1.2236...$, $x_4 = 1.2554...$,
$x_5 = 1.2679...$, $x_6 = 1.2727...$, $x_7 = 1.2745...$, $x_8 = 1.2752...$,
$x_9 = 1.2755...$, $x_{10} = 1.2756...$, $x_{11} = 1.2756...$, $x_{12} = 1.2756....$

⚠ In the calculations the full calculator values of x_r were used, but only the first 4 decimal places have been written down.

The process has clearly converged, but in this case not to the root for which you were looking: you have identified the root in the interval [1, 2]. If instead you had taken $x_1 = 0$ as your starting point and applied the second formula, you would have obtained a sequence converging to the value –1.6180, the root in the interval [–2, –1].

The choice of g(*x*)

A particular rearrangement of the equation $f(x) = 0$ into the form $x = g(x)$ will allow convergence to a root a of the equation, provided that $-1 < g'(a) < 1$ for values of x close to the root.

Look again at the two rearrangements of $x^5 - 5x + 3 = 0$ which were suggested. When you look at the graph of

$$y = g(x) = \sqrt[5]{5x - 3},$$

as shown in figure 6.13, you can see that its gradient near A, the root you were seeking, is greater than 1. This makes

$$x_{r+1} = \sqrt[5]{5x_r - 3},$$

an unsuitable iterative formula for finding the root in the interval [0, 1], as you saw earlier.

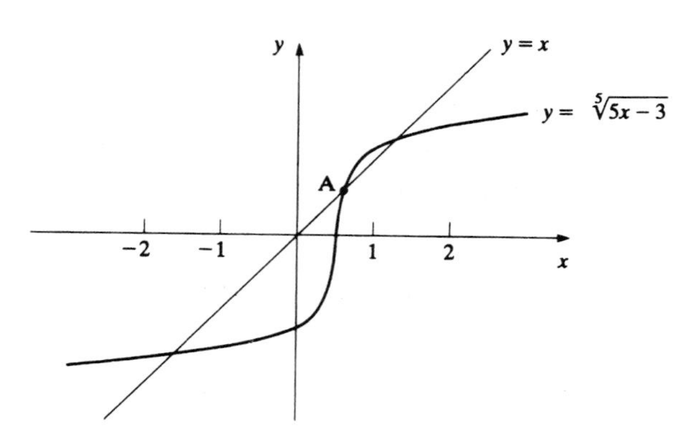

Figure 6.13

When an equation has two or more roots, a single rearrangement will not usually find all of them. This is demonstrated in figure 6.14.

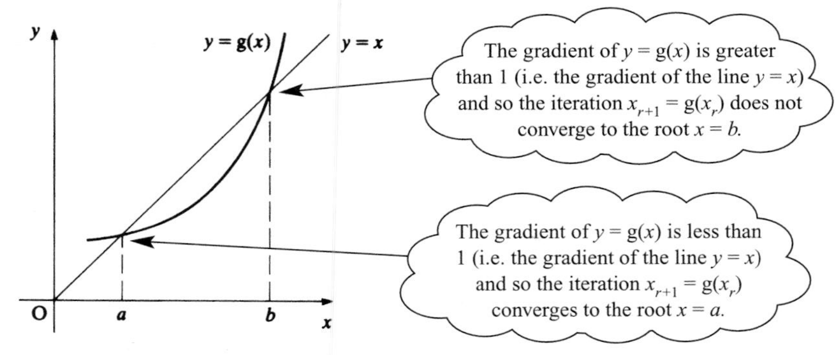

Figure 6.14

ACTIVITY 6.3 Try using the iterative formula $x_{r+1} = \dfrac{x_r^5 + 3}{5}$ to find the roots in the intervals $[-2, -1]$ and $[1, 2]$. In both cases use each end point of the interval as a starting point. What happens?

Explain what you find by referring to a sketch of the curve $y = \dfrac{x^5 + 3}{5}$.

Accuracy of method of rearranging equation

Iterative procedures give you a sequence of point estimates. A staircase diagram, for example, might give the following.

1, 0.8, 0.6655, 0.6261, 0.6192

What can you say at this stage?

Looking at the pattern of convergence it seems as though the root lies between 0.61 and 0.62, but you cannot be absolutely certain from the available evidence. To be certain you must look for a change of sign.

$f(0.61) = +0.034\ldots \quad f(0.62) = -0.0083\ldots$

---

p Explain why you can now be quite certain that your judgement is correct.

Note

Estimates from a cobweb diagram oscillate above and below the root and so naturally provide you with bounds.

When does this method fail?

It is always possible to rearrange an equation $f(x) = 0$ into the form $x = g(x)$, but this only leads to a successful iteration if successive iterations converge and they converge to the root for which you are looking.

When deciding on the suitablity or otherwise of a particular rearrangment you must check its gradient near the root you are seeking. In most cases, it is adequate to do this by comparing the gradient with that of $y = x$ or $y = -x$.

A graphic calculator or computer package is particularly helpful here.

EXERCISE 6B

1 (i) Show that the equation $x^3 - x - 2 = 0$ has a root between 1 and 2.

(ii) The equation is rearranged into the form $x = \mathrm{g}(x)$, where

$$\mathrm{g}(x) = \sqrt[3]{x + 2}.$$

Sketch $y = \mathrm{g}(x)$ and show that $-1 < \mathrm{g}'(x) < 1$ for values of x in the interval $[1, 2]$.

(iii) Use the iterative formula suggested by this rearrangement to find the value of the root to 3 decimal places.

2 (i) Show that the equation $\mathrm{e}^{-x} - x + 2 = 0$ has a root in the interval $[2, 3]$.

(ii) The equation is rearranged into the form $x = \mathrm{g}(x)$ where $\mathrm{g}(x) = \mathrm{e}^{-x} + 2$. Show that $-1 < \mathrm{g}'(x) < 1$ for values of x in the interval $[2, 3]$.

(iii) Use the iterative formula suggested by this rearrangement to find the value of the root to 3 decimal places.

3 (i) By considering $\mathrm{f}'(x)$, where $\mathrm{f}(x) = x^3 + x - 3$, show that there is exactly one real root of the equation $x^3 + x - 3 = 0$.

(ii) Show that the root lies in the interval $[1, 2]$.

(iii) Rearrange the equation into the form $x = \mathrm{g}(x)$ where $-1 < \mathrm{g}'(x) < 1$ for values of x close to the root and illustrate this.

(iv) Hence find the root correct to 4 decimal places.

4 (i) Show that the equation $\mathrm{e}^x + x - 6 = 0$ has a root in the interval $[1, 2]$.

(ii) Show that this equation may be written in the form $x = \ln(6 - x)$.

(iii) Hence find the root correct to 3 decimal places.

5 (i) Sketch the curves $y = \mathrm{e}^x$ and $y = x^2 + 2$ on the same graph.

(ii) Use your sketch to explain why the equation $\mathrm{e}^x - x^2 - 2 = 0$ has only one root.

(iii) Rearrange this equation in the form $x = \mathrm{g}(x)$.

(iv) Find the root correct to 3 decimal places

6 (i) Show that $x^2 = \ln(x + 1)$ for $x = 0$ and for one other value of x.

(ii) Use the method of fixed point iteration to find the second value to 3 decimal places.

7 (i) Sketch the graphs of $y = x$ and $y = \cos x$ on the same axes, for $0 \leqslant x \leqslant \frac{\pi}{2}$.

(ii) Find the solution of the equation $x = \cos x$ to 5 decimal places.

ACTIVITY 6.4

(i) Show that the equation $\ln x - \sin x = 0$ has only one root.

(ii) Rearrange the equation in the form $x = g(x)$.

(iii) Explain your results when you try to find the root using the iteration

$$x_{r+1} = g(x_r).$$

The Newton–Raphson method

This is another fixed point iteration method and, as for the previous method, it is necessary to use an estimate of the root as a starting point.

You start with an estimate, x_1, for a root of $f(x) = 0$. You then draw the tangent to the curve $y = f(x)$ at the point $(x_1, f(x_1))$. The point at which the tangent cuts the x axis then gives the next approximation for the root, and the process is repeated, as shown in figure 6.15.

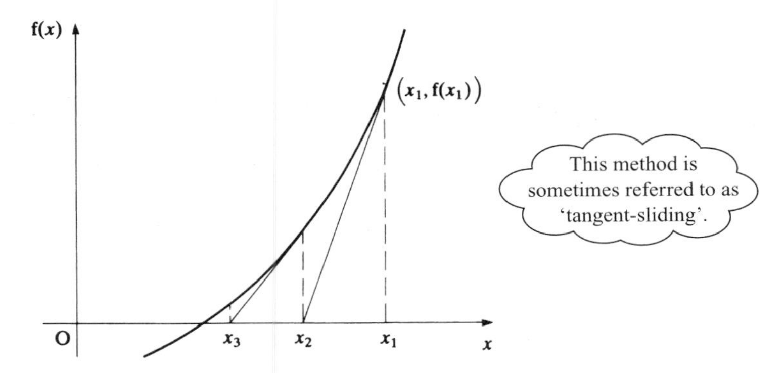

Figure 6.15

The gradient of the tangent at $(x_1, f(x_1))$ is $f'(x_1)$. Since the equation of a straight line can be written

$$y - y_1 = m(x - x_1),$$

the equation of the tangent is

$$y - f(x_1) = f'(x_1)[x - x_1].$$

This tangent cuts the x axis at $(x_2, 0)$, so

$$0 - f(x_1) = f'(x_1)[x_2 - x_1].$$

Rearranging this gives

$$x_2 = x_1 - \frac{f(x_1)}{f'(x_1)}.$$

This gives rise to the Newton–Raphson iterative formula

$$x_{r+1} = x_r - \frac{f(x_r)}{f'(x_r)}.$$

Returning to the equation $x^5 - 5x + 3 = 0$, which has a root in the interval [0, 1], you can write

$$f(x) = x^5 - 5x + 3 \text{ and so } f'(x) = 5x^4 - 5.$$

The iterative formula is therefore

$$\begin{aligned} x_{r+1} &= x_r - \frac{f(x_r)}{f'(x_r)} \\ &= x_r - \frac{x_r^5 - 5x_r + 3}{5x_r^4 - 5} \\ &= \frac{4x_r^5 - 3}{5x_r^4 - 5} \end{aligned}$$

Starting with $x_1 = 0$ gives

$x_2 = 0.6$, $x_3 = 0.617\,867\,6\ldots$, $x_4 = 0.618\,033\,9\ldots$, …

which is a faster rate of convergence than any of the earlier methods gave.

INVESTIGATION

What happens when you try $x_1 = 1$ as a starting point in the iteration

$$x_{r+1} = x_r - \frac{x_r^5 - 5x_r + 3}{5x_r^4 - 5}\ ?$$

Illustrate this on a graph.

In this example the Newton–Raphson method gives an extremely rapid rate of convergence. This is the case for most examples, even when the first approximation is not particularly good. A discussion of the rate of convergence of this method is beyond the scope of this text, but for manual calculations it is almost always the most efficient method.

Problems with the Newton–Raphson method

Most problems that arise with the Newton–Raphson method fall into one or other of the following three categories.

Poor choice of starting value

If your initial value is close enough to a root, the method will nearly always give convergence to it. However if the initial value is not close to the root, or is near a turning point of $y = f(x)$, the iteration may diverge, or converge to another root.

When the first approximation is close to a turning point, $f'(x_1)$ will be very small. In most cases this will mean that x_2 is not very close to the root, as shown in figure 6.16.

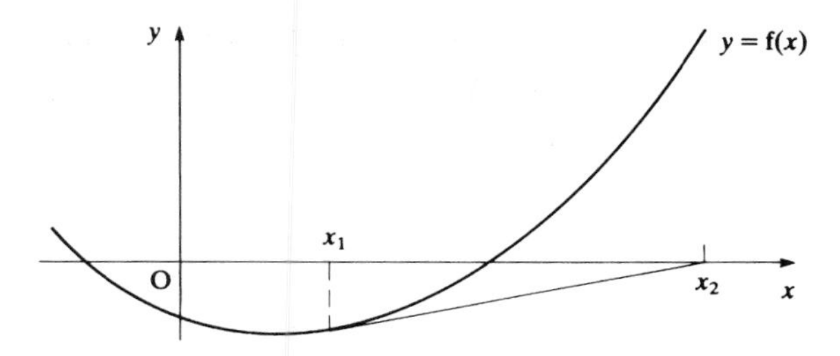

Figure 6.16

In this case you may find that after two or three steps the values you compute are converging rapidly, but they may be converging to a root other than the one which you are trying to locate.

When the first approximation is at a stationary point, $f'(x_1) = 0$ so the method cannot proceed.

The function is discontinuous

As with all numerical methods for solving equations, this method can break down when the equation is that of a discontinuous function.

The function is not defined over the whole of $\mathbb{R}$

In this case the tangent at $(x_i, f(x_i))$ may meet the axis at a point outside the domain of the function.

EXERCISE 6C

1 **(i)** Sketch the curve $f(x) = \frac{x^3}{3} - x + 2$.

(ii) Using the Newton–Raphson method find the root of the equation $f(x) = 0$, starting with $x_1 = -5$, correct to 3 decimal places.

(iii) What happens if the starting value is taken to be $x_1 = 0.5$?

2 **(i)** Show that the equation $x^4 - 7x^3 + 1 = 0$ has a root in the interval $[0, 1]$.

(ii) Use the Newton–Raphson method to find this root correct to 2 decimal places, starting with $x_1 = 1$.

(iii) Explain why $x_1 = 0$ is not a suitable starting point.

3 **(i)** Show that the equation $e^x - 3x^2 = 0$ has three roots in the interval $[-1, 4]$.

(ii) Use the Newton–Raphson method to find each of the roots correct to 2 decimal places. In each case state the starting value which gave convergence to the particular root.

(iii) A starting value $x_1 = 0$, gives $x_2 = -1$. Explain this result.

4 **(i)** Show that the equation $x^2 - 3x \ln x = 0$ has two roots in the interval $[1, 5]$.

(ii) Use the Newton–Raphson method to find each root correct to 2 decimal places.

5 Using the Newton–Raphson method or otherwise find, correct to 3 decimal places, the value of x for which $x = e^{-x}$.

[MEI]

6 (i) Show that the equation $x^3 - x^2 - 2x + 1 = 0$ has three roots in the interval $[-2, 2]$.

(ii) Use the Newton–Raphson method to find each of the three roots correct to 4 decimal places.

(iii) Investigate whether the root found is always that nearest the starting point.

7 (i) Show that the equation $x^3 - 3x^2 + 1 = 0$ has exactly three roots.

(ii) Use the Newton–Raphson method to find each of the two smaller roots correct to 3 decimal places.

(iii) Find the largest root to the limit of the accuracy of your calculator, using $x_1 = 20$ as a starting point.

(iv) Investigate how many digits the method has fixed after each iteration, and comment on your findings.

8 (i) Sketch the curves $y = e^x$ and $y = \frac{4}{x}$. At how many points do they intersect?

(ii) Sketch the graph of the function $\frac{4}{x} - e^x$ for all values of x.

(iii) Use the Newton–Raphson method to find the value of x where the curve $y = \frac{4}{x} - e^x$ crosses the x axis, correct to 3 decimal places, taking $x_1 = 2$.

(iv) Explain what happens if you use a starting value of $x_1 = 3$.

The following investigations illustrate cases where problems arise when using the Newton–Raphson method. In each case finish the investigation by suggesting how the roots can be found as easily as possible.

INVESTIGATIONS

1 The function $f(x) = \ln(x + 2) - x$ is not defined for $x \leqslant -2$. The line $x = -2$ is an asymptote, as shown in figure 6.17.

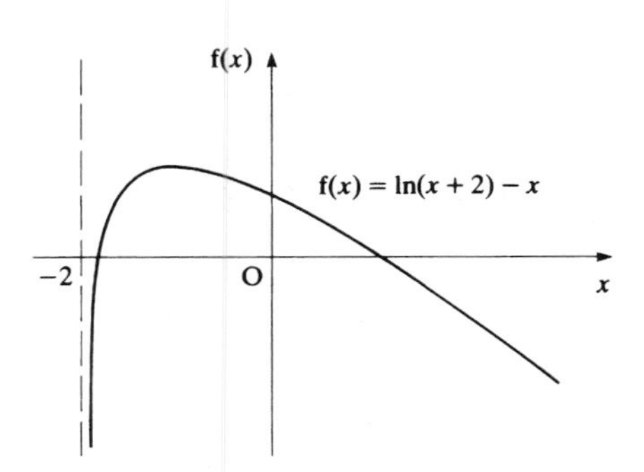

Figure 6.17

A systematic search for a sign change reveals that there are roots in the intervals $[-2, -1]$ and $[1, 2]$. Using the Newton–Raphson method with $x_1 = -1$, try to find the smaller root. Describe what happens.

Now try $x_1 = -1.5$. What happens now?

2 When using the sign-change principle to locate the roots of $f(x) = 0$, where

$$f(x) = 9 - \frac{1}{x^2 - 4x + 4.1},$$

the following results are obtained.

x	0	1	2	3	4
$f(x)$	8.76	8.09	–1	8.09	8.76

This shows that there are roots in each of the intervals [1, 2] and [2, 3].

Investigate what happens when the Newton–Raphson method is used to find the smaller root using 1, 1.2, 1.4, 1.6, 1.8 and 2 as starting points.

KEY POINTS

Interval estimation

1 When $f(x)$ is a continuous function, if $f(a)$ and $f(b)$ have opposite signs, there will be at least one root of $f(x) = 0$ in the interval $[a, b]$.

2 When an interval $[a, b]$ containing a root has been found, this interval may be reduced systematically by one of the following methods.

- Decimal search within the interval
- Interval bisection
- (e) Linear interpolation

3 Solution bounds are provided automatically by these methods.

Fixed point iteration

4 Fixed point iteration may be used to solve an equation $f(x) = 0$ by either of the following methods.

- Rearranging the equation $f(x) = 0$ into the form $x = g(x)$ where $-1 < g'(x) < 1$ near the root, and using the iteration

$$x_{r+1} = g(x_r).$$

- The Newton–Raphson method using the iteration

$$x_{r+1} = x_r - \frac{f(x_r)}{f'(x_r)}.$$

5 Solution bounds are usually confirmed by demonstrating a change of sign of $f(x)$ between them.

Applications of Advanced Mathematics

7 Algebra

At the age of twenty-one he wrote a treatise upon the Binomial Theorem. ... On the strength of it, he won the Mathematical Chair at one of our smaller Universities.

Sherlock Holmes on Professor Moriarty
'The Final Problem' by Sir Arthur Conan Doyle

How would you find $\sqrt{101}$ correct to 3 decimal places, without using a calculator?

Many people are able to develop a very high degree of skill in mental arithmetic, particularly those, such as bookmakers, whose work calls for quick reckoning. There are also those who have quite exceptional innate skills. M. Hari Prasad, pictured right, is famous for his mathematical speed; on one occasion he found the square root of a six-digit number in just 1 minute 3.8 seconds.

While most mathematicians do not have M. Hari Prasad's high level of talent with numbers, they do acquire a sense of when something looks right or wrong. This often involves finding approximate values of numbers, such as $\sqrt{101}$, using methods that are based on series expansions, and these are the subject of the first part of this chapter.

INVESTIGATION

Using your calculator, write down the values of $\sqrt{1.02}$, $\sqrt{1.04}$, $\sqrt{1.06}$, ..., giving your answers correct to 2 decimal places. What do you notice?

Use your results to complete the following, giving the value of the constant k.

$$\sqrt{1.02} = (1 + 0.02)^{\frac{1}{2}} \approx 1 + 0.02k$$

$$\sqrt{1.04} = (1 + 0.04)^{\frac{1}{2}} \approx 1 + 0.04k$$

What is the largest value of x such that $\sqrt{1 + x} \approx 1 + kx$ is true for the same value of k?

The general binomial expansion

You have already met the binomial expansion in the form

$$(1+x)^n = 1 + \binom{n}{1}x + \binom{n}{2}x^2 + \binom{n}{3}x^3 + \ldots + \binom{n}{r}x^r + \ldots$$

which holds when n is any positive integer (or zero), that is $n \in \mathbb{N}$.

This may also be written as

$$(1+x)^n = 1 + nx + \frac{n(n-1)}{2!}x^2 + \frac{n(n-1)(n-2)}{3!}x^3 + \ldots$$
$$+ \frac{n(n-1)(n-2)\ldots(n-r+1)}{r!}x^r + \ldots$$

which, being the same expansion as above, also holds when $n \in \mathbb{N}$.

The general binomial theorem states that this second form, that is

$$(1+x)^n = 1 + nx + \frac{n(n-1)}{2!}x^2 + \frac{n(n-1)(n-2)}{3!}x^3 + \ldots$$
$$+ \frac{n(n-1)(n-2)\ldots(n-r+1)}{r!}x^r + \ldots$$

is true when ***n* is any real number**, but there are two important differences to note when $n \notin \mathbb{N}$.

- The series is infinite (or non-terminating).
- The expansion of $(1+x)^n$ is valid only if $|x| < 1$.

Proving this result is beyond the scope of an A-level course but you can assume that it is true.

Consider now the coefficients in the binomial expansion:

$$1 \quad n \quad \frac{n(n-1)}{2!} \quad \frac{n(n-1)(n-2)}{3!} \quad \frac{n(n-1)(n-2)(n-3)}{4!} \ldots$$

When $n = 0$, we get	1	0	0	0	0	…	(infinitely many zeros)
$n = 1$	1	1	0	0	0	…	ditto
$n = 2$	1	2	1	0	0	…	ditto
$n = 3$	1	3	3	1	0	…	ditto
$n = 4$	1	4	6	4	1	…	ditto

so that, for example

$$(1+x)^2 = 1 + 2x + x^2 + 0x^3 + 0x^4 + 0x^5 + \dots$$

$$(1+x)^3 = 1 + 3x + 3x^2 + x^3 + 0x^4 + 0x^5 + \dots$$

$$(1+x)^4 = 1 + 4x + 6x^2 + 4x^3 + x^4 + 0x^5 + \dots$$

Of course, it is usual to discard all the zeros and write these binomial coefficients in the familiar form of Pascal's triangle:

$$\begin{array}{ccccccccc} & & & & 1 & & & & \\ & & & 1 & & 1 & & & \\ & & 1 & & 2 & & 1 & & \\ & 1 & & 3 & & 3 & & 1 & \\ 1 & & 4 & & 6 & & 4 & & 1 \end{array}$$

and the expansions as

$$(1+x)^2 = 1 + 2x + x^2$$

$$(1+x)^3 = 1 + 3x + 3x^2 + x^3$$

$$(1+x)^4 = 1 + 4x + 6x^2 + 4x^3 + x^4$$

However, for other values of n (where $n \notin \mathbb{N}$) there are no zeros in the row of binomial coefficients and so we obtain an infinite sequence of non-zero terms. For example:

$$n = -3 \quad \text{gives} \quad 1 \quad -3 \quad \frac{(-3)(-4)}{2!} \quad \frac{(-3)(-4)(-5)}{3!} \quad \frac{(-3)(-4)(-5)(-6)}{4!} \dots$$

$$\text{that is} \quad 1 \quad -3 \quad 6 \quad -10 \quad 15 \dots$$

$$n = \tfrac{1}{2} \quad \text{gives} \quad 1 \quad \tfrac{1}{2} \quad \frac{\left(\frac{1}{2}\right)\left(-\frac{1}{2}\right)}{2!} \quad \frac{\left(\frac{1}{2}\right)\left(-\frac{1}{2}\right)\left(-\frac{3}{2}\right)}{3!} \quad \frac{\left(\frac{1}{2}\right)\left(-\frac{1}{2}\right)\left(-\frac{3}{2}\right)\left(-\frac{5}{2}\right)}{4!} \dots$$

$$\text{that is} \quad 1 \quad \tfrac{1}{2} \quad -\tfrac{1}{8} \quad \tfrac{1}{16} \quad -\tfrac{5}{128} \dots$$

so that $\quad (1+x)^{-3} = 1 - 3x + 6x^2 - 10x^3 + 15x^4 + \dots$

and $\quad (1+x)^{\frac{1}{2}} = 1 + \frac{1}{2}x - \frac{1}{8}x^2 + \frac{1}{16}x^3 - \frac{5}{128}x^4 + \dots$

But remember: these two expansions are valid only if $|x| < 1$.

---

p Show that the expansion of $(1+x)^{\frac{1}{2}}$ is not valid when $x = 8$.

These examples confirm that there will be an infinite sequence of non-zero coefficients when $n \notin \mathbb{N}$. You can also see that, after a certain stage, the remaining terms of the sequence will alternate in sign.

In the investigation at the beginning of this chapter you showed that

$$\sqrt{1+x} \approx 1 + \tfrac{1}{2}x$$

is a good approximation for small values of x. Notice that these are the first two terms of the binomial expansion for $n = \frac{1}{2}$. If you include the third term, the approximation is

$$\sqrt{1+x} \approx 1 + \tfrac{1}{2}x - \tfrac{1}{8}x^2.$$

Take $y = 1 + \frac{1}{2}x$, $y = 1 + \frac{1}{2}x - \frac{1}{8}x^2$ and $y = \sqrt{1+x}$.

They are shown in the graph in figure 7.1 for values of x between –1 and 1.

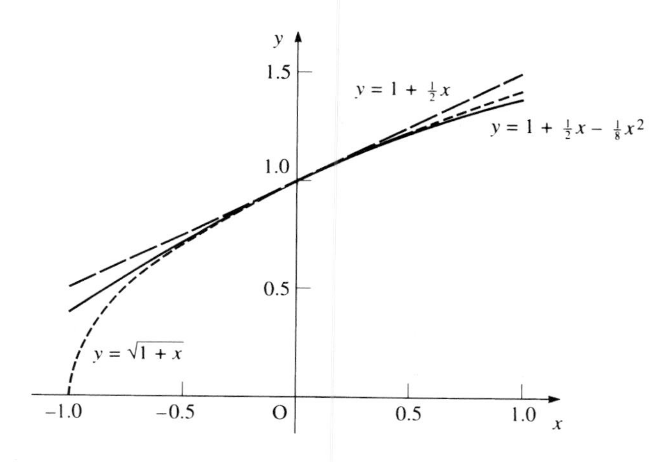

Figure 7.1

INVESTIGATION

For $n = \frac{1}{2}$ the first three terms of the binomial expansion are $1 + \frac{1}{2}x - \frac{1}{8}x^2$. Use your calculator to verify the approximate result

$$\sqrt{1+x} \approx 1 + \tfrac{1}{2}x - \tfrac{1}{8}x^2$$

for 'small' values of x.
What values of x can be considered as 'small' if you want the result to be correct to 2 decimal places?

Now take $n = -3$. Using the coefficients found earlier suggests the approximate result

$$(1+x)^{-3} \approx 1 - 3x + 6x^2.$$

Comment on values of x for which this approximation is correct to 2 decimal places.

When $|x| < 1$, the magnitudes of $x^2, x^3, x^4, x^5, \ldots$ form a decreasing geometric sequence. In this case, the binomial expansion converges (just as a geometric series converges for $-1 < r < 1$, where r is the common ratio) and has a sum to infinity.

ACTIVITY 7.1 Compare the geometric series $1 - x + x^2 - x^3 + \ldots$ with the series obtained by putting $n = -1$ in the binomial expansion. What do you notice?

To summarise: when n is not a positive integer or zero, the binomial expansion of $(1 + x)^n$ becomes an infinite series, and is only valid when some restriction is placed on the values of x.

The binomial theorem states that for any value of n:

$$(1 + x)^n = 1 + nx + \frac{n(n-1)}{2!}x^2 + \frac{n(n-1)(n-2)}{3!}x^3 + \ldots$$

where

- if $n \in \mathbb{N}$, x may take any value;
- if $n \notin \mathbb{N}$, $|x| < 1$.

Note

The full statement is the binomial *theorem*, and the right-hand side is referred to as the binomial *expansion*.

EXAMPLE 7.1

Expand $(1 - x)^{-2}$ as a series of ascending powers of x up to and including the term in x^3, stating the set of values of x for which the expansion is valid.

SOLUTION

$$(1 + x)^n = 1 + nx + \frac{n(n-1)}{2!}x^2 + \frac{n(n-1)(n-2)}{3!}x^3 + \ldots$$

Replacing n by -2, and x by $(-x)$ gives

$$(1 + (-x))^{-2} = 1 + (-2)(-x) + \frac{(-2)(-3)}{2!}(-x)^2 + \frac{(-2)(-3)(-4)}{3!}(-x)^3 + \ldots \quad \text{when } |-x| < 1$$

It is important to put brackets round the term $-x$, since, for example, $(-x)^2$ is not the same as $-x^2$.

which leads to

$$(1 - x)^{-2} \approx 1 + 2x + 3x^2 + 4x^3 \quad \text{when } |x| < 1.$$

Note

In this example the coefficients of the powers of x form a recognisable sequence, and it would be possible to write down a general term in the expansion. The coefficient is always one more than the power, so the rth term would be rx^{r-1}. Using sigma notation, the infinite series could be written as

$$\sum_{r=1}^{\infty} rx^{r-1}.$$

EXAMPLE 7.2

Find a quadratic approximation for $\frac{1}{\sqrt{1+2t}}$ and state for which values of t the expansion is valid.

SOLUTION

$$\frac{1}{\sqrt{1+2t}} = \frac{1}{(1+2t)^{\frac{1}{2}}} = (1+2t)^{-\frac{1}{2}}$$

The binomial theorem states that

$$(1+x)^n = 1 + nx + \frac{n(n-1)}{2!}x^2 + \frac{n(n-1)(n-2)}{3!}x^3 + \ldots$$

Replacing n by $-\frac{1}{2}$ and x by $2t$ gives

$$(1+2t)^{-\frac{1}{2}} = 1 + \left(-\tfrac{1}{2}\right)(2t) + \frac{\left(-\frac{1}{2}\right)\left(-\frac{3}{2}\right)}{2!}(2t)^2 + \ldots \quad \text{when } |2t| < 1$$

Remember to put brackets round the term $2t$, since $(2t)^2$ is not the same as $2t^2$.

$$\Rightarrow \quad (1+2t)^{-\frac{1}{2}} \approx 1 - t + \tfrac{3}{2}t^2 \quad \text{when } |t| < \tfrac{1}{2}.$$

INVESTIGATION

Example 7.1 showed how using the binomial expansion for $(1-x)^{-2}$ gave a sequence of coefficients of powers of x which was easily recognisable, so that the particular binomial expansion could be written using sigma notation.

Investigate whether a recognisable pattern is formed by the coefficients in the expansions of $(1-x)^n$ for any other negative integers n.

The equivalent binomial expansion of $(a+x)^n$ when n is not a positive integer is rather unwieldy. It is easier to start by taking a outside the brackets:

$$(a+x)^n = a^n\left(1 + \frac{x}{a}\right)^n$$

The first entry inside the bracket is now 1 and so the first few terms of the expansion are

$$(a+x)^n = a^n\left[1 + n\left(\frac{x}{a}\right) + \frac{n(n-1)}{2!}\left(\frac{x}{a}\right)^2 + \frac{n(n-1)(n-2)}{3!}\left(\frac{x}{a}\right)^3 + \ldots\right]$$

for $\left|\frac{x}{a}\right| < 1$.

Note

Since the bracket is raised to the power n, any quantity you take out must be raised to the power n too, as in the following example.

EXAMPLE 7.3

Expand $(2+x)^{-3}$ as a series of ascending powers of x up to and including the term in x^2, stating the values of x for which the expansion is valid.

SOLUTION

$$(2+x)^{-3} = \frac{1}{(2+x)^3}$$

$$= \frac{1}{2^3\left(1+\frac{x}{2}\right)^3}$$

$$= \frac{1}{8}\left(1+\frac{x}{2}\right)^{-3}$$

Notice that this is the same as $2^{-3}\left(1+\frac{x}{2}\right)^{-3}$.

Take the binomial expansion

$$(1+x)^n = 1 + nx + \frac{n(n-1)}{2!}x^2 + \frac{n(n-1)(n-2)}{3!}x^3 + \ldots$$

and replace n by -3 and x by $\frac{x}{2}$ to give

$$\frac{1}{8}\left(1+\frac{x}{2}\right)^{-3} = \frac{1}{8}\left[1 + (-3)\left(\frac{x}{2}\right) + \frac{(-3)(-4)}{2!}\left(\frac{x}{2}\right)^2 + \ldots\right] \quad \text{when } \left|\frac{x}{2}\right| < 1$$

$$\approx \frac{1}{8} - \frac{3x}{16} + \frac{3x^2}{16} \quad \text{when } |x| < 2.$$

The chapter began by asking how you would find $\sqrt{101}$ to 3 decimal places without using a calculator. How would you find it?

EXAMPLE 7.4

Find a quadratic approximation for $\frac{(2+x)}{(1-x^2)}$, stating the values of x for which the expansion is valid.

SOLUTION

$$\frac{(2+x)}{(1-x^2)} = (2+x)(1-x^2)^{-1}$$

Take the binomial expansion

$$(1+x)^n = 1 + nx + \frac{n(n-1)}{2!}x^2 + \frac{n(n-1)(n-2)}{3!}x^3 + \ldots$$

and replace n by -1 and x by $(-x^2)$ to give

$$(1 + (-x^2))^{-1} = 1 + (-1)(-x^2) + \frac{(-1)(-2)(-x^2)^2}{2!} + \dots \qquad \text{when } |-x^2| < 1$$

$$(1 - x^2)^{-1} = 1 + x^2 + \dots \qquad \text{when } |x^2| < 1, \text{ i.e. when } |x| < 1.$$

Multiply both sides by $(2 + x)$ to obtain $(2 + x)(1 - x^2)^{-1}$:

$$(2 + x)(1 - x^2)^{-1} \approx (2 + x)(1 + x^2)$$

$$\approx 2 + x + 2x^2 \qquad \text{when } |x| < 1.$$

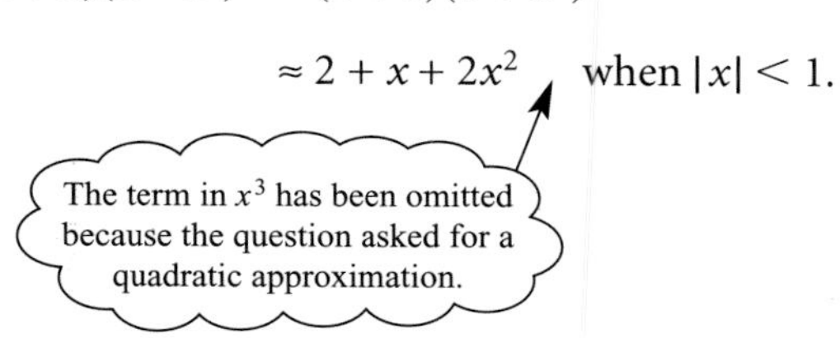

Sometimes two or more binomial expansions may be used together. If these impose different restrictions on the values of x, you need to decide which is the strictest.

EXAMPLE 7.5

Find a and b such that

$$\frac{1}{(1 - 2x)(1 + 3x)} \approx a + bx$$

and state the values of x for which the expansions you use are valid.

SOLUTION

$$\frac{1}{(1 - 2x)(1 + 3x)} = (1 - 2x)^{-1}(1 + 3x)^{-1}$$

Using the binomial expansion:

$$(1 - 2x)^{-1} \approx 1 + (-1)(-2x) \qquad \text{for } |-2x| < 1$$

and $$(1 + 3x)^{-1} \approx 1 + (-1)(3x) \qquad \text{for } |3x| < 1$$

$$\Rightarrow \quad (1 - 2x)^{-1}(1 + 3x)^{-1} \approx (1 + 2x)(1 - 3x)$$

$$\approx 1 - x \qquad \text{(ignoring higher powers of } x\text{)}$$

giving $a = 1$ and $b = -1$.

For the result to be valid, both $|2x| < 1$ and $|3x| < 1$ need to be satisfied.

$$|2x| < 1 \quad \Rightarrow \quad -\tfrac{1}{2} < x < \tfrac{1}{2}$$

and $$|3x| < 1 \quad \Rightarrow \quad -\tfrac{1}{3} < x < \tfrac{1}{3}.$$

Both of these restrictions are satisfied if $-\frac{1}{3} < x < \frac{1}{3}$. This is the stricter restriction.

Note

The binomial expansion may also be used when the first term is the variable. For example:

$$(x+2)^{-1} \text{ may be written as } (2+x)^{-1} = 2^{-1}\left(1+\frac{x}{2}\right)^{-1}$$

and
$$\begin{aligned}(2x-1)^{-3} &= [(-1)(1-2x)]^{-3}\\ &= (-1)^{-3}(1-2x)^{-3}\\ &= -(1-2x)^{-3}.\end{aligned}$$

What happens when you try to rearrange $\sqrt{x-1}$ so that the binomial expansion can be used?

EXERCISE 7A

1 For each of the functions below

(a) write down the first three non-zero terms in their expansions as a series of ascending powers of x

(b) state the values of x for which the expansion is valid

(c) substitute $x = 0.1$ in both the function and its expansion and calculate the relative error, where

$$\text{relative error} = \frac{\text{absolute error} \times 100}{\text{true value}}\%.$$

(d) If you have access to a graphic calculator or suitable computer package, draw the graphs of each function and the first three terms of its binomial expansion on the same axes. In each case, notice how the graphs illustrate the need for some restriction on the values of x.

(i) $(1+x)^{-2}$ **(ii)** $\dfrac{1}{1+2x}$ **(iii)** $\sqrt{1-x^2}$

(iv) $\dfrac{1+2x}{1-2x}$ **(v)** $(3+x)^{-1}$ **(vi)** $(1-x)\sqrt{4+x}$

(vii) $\dfrac{x+2}{x-3}$ **(viii)** $\dfrac{1}{\sqrt{3x+4}}$ **(ix)** $\dfrac{1+2x}{(2x-1)^2}$

(x) $\dfrac{1+x^2}{1-x^2}$ **(xi)** $\sqrt[3]{1+2x^2}$ **(xii)** $\dfrac{1}{(1+2x)(1+x)}$

2 **(i)** Write down the expansion of $(1+x)^3$.

(ii) Find the first four terms in the expansion of $(1-x)^{-4}$ in ascending powers of x. For what values of x is this expansion valid?

(iii) When the expansion is valid

$$\frac{(1+x)^3}{(1-x)^4} = 1 + 7x + ax^2 + bx^3 + \ldots .$$

Find the values of a and b. [MEI]

3 (i) Write down the expansion of $(2 - x)^4$.

(ii) Find the first four terms in the expansion of $(1 + 2x)^{-3}$ in ascending powers of x. For what range of values of x is this expansion valid?

(iii) When the expansion is valid

$$\frac{(2 - x)^4}{(1 + 2x)^3} = 16 + ax + bx^2 + \dots .$$

Find the values of a and b.

[MEI]

4 Write down the expansions of the following expressions in ascending powers of x, as far as the term containing x^3. In each case state the values of x for which the expansion is valid.

(i) $(1 - x)^{-1}$ **(ii)** $(1 + 2x)^{-2}$ **(iii)** $\dfrac{1}{(1 - x)(1 + 2x)^2}$

[MEI]

5 (i) Show that $\dfrac{1}{\sqrt{4 - x}} = \dfrac{1}{2}\left(1 - \dfrac{x}{4}\right)^{-\frac{1}{2}}$.

(ii) Write down the first three terms in the binomial expansion of $\left(1 - \dfrac{x}{4}\right)^{-\frac{1}{2}}$ in ascending powers of x, stating the range of values of x for which this expansion is valid.

(iii) Find the first three terms in the expansion of $\dfrac{2(1 + x)}{\sqrt{4 - x}}$ in ascending powers of x, for small values of x.

[MEI]

6 (i) Expand $(1 + y)^{-1}$, where $-1 < y < 1$, as a series in powers of y, giving the first four terms.

(ii) Hence find the first four terms of the expansion of $\left(1 + \dfrac{2}{x}\right)^{-1}$ where $-1 < \dfrac{2}{x} < 1$.

(iii) Show that $\left(1 + \dfrac{2}{x}\right)^{-1} = \dfrac{x}{x + 2} = \dfrac{x}{2}\left(1 + \dfrac{x}{2}\right)^{-1}$.

(iv) Find the first four terms of the expansion of $\dfrac{x}{2}\left(1 + \dfrac{x}{2}\right)^{-1}$ where $-1 < \dfrac{x}{2} < 1$.

(v) State the conditions on x under which your expansions for $\left(1 + \dfrac{2}{x}\right)^{-1}$ and $\dfrac{x}{2}\left(1 + \dfrac{x}{2}\right)^{-1}$ are valid and explain briefly why your expansions are different.

[MEI]

7 (i) Use integration by parts to show that

$$\int_1^k t \ln t \,\mathrm{d}t = \tfrac{1}{2}k^2 \ln k - \tfrac{1}{4}k^2 + \tfrac{1}{4}$$

where k is positive.

(ii) Expand $(1 - 2x)^{-\frac{1}{2}}$ in ascending powers of x, up to and including the term in x^3, giving your answer in simplified form.
State the range of values of x for which the expansion is valid.

(iii) Hence show that, provided x is small, $(1 - 2x)^{-\frac{1}{2}} \ln(1 + x)$ is approximately equal to $t \ln t$, where $t = 1 + x$.

Hence find an approximate value for $\displaystyle\int_0^{0.1} \frac{\ln(1 + x)}{\sqrt{1 - 2x}}\,\mathrm{d}x$.

[MEI]

Review of algebraic fractions

If $f(x)$ and $g(x)$ are polynomials, the expression $\frac{f(x)}{g(x)}$ is an *algebraic fraction* or *rational function*. It may also be called a *rational expression*. There are many occasions in mathematics when a problem reduces to the manipulation of algebraic fractions, and the rules for this are exactly the same as those for numerical fractions.

Simplifying fractions

To simplify a fraction, you look for a factor common to both the numerator (top line) and the denominator (bottom line) and cancel by it.

For example, in arithmetic

$$\frac{15}{20}=\frac{5\times 3}{5\times 4}=\frac{3}{4}$$

and in algebra

$$\frac{6a}{9a^2}=\frac{2\times 3\times a}{3\times 3\times a\times a}=\frac{2}{3a}.$$

Notice how you must *factorise* both the numerator and denominator before cancelling, since it is only possible to cancel by a *common factor*. In some cases this involves putting brackets in.

$$\frac{2a+4}{a^2-4}=\frac{2(a+2)}{(a+2)(a-2)}=\frac{2}{(a-2)}$$

Multiplying and dividing fractions

Multiplying fractions involves cancelling any factors common to the numerator and denominator. For example:

$$\frac{10a}{3b^2}\times\frac{9ab}{25}=\frac{2\times 5\times a}{3\times b\times b}\times\frac{3\times 3\times a\times b}{5\times 5}=\frac{6a^2}{5b}.$$

As with simplifying, it is often necessary to factorise any algebraic expressions first.

$$\frac{a^2+3a+2}{9}\times\frac{12}{a+1}=\frac{(a+1)(a+2)}{3\times 3}\times\frac{3\times 4}{(a+1)}$$

$$=\frac{(a+2)}{3}\times\frac{4}{1}$$

$$=\frac{4(a+2)}{3}$$

Remember that when one fraction is divided by another, you change ÷ to × and invert the fraction which follows the ÷ symbol. For example:

$$\frac{12}{x^2-1} \div \frac{4}{x+1} = \frac{12}{(x+1)(x-1)} \times \frac{(x+1)}{4}$$

$$= \frac{3}{(x-1)}.$$

Addition and subtraction of fractions

To add or subtract two fractions they must be replaced by equivalent fractions, both of which have the same denominator.

For example:

$$\frac{2}{3} + \frac{1}{4} = \frac{8}{12} + \frac{3}{12} = \frac{11}{12}.$$

Similarly, in algebra:

$$\frac{2x}{3} + \frac{x}{4} = \frac{8x}{12} + \frac{3x}{12} = \frac{11x}{12}$$

and $\quad \frac{2}{3x} + \frac{1}{4x} = \frac{8}{12x} + \frac{3}{12x} = \frac{11}{12x}.$

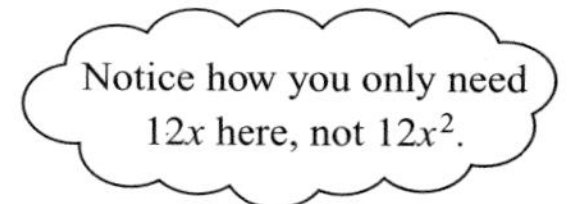

You must take particular care when the subtraction of fractions introduces a sign change. For example:

$$\frac{4x-3}{6} - \frac{2x+1}{4} = \frac{2(4x-3) - 3(2x+1)}{12}$$

$$= \frac{8x-6-6x-3}{12}$$

$$= \frac{2x-9}{12}.$$

Notice how in addition and subtraction, the new denominator is the *lowest common multiple* of the original denominators. When two denominators have no *common factor*, their product gives the new denominator. For example:

$$\frac{2}{y+3} + \frac{3}{y-2} = \frac{2(y-2) + 3(y+3)}{(y+3)(y-2)}$$

$$= \frac{2y-4+3y+9}{(y+3)(y-2)}$$

$$= \frac{5y+5}{(y+3)(y-2)}$$

$$= \frac{5(y+1)}{(y+3)(y-2)}.$$

It may be necessary to factorise denominators in order to identify common factors, as shown here.

$$\frac{2b}{a^2-b^2}-\frac{3}{a+b}=\frac{2b}{(a+b)(a-b)}-\frac{3}{(a+b)}$$

$$=\frac{2b-3(a-b)}{(a+b)(a-b)}$$

$$=\frac{5b-3a}{(a+b)(a-b)}.$$

$(a + b)$ is a common factor.

EXERCISE 7B

Simplify the expressions in questions 1–10.

1 $\frac{6a}{b}\times\frac{a}{9b^2}$

2 $\frac{5xy}{3}\div 15xy^2$

3 $\frac{x^2-9}{x^2-9x+18}$

4 $\frac{5x-1}{x+3}\times\frac{x^2+6x+9}{5x^2+4x-1}$

5 $\frac{4x^2-25}{4x^2+20x+25}$

6 $\frac{a^2+a-12}{5}\times\frac{3}{4a-12}$

7 $\frac{4x^2-9}{x^2+2x+1}\div\frac{2x-3}{x^2+x}$

8 $\frac{2p+4}{5}\div(p^2-4)$

9 $\frac{a^2-b^2}{2a^2+ab-b^2}$

10 $\frac{x^2+8x+16}{x^2+6x+9}\times\frac{x^2+2x-3}{x^2+4x}$

In questions 11–24 write each of the expressions as a single fraction in its simplest form.

11 $\frac{1}{4x}+\frac{1}{5x}$

12 $\frac{x}{3}-\frac{(x+1)}{4}$

13 $\frac{a}{a+1}+\frac{1}{a-1}$

14 $\frac{2}{x-3}+\frac{3}{x-2}$

15 $\frac{x}{x^2-4}-\frac{1}{x+2}$

16 $\frac{p^2}{p^2-1}-\frac{p^2}{p^2+1}$

17 $\frac{2}{a+1}-\frac{a}{a^2+1}$

18 $\frac{2y}{(y+2)^2}-\frac{4}{y+4}$

19 $x+\frac{1}{x+1}$

20 $\frac{2}{b^2+2b+1}-\frac{3}{b+1}$

21 $\frac{2}{3(x-1)}+\frac{3}{2(x+1)}$

22 $\frac{6}{5(x+2)}-\frac{2x}{(x+2)^2}$

23 $\frac{2}{a+2}-\frac{a-2}{2a^2+a-6}$

24 $\frac{1}{x-2}+\frac{1}{x}+\frac{1}{x+2}$

Equations involving algebraic fractions

The easiest way to solve an equation involving fractions is usually to multiply both sides by an expression which will cancel out the fractions.

EXAMPLE 7.6

Solve $\frac{x}{3} + \frac{2x}{5} = 4$.

SOLUTION

Multiplying by 15 (the lowest common multiple of 3 and 5) gives

$$15 \times \frac{x}{3} + 15 \times \frac{2x}{5} = 15 \times 4$$

Notice that all three terms must be multiplied by 15.

$$\Rightarrow \quad 5x + 6x = 60$$

$$\Rightarrow \quad 11x = 60$$

$$\Rightarrow \quad x = \frac{60}{11}.$$

A similar method applies when the denominator is algebraic.

EXAMPLE 7.7

Solve $\frac{5}{x} - \frac{4}{x+1} = 1$.

SOLUTION

Multiplying by $x(x + 1)$ (the lowest common multiple of x and $x + 1$) gives

$$\frac{5x(x+1)}{x} - \frac{4x(x+1)}{x+1} = x(x+1)$$

$$\Rightarrow \quad 5(x+1) - 4x = x(x+1)$$

$$\Rightarrow \quad 5x + 5 - 4x = x^2 + x$$

$$\Rightarrow \quad x^2 = 5$$

$$\Rightarrow \quad x = \pm\sqrt{5}.$$

In Example 7.7, the lowest common multiple of the denominators is their product, but this is not always the case.

EXAMPLE 7.8

Solve $\frac{1}{(x-3)(x-1)} + \frac{1}{x(x-1)} = -\frac{1}{x(x-3)}$.

SOLUTION

Here you only need to multiply by $x(x-3)(x-1)$ to eliminate all the fractions. This gives

$$\frac{x(x-3)(x-1)}{(x-3)(x-1)} + \frac{x(x-3)(x-1)}{x(x-1)} = \frac{-x(x-3)(x-1)}{x(x-3)}$$

$$\Rightarrow \quad x + (x-3) = -(x-1)$$

$$\Rightarrow \quad 2x - 3 = -x + 1$$

$$\Rightarrow \quad 3x = 4$$

$$\Rightarrow \quad x = \tfrac{4}{3}.$$

Fractional algebraic equations arise in a number of situations, including, as in the following example, problems connecting distance, speed and time. The relationship

$$\text{time} = \frac{\text{distance}}{\text{speed}}$$

is useful here.

EXAMPLE 7.9

Each day I travel 10 km from home to work. One day, because of road works, my average speed was 5 km h^{-1} slower than usual, and my journey took an extra 10 minutes.

Take x km h^{-1} as my usual speed.

(i) Write down an expression in x which represents my usual time in hours.

(ii) write down an expression in x which represents my time when I travelled 5 km h^{-1} slower than usual.

(iii) Use these expressions to form an equation in x and solve it.

(iv) How long does my journey usually take?

SOLUTION

(i) $\text{Time} = \frac{\text{distance}}{\text{speed}} \quad \Rightarrow \quad \text{usual time} = \frac{10}{x}.$

(ii) I now travel at $(x-5)$ km h^{-1}, so the longer time $= \frac{10}{x-5}$.

(iii) The difference in these times is 10 minutes, or $\frac{1}{6}$ hour, so

$$\frac{10}{x-5} - \frac{10}{x} = \frac{1}{6}.$$

Multiplying by $6x(x-5)$ gives

$$\frac{60x(x-5)}{(x-5)} - \frac{60x(x-5)}{x} = \frac{6x(x-5)}{6}$$

$$\Rightarrow \quad 60x - 60(x-5) = x(x-5)$$

$$\Rightarrow \quad 60x - 60x + 300 = x^2 - 5x$$

$$\Rightarrow \quad x^2 - 5x - 300 = 0$$

$$\Rightarrow \quad (x-20)(x+15) = 0$$

$$\Rightarrow \quad x = 20 \text{ or } x = -15.$$

(iv) Reject $x = -15$, since $x \text{ km h}^{-1}$ is a speed.
Usual speed = 20 km h^{-1}.
Usual time $= \dfrac{10}{x}$ hours = 30 minutes.

EXERCISE 7C

1 Solve the following equations.

(i) $\dfrac{2x}{7} - \dfrac{x}{4} = 3$

(ii) $\dfrac{5}{4x} + \dfrac{3}{2x} = \dfrac{11}{16}$

(iii) $\dfrac{2}{x} - \dfrac{5}{2x-1} = 0$

(iv) $x - 3 = \dfrac{x+2}{x-2}$

(v) $\dfrac{1}{x} + x + 1 = \dfrac{13}{3}$

(vi) $\dfrac{2x}{x+1} - \dfrac{1}{x-1} = 1$

(vii) $\dfrac{x}{x-1} - \dfrac{x-1}{x} = 2$

(viii) $\dfrac{2}{p+1} - \dfrac{3}{1-3p} = 0$

(ix) $\dfrac{18}{4a-1} - \dfrac{1}{a+1} = 1$

(x) $\dfrac{2}{2r-1} - \dfrac{6}{r+1} = 11$

2 The numerator of a fraction is five less than the denominator.
If the numerator and denominator are each increased by nine, the value of the new fraction formed is $\frac{3}{4}$.
Find the original fraction.

3 Lucy has constructed a new website and so far this has received 156 hits.
If it gets 54 hits next week, the average number of hits per week will increase by four.

(i) Write down an equation for n, the number of weeks since this site was launched.

(ii) Solve this equation to find n.

4 I have £6 to spend on crisps for a party.

When I get to the shop I find that the price has been reduced by 1 penny per packet, and I can buy one packet more than I expected.

Take x pence as the original cost of a packet of crisps.

(i) Write down an expression in x which represents the number of packets that I expected to buy.

(ii) Write down an expression in x which represents the number of packets bought at the reduced price.

(iii) Form an equation in x and solve it to find the original cost.

5 The distance from Manchester to Oxford is 270 km.

One day, road works on the M6 meant that my average speed was 10 km h^{-1} less than I had anticipated, and so I arrived 18 minutes later than planned.

Take x km h^{-1} as the anticipated average speed.

(i) Write down an expression in x for the anticipated and actual times of the journey.

(ii) Form an equation in x and solve it.

(iii) Find the time of my arrival in Oxford if I left home at 10 am.

6 Of the three statements given below, one is true for all values of x, one is true for just one value of x and one is true for just two values of x.

Identify the one that is true for all values of x and solve the other two.

(i) $\dfrac{x+1}{x-1} - \dfrac{x-1}{x+1} = \dfrac{4x}{x^2-1}$

(ii) $\dfrac{x+1}{x-1} - \dfrac{x-1}{x+1} = \dfrac{2}{x^2-1}$

(iii) $\dfrac{x+1}{x-1} - \dfrac{x-1}{x+1} = \dfrac{5}{6}$

7 Each time someone leaves the firm of Honeys, he or she is taken out for a meal by the rest of the staff.

On one such occasion the bill came to £272, and each member of staff remaining with the firm paid £1 extra to cover the cost of the meal for the one who was leaving.

Taking £x as the cost of the meal, write down an equation in x and solve it.

How many staff were left working for Honeys?

8 A Swiss roll cake is 21 cm long. When I cut it into slices, I can get two extra slices if I reduce the thickness of each slice by $\frac{1}{4}$ cm.

Taking x as the number of thicker slices, write down an equation in x and solve it.

9 Two electrical resistances may be connected in series or in parallel. In series, the equivalent single resistance is the sum of the two resistances, but in parallel, the two resistances R_1 and R_2 are equivalent to a single resistance R where

$$\frac{1}{R_1} + \frac{1}{R_2} = \frac{1}{R}.$$

(i) Find the single resistance which is equivalent to resistances of 3 and 4 ohms connected in parallel.

(ii) What resistance must be added in parallel to a resistance of 6 ohms to give a resistance of 2.4 ohms?

(iii) What is the effect of connecting two equal resistances in parallel?

P Prove that the equation

$$\frac{x}{x-1} + \frac{x-1}{x} = 2$$

has no solution.

Partial fractions

Until this point, any instruction to simplify an algebraic fractional expression was asking you to give the expansion as a single fraction. Sometimes, however, it is easier to deal with two or three simple separate fractions than it is to handle one more complicated one. This is the case when you are using the binomial theorem to obtain a series expansion.

For example:

$$\frac{1}{(1+2x)(1+x)}$$

may be written as

$$\frac{2}{(1+2x)} - \frac{1}{(1+x)}.$$

The two-part expression $\frac{2}{(1+2x)} - \frac{1}{(1+x)}$ is much easier to expand than $\frac{1}{(1+2x)(1+x)}$.

When integrating, it is even more important to work with a number of simple fractions than to combine them into one. For example, the only analytical method for integrating $\frac{1}{(1+2x)(1+x)}$ involves first writing it as $\frac{2}{(1+2x)} - \frac{1}{(1+x)}$.

You will meet this application in Chapter 10.

This process of taking an expression such as $\frac{1}{(1+2x)(1+x)}$ and writing it in the form $\frac{2}{(1+2x)} - \frac{1}{(1+x)}$ is called expressing the algebraic fraction in *partial fractions*.

How can this be done in general?

It is sufficient to consider only *proper* algebraic fractions, that is fractions where the order of the numerator (top line) is strictly less than that of the denominator (bottom line). The following, for example, are proper fractions:

$$\frac{2}{1+x}, \frac{5x-1}{x^2-3}, \frac{7x}{(x+1)(x-2)}.$$

Examples of improper fractions are

$$\frac{2x}{x+1} \qquad \left(\text{which can be written as } 2 - \frac{2}{x+1}\right)$$

and

$$\frac{x^2}{x-2} \qquad \left(\text{which can be written as } x + 2 + \frac{4}{x-2}\right).$$

It can be shown that, when a proper algebraic fraction is decomposed into its partial fractions, each of the partial fractions will be a proper fraction.

When finding partial fractions you must always assume the most general numerator possible, and the method for doing this is illustrated in the following examples.

Type 1: denominators of the form $(ax + b)(cx + d)$

EXAMPLE 7.10

Express $\frac{4+x}{(1+x)(2-x)}$ as a sum of partial fractions.

SOLUTION

Assume

$$\frac{4+x}{(1+x)(2-x)} \equiv \frac{A}{1+x} + \frac{B}{2-x}.$$

Remember: a linear denominator ⇒ a constant numerator if the fraction is to be a proper fraction.

Multiplying both sides by $(1+x)(2-x)$ gives

$$4 + x \equiv A(2-x) + B(1+x). \qquad ①$$

This is an identity; it is true for all values of x.

There are two possible ways in which you can find the constants A and B. You can either

- substitute *any two* values of x in ① (two values are needed to give two equations to solve for the two unknowns A and B); or
- equate the constant terms to give one equation (this is the same as putting $x = 0$) and the coefficients of x to give another.

Sometimes one method is easier than the other, and in practice you will often want to use a combination of the two.

Method 1: Substitution

Although you can substitute any two values of x, the easiest to use are $x = 2$ and $x = -1$, since each makes the value of one bracket zero in the identity

$$4 + x \equiv A(2 - x) + B(1 + x).$$

$$x = 2 \quad \Rightarrow \quad 4 + 2 = A(2 - 2) + B(1 + 2)$$

$$6 = 3B \quad \Rightarrow \quad B = 2$$

$$x = -1 \quad \Rightarrow \quad 4 - 1 = A(2 + 1) + B(1 - 1)$$

$$3 = 3A \quad \Rightarrow \quad A = 1$$

Substituting these values for A and B gives

$$\frac{4 + x}{(1 + x)(2 - x)} \equiv \frac{1}{1 + x} + \frac{2}{2 - x}.$$

Method 2: Equating coefficients

In this method, you write the right-hand side of

$$4 + x \equiv A(2 - x) + B(1 + x)$$

as a polynomial in x, and then compare the coefficients of the various terms.

$$4 + x \equiv 2A - Ax + B + Bx$$

$$4 + 1x \equiv (2A + B) + (-A + B)x$$

Equating the constant terms: $\quad 4 = 2A + B.$

Equating the coefficients of x: $\quad 1 = -A + B.$

These are simultaneous equations in A and B.

Solving these simultaneous equations gives $A = 1$ and $B = 2$ as before.

? In each of these methods the identity (≡) was later replaced by equality (=). Why was this done?

In some cases it is necessary to factorise the denominator before finding the partial fractions.

EXAMPLE 7.11

Express $\frac{2}{4-x^2}$ as a sum of partial fractions.

SOLUTION

$$\frac{2}{4-x^2} \equiv \frac{2}{(2+x)(2-x)}$$

$$\equiv \frac{A}{2+x} + \frac{B}{2-x}$$

Multiplying both sides by $(2+x)(2-x)$ gives

$$2 \equiv A(2-x) + B(2+x) \quad ①$$

$$2 \equiv (2A + 2B) + x(B - A).$$

Equating constant terms: $2 = 2A + 2B$. ②

Equating coefficients of x: $0 = B - A$, so $B = A$.

Substituting in ② gives $A = B = \frac{1}{2}$.

Using these values

$$\frac{2}{(2+x)(2-x)} \equiv \frac{\frac{1}{2}}{2+x} + \frac{\frac{1}{2}}{2-x}$$

$$\equiv \frac{1}{2(2+x)} + \frac{1}{2(2-x)}.$$

EXERCISE 7D

1 Express each of the following fractions as a sum of partial fractions.

(i) $\frac{5}{(x-2)(x+3)}$ **(ii)** $\frac{1}{x(x+1)}$ **(iii)** $\frac{6}{(x-1)(x-4)}$

(iv) $\frac{x+5}{(x-1)(x+2)}$ **(v)** $\frac{3x}{(2x-1)(x+1)}$ **(vi)** $\frac{4}{x^2-2x}$

(vii) $\frac{2}{(x-1)(3x-1)}$ **(viii)** $\frac{x-1}{x^2-3x-4}$ **(ix)** $\frac{x+2}{2x^2-x}$

(x) $\frac{7}{2x^2+x-6}$ **(xi)** $\frac{2x-1}{2x^2+3x-20}$ **(xii)** $\frac{2x+5}{18x^2-8}$

Type 2: denominators of the form $(ax + b)(cx^2 + d)$

EXAMPLE 7.12

Express $\frac{2x+3}{(x-1)(x^2+4)}$ as a sum of partial fractions.

SOLUTION

You need to assume a numerator of order 1 for the partial fraction with a denominator of $x^2 + 4$, which is of order 2.

$$\frac{2x+3}{(x-1)(x^2+4)} \equiv \frac{A}{x-1} + \frac{Bx+C}{x^2+4}$$

$Bx + C$ is the most general numerator of order 1.

Multiplying both sides by $(x-1)(x^2+4)$ gives

$$2x+3 \equiv A(x^2+4)+(Bx+C)(x-1) \qquad ①$$

$$x=1 \quad \Rightarrow \quad 5=5A \quad \Rightarrow \quad A=1.$$

The other two unknowns, B and C, are most easily found by equating coefficients. Identity ① may be rewritten as

$$2x+3 \equiv (A+B)x^2+(-B+C)x+(4A-C).$$

Equating coefficients of x^2: $\quad 0=A+B \quad \Rightarrow \quad B=-1.$

Equating constant terms: $\quad 3=4A-C \quad \Rightarrow \quad C=1.$

This gives

$$\frac{2x+3}{(x-1)(x^2+4)} \equiv \frac{1}{x-1}+\frac{1-x}{x^2+4}.$$

Note

Notice how Example 7.12 uses a combination of the two methods.

Type 3: denominators of the form $(ax+b)(cx+d)^2$

The factor $(cx+d)^2$ is of order 2, so it would have an order 1 numerator in the partial fractions. However, in the case of a repeated factor there is a simpler form.

Consider $\quad \dfrac{4x+5}{(2x+1)^2}.$

This can be written as

$$\frac{2(2x+1)+3}{(2x+1)^2}$$

$$\equiv \frac{2(2x+1)}{(2x+1)^2}+\frac{3}{(2x+1)^2}$$

$$\equiv \frac{2}{(2x+1)}+\frac{3}{(2x+1)^2}.$$

Note

In this form, both the numerators are constant.

In a similar way, any fraction of the form $\dfrac{px+q}{(cx+d)^2}$ can be written as

$$\frac{A}{(cx+d)}+\frac{B}{(cx+d)^2}.$$

When expressing an algebraic fraction in partial fractions, you are aiming to find the simplest partial fractions possible, so you would want the form where the numerators are constant.

EXAMPLE 7.13

Express $\dfrac{x+1}{(x-1)(x-2)^2}$ as a sum of partial fractions.

SOLUTION

Let $\dfrac{x+1}{(x-1)(x-2)^2} \equiv \dfrac{A}{(x-1)} + \dfrac{B}{(x-2)} + \dfrac{C}{(x-2)^2}$.

Notice that you only need $(x-2)^2$ here and not $(x-2)^3$.

Multiplying both sides by $(x-1)(x-2)^2$ gives

$$x + 1 \equiv A(x-2)^2 + B(x-1)(x-2) + C(x-1).$$

$x = 1$ (so that $x - 1 = 0$) $\Rightarrow$ $2 = A(-1)^2$ $\Rightarrow A = 2$

$x = 2$ (so that $x - 2 = 0$) $\Rightarrow$ $3 = C$

Equating coefficients of x^2 $\Rightarrow$ $0 = A + B$ $\Rightarrow$ $B = -2$.

This gives

$$\frac{x+1}{(x-1)(x-2)^2} \equiv \frac{2}{x-1} - \frac{2}{x-2} + \frac{3}{(x-2)^2}.$$

EXAMPLE 7.14

Express $\dfrac{5x^2-3}{x^2(x+1)}$ as a sum of partial fractions.

SOLUTION

Let $\dfrac{5x^2-3}{x^2(x+1)} \equiv \dfrac{A}{x} + \dfrac{B}{x^2} + \dfrac{C}{x+1}$.

Multiplying both sides by $x^2(x+1)$ gives

$$5x^2 - 3 \equiv Ax(x+1) + B(x+1) + Cx^2.$$

$x = 0$ $\Rightarrow$ $-3 = B$

$x = -1$ $\Rightarrow$ $+2 = C$

Equating coefficients of x^2: $+5 = A + C$ $\Rightarrow$ $A = 3$.

This gives

$$\frac{5x^2-3}{x^2(x+1)} \equiv \frac{3}{x} - \frac{3}{x^2} + \frac{2}{x+1}.$$

EXERCISE 7E

1 Express each of the following fractions as a sum of partial fractions.

(i) $\dfrac{4}{(1-3x)(1-x)^2}$ **(ii)** $\dfrac{4+2x}{(2x-1)(x^2+1)}$ **(iii)** $\dfrac{5-2x}{(x-1)^2(x+2)}$

(iv) $\dfrac{2x+1}{(x-2)(x^2+4)}$ **(v)** $\dfrac{2x^2+x+4}{(2x^2-3)(x+2)}$ **(vi)** $\dfrac{x^2-1}{x^2(2x+1)}$

(vii) $\dfrac{x^2+3}{x(3x^2-1)}$ **(viii)** $\dfrac{2x^2+x+2}{(2x^2+1)(x+1)}$ **(ix)** $\dfrac{4x^2-3}{x(2x-1)^2}$

2 Given that

$$\frac{x^2 + 2x + 7}{(2x + 3)(x^2 + 4)} \equiv \frac{A}{(2x + 3)} + \frac{Bx + C}{(x^2 + 4)}$$

find the values of the constants A, B and C.

[MEI, *part*]

3 Calculate the values of the constants A, B and C for which

$$\frac{x^2 - 4x + 23}{(x - 5)(x^2 + 3)} \equiv \frac{A}{(x - 5)} + \frac{Bx + C}{(x^2 + 3)}.$$

[MEI, *part*]

Using partial fractions with the binomial expansion

One of the most common reasons for writing an expression in partial fractions is to enable binomial expansions to be applied, as in the following example.

EXAMPLE 7.15

Express $\frac{2x + 7}{(x - 1)(x + 2)}$ in partial fractions and hence find the first three terms of its binomial expansion, stating the values of x for which this is valid.

SOLUTION

$$\frac{2x + 7}{(x - 1)(x + 2)} \equiv \frac{A}{(x - 1)} + \frac{B}{(x + 2)}$$

Multiplying both sides by $(x - 1)(x + 2)$ gives

$$2x + 7 \equiv A(x + 2) + B(x - 1).$$

$$x = 1 \quad \Rightarrow \quad 9 = 3A \quad \Rightarrow \quad A = 3$$

$$x = -2 \quad \Rightarrow \quad 3 = -3B \quad \Rightarrow \quad B = -1$$

This gives

$$\frac{2x + 7}{(x - 1)(x + 2)} \equiv \frac{3}{(x - 1)} - \frac{1}{(x + 2)}.$$

In order to obtain the binomial expansion, each bracket must be of the form $(1 \pm \ldots)$, giving

$$\frac{2x + 7}{(x - 1)(x + 2)} \equiv \frac{-3}{(1 - x)} - \frac{1}{2\left(1 + \frac{x}{2}\right)}$$

$$\equiv -3(1 - x)^{-1} - \frac{1}{2}\left(1 + \frac{x}{2}\right)^{-1}. \quad ①$$

The two binomial expansions are

$$(1 - x)^{-1} = 1 + (-1)(-x) + \frac{(-1)(-2)}{2!}(-x)^2 + \ldots \quad \text{for } |x| < 1$$

$$\approx 1 + x + x^2$$

and $\left(1+\frac{x}{2}\right)^{-1} = 1 + (-1)\left(\frac{x}{2}\right) + \frac{(-1)(-2)}{2!}\left(\frac{x}{2}\right)^2 + \dots$ for $\left|\frac{x}{2}\right| < 1$

$$\approx 1 - \frac{x}{2} + \frac{x^2}{4}.$$

Substituting these in ① gives

$$\frac{2x+7}{(x-1)(x+2)} \approx -3(1+x+x^2) - \frac{1}{2}\left(1 - \frac{x}{2} + \frac{x^2}{4}\right)$$

$$= -\frac{7}{2} - \frac{11x}{4} - \frac{25x^2}{8}.$$

The expansion is valid when $|x| < 1$ and $\left|\frac{x}{2}\right| < 1$. The stricter of these is $|x| < 1$

INVESTIGATION

Find a binomial expansion for the function

$$f(x) = \frac{1}{(1+2x)(1-x)}$$

and state the values of x for which it is valid

(i) by writing it as $(1 + 2x)^{-1}(1 - x)^{-1}$
(ii) by writing it as $[1 + (x - 2x^2)]^{-1}$ and treating $(x - 2x^2)$ as one term
(iii) by first expressing $f(x)$ as a sum of partial fractions.

Decide which method you find simplest for the following cases.
(a) When a linear approximation for $f(x)$ is required.
(b) When a quadratic approximation for $f(x)$ is required.
(c) When the coefficient of x^n is required.

EXERCISE 7F

1 Find the first three terms in the binomial expansion of the following fractions.

(i) $\frac{4}{(1-3x)(1-x)^2}$ **(ii)** $\frac{4+2x}{(2x-1)(x^2+1)}$

(iii) $\frac{5-2x}{(x-1)^2(x+2)}$ **(iv)** $\frac{2x+1}{(x-2)(x^2+4)}$

2 (i) Express $\frac{7-4x}{(2x-1)(x+2)}$ in partial fractions as $\frac{A}{(2x-1)} + \frac{B}{(x+2)}$ where A and B are to be found.

(ii) Find the expansion of $\frac{1}{(1-2x)}$ in the form $a + bx + cx^2 + \dots$ where a, b and c are to be found.
Give the range of values of x for which this expansion is valid.

(iii) Find the expansion of $\frac{1}{(2+x)}$ as far as the term containing x^2.
Give the range of values of x for which this expansion is valid.

(iv) Hence find a quadratic approximation for $\frac{7-4x}{(2x-1)(x+2)}$ when $|x|$ is small.

Find the relative error in this approximation when $x = 0.1$.

[MEI]

3 (i) Expand $(2-x)(1+x)$.

Hence express $\frac{3x}{2+x-x^2}$ in partial fractions.

(ii) Use the binomial expansion of the partial fractions in part **(i)** to show that

$$\frac{3x}{2+x-x^2} = \frac{3}{2}x - \frac{3}{4}x^2 + \dots .$$

State the range of values of x for which this result is valid.

[MEI, *part*]

4 (i) Given that $f(x) = \frac{8x-6}{(1-x)(3-x)}$, express $f(x)$ in partial fractions.

Hence show that

$$f'(x) = (1-x)^{-2} - \left(1 - \frac{x}{3}\right)^{-2}.$$

(ii) Using the results in part **(i)**, or otherwise, find the x co-ordinates of the turning points on the graph of $y = f(x)$.

(iii) Use the binomial expansion, together with the result in part **(i)**, to expand $f'(x)$ in powers of x up to and including the term in x^2.

(iv) Show that, when $f'(x)$ is expanded in powers of x, the coefficients of all the powers of x are positive.

[MEI]

KEY POINTS

1 The general binomial expansion for $n \in \mathbb{R}$ is

$$(1 + x)^n = 1 + nx + \frac{n(n-1)}{2!}x^2 + \frac{n(n-1)(n-2)}{3!}x^3 + \dots .$$

In the special case when $n \in \mathbb{N}$, the series expansion is finite and valid for all x.

When $n \notin \mathbb{N}$, the series expansion is non-terminating (infinite) and valid only if $|x| < 1$.

2 When $n \notin \mathbb{N}$, $(a + x)^n$ should be written as $a^n\left(1 + \frac{x}{a}\right)^n$ before obtaining the binomial expansion.

3 When multiplying algebraic fractions, you can only cancel when the same factor occurs in both the numerator and the denominator.

4 When adding or subtracting algebraic fractions, you first need to find a common denominator.

5 The easiest way to solve any equation involving fractions is usually to multiply both sides by a quantity which will eliminate the fractions.

6 A proper algebraic fraction with a denominator which factorises can be decomposed into a sum of proper partial fractions.

7 The following forms of partial fraction should be used.

$$\frac{px + q}{(ax + b)(cx + d)} \equiv \frac{A}{ax + b} + \frac{B}{cx + d}$$

$$\frac{px^2 + qr + r}{(ax + b)(cx^2 + d)} \equiv \frac{A}{ax + b} + \frac{Bx + C}{cx^2 + d}$$

$$\frac{px^2 + qx + r}{(ax + b)(cx + d)^2} \equiv \frac{A}{ax + b} + \frac{B}{cx + d} + \frac{C}{(cx + d)^2}$$

8 Trigonometry

Music, when soft voices die,
Vibrates in the memory –

P.B. Shelley

❓ Both of these photographs show forms of waves. In each case, estimate the wavelength and the amplitude in metres (see figure 8.1).

Use your measurements to suggest, for each curve, values of a and b which would make $y = a\sin bx$ a suitable model for the curve.

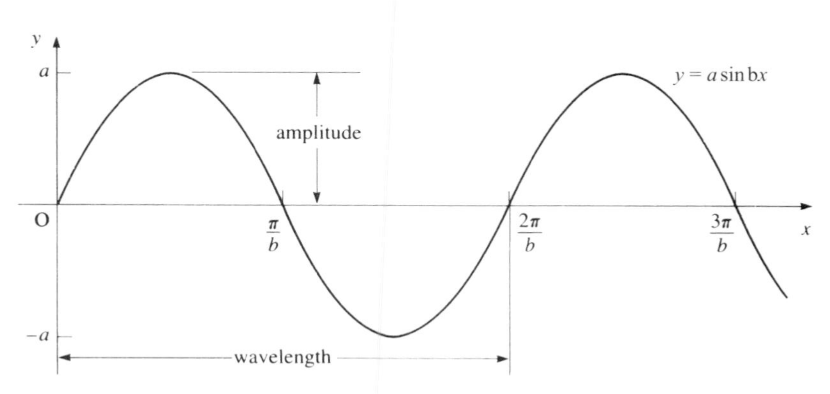

Figure 8.1

Reciprocal trigonometrical functions

As well as the three main trigonometrical functions, there are three more which are commonly used. These are their reciprocals – cosecant (cosec), secant (sec) and cotangent (cot), defined by

$$\operatorname{cosec}\theta = \frac{1}{\sin\theta}; \qquad \sec\theta = \frac{1}{\cos\theta}; \qquad \cot\theta = \frac{1}{\tan\theta}\left(= \frac{\cos\theta}{\sin\theta}\right).$$

Each of these is undefined for certain values of θ. For example, cosec θ is undefined for $\theta = 0°, 180°, 360°, \ldots$ since $\sin\theta$ is zero for these values of θ.

Figure 8.2 shows the graphs of these functions. Notice how all three of the functions have asymptotes at intervals of 180°. Each of the graphs shows one of the main trigonometrical functions as a broken line and the related reciprocal function as a solid line.

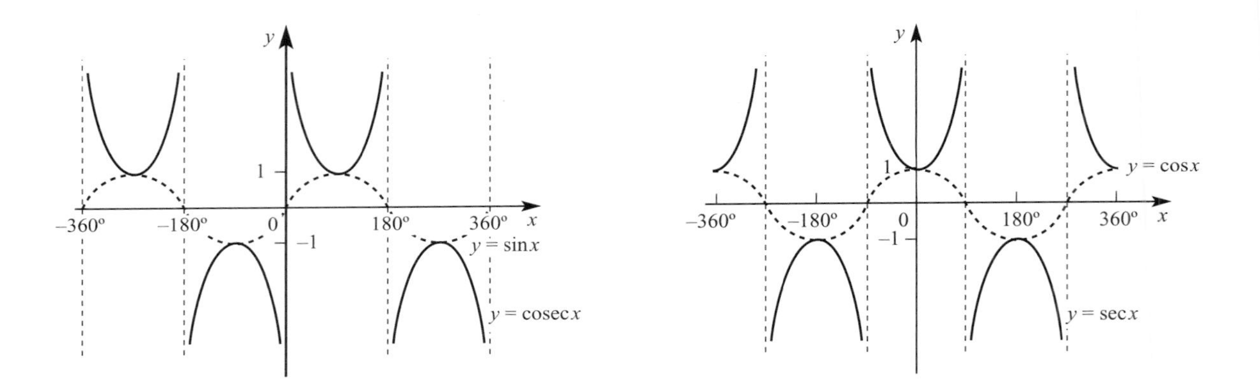

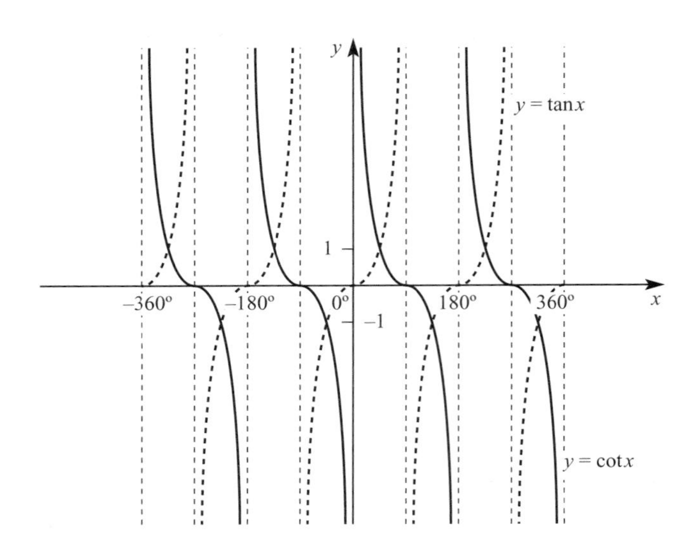

Figure 8.2

Using the definitions of the reciprocal functions two alternative trigonometrical forms of Pythagoras' theorem can be obtained.

(i) $\sin^2\theta + \cos^2\theta \equiv 1$

Dividing both sides by $\cos^2\theta$: $\dfrac{\sin^2\theta}{\cos^2\theta} + \dfrac{\cos^2\theta}{\cos^2\theta} \equiv \dfrac{1}{\cos^2\theta}$

$$\Rightarrow \quad \tan^2\theta + 1 \equiv \sec^2\theta.$$

This identity is sometimes used in mechanics.

(ii) $\sin^2\theta + \cos^2\theta \equiv 1$

Dividing both sides by $\sin^2\theta$: $\dfrac{\sin^2\theta}{\sin^2\theta} + \dfrac{\cos^2\theta}{\sin^2\theta} \equiv \dfrac{1}{\sin^2\theta}$

$$\Rightarrow \quad 1 + \cot^2\theta \equiv \operatorname{cosec}^2\theta.$$

Questions concerning reciprocal functions are usually most easily solved by considering the related function, as in the following examples.

EXAMPLE 8.1

Find cosec 120° leaving your answer in surd form.

SOLUTION

$$\begin{aligned} \operatorname{cosec} 120° &= \frac{1}{\sin 120°} \\ &= 1 \div \frac{\sqrt{3}}{2} \\ &= \frac{2}{\sqrt{3}} \end{aligned}$$

EXAMPLE 8.2

Find values of θ in the interval $0° \leqslant \theta \leqslant 360°$ for which $\sec^2\theta = 4 + 2\tan\theta$.

SOLUTION

First you need to obtain an equation containing only one trigonometrical function.

$$\sec^2\theta = 4 + 2\tan\theta$$

$$\Rightarrow \quad \tan^2\theta + 1 = 4 + 2\tan\theta$$

$$\Rightarrow \quad \tan^2\theta - 2\tan\theta - 3 = 0$$

$$\Rightarrow \quad (\tan\theta - 3)(\tan\theta + 1) = 0$$

$$\Rightarrow \quad \tan\theta = 3 \text{ or } \tan\theta = -1$$

$\tan\theta = 3 \quad \Rightarrow \quad \theta = 71.6°$ (calculator)

or $\quad \theta = 71.6° + 180° = 251.6°$ (see figure 8.3)

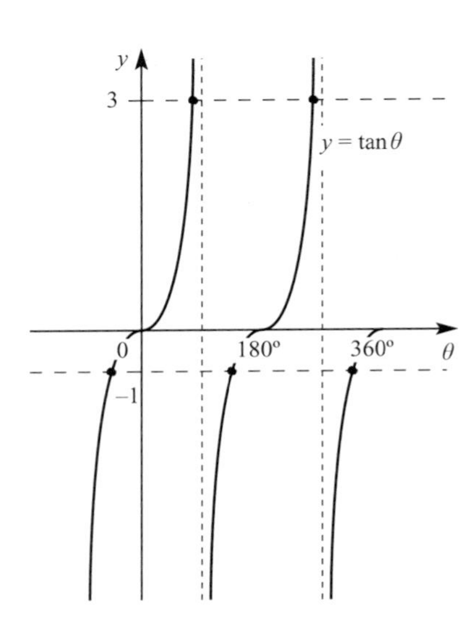

Figure 8.3

$\tan\theta = -1 \quad \Rightarrow \quad \theta = -45°$ (not in the required range)

or $\quad \theta = -45° + 180° = 135°$ (see figure 8.3)

or $\quad \theta = 135° + 180° = 315°$

The values of θ are 71.6°, 135°, 251.6°, 315°.

EXERCISE 8A

1 Solve the following equations for $0° \leqslant x \leqslant 360°$.

(i) $\operatorname{cosec} x = 1$ **(ii)** $\sec x = 2$ **(iii)** $\cot x = 4$

(iv) $\sec x = -3$ **(v)** $\cot x = -1$ **(vi)** $\operatorname{cosec} x = -2$

2 Find the following giving your answers as fractions or in surd form.
You should not need your calculator.

(i) $\cot 135°$ **(ii)** $\sec 150°$ **(iii)** $\operatorname{cosec} 240°$

(iv) $\sec 210°$ **(v)** $\cot 270°$ **(vi)** $\operatorname{cosec} 225°$

3 In triangle ABC, angle $A = 90°$ and $\sec B = 2$.

(i) Find the angles B and C.

(ii) Find $\tan B$.

(iii) Show that $1 + \tan^2 B = \sec^2 B$.

4 In triangle LMN, angle $M = 90°$ and $\cot N = 1$.

(i) Find the angles L and N.

(ii) Find $\sec L$, $\operatorname{cosec} L$, and $\tan L$.

(iii) Show that $1 + \tan^2 L = \sec^2 L$.

5 Malini is 1.5 m tall.
At 8 pm one evening her shadow is 6 m long.
Given that the angle of elevation of the sun at that moment is α

(i) show that $\cot\alpha = 4$

(ii) find α.

6 (i) For what values of a, where $0° \leqslant a \leqslant 360°$, are $\sec a$, $\operatorname{cosec} a$ and $\cot a$ all positive?

(ii) Are there any values of a for which $\sec a$, $\operatorname{cosec} a$ and $\cot a$ are all negative? Explain your answer.

(iii) Are there any values of a for which $\sec a$, $\operatorname{cosec} a$ and $\cot a$ are all equal? Explain your answer.

7 Solve the following equations for $0° \leqslant x \leqslant 360°$.

(i) $\cos x = \sec x$ **(ii)** $\operatorname{cosec} x = \sec x$

(iii) $2 \sin x = 3 \cot x$ **(iv)** $\operatorname{cosec}^2 x + \cot^2 x = 2$

(v) $3 \sec^2 x - 10 \tan x = 0$ **(vi)** $1 + \cot^2 x = 2 \tan^2 x$

The photographs at the start of this chapter show just two of the countless examples of waves and oscillations that are part of the world around us.

Because such phenomena are modelled by trigonometrical (and especially sine and cosine) functions, trigonometry has an importance in mathematics far beyond its origins in right-angled triangles.

Compound-angle formulae

ACTIVITY 8.1 Find an acute angle θ so that $\sin(\theta + 60°) = \cos(\theta - 60°)$.

Hint: Try drawing graphs and searching for a numerical solution.

You should be able to find the solution using either of these methods, but replacing 60° by, for example, 35° would make both of these methods rather tedious. In this chapter you will meet some formulae which help you to solve such equations more efficiently.

It is tempting to think that $\sin(\theta + 60°)$ should equal $\sin\theta + \sin 60°$, but this is not so, as you can see by substituting a numerical value of θ. For example, putting $\theta = 30°$ gives $\sin(\theta + 60°) = 1$, but $\sin\theta + \sin 60° \approx 1.366$.

To find an expression for $\sin(\theta + 60°)$, you would use the *compound-angle formula*

$$\sin(\theta + \phi) = \sin\theta \cos\phi + \cos\theta \sin\phi.$$

This is proved below in the case when θ and ϕ are acute angles. It is, however, true for all values of the angles. It is an *identity*.

As you work through this proof make a list of all the results you are assuming.

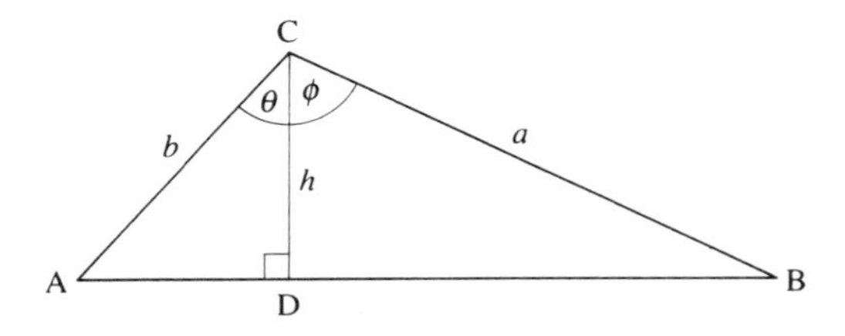

Figure 8.4

Using the trigonometrical formula for the area of a triangle in figure 8.4:

$$\text{area ABC} = \text{area ADC} + \text{area DBC}$$

$$\tfrac{1}{2}ab\sin(\theta + \phi) = \tfrac{1}{2}bh\sin\theta + \tfrac{1}{2}ah\sin\phi$$

$h = a\cos\phi$ from $\triangle$DBC

$h = b\cos\theta$ from $\triangle$ADC

$$ab\sin(\theta + \phi) = ab\sin\theta\cos\phi + ab\cos\theta\sin\phi$$

which gives

$$\sin(\theta + \phi) = \sin\theta\cos\phi + \cos\theta\sin\phi \qquad ①$$

This is the first of the compound-angle formulae (or expansions), and it can be used to prove several more. These are true for all values of θ and ϕ.

Replacing ϕ by $-\phi$ in ① gives

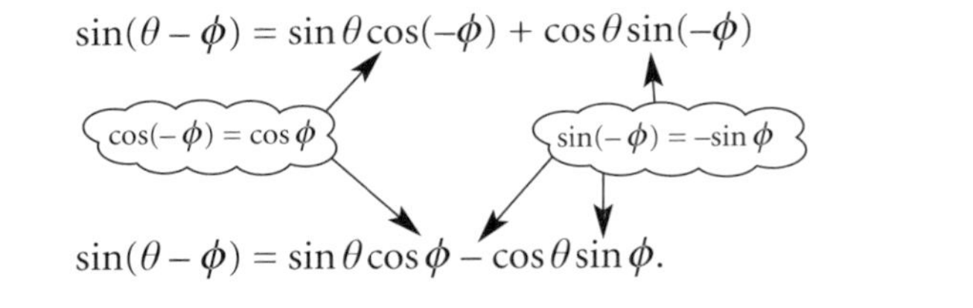

$$\sin(\theta - \phi) = \sin\theta\cos(-\phi) + \cos\theta\sin(-\phi)$$

$$\Rightarrow \quad \sin(\theta - \phi) = \sin\theta\cos\phi - \cos\theta\sin\phi. \qquad ②$$

ACTIVITY 8.2 Derive the rest of these formulae.

(i) To find an expansion for $\cos(\theta - \phi)$ replace θ by $(90° - \theta)$ in the expansion of $\sin(\theta + \phi)$.

Hint: $\sin(90° - \theta) = \cos\theta$ and $\cos(90° - \theta) = \sin\theta$

(ii) To find an expansion for $\cos(\theta + \phi)$ replace ϕ by $(-\phi)$ in the expansion of $\cos(\theta - \phi)$.

(iii) To find an expansion for $\tan(\theta + \phi)$, write $\tan(\theta + \phi) = \dfrac{\sin(\theta + \phi)}{\cos(\theta + \phi)}$.

Hint: After using the expansions of $\sin(\theta + \phi)$ and $\cos(\theta + \phi)$, divide the numerator and the denominator of the resulting fraction by $\cos\theta\cos\phi$ to give an expansion in terms of $\tan\theta$ and $\tan\phi$.

(iv) To find an expansion for $\tan(\theta - \phi)$ in terms of $\tan\theta$ and $\tan\phi$, replace ϕ by $(-\phi)$ in the expansion of $\tan(\theta + \phi)$.

p Are your results valid for all values of θ and ϕ?

Test your results with $\theta = 60°$, $\phi = 30°$.

The four results obtained in Activity 8.2, together with the two previous results, form the set of compound-angle formulae.

$$\sin(\theta + \phi) = \sin\theta\cos\phi + \cos\theta\sin\phi$$

$$\sin(\theta - \phi) = \sin\theta\cos\phi - \cos\theta\sin\phi$$

$$\cos(\theta + \phi) = \cos\theta\cos\phi - \sin\theta\sin\phi$$

$$\cos(\theta - \phi) = \cos\theta\cos\phi + \sin\theta\sin\phi$$

$$\tan(\theta + \phi) = \frac{\tan\theta + \tan\phi}{1 - \tan\theta\tan\phi} \qquad \theta, \phi \text{ and } (\theta + \phi) \neq 90°, 270°, \ldots$$

$$\tan(\theta - \phi) = \frac{\tan\theta - \tan\phi}{1 + \tan\theta\tan\phi} \qquad \theta, \phi \text{ and } (\theta - \phi) \neq 90°, 270°, \ldots$$

You are now in a position to solve the earlier problem more easily. To find an acute angle θ such that $\sin(\theta + 60°) = \cos(\theta - 60°)$, you expand each side using the compound-angle formulae.

$$\sin(\theta + 60°) = \sin\theta\cos 60° + \cos\theta\sin 60°$$

$$= \frac{1}{2}\sin\theta + \frac{\sqrt{3}}{2}\cos\theta \qquad ①$$

$$\cos(\theta - 60°) = \cos\theta\cos 60° + \sin\theta\sin 60°$$

$$= \frac{1}{2}\cos\theta + \frac{\sqrt{3}}{2}\sin\theta \qquad ②$$

From ① and ②

$$\frac{1}{2}\sin\theta + \frac{\sqrt{3}}{2}\cos\theta = \frac{1}{2}\cos\theta + \frac{\sqrt{3}}{2}\sin\theta$$

$$\sin\theta + \sqrt{3}\cos\theta = \cos\theta + \sqrt{3}\sin\theta.$$

Collect like terms:

$$\Rightarrow \quad (\sqrt{3} - 1)\cos\theta = (\sqrt{3} - 1)\sin\theta$$

$$\cos\theta = \sin\theta.$$

Divide by $\cos\theta$:

This gives an equation in one trigonometrical ratio.

$$1 = \tan\theta$$

$$\theta = 45°.$$

Since an acute angle was required, this is the only root.

When do you use the compound-angle formulae?

You have already seen compound-angle formulae used in solving a trigonometrical equation and this is quite a common application of them. However, their significance goes well beyond that since they form the basis for a number of important techniques. Those covered in this book are as follows.

- **The derivation of double-angle formulae**
  The derivation and uses of these are covered on pages 192 to 196.
- **The addition of different sine and cosine functions**
  This is covered on pages 197 to 200 and 201 to 204 of this chapter. The work on pages 197 to 200 is enrichment material. It is included here because the basic wave form is a sine curve. It has many applications, for example in applied mathematics, physics and chemistry.
- **Calculus of trigonometrical functions**
  This was introduced in Chapter 4 but is covered more rigorously later in this chapter. Proofs of the results depend on using either the compound-angle formulae or the factor formulae which are derived from them.

You will see from this that the compound-angle formulae are important in the development of the subject. Some people learn them by heart, others think it is safer to look them up when they are needed. Whichever policy you adopt, you should understand these formulae and recognise their form. Without that you will be unable to do the next example, which uses one of them in reverse.

EXAMPLE 8.3

Simplify $\cos\theta\cos 3\theta - \sin\theta\sin 3\theta$.

SOLUTION

The formula which has the same pattern of cos cos – sin sin is

$$\cos(\theta + \phi) = \cos\theta\cos\phi - \sin\theta\sin\phi$$

Using this, and replacing ϕ by 3θ, gives

$$\begin{aligned}\cos\theta\cos 3\theta - \sin\theta\sin 3\theta &= \cos(\theta + 3\theta)\\ &= \cos 4\theta.\end{aligned}$$

EXERCISE 8B

1 Use the compound-angle formulae to write the following as surds.

(i) $\sin 75° = \sin(45° + 30°)$ **(ii)** $\cos 135° = \cos(90° + 45°)$
(iii) $\tan 15° = \tan(45° - 30°)$ **(iv)** $\tan 75° = \tan(45° + 30°)$

2 Expand each of the following expressions.

(i) $\sin(\theta + 45°)$ **(ii)** $\cos(\theta - 30°)$
(iii) $\sin(60° - \theta)$ **(iv)** $\cos(2\theta + 45°)$
(v) $\tan(\theta + 45°)$ **(vi)** $\tan(\theta - 45°)$

3 Simplify each of the following expressions.

(i) $\sin 2\theta \cos\theta - \cos 2\theta \sin\theta$

(ii) $\cos\phi \cos 3\phi - \sin\phi \sin 3\phi$

(iii) $\sin 120° \cos 60° + \cos 120° \sin 60°$

(iv) $\cos\theta \cos\theta - \sin\theta \sin\theta$

4 Solve the following equations for values of θ in the range $0° \leqslant \theta \leqslant 180°$.

(i) $\cos(60° + \theta) = \sin\theta$

(ii) $\sin(45° - \theta) = \cos\theta$

(iii) $\tan(45° + \theta) = \tan(45° - \theta)$

(iv) $2\sin\theta = 3\cos(\theta - 60°)$

(v) $\sin\theta = \cos(\theta + 120°)$

5 Solve the following equations for values of θ in the range $0 \leqslant \theta \leqslant \pi$.
(When the range is given in radians, the solutions should be in radians, using multiples of π where appropriate.)

(i) $\sin\left(\theta + \frac{\pi}{4}\right) = \cos\theta$

(ii) $2\cos\left(\theta - \frac{\pi}{3}\right) = \cos\left(\theta + \frac{\pi}{2}\right)$

6 Calculators are not to be used in this question.
The diagram shows three points L(–2, 1), M(0, 2) and N(3, –2) joined to form a triangle. The angles α and β and the point P are shown in the diagram.

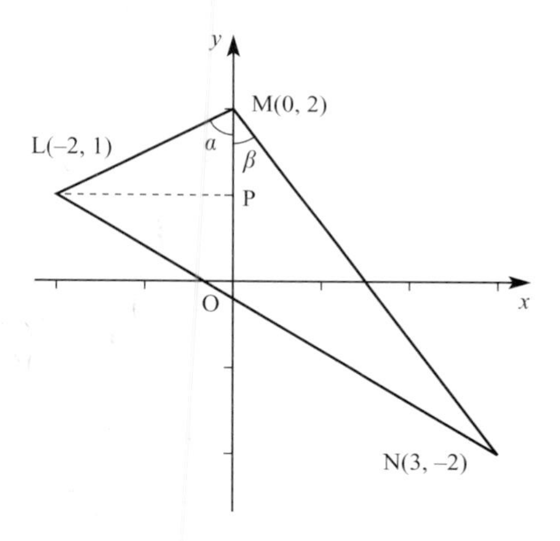

(i) Show that $\sin\alpha = \dfrac{2}{\sqrt{5}}$ and write down the value of $\cos\alpha$.

(ii) Find the values of $\sin\beta$ and $\cos\beta$.

(iii) Show that $\sin\angle\text{LMN} = \dfrac{11}{5\sqrt{5}}$.

(iv) Show that $\tan\angle\text{LNM} = \dfrac{11}{27}$.

[MEI]

7 **(i)** Find $\int x \cos kx \, dx$, where k is a non-zero constant.

(ii) Show that

$$\cos(A - B) - \cos(A + B) = 2 \sin A \sin B.$$

Hence express $2 \sin 5x \sin 3x$ as the difference of two cosines.

(iii) Use the results in parts **(i)** and **(ii)** to show that

$$\int_0^{\frac{\pi}{4}} x \sin 5x \sin 3x \, dx = \frac{\pi - 2}{16}.$$

[MEI]

8 **(i)** Use the formulae for $\cos(\theta + \phi)$ and $\cos(\theta - \phi)$ to prove that

$$\cos(\theta - \phi) - \cos(\theta + \phi) = 2 \sin \theta \sin \phi. \quad (*)$$

Prove also that $\sin(\pi - \theta) = \sin \theta$.

In triangle PQR, angle P $= \frac{1}{6}\pi$ radians, angle Q $= \alpha$ radians, and QR $= 1$ unit. The point S is at the foot of the perpendicular from R to PQ, as shown in the diagram.

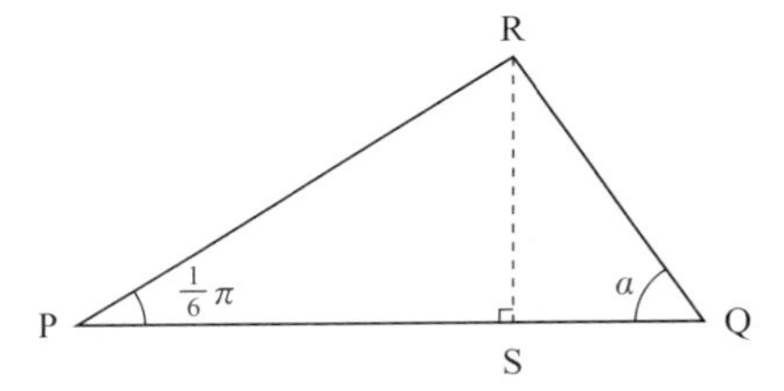

(ii) Show that PQ $= 2 \sin\left(\alpha + \frac{1}{6}\pi\right)$.
By finding RS in terms of α, deduce that the area A of the triangle is given by

$$A = \sin\left(\alpha + \tfrac{1}{6}\pi\right) \sin \alpha.$$

Find the value of α for which the area A is a maximum. [You may find the result (*) helpful.]

(iii) Expand $\sin\left(\alpha + \frac{1}{6}\pi\right)$, and hence show that, for small values of α, $A \approx p\alpha + q\alpha^2$, where p and q are contants to be determined.

$\left[\text{For small } \theta, \sin \theta \approx \theta \text{ and } \cos \theta \approx 1.\right]$

Find the value of this expression when $\alpha = 0.1$, and find also the corresponding value of A given by the expression in part **(ii)**. [MEI]

Double-angle formulae

p As you work through these proofs, think how you can check the results.

Is a check the same as a proof?

Substituting $\phi = \theta$ in the relevant compound formulae leads immediately to expressions for $\sin 2\theta$, $\cos 2\theta$ and $\tan 2\theta$, as follows.

(i) $\sin(\theta + \phi) = \sin\theta\cos\phi + \cos\theta\sin\phi$

When $\phi = \theta$, this becomes

$$\sin(\theta + \theta) = \sin\theta\cos\theta + \cos\theta\sin\theta$$

giving $\sin 2\theta = 2\sin\theta\cos\theta$.

(ii) $\cos(\theta + \phi) = \cos\theta\cos\phi - \sin\theta\sin\phi$

When $\phi = \theta$, this becomes

$$\cos(\theta + \theta) = \cos\theta\cos\theta - \sin\theta\sin\theta$$

giving $\cos 2\theta = \cos^2\theta - \sin^2\theta$.

Using the Pythagorean identity $\cos^2\theta + \sin^2\theta = 1$, two other forms for $\cos 2\theta$ can be obtained.

$$\cos 2\theta = (1 - \sin^2\theta) - \sin^2\theta \quad \Rightarrow \quad \cos 2\theta = 1 - 2\sin^2\theta$$

$$\cos 2\theta = \cos^2\theta - (1 - \cos^2\theta) \quad \Rightarrow \quad \cos 2\theta = 2\cos^2\theta - 1$$

These alternative forms are often more useful since they contain only one trigonometrical function.

(iii) $\tan(\theta + \phi) = \dfrac{\tan\theta + \tan\phi}{1 - \tan\theta\tan\phi} \qquad (\theta + \phi) \neq 90°, 270°, \ldots$

When $\phi = \theta$ this becomes

$$\tan(\theta + \theta) = \frac{\tan\theta + \tan\theta}{1 - \tan\theta\tan\theta}$$

giving $\tan 2\theta = \dfrac{2\tan\theta}{1 - \tan^2\theta} \qquad \theta \neq 45°, 135°, \ldots$.

Uses of the double-angle formulae

In modelling situations

You will meet situations, such as that below, where using a double-angle formula not only allows you to write an expression more neatly but also thereby allows you to interpret its meaning more clearly.

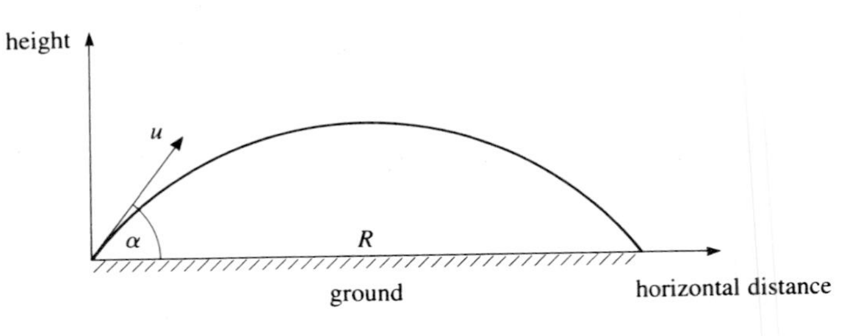

Figure 8.5

When an object is projected, such as a golf ball being hit as in figure 8.5, with speed u at an angle α to the horizontal over level ground, the horizontal distance it travels before striking the ground, called its range, R, is given by the product of the horizontal component of the velocity $u\cos\alpha$ and its time of flight $\frac{(2u\sin\alpha)}{g}$.

$$R = \frac{2u^2\sin\alpha\cos\alpha}{g}$$

Using the double-angle formula, $\sin 2\alpha = 2\sin\alpha\cos\alpha$ allows this to be written as

$$R = \frac{u^2\sin 2\alpha}{g}.$$

Since the maximum value of $\sin 2\alpha$ is 1, it follows that the greatest value of the range R is $\frac{u^2}{g}$ and that this occurs when $2\alpha = 90°$ and so $\alpha = 45°$. Thus an angle of projection of 45° will give the maximum range of the projectile over level ground. (This assumes that air resistance may be ignored.)

In this example, the double-angle formula enabled the expression for R to be written tidily. However, it did more than that because it made it possible to find the maximum value of R by inspection and without using calculus.

In calculus

The double-angle formulae allow a number of functions to be integrated and you will meet some of these later in this chapter.

The formulae for $\cos 2\theta$ are particularly useful in this respect since

$$\cos 2\theta = 1 - 2\sin^2\theta \quad \Rightarrow \quad \sin^2\theta = \tfrac{1}{2}(1 - \cos 2\theta)$$

and

$$\cos 2\theta = 2\cos^2\theta - 1 \quad \Rightarrow \quad \cos^2\theta = \tfrac{1}{2}(1 + \cos 2\theta)$$

and these identities allow you to integrate $\sin^2\theta$ and $\cos^2\theta$.

In solving equations

You will sometimes need to solve equations involving both single and double angles as shown by the next two examples.

EXAMPLE 8.4

Solve the equation $\sin 2\theta = \sin\theta$ for $0° \leqslant \theta \leqslant 360°$.

SOLUTION

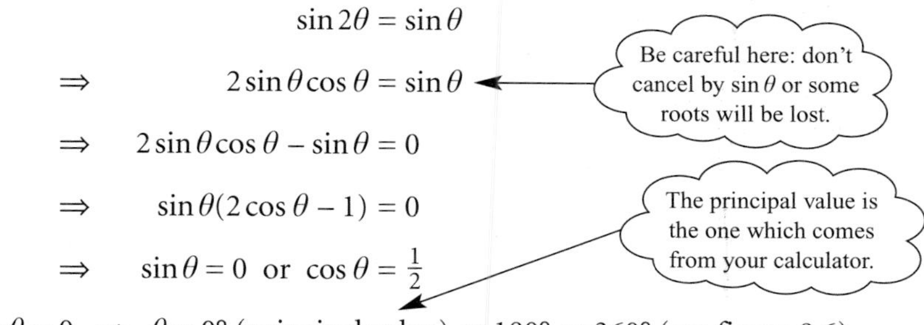

$$\sin 2\theta = \sin\theta$$

$$\Rightarrow \quad 2\sin\theta\cos\theta = \sin\theta$$

$$\Rightarrow \quad 2\sin\theta\cos\theta - \sin\theta = 0$$

$$\Rightarrow \quad \sin\theta(2\cos\theta - 1) = 0$$

$$\Rightarrow \quad \sin\theta = 0 \text{ or } \cos\theta = \tfrac{1}{2}$$

$\sin\theta = 0 \Rightarrow \theta = 0°$ (principal value) or $180°$ or $360°$ (see figure 8.6).

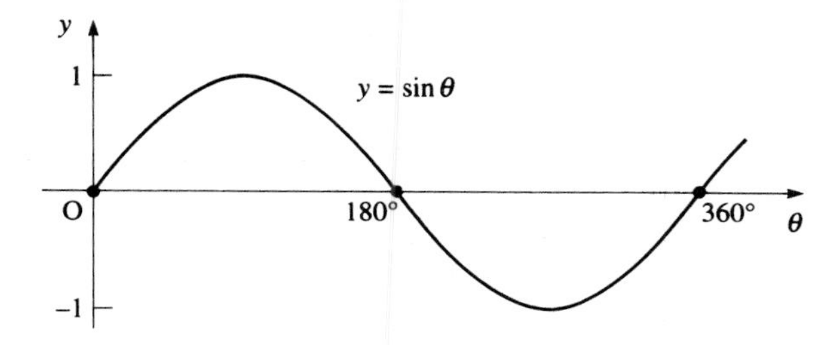

Figure 8.6

$\cos\theta = \frac{1}{2} \Rightarrow \theta = 60°$ (principal value) or $300°$ (see figure 8.7).

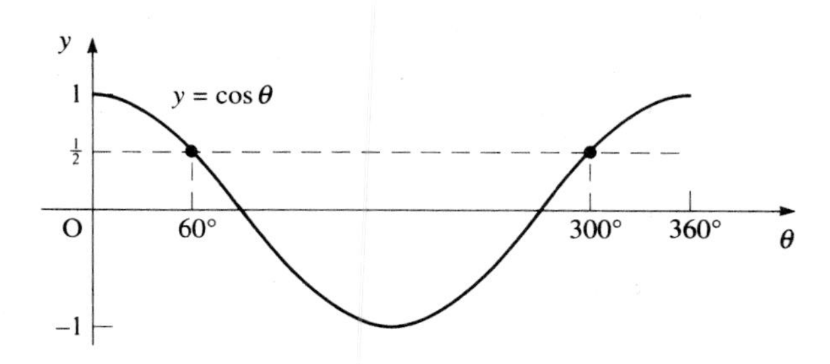

Figure 8.7

The full set of roots for $0° \leqslant \theta \leqslant 360°$ is $\theta = 0°, 60°, 180°, 300°, 360°$.

When an equation contains $\cos 2\theta$, you will save time if you take care to choose the most suitable expansion.

EXAMPLE 8.5

Solve $2 + \cos 2\theta = \sin\theta$ for $0 \leqslant \theta \leqslant 2\pi$. (Notice that the request for $0 \leqslant \theta \leqslant 2\pi$, i.e. in radians, is an invitation to give the answer in radians.)

SOLUTION

Using $\cos 2\theta = 1 - 2\sin^2\theta$ gives

This is the most suitable expansion since the right-hand side contains $\sin\theta$.

$$2 + (1 - 2\sin^2\theta) = \sin\theta$$

$$\Rightarrow \quad 2\sin^2\theta + \sin\theta - 3 = 0$$

$$\Rightarrow \quad (2\sin\theta + 3)(\sin\theta - 1) = 0$$

$$\Rightarrow \quad \sin\theta = -\tfrac{3}{2} \text{ (not valid since } -1 \leqslant \sin\theta \leqslant 1)$$

or $\quad \sin\theta = 1.$

Figure 8.8 shows that the principal value $\theta = \dfrac{\pi}{2}$ is the only root for $0 \leqslant \theta \leqslant 2\pi$.

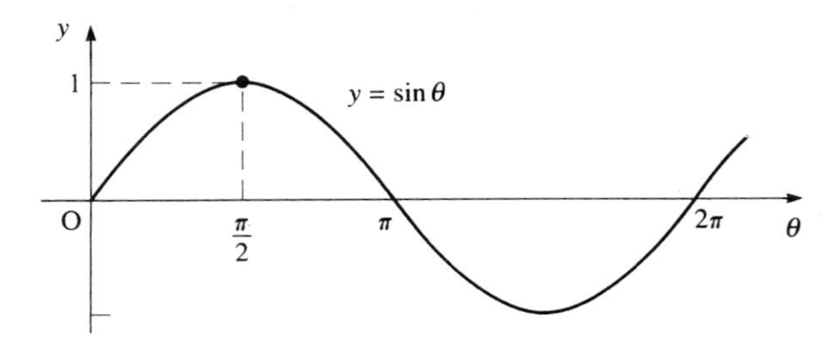

Figure 8.8

EXERCISE 8C

1 Solve the following equations for $0° \leqslant \theta \leqslant 360°$.

(i) $2\sin 2\theta = \cos\theta$ **(ii)** $\tan 2\theta = 4\tan\theta$ **(iii)** $\cos 2\theta + \sin\theta = 0$

(iv) $\tan\theta\tan 2\theta = 1$ **(v)** $2\cos 2\theta = 1 + \cos\theta$

2 Solve the following equations for $-\pi \leqslant \theta \leqslant \pi$.

(i) $\sin 2\theta = 2\sin\theta$ **(ii)** $\tan 2\theta = 2\tan\theta$ **(iii)** $\cos 2\theta - \cos\theta = 0$

(iv) $1 + \cos 2\theta = 2\sin^2\theta$ **(v)** $\sin 4\theta = \cos 2\theta$

(**Hint:** Write the expression in part **(v)** as an equation in 2θ.)

3 By first writing $\sin 3\theta$ as $\sin(2\theta + \theta)$, express $\sin 3\theta$ in terms of $\sin\theta$. Hence solve the equation $\sin 3\theta = \sin\theta$ for $0 \leqslant \theta \leqslant 2\pi$.

4 Solve $\cos 3\theta = 1 - 3\cos\theta$ for $0° \leqslant \theta \leqslant 360°$.

5 Simplify $\dfrac{1 + \cos 2\theta}{\sin 2\theta}$.

6 Express $\tan 3\theta$ in terms of $\tan\theta$.

7 Show that $\dfrac{1 - \tan^2\theta}{1 + \tan^2\theta} = \cos 2\theta$.

8 (i) Show that $\tan\left(\frac{\pi}{4}+\theta\right)\tan\left(\frac{\pi}{4}-\theta\right)=1$.

(ii) Given that $\tan 26.6° = 0.5$, solve $\tan\theta = 2$ without using your calculator. Give θ to 1 decimal place, where $0° < \theta < 90°$.

9 (i) Sketch on the same axes the graphs of

$$y = \cos 2x \quad \text{and} \quad y = 3\sin x - 1 \quad \text{for} \quad 0 \leqslant x \leqslant 2\pi.$$

(ii) Show that these curves meet at points whose x co-ordinates are solutions of the equation $2\sin^2 x + 3\sin x - 2 = 0$.

(iii) Solve this equation to find the values of x in terms of π for $0 \leqslant x \leqslant 2\pi$.

[MEI]

e The factor formulae

In algebra, the term 'factorising' means writing expressions as products. For example, 'factorise $x^2 - 3x + 2$' means 'write $x^2 - 3x + 2$ as $(x-1)(x-2)$'. The same idea of factorising applies in trigonometry: you write sums or differences of trigonometrical functions as products.

---

p A student writes '$\sin\alpha + \sin\beta = \sin(\alpha + \beta)$'.

There are two ways to prove this is wrong. What are they?

The factor formulae are derived from the compound-angle formulae.

Start with the compound-angle formulae for $\sin(\theta + \phi)$ and $\sin(\theta - \phi)$.

$$\sin(\theta + \phi) = \sin\theta\cos\phi + \cos\theta\sin\phi \quad ①$$

$$\sin(\theta - \phi) = \sin\theta\cos\phi - \cos\theta\sin\phi \quad ②$$

Adding ① and ② gives

$$\sin(\theta + \phi) + \sin(\theta - \phi) = 2\sin\theta\cos\phi. \quad ③$$

At this point, it is helpful to change variables by writing

$$\theta + \phi = \alpha \quad \text{and} \quad \theta - \phi = \beta$$

so that $\theta = \frac{1}{2}(\alpha + \beta)$ and $\phi = \frac{1}{2}(\alpha - \beta)$.

Substituting for θ and ϕ in ③ gives

$$\sin\alpha + \sin\beta = 2\sin\left(\frac{\alpha+\beta}{2}\right)\cos\left(\frac{\alpha-\beta}{2}\right).$$

The left-hand side is a sum and the right-hand side is a product, so the expression has been factorised.

Similarly, subtracting ② from ① gives

$$\sin\alpha - \sin\beta = 2\cos\left(\frac{\alpha+\beta}{2}\right)\sin\left(\frac{\alpha-\beta}{2}\right).$$

ACTIVITY 8.3

Write down the expressions for $\cos(\theta + \phi)$ and $\cos(\theta - \phi)$ and use these to obtain factor formulae for $\cos\alpha + \cos\beta$ and for $\cos\alpha - \cos\beta$.

e When do you use the factor formulae?

e *Addition of waveforms*

The factor formulae allow you to add together sine and cosine functions. This operation is equivalent to the physical situation of combining waves of the same size (amplitude).

INVESTIGATION

e *Two musicians playing in tune*

The sound of two musicians playing in tune with the same loudness may be modelled as two waves given by $x_1 = a\sin\omega t$ and $x_2 = a\sin(\omega t + \varepsilon)$.

The constant ω is related to the frequency of these waves and so to the pitch of the musical notes. (The frequency is given by $\frac{\omega}{2\pi}$). The two waves are not in phase and this is represented by the constant ε in the expression for x_2 (see figure 8.9).

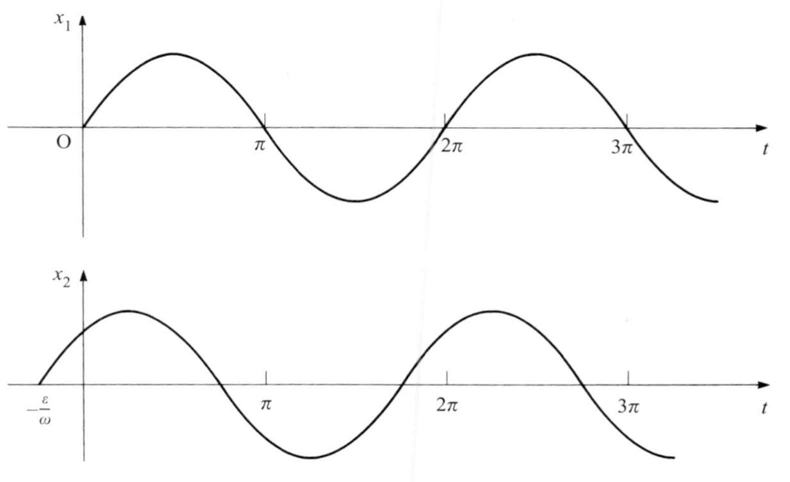

Figure 8.9

Show that $x_1 + x_2$ is a single wave. That is, the musicians sound as one but louder.

ⓔ *Two musicians playing slightly out of tune*

In this case, the waves are given by $x_1 = a\sin\omega t$ and $x_2 = a\sin(\omega + \delta)t$, where δ is very small compared to ω.
Find the expression for $x_1 + x_2$.

Explain how this makes the combined note of the musicians vary in loudness, a phenomenon known as *beats*. How do beats help a piano tuner?

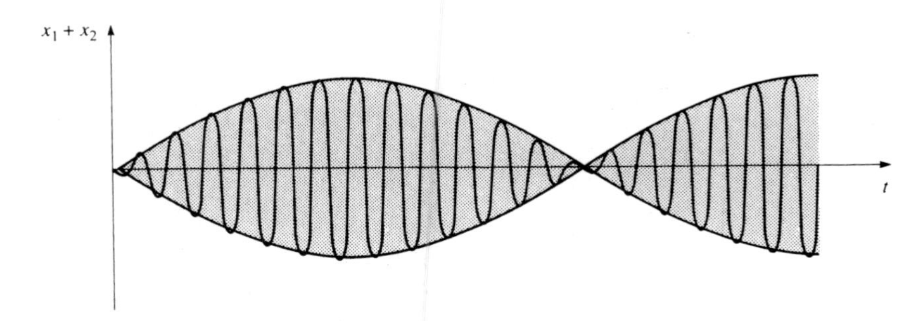

Figure 8.10

ⓔ *Manipulation*

The factor formulae are often useful in tidying up expressions and in solving equations, as in the next example.

EXAMPLE 8.6

Solve $\sin 3\theta + \sin\theta = 0$ for $0° \leqslant \theta \leqslant 360°$.

SOLUTION

Using

$$\sin\alpha + \sin\beta = 2\sin\left(\frac{\alpha+\beta}{2}\right)\cos\left(\frac{\alpha-\beta}{2}\right)$$

and putting $\alpha = 3\theta$ and $\beta = \theta$ gives

$$\sin 3\theta + \sin\theta = 2\sin 2\theta\cos\theta$$

so the equation becomes

$$2\sin 2\theta\cos\theta = 0$$

$$\Rightarrow \quad \cos\theta = 0 \quad \text{or} \quad \sin 2\theta = 0.$$

From the graphs for $y = \cos\theta$ and $y = \sin\theta$

$$\cos\theta = 0 \quad \text{gives} \quad \theta = 90° \text{ or } 270°$$

$$\sin 2\theta = 0 \quad \text{gives} \quad 2\theta = 0°, 180°, 360°, 540° \text{ or } 720°$$

$$\text{so} \quad \theta = 0°, 90°, 180°, 270° \text{ or } 360°.$$

You should only list each root once in the final answer.

The complete set of roots in the range given is $\theta = 0°, 90°, 180°, 270°, 360°$.

EXERCISE 8D

The questions in this exercise relate to enrichment material.

1 Factorise the following expressions.

(i) $\sin 4\theta - \sin 2\theta$

(ii) $\cos 5\theta + \cos\theta$

(iii) $\cos 7\theta - \cos 3\theta$

(iv) $\cos(\theta + 60°) + \cos(\theta - 60°)$

(v) $\sin(3\theta + 45°) + \sin(3\theta - 45°)$

2 Factorise $\cos 4\theta + \cos 2\theta$. Hence, for $0° < \theta < 180°$, solve

$$\cos 4\theta + \cos 2\theta = \cos\theta.$$

3 Simplify $\dfrac{\sin 5\theta + \sin 3\theta}{\sin 5\theta - \sin 3\theta}$.

4 Solve the equation $\sin 3\theta - \sin\theta = 0$ for $0 \leqslant \theta \leqslant 2\pi$.

5 Factorise $\sin(\theta + 73°) - \sin(\theta + 13°)$ and use your result to sketch the graph of $y = \sin(\theta + 73°) - \sin(\theta + 13°)$.

6 Prove that $\sin^2 A - \sin^2 B = \sin(A - B)\sin(A + B)$.

7 **(i)** Use a suitable factor formula to show that

$$\sin 3\theta + \sin\theta = 4\sin\theta\cos^2\theta.$$

(ii) Hence show that $\sin 3\theta = 3\sin\theta - 4\sin^3\theta$.

The forms $r\cos(\theta \pm \alpha)$, $r\sin(\theta \pm \alpha)$

Another modification of the compound-angle formulae allows you to simplify expressions such as $4\sin\theta + 3\cos\theta$ and hence solve equations of the form

$$a\sin\theta + b\cos\theta = c.$$

To find a single expression for $4\sin\theta + 3\cos\theta$, you match it to the expression

$$r\sin(\theta + \alpha) = r(\sin\theta\cos\alpha + \cos\theta\sin\alpha).$$

This is because the expansion of $r\sin(\theta + \alpha)$ has $\sin\theta$ in the first term, $\cos\theta$ in the second term and a plus sign in between them. It is then possible to choose appropriate values of r and α.

$$4\sin\theta + 3\cos\theta \equiv r(\sin\theta\cos\alpha + \cos\theta\sin\alpha)$$

Coefficients of $\sin\theta$: $\quad 4 = r\cos\alpha$

Coefficients of $\cos\theta$: $\quad 3 = r\sin\alpha.$

Looking at the right-angled triangle in figure 8.11 gives the values for r and α.

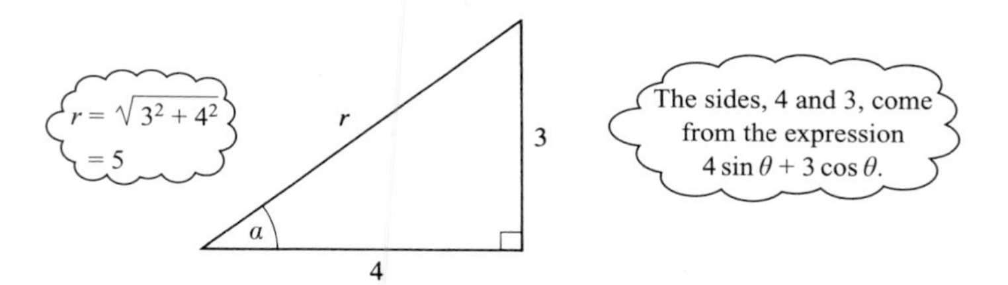

Figure 8.11

In this triangle, the hypotenuse is $\sqrt{4^2 + 3^2} = 5$, which corresponds to r in the expression above.

The angle α is given by

$$\sin\alpha = \tfrac{3}{5} \quad \text{and} \quad \cos\alpha = \tfrac{4}{5} \quad \Rightarrow \quad \alpha = 36.9°.$$

So the expression becomes

$$4\sin\theta + 3\cos\theta = 5\sin(\theta + 36.9°).$$

The steps involved in this procedure can be generalised to write

$$a\sin\theta + b\cos\theta = r\sin(\theta + \alpha)$$

where

$$r = \sqrt{a^2 + b^2} \qquad \sin\alpha = \frac{b}{\sqrt{a^2 + b^2}} \qquad \cos\alpha = \frac{a}{\sqrt{a^2 + b^2}}.$$

The same expression may also be written as a cosine function. In this case, rewrite $4\sin\theta + 3\cos\theta$ as $3\cos\theta + 4\sin\theta$ and notice that:

(i) The expansion of $\cos(\theta - \beta)$ starts with $\cos\theta$ ... just like the expression $3\cos\theta + 4\sin\theta$.

(ii) The expansion of $\cos(\theta - \beta)$ has + in the middle, just like the expression $3\cos\theta + 4\sin\theta$.

The expansion of $r\cos(\theta - \beta)$ is given by

$$r\cos(\theta - \beta) = r(\cos\theta\cos\beta + \sin\theta\sin\beta).$$

To compare this with $3\cos\theta + 4\sin\theta$, look at the triangle in figure 8.12 in which

$$r = \sqrt{3^2 + 4^2} = 5 \qquad \cos\beta = \tfrac{3}{5} \qquad \sin\beta = \tfrac{4}{5} \qquad \Rightarrow \qquad \beta = 53.1°.$$

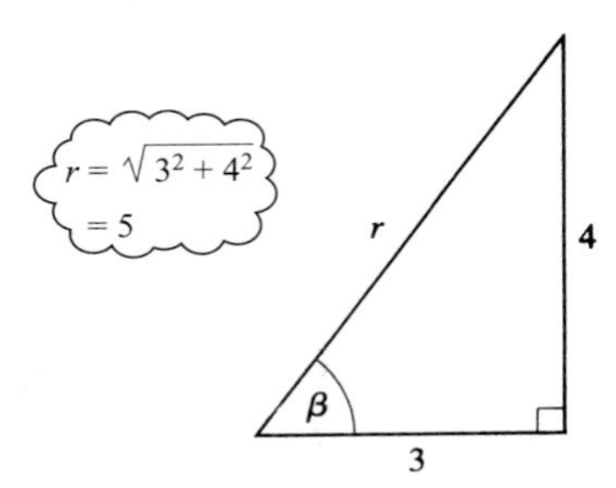

Figure 8.12

This means that you can write $3\cos\theta + 4\sin\theta$ in the form

$$r\cos(\theta - \beta) = 5\cos(\theta - 53.1°).$$

The procedure used here can be generalised to give the result

$$a\cos\theta + b\sin\theta = r\cos(\theta - a)$$

where $\quad r = \sqrt{a^2 + b^2} \qquad \cos a = \frac{a}{r} \qquad \sin a = \frac{b}{r}.$

Note

The value of r will always be positive, but $\cos\alpha$ and $\sin\alpha$ may be positive or negative, depending on the values of a and b. In all cases, it is possible to find an angle α for which $-180° < \alpha < 180°$.

You can derive alternative expressions of this type based on other compound-angle formulae if you wish a to be an acute angle, as is done in the next example.

EXAMPLE 8.7

(i) Express $\sqrt{3}\sin\theta - \cos\theta$ in the form $r\sin(\theta - \alpha)$, where $r > 0$ and $0 < \alpha < \frac{\pi}{2}$.

(ii) State the maximum and minimum values of $\sqrt{3}\sin\theta - \cos\theta$.

(iii) Sketch the graph of $y = \sqrt{3}\sin\theta - \cos\theta$ for $0 \leqslant \theta \leqslant 2\pi$.

(iv) Solve the equation $\sqrt{3}\sin\theta - \cos\theta = 1$ for $0 \leqslant \theta \leqslant 2\pi$.

SOLUTION

(i) $r\sin(\theta - \alpha) = r(\sin\theta\cos\alpha - \cos\theta\sin\alpha)$

$$= (r\cos\alpha)\sin\theta - (r\sin\alpha)\cos\theta.$$

Comparing this with $\sqrt{3}\sin\theta - \cos\theta$, the two expressions are identical if

$$r\cos\alpha = \sqrt{3} \qquad \text{and} \qquad r\sin\alpha = 1.$$

From the triangle in figure 8.13

$$r = \sqrt{1+3} = 2 \quad \text{and} \quad \tan\alpha = \frac{1}{\sqrt{3}} \quad \Rightarrow \quad \alpha = \frac{\pi}{6}$$

so $$\sqrt{3}\sin\theta - \cos\theta = 2\sin\left(\theta - \frac{\pi}{6}\right).$$

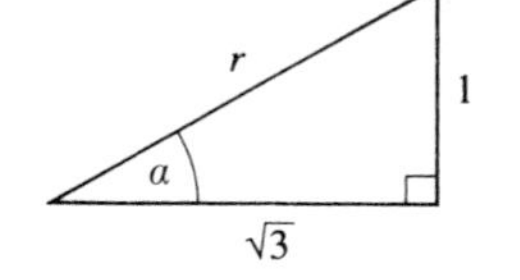

Figure 8.13

(ii) The sine function oscillates between 1 and –1, so $2\sin\left(\theta - \frac{\pi}{6}\right)$ oscillates between 2 and –2.

Maximum value = 2

Minimum value = –2.

(iii) The graph of $y = 2\sin\left(\theta - \frac{\pi}{6}\right)$ in figure 8.14 is obtained from the graph of $y = \sin\theta$ by a translation $\begin{pmatrix} \frac{\pi}{6} \\ 0 \end{pmatrix}$ and a stretch of factor 2 parallel to the y axis.

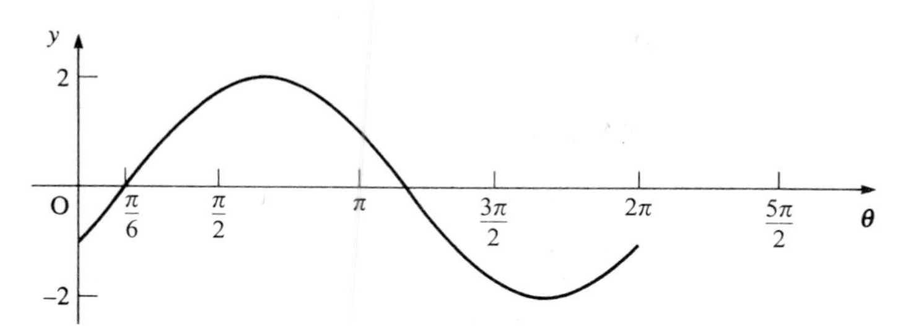

Figure 8.14

(iv) The equation $\sqrt{3}\sin\theta - \cos\theta = 1$ is equivalent to

$$2\sin\left(\theta - \frac{\pi}{6}\right) = 1$$

$$\Rightarrow \quad \sin\left(\theta - \frac{\pi}{6}\right) = \frac{1}{2}.$$

Let $x = \left(\theta - \frac{\pi}{6}\right)$ and solve $\sin x = \frac{1}{2}$.

Solving $\sin x = \frac{1}{2}$ gives $x = \frac{\pi}{6}$ (principal value)

or $\quad x = \pi - \frac{\pi}{6} = \frac{5\pi}{6}$ (from the graph in figure 8.15)

giving $\quad \theta = \frac{\pi}{6} + \frac{\pi}{6} = \frac{\pi}{3} \quad$ or $\quad \theta = \frac{5\pi}{6} + \frac{\pi}{6} = \pi.$

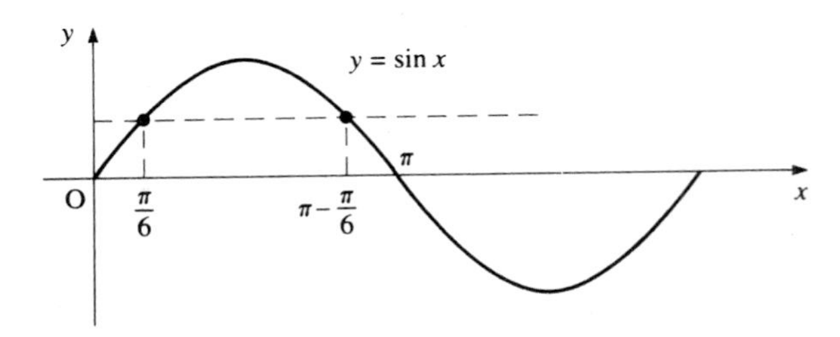

Figure 8.15

The roots in $0 \leqslant \theta \leqslant 2\pi$ are $\theta = \frac{\pi}{3}$ and π.

Always check (for example by reference to a sketch graph) that the number of roots you have found is consistent with the number you are expecting. When solving equations of the form $\sin(\theta - \alpha) = c$ by considering $\sin x = c$, it is sometimes necessary to go outside the range specified for θ since, for example, $0 \leqslant \theta \leqslant 2\pi$ is the same as $-\alpha \leqslant x \leqslant 2\pi - \alpha$.

Using these forms

There are many situations, as on page 201, which produce expressions which can be tidied up using these forms. They are also particularly useful for solving equations involving both the sine and cosine of the same angle.

The fact that $a\cos\theta + b\sin\theta$ can be written as $r\cos(\theta - \alpha)$ is an illustration of the fact that any two waves of the same frequency, whatever their amplitudes, can be added together to give a single combined wave, also of the same frequency.

EXERCISE 8E

1 Express each of the following in the form $r\cos(\theta - \alpha)$, where $r > 0$ and $0° < \alpha < 90°$.

(i) $\cos\theta + \sin\theta$ **(ii)** $3\cos\theta + 4\sin\theta$

(iii) $\cos\theta + \sqrt{3}\sin\theta$ **(iv)** $\sqrt{5}\cos\theta + 2\sin\theta$

2 Express each of the following in the form $r\cos(\theta + \alpha)$, where $r > 0$ and $0 < \alpha < \frac{\pi}{2}$.

(i) $\cos\theta - \sin\theta$ **(ii)** $\sqrt{3}\cos\theta - \sin\theta$

3 Express each of the following in the form $r\sin(\theta + \alpha)$, where $r > 0$ and $0° < \alpha < 90°$.

(i) $\sin\theta + 2\cos\theta$ **(ii)** $3\sin\theta + 4\cos\theta$

4 Express each of the following in the form $r\sin(\theta - \alpha)$, where $r > 0$ and $0 < \alpha < \frac{\pi}{2}$.

(i) $\sin\theta - \cos\theta$ **(ii)** $\sqrt{3}\sin\theta - \cos\theta$

5 Express each of the following in the form $r\cos(\theta - \alpha)$, where $r > 0$ and $-180° < \alpha < 180°$.

(i) $\cos\theta - \sqrt{3}\sin\theta$ **(ii)** $2\sqrt{2}\cos\theta - 2\sqrt{2}\sin\theta$

(iii) $\sin\theta + \sqrt{3}\cos\theta$ **(iv)** $5\sin\theta + 12\cos\theta$

(v) $\sin\theta - \sqrt{3}\cos\theta$ **(vi)** $\sqrt{2}\sin\theta - \sqrt{2}\cos\theta$

6 **(i)** Express $5\cos\theta - 12\sin\theta$ in the form $r\cos(\theta + \alpha)$, where $r > 0$ and $0° < \alpha < 90°$.

(ii) State the maximum and minimum values of $5\cos\theta - 12\sin\theta$.

(iii) Sketch the graph of $y = 5\cos\theta - 12\sin\theta$ for $0° \leqslant \theta \leqslant 360°$.

(iv) Solve the equation $5\cos\theta - 12\sin\theta = 4$ for $0° \leqslant \theta \leqslant 360°$.

7 **(i)** Express $3\sin\theta - \sqrt{3}\cos\theta$ in the form $r\sin(\theta - \alpha)$, where $r > 0$ and $0 < \alpha < \frac{\pi}{2}$.

(ii) State the maximum and minimum values of $3\sin\theta - \sqrt{3}\cos\theta$ and the smallest positive values of θ for which they occur.

(iii) Sketch the graph of $y = 3\sin\theta - \sqrt{3}\cos\theta$ for $0 \leqslant \theta \leqslant 2\pi$.

(iv) Solve the equation $3\sin\theta - \sqrt{3}\cos\theta = \sqrt{3}$ for $0 \leqslant \theta \leqslant 2\pi$.

8 **(i)** Express $2\sin 2\theta + 3\cos 2\theta$ in the form $r\sin(2\theta + \alpha)$, where $r > 0$ and $0° < \alpha < 90°$.

(ii) State the maximum and minimum values of $2\sin 2\theta + 3\cos 2\theta$ and the smallest positive values of θ for which they occur.

(iii) Sketch the graph of $y = 2\sin 2\theta + 3\cos 2\theta$ for $0° \leqslant \theta \leqslant 360°$.

(iv) Solve the equation $2\sin 2\theta + 3\cos 2\theta = 1$ for $0° \leqslant \theta \leqslant 360°$.

9 **(i)** Express $\cos\theta + \sqrt{2}\sin\theta$ in the form $r\cos(\theta - \alpha)$, where $r > 0$ and $0° < \alpha < 90°$.

(ii) State the maximum and minimum values of $\cos\theta + \sqrt{2}\sin\theta$ and the smallest positive values of θ for which they occur.

(iii) Sketch the graph of $y = \cos\theta + \sqrt{2}\sin\theta$ for $0° \leqslant \theta \leqslant 360°$.

(iv) State the maximum and minimum values of

$$\frac{1}{3 + \cos\theta + \sqrt{2}\sin\theta}$$

and the smallest positive values of θ for which they occur.

10 The diagram shows a table jammed in a corridor. The table is 120 cm long and 80 cm wide, and the width of the corridor is 130 cm.

(i) Show that $12\sin\theta + 8\cos\theta = 13$.

(ii) Hence find the angle θ. (There are two answers.)

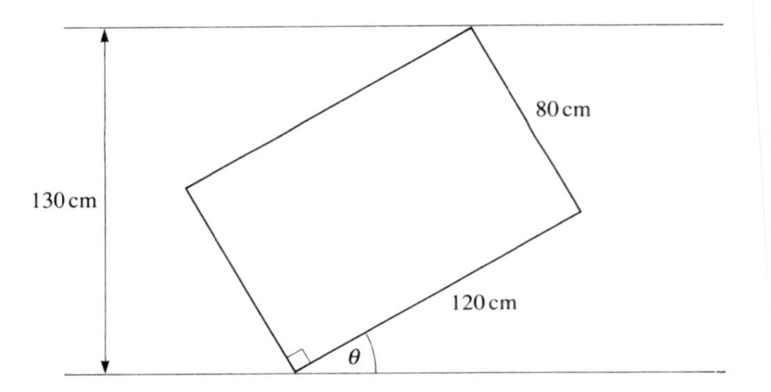

11 **(i)** Use a trigonometrical formula to expand $\cos(x + \alpha)$.

(ii) Express $y = 2\cos x - 5\sin x$ in the form $r\cos(x + \alpha)$, giving the positive value of r and the smallest positive value of α.

(iii) State the maximum and minimum values of y and the corresponding values of x for $0° \leqslant x \leqslant 360°$.

(iv) Solve the equation

$$2\cos x - 5\sin x = 3, \quad \text{for } 0° \leqslant x \leqslant 360°.$$

[MEI]

12 **(i)** Find the value of the acute angle α for which

$$5\cos x - 3\sin x = \sqrt{34}\cos(x + \alpha)$$

for all x.

Giving your answers correct to 1 decimal place,

(ii) solve the equation $5\cos x - 3\sin x = 4$ for $0° \leqslant x \leqslant 360°$

(iii) solve the equation $5\cos 2x - 3\sin 2x = 4$ for $0° \leqslant x \leqslant 360°$.

[MEI]

13 **(i)** Find the positive value of R and the acute angle α for which

$$6\cos x + 8\sin x = R\cos(x - \alpha).$$

(ii) Sketch the curve with equation

$$y = 6\cos x + 8\sin x, \quad \text{for } 0° \leqslant x \leqslant 360°.$$

Mark your axes carefully and indicate the angle α on the x axis.

(iii) Solve the equation

$$6\cos x + 8\sin x = 4, \quad \text{for } 0° \leqslant x \leqslant 360°.$$

(iv) Solve the equation

$$8\cos\theta + 6\sin\theta = 4, \quad \text{for } 0° \leqslant \theta \leqslant 360°.$$

[MEI]

14 In the diagram below, angle QPT = angle SQR = θ, angle QPR = α, PQ = a, QR = b, PR = c, angle QSR = angle QTP = 90°, SR = TU.

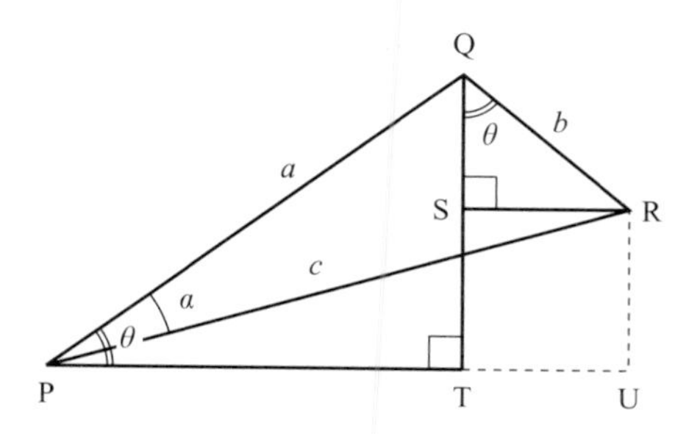

(i) Show that angle PQR = 90°, and write down the length of c in terms of a and b.

(ii) Show that PU may be written as $a\cos\theta + b\sin\theta$ and as $c\cos(\theta - \alpha)$. Write down the value of $\tan\alpha$ in terms of a and b.

(iii) In the case when $a = 4$, $b = 3$, find the acute angle α.

(iv) Solve the equation

$$4\cos\theta + 3\sin\theta = 2 \quad \text{for} \quad 0° \leqslant \theta \leqslant 360°.$$

[MEI]

15 The diagram shows the graph, for $-1 \leqslant x \leqslant 4$, of $y = \text{f}(x)$, where

$$\text{f}(x) = 2(2\cos x - \sin x)\sin x$$

and x is in radians.

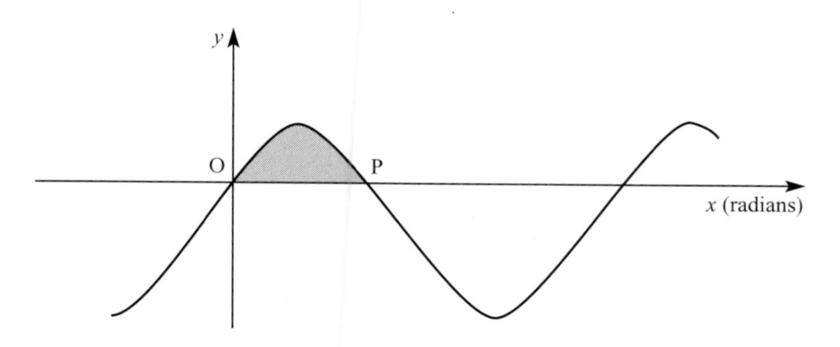

The x co-ordinate of the point P (where the graph crosses the x axis) is λ.

(i) Show that $\tan\lambda = 2$.
Find the *exact* value of $\sin\lambda$.

(ii) Show that $\text{f}(x)$ can be expressed in the form $a\sin 2x + b\cos 2x - 1$, where a and b are constants to be determined.

(iii) Show that $\text{f}(x) = R\cos(2x - \lambda) - 1$, where R is a constant to be determined.
Deduce the *exact* range of the function $\text{f}(x)$.

(iv) Show that the area of the shaded region is $2 - \lambda$.

[MEI]

16 **(i)** Express $3\cos x + \sin x$ in the form $R\cos(x - \alpha)$, giving the value of R and the smallest positive value of α.

(ii) Use your answer to part **(i)** to solve the equation

$$3\cos x + \sin x = 1, \quad \text{for } 0° \leqslant x \leqslant 360°.$$

(iii) Solve the equation $(3\cos x)^2 = (1 - \sin x)^2$ by substituting for $\cos^2 x$ in terms of $\sin x$ and solving the resulting quadratic equation in $\sin x$.

(iv) Explain why the answers to parts **(ii)** and **(iii)** are not the same.

[MEI]

17 In the diagram, OAB is a bent rod, wth OA = 1 metre, AB = 2 metres and angle OAB = 120°.
The bent rod is in a vertical plane. It is free to rotate in this plane about the point O.

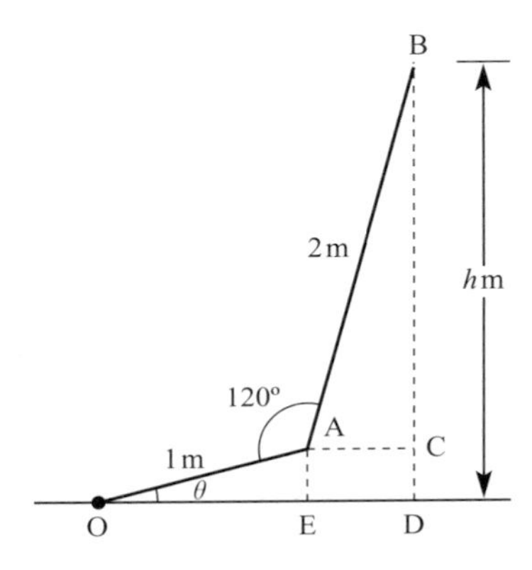

OA makes an angle θ with the horizontal, where $-90° < \theta < 90°$.
The vertical height BD of B above the level of O is h metres.
The horizontal through A meets BD at C.

(i) Show that angle BAC = $\theta + 60°$, and show that $h = \sin\theta + 2\sin(\theta + 60°)$.

(ii) Hence show that $h = 2\sin\theta + \sqrt{3}\cos\theta$, and find the angle θ for which $h = 0$.

(iii) Express $2\sin\theta + \sqrt{3}\cos\theta$ in the form $R\sin(\theta + \alpha)$.
Hence or otherwise find the maximum value of h, and find an angle θ for which $h = 2.5$.

[MEI]

INVESTIGATION

The simplest alternating current is one which varies with time t according to

$I = A\sin 2\pi ft,$

where f is the frequency and A is the maximum value. The frequency of the public AC supply is 50 hertz (cycles per second).

Investigate what happens when two alternating currents $A_1 \sin 2\pi ft$ and $A_2 \sin(2\pi ft + \alpha)$ with the same frequency f but a phase difference of α are added together.

The previous exercises have each concentrated on just one of the many trigonometrical techniques which you will need to apply confidently. The following exercise requires you to identify which technique is the correct one.

EXERCISE 8F

1 Simplify the following.

(i) $2\sin 3\theta \cos 3\theta$

(ii) $\cos^2 3\theta - \sin^2 3\theta$

(iii) $\cos^2 3\theta + \sin^2 3\theta$

(iv) $1 - 2\sin^2 \dfrac{\theta}{2}$

(v) $\sin(\theta - \alpha)\cos\alpha + \cos(\theta - \alpha)\sin\alpha$

(vi) $3\sin\theta\cos\theta$

(vii) $\dfrac{\sin 2\theta}{2\sin\theta}$

(viii) $\cos 2\theta - 2\cos^2\theta$

2 Express

(i) $(\cos x - \sin x)^2$ in terms of $\sin 2x$

(ii) $\cos^4 x - \sin^4 x$ in terms of $\cos 2x$

(iii) $2\cos^2 x - 3\sin^2 x$ in terms of $\cos 2x$.

3 Prove that

(i) $\dfrac{1 - \cos 2\theta}{1 + \cos 2\theta} \equiv \tan^2\theta$

(ii) $\operatorname{cosec} 2\theta + \cot 2\theta \equiv \cot\theta$

(iii) $\tan 4\theta \equiv \dfrac{4t(1 - t^2)}{1 - 6t^2 + t^4}$ where $t = \tan\theta$.

4 Solve the following equations.

(i)	$\sin(\theta + 40°) = 0.7$	$0° \leqslant \theta \leqslant 360°$
(ii)	$3\cos^2\theta + 5\sin\theta - 1 = 0$	$0° \leqslant \theta \leqslant 360°$
(iii)	$2\cos\left(\theta - \frac{\pi}{6}\right) = 1$	$-\pi \leqslant \theta \leqslant \pi$
(iv)	$\cos(45° - \theta) = 2\sin(30° + \theta)$	$-180° \leqslant \theta \leqslant 180°$
(v)	$\cos 2\theta + 3\sin\theta = 2$	$0 \leqslant \theta \leqslant 2\pi$
(vi)	$\cos\theta + 3\sin\theta = 2$	$0° \leqslant \theta \leqslant 360°$
(vii)	$\tan^2 x - 3\tan x - 4 = 0$	$0° \leqslant \theta \leqslant 180°$

Small-angle approximations

In this section θ is in radians, not degrees.

Figure 8.16 shows the graphs of $y = \theta$, $y = \sin\theta$ and $y = \tan\theta$ on the same axes, for $0 \leqslant \theta \leqslant \frac{\pi}{2}$. The same scale is used for both axes.

From this, it appears that in this interval, $\sin\theta < \theta < \tan\theta$.

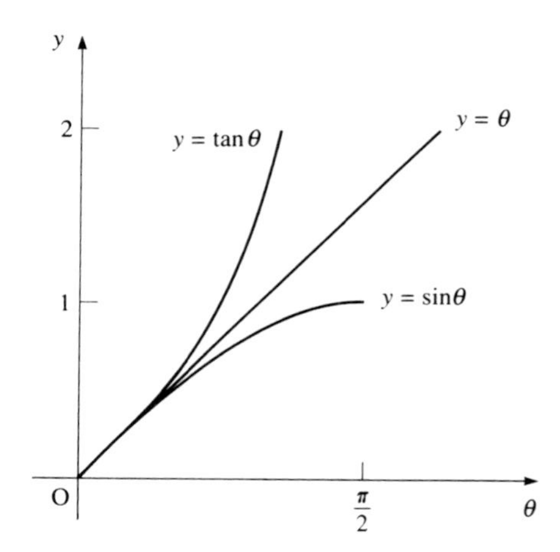

Figure 8.16

To prove this result, look at figure 8.17. PT is a tangent to the circle, radius r units and centre O.

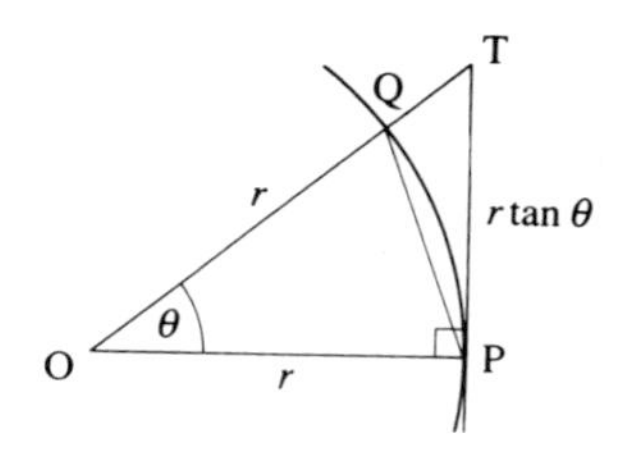

Figure 8.17

P Why does θ need to be in radians?

Considering areas:

$$\triangle\text{OPQ} < \text{sector OPQ} < \triangle\text{OPT}$$

$$\Rightarrow \quad \tfrac{1}{2}r^2\sin\theta < \tfrac{1}{2}r^2\theta < \tfrac{1}{2}\times r\times r\tan\theta$$

$$\Rightarrow \quad \sin\theta < \theta < \tan\theta.$$

θ must be in radians for this formula for the area of a sector.

$\frac{1}{2}ab\sin C$

$\frac{1}{2}$ base × height

Use a graphic calculator to draw $y = \theta$, $y = \sin\theta$ and $y = \tan\theta$ on the same axes, for $0 \leqslant \theta \leqslant 0.2$ radians. Notice how close the graphs are. This suggests that for small values of θ, $\sin\theta \approx \theta$ and $\tan\theta \approx \theta$.

The result $\sin\theta \approx \theta$ for small angles θ is a fundamental result which you will meet again later in this chapter when you differentiate trigonometrical functions. To prove this, take the relationship $\sin\theta < \theta < \tan\theta$ proved earlier for $0 < \theta < \frac{\pi}{2}$ and divide through by $\sin\theta$ to give

$$1 < \frac{\theta}{\sin\theta} < \frac{\tan\theta}{\sin\theta}$$

$$\Rightarrow \quad 1 < \frac{\theta}{\sin\theta} < \frac{1}{\cos\theta}.$$

As $\theta \to 0$, $\cos\theta \to 1$, so $\dfrac{\theta}{\sin\theta}$ is sandwiched between 1 and something approaching 1, showing that as $\theta \to 0$, $\sin\theta \approx \theta$. This can be written formally as

$$\lim_{\theta\to 0}\frac{\theta}{\sin\theta} = 1$$

Dividing each term in the relationship $\sin\theta < \theta < \tan\theta$ by $\tan\theta$ gives

$$\frac{\sin\theta}{\tan\theta} < \frac{\theta}{\tan\theta} < 1$$

$$\Rightarrow \quad \cos\theta < \frac{\theta}{\tan\theta} < 1.$$

As $\theta \to 0$, $\cos\theta \to 1$, showing that $\displaystyle\lim_{\theta\to 0}\frac{\theta}{\tan\theta} = 1$.

You know that $\cos 0 = 1$, and for small values of θ, $\cos\theta \approx 1$ but it is easy to obtain a closer approximation.

Using the double-angle formula $\cos 2\theta = 1 - 2\sin^2\theta$ and replacing 2θ by θ $\left(\text{and } \theta \text{ by } \frac{\theta}{2}\right)$ gives

$$\cos\theta = 1 - 2\sin^2\frac{\theta}{2}. \qquad ①$$

When θ is small, so is $\frac{\theta}{2}$, so $\sin\frac{\theta}{2} \approx \frac{\theta}{2}$. In ① this gives

$$\cos\theta \approx 1 - 2\left(\frac{\theta}{2}\right)^2$$

$$\Rightarrow \quad \cos\theta \approx 1 - \frac{\theta^2}{2}.$$

All of these approximations are very good for $-0.1 \leqslant \theta \leqslant 0.1$ radians.

? What do you think is meant by the expression 'very good' above?
Can you quantify it by calculating the maximum percentage error?

EXAMPLE 8.8

Given that θ is small, show that $\tan\left(\frac{\pi}{4} - \theta\right) \approx \frac{1-\theta}{1+\theta}$.

SOLUTION

$$\tan\left(\frac{\pi}{4} - \theta\right) = \frac{\tan\frac{\pi}{4} - \tan\theta}{1 + \tan\frac{\pi}{4}\tan\theta}$$

$$= \frac{1 - \tan\theta}{1 + \tan\theta} \qquad \text{since } \tan\frac{\pi}{4} = 1$$

$$\approx \frac{1-\theta}{1+\theta}.$$

These approximations can also be used to find the limit of a fractional expression as $\theta \to 0$ in cases when substituting $\theta = 0$ gives $\frac{0}{0}$, which is undefined.

ACTIVITY 8.4

(i) Show that substituting $\theta = 0$ into the expression

$$\frac{\cos\theta - \cos 2\theta}{\theta^2}$$

gives $\frac{0}{0}$, which is undefined.

(ii) Investigate the behaviour of this expression as $\theta \to 0$ by evaluating

$$\frac{\cos\theta - \cos 2\theta}{\theta^2}$$

for values of θ (in radians) starting with $\theta = 0.2$ and decreasing in steps of 0.02.

EXAMPLE 8.9

(i) Find an approximation for $\cos\theta - \cos 2\theta$ when θ and 2θ are both small.

(ii) Hence find

$$\lim_{\theta \to 0} \frac{\cos\theta - \cos 2\theta}{\theta^2}.$$

SOLUTION

(i) When θ and 2θ are both small

$$\cos\theta \approx 1 - \frac{\theta^2}{2}$$

and $$\cos 2\theta \approx 1 - \frac{(2\theta)^2}{2}$$

$$\approx 1 - 2\theta^2.$$

Using these approximations, when θ is small

$$\cos\theta - \cos 2\theta \approx \left(1 - \frac{\theta^2}{2}\right) - (1 - 2\theta^2)$$

$$= \frac{3\theta^2}{2}.$$

(ii) $$\frac{\cos\theta - \cos 2\theta}{\theta^2} \approx \frac{3\theta^2}{2\theta^2}$$

$$\approx \frac{3}{2}$$

This is consistent with the result in Activity 8.4 and may be written as

$$\lim_{\theta \to 0} \frac{\cos\theta - \cos 2\theta}{\theta^2} = \frac{3}{2}.$$

EXAMPLE 8.10

(i) Simplify $\tan\left(\frac{\pi}{4} + \theta\right)$ when θ is small.

(ii) Hence use the binomial theorem to find a quadratic approximation for $\tan\left(\frac{\pi}{4} + \theta\right)$ when θ is small.

SOLUTION

(i) $$\tan\left(\frac{\pi}{4} + \theta\right) = \frac{\tan\frac{\pi}{4} + \tan\theta}{1 - \tan\frac{\pi}{4}\tan\theta}$$

$$= \frac{1 + \tan\theta}{1 - \tan\theta}$$

$$\approx \frac{1 + \theta}{1 - \theta} \quad \text{when } \theta \text{ is small.}$$

(ii) $$\frac{1 + \theta}{1 - \theta} = (1 + \theta)(1 - \theta)^{-1}$$

$$= (1 + \theta)\left[1 + (-1)(-\theta) + \frac{(-1)(-2)(-\theta)^2}{2!} + \ldots\right]$$

$$\approx (1 + \theta)(1 + \theta + \theta^2)$$

$$\approx 1 + 2\theta + 2\theta^2$$

Differentiating $y = \sin x$ from first principles

In Chapter 4 you deduced the result $\frac{\mathrm{d}}{\mathrm{d}x}(\sin x) = \cos x$ by looking at the graph of $y = \frac{\mathrm{d}}{\mathrm{d}x}(\sin x)$. You are now able to prove this result.

P As you work through the proof, list what you now know (but did not know earlier) that allows you to prove the result.

Figure 8.18 shows part of the graph of $y = \sin x$. The point P is a general point $(x, \sin x)$ on the graph. The point Q is a very small distance further on, so it has x co-ordinate $x + \delta x$, where δx is very small, and y co-ordinate $\sin(x + \delta x)$.

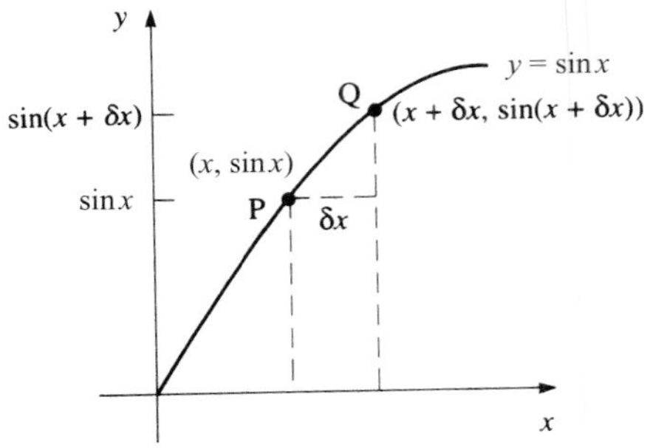

Figure 8.18

You can find the gradient at the point P by finding the limit of the gradient of the chord PQ as δx approaches zero.

$$\frac{\mathrm{d}y}{\mathrm{d}x} = \lim_{\delta x \to 0} \frac{\sin(x + \delta x) - \sin x}{\delta x}$$

$\sin(x + \delta x)$ may be simplified by using the compound-angle formula.

$$\sin(x + \delta x) = \sin x \cos \delta x + \cos x \sin \delta x$$

As δx is small, you can replace $\cos \delta x$ and $\sin \delta x$ by their small-angle approximations

$$\cos \delta x \approx 1 - \tfrac{1}{2}(\delta x)^2 \qquad \sin \delta x \approx \delta x$$

which leads to

$$\begin{aligned} \sin(x + \delta x) &\approx (\sin x)[1 - \tfrac{1}{2}(\delta x)^2] + (\cos x)\delta x \\ &= \sin x - \tfrac{1}{2}(\sin x)(\delta x)^2 + (\cos x)\delta x. \end{aligned}$$

Substituting this in the expression $\frac{\sin(x + \delta x) - \sin x}{\delta x}$ gives

$$\begin{aligned} &\frac{\sin x - \tfrac{1}{2}(\sin x)(\delta x)^2 + (\cos x)\delta x - \sin x}{\delta x} \\ &= \frac{-\tfrac{1}{2}(\sin x)(\delta x)^2 + (\cos x)\delta x}{\delta x} \\ &= -\tfrac{1}{2}(\sin x)\delta x + \cos x. \end{aligned}$$

In the limit as $\delta x \to 0$, this becomes simply $\cos x$. So

$$\frac{dy}{dx} = \cos x.$$

You have now proved the result which you found in Activity 4.4 by sketching the gradient graph.

EXERCISE 8G

1 When θ is small enough for θ^3 to be ignored, find approximate expressions for the following.

(i) $\dfrac{\theta \sin\theta}{1-\cos\theta}$ **(ii)** $2\cos\left(\dfrac{\pi}{3}+\theta\right)$

(iii) $\cos\theta\cos 2\theta$ **(iv)** $\dfrac{\theta\tan\theta}{1-\cos 2\theta}$

(v) $\dfrac{\cos 4\theta - \cos 2\theta}{\sin 4\theta - \sin 2\theta}$ **(vi)** $\sin(\alpha+\theta)\sin\theta$ (Note: α is not small.)

2 (i) Find an approximate expression for $\sin 2\theta + \tan 3\theta$ when θ is small enough for 3θ to be considered as small.

(ii) Hence find

$$\lim_{\theta\to 0} \frac{\sin 2\theta + \tan 3\theta}{\theta}.$$

3 (i) Find an approximate expression for $1-\cos\theta$ when θ is small.

(ii) Hence find

$$\lim_{\theta\to 0} \frac{1-\cos\theta}{4\theta\sin\theta}.$$

4 (i) Find an approximate expression for $\sin\theta\left[\sin\left(\dfrac{\pi}{6}+\theta\right)-\sin\dfrac{\pi}{6}\right]$ when θ is small.

(ii) Find an approximate expression for $1-\cos 2\theta$ when θ is small.

(iii) Hence find

$$\lim_{\theta\to 0} \frac{\sin\theta\left[\sin\left(\frac{\pi}{6}+\theta\right)-\sin\frac{\pi}{6}\right]}{1-\cos 2\theta}.$$

5 (i) Find an approximate expression for $1-\cos 4\theta$ when θ is small enough for 4θ to be considered as small.

(ii) Find an approximate expression for $\tan^2 2\theta$ when θ is small enough for 2θ to be considered as small.

(iii) Hence find

$$\lim_{\theta\to 0} \frac{1-\cos 4\theta}{\tan^2 2\theta}.$$

6 (i) Find an approximate expression for $\dfrac{1}{1+\tan\theta}$ when θ is small.

(ii) Hence use the binomial theorem to find a quadratic approximation for $\dfrac{1}{1+\tan\theta}$.

(iii) When $\theta = 0.1$ radians, find the percentage errors which arise when you use each of the expressions you have derived in parts **(i)** and **(ii)** in place of $\dfrac{1}{1+\tan\theta}$.

7 (i) Find an approximate expression for $\sqrt{1+\sin\theta}$ when θ is small.

(ii) Hence use the binomial theorem to find a quadratic approximation for $\sqrt{1+\sin\theta}$.

(iii) Say which of these approximations you would expect to be the more accurate, and give a reason for your answer.

(iv) Check your answer to part **(iii)** by substituting $\theta = 0.1$ radians.

8 (i) By writing $\sec\theta$ as $\dfrac{1}{\cos\theta}$ find an approximate expression for $\sec\theta$ when θ is small.

(ii) Hence use the binomial theorem to find a quadratic approximation for $\sec\theta$.

(iii) Use a trial and improvement method to find the largest value of θ for which the error incurred in using your answer to part **(ii)** in place of $\sec\theta$ is less than 1%.

(iv) Comment on your answer to part **(iii)**.

9 There are regulations in fencing to ensure that the blades used are not too bent. For épées, the rule states that the blade must not depart by more than 1 cm from the straight line joining the base to the point (see figure A). For sabres, the corresponding rule states that the point must not be more than 4 cm out of line, i.e. away from the tangent at the base of the blade (see figure B).

Suppose that a blade AB is bent to form an arc of a circle of radius r, and that AB subtends an angle 2θ at the centre O of the circle. Then with the notation of figure C, the épée bend is measured by CD, and the sabre bend by BE.

Figure A

Figure B

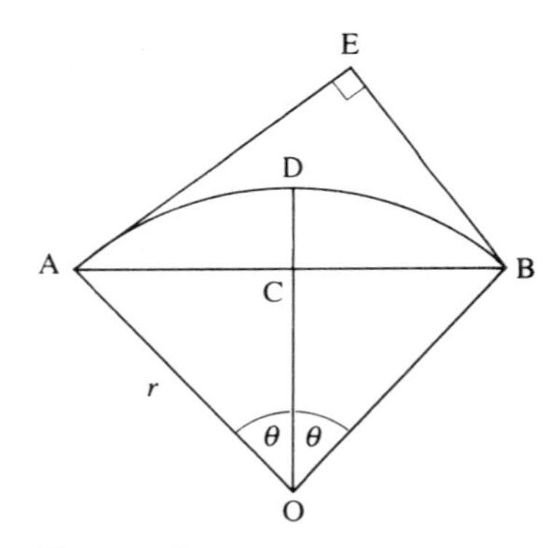

Figure C

(i) Show that $CD = r(1 - \cos\theta)$.

(ii) Explain why angle $BAE = \theta$.

(iii) Show that $BE = 2r\sin^2\theta$.

(iv) Deduce that if θ is small, $BE \approx 4CD$ and hence that the rules for épée and sabre amount to the same thing.

10 **(i)** Solve the equation $\sin 2x + \cos 2x = 0$ for $-\frac{\pi}{2} \leqslant x \leqslant \frac{\pi}{2}$, giving your answers in radians.

(ii) Show that $\cos 2x \approx 1 - 2x^2$ for small values of x.
Write down a small-angle approximation for $\sin 2x$.

(iii) Using the results in part **(ii)**, find a quadratic function $Q(x)$ which is an approximation to $\sin 2x + \cos 2x$ for small values of x.

(iv) Solve the equation $Q(x) = 0$.

(v) Comment on your answers to parts **(i)** and **(iv)**.

[MEI]

11 **(i)** Express $\dfrac{2}{(2-x)(1-x)}$ in partial fractions.

Show that, for small values of x,

$$\frac{2}{(2-x)(1-x)} \approx 1 + kx + \tfrac{7}{4}x^2$$

where k is to be found.

(ii) By using a suitable small-angle approximation for $\cos\theta$, together with the result of part **(i)**, show that, for small values of θ

$$\frac{2}{(1+\cos\theta)\cos\theta} \approx 1 + \tfrac{3}{4}\theta^2.$$

(iii) Given that θ is small, find an approximate solution of the equation

$$\frac{2}{(1+\cos\theta)\cos\theta} = 0.99 + \sin^2\theta.$$

[MEI]

12 **(i)** Use a compound-angle formula to write down an expression for $\sin(x + \delta x)$.

(ii) Rewrite your answer to part **(i)** using small-angle approximations for $\sin\delta x$ and $\cos\delta x$.

(iii) Use your answer to part **(ii)** to write down an expression for

$$\frac{\sin(x+\delta x) - \sin x}{\delta x}.$$

(iv) State

$$\lim_{\delta x \to 0} \frac{\sin(x+\delta x) - \sin x}{\delta x}.$$

(v) Explain the significance of your answer to part **(iv)**.

13 (i) Find $\int \theta \cos 2\theta \, d\theta$.

(ii) Find the expansion of $(1 + 2x)^{-3}$ up to and including the term in x^3, giving the coefficients in their simplest form.
State the range of values of x for which the expansion is valid.

(iii) Show that, provided θ is small, $\cos 2\theta \approx 1 - 2\theta^2$.

Hence find a and b such that $(\cos 2\theta)^{-3}$ is approximately $a + b\theta^2$, provided θ is small.

Use this approximation to find an estimate for

$$\int_0^{0.1} \frac{\theta}{(\cos 2\theta)^3} \, d\theta.$$

[MEI]

14 (i) (a) Find the exact value of $\int_0^{\frac{1}{2}\pi} x \cos 2x \, dx$.

(b) By writing $\cos^2 x$ in terms of $\cos 2x$, show that

$$\int_0^{\frac{1}{2}\pi} x \cos^2 x \, dx = \tfrac{1}{16}(\pi^2 - 4).$$

(ii) The variables x and y satisfy $\frac{dy}{dx} = x\sqrt{\cos x}$, and $y = 0$ when $x = 0$.

(a) Using the approximation $\cos x \approx 1 - \frac{1}{2}x^2$ and a suitable substitution, show by integration that, for small values of x,

$$y \approx \tfrac{2}{3} - \tfrac{2}{3}(1 - \tfrac{1}{2}x^2)^{\frac{3}{2}}.$$

(b) Using a binomial expansion on this result, show that for small values of x

$$y \approx ax^2 + bx^4,$$

where a and b are constants to be determined.

[MEI]

INVESTIGATION

Explain why tan 89° is approximately but not exactly equal to the number of degrees in a radian.

e The general solutions of trigonometrical equations

The equation $\tan \theta = 1$ has infinitely many roots:

$$\ldots, -315°, \; -135°, \; 45°, \; 225°, \; 405°, \ldots \text{ (in degrees)}$$

$$\ldots, -\frac{7\pi}{4}, \; -\frac{3\pi}{4}, \; \frac{\pi}{4}, \; \frac{5\pi}{4}, \; \frac{9\pi}{4}, \ldots \quad \text{(in radians).}$$

Only one of these roots, namely 45° or $\frac{\pi}{4}$, is denoted by the function arctan 1. This is the value which your calculator will give you. It is called the *principal value.*

The principal value for any inverse trigonometrical function is unique and lies within a specified range:

$$-\frac{\pi}{2} < \arctan x < \frac{\pi}{2}$$

$$-\frac{\pi}{2} \leqslant \arcsin x \leqslant \frac{\pi}{2}$$

$$0 \leqslant \arccos x \leqslant \pi.$$

It is possible to deduce all other roots from the principal value and this is shown below.

To solve the equation $\tan\theta = c$, notice how all possible values of θ occur at intervals of 180° or π radians (see figure 8.19). So the general solution is

$$\theta = \arctan c + n\pi \quad n \in \mathbb{Z} \qquad \text{(in radians).}$$

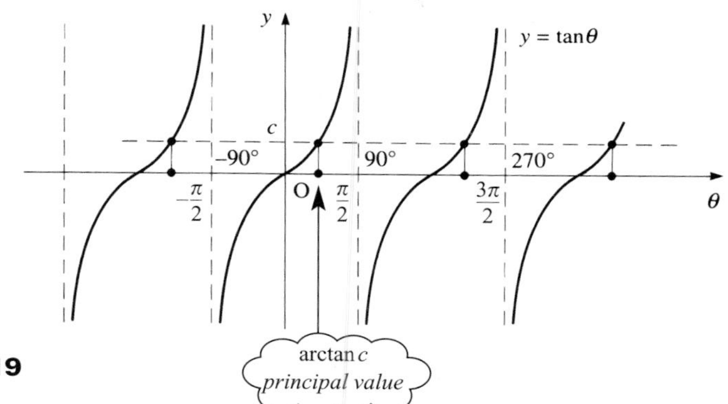

Figure 8.19

The cosine graph (see figure 8.20) has the y axis as a line of symmetry. Notice how the values $\pm\arccos c$ generate all the other roots at intervals of 360° or 2π. So the general solution is

$$\theta = \pm\arccos c + 2n\pi \qquad n \in \mathbb{Z} \qquad \text{(in radians).}$$

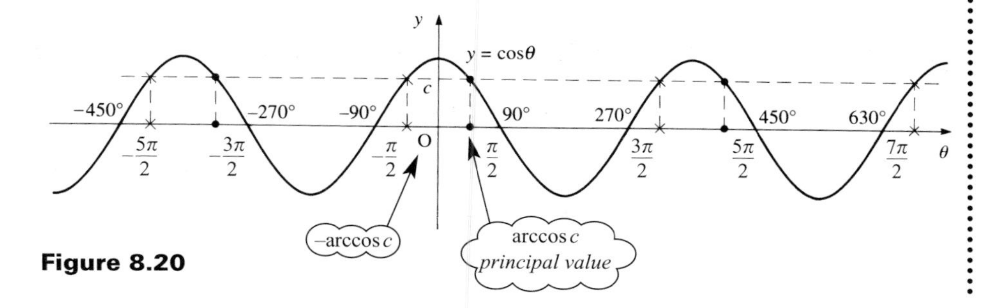

Figure 8.20

To solve the equation $\sin\theta = c$, notice that there are two roots located symmetrically each side of $\theta = \frac{\pi}{2}$, which generate all the other possible roots (see figure 8.21). This gives rise to the slightly more complicated expressions

$$\theta = \frac{\pi}{2} \pm \left(\frac{\pi}{2} - \arcsin c\right) + 2n\pi$$

or $$\theta = \left(2n + \frac{1}{2}\right)\pi \pm \left(\frac{\pi}{2} - \arcsin c\right) \quad n \in \mathbb{Z}.$$

You may, however, find it easier to remember these as two separate formulae:

$$\theta = 2n\pi + \arcsin c \qquad \text{or} \qquad \theta = (2n+1)\pi - \arcsin c.$$

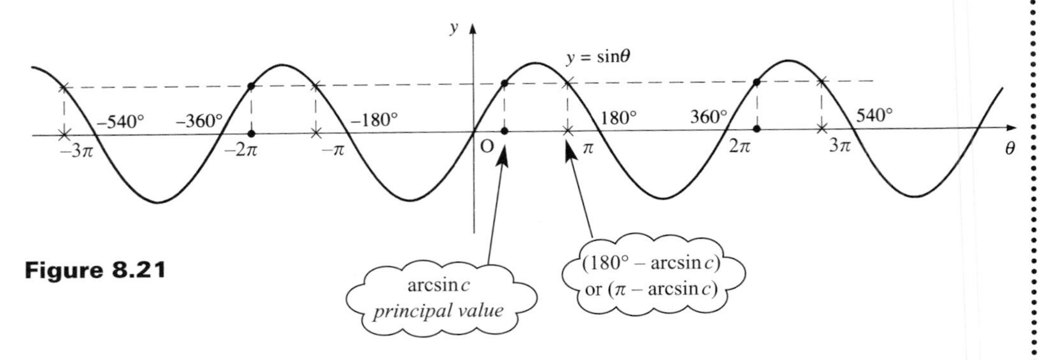

Figure 8.21

ACTIVITY 8.5 Show that the general solution of the equation $\sin\theta = c$ may also be written

$$\theta = n\pi + (-1)^n \arcsin c.$$

e Using trigonometrical identities in integration

Sometimes, when it is not immediately obvious how to integrate a function involving trigonometrical functions, it may help to rewrite the function using one of the trigonometrical identities.

EXAMPLE 8.11

Find $\int \sin^2 x \, dx$.

SOLUTION

A substitution cannot be used in this case. However, you know the identity

$$\cos 2x = 1 - 2\sin^2 x.$$

(Remember that this is just one of the three expressions for $\cos 2x$.)

This identity may be rewritten as

$$\sin^2 x = \tfrac{1}{2}(1 - \cos 2x).$$

By putting $\sin^2 x$ in this form, you will be able to perform the integration:

$$\int \sin^2 x \, dx = \tfrac{1}{2}\int (1 - \cos 2x) \, dx$$
$$= \tfrac{1}{2}(x - \tfrac{1}{2}\sin 2x) + c$$
$$= \tfrac{1}{2}x - \tfrac{1}{4}\sin 2x + c.$$

You can integrate $\cos^2 x$ in the same way, by using $\cos^2 x = \frac{1}{2}(\cos 2x + 1)$. Other even powers of $\sin x$ or $\cos x$ can also be integrated in a similar way, but you have to use the identity twice or more.

EXAMPLE 8.12

Find $\int \cos^4 x \, dx$.

SOLUTION

First express $\cos^4 x$ as $(\cos^2 x)^2$:

$$\cos^4 x = \left[\tfrac{1}{2}\left(\cos 2x + 1\right)\right]^2$$
$$= \tfrac{1}{4}\left(\cos^2 2x + 2\cos 2x + 1\right).$$

Next, apply the same identity to $\cos^2 2x$:

$$\cos^2 2x = \tfrac{1}{2}\left(\cos 4x + 1\right).$$

Hence $\cos^4 x = \frac{1}{4}\left(\frac{1}{2}\cos 4x + \frac{1}{2} + 2\cos 2x + 1\right)$

$$= \tfrac{1}{4}\left(\tfrac{1}{2}\cos 4x + 2\cos 2x + \tfrac{3}{2}\right)$$
$$= \tfrac{1}{8}\cos 4x + \tfrac{1}{2}\cos 2x + \tfrac{3}{8}.$$

This can now be integrated:

$$\int \cos^4 x \, dx = \int \left(\tfrac{1}{8}\cos 4x + \tfrac{1}{2}\cos 2x + \tfrac{3}{8}\right) dx$$
$$= \tfrac{1}{32}\sin 4x + \tfrac{1}{4}\sin 2x + \tfrac{3}{8}x + c.$$

For odd powers of $\sin x$ or $\cos x$, a different technique is used, as in the next example.

EXAMPLE 8.13

Find $\int \cos^3 x \, dx$.

SOLUTION

First write $\cos^3 x = \cos x \cos^2 x$.

Now remember that

$$\cos^2 x + \sin^2 x = 1 \quad \Rightarrow \quad \cos^2 x = 1 - \sin^2 x.$$

This gives

$$\cos^3 x = \cos x(1 - \sin^2 x)$$
$$= \cos x - \cos x \sin^2 x.$$

The first part of this expression, $\cos x$, is easily integrated to give $\sin x$.

The second part is more complicated, but you can see that it is of a type that you have met already, as it is a product of two functions, one of which is a function of $\sin x$ and the other of which is the derivative of $\sin x$. This can be integrated either by making the substitution $u = \sin x$ or simply in your head (by inspection). So

$$\int \cos^3 x\,dx = \int (\cos x - \cos x \sin^2 x)\,dx$$
$$= \sin x - \tfrac{1}{3}\sin^3 x + c.$$

Any odd power of $\sin x$ or $\cos x$ can be integrated in this way, but again it may be necessary to use the identity more than once. For example:

$$\sin^5 x = \sin x(\sin^2 x)(\sin^2 x) = \sin x(1 - \cos^2 x)^2$$
$$= \sin x(1 - 2\cos^2 x + \cos^4 x)$$
$$= \sin x - 2\sin x\cos^2 x + \sin x\cos^4 x.$$

This can now be integrated.

KEY POINTS

1 $\sec\theta = \dfrac{1}{\cos\theta}$; $\operatorname{cosec}\theta = \dfrac{1}{\sin\theta}$; $\cot\theta = \dfrac{1}{\tan\theta}$

2 $\tan^2\theta + 1 = \sec^2\theta$; $1 + \cot^2\theta = \operatorname{cosec}^2\theta$

3 **Compound-angle formulae**

- $\sin(\theta + \phi) = \sin\theta\cos\phi + \cos\theta\sin\phi$
- $\sin(\theta - \phi) = \sin\theta\cos\phi - \cos\theta\sin\phi$
- $\cos(\theta + \phi) = \cos\theta\cos\phi - \sin\theta\sin\phi$
- $\cos(\theta - \phi) = \cos\theta\cos\phi + \sin\theta\sin\phi$
- $\tan(\theta + \phi) = \dfrac{\tan\theta + \tan\phi}{1 - \tan\theta\tan\phi}$ $\quad (\theta + \phi) \neq 90°, 270°, \ldots$
- $\tan(\theta - \phi) = \dfrac{\tan\theta - \tan\phi}{1 + \tan\theta\tan\phi}$ $\quad (\theta - \phi) \neq 90°, 270°, \ldots$

4 **Double-angle and related formulae**

- $\sin 2\theta = 2\sin\theta\cos\theta$
- $\cos 2\theta = \cos^2\theta - \sin^2\theta = 1 - 2\sin^2\theta = 2\cos^2\theta - 1$
- $\tan 2\theta = \dfrac{2\tan\theta}{1 - \tan^2\theta}$ $\quad \theta \neq 45°, 135°, \ldots$
- $\sin^2\theta = \tfrac{1}{2}(1 - \cos 2\theta)$
- $\cos^2\theta = \tfrac{1}{2}(1 + \cos 2\theta)$

5 The r, α formulae

- $a\sin\theta + b\cos\theta = r\sin(\theta + \alpha)$
- $a\sin\theta - b\cos\theta = r\sin(\theta - \alpha)$
- $a\cos\theta + b\sin\theta = r\cos(\theta - \alpha)$
- $a\cos\theta - b\sin\theta = r\cos(\theta + \alpha)$

where $r = \sqrt{a^2 + b^2}$, $\cos\alpha = \dfrac{a}{r}$, $\sin\alpha = \dfrac{b}{r}$

6 The small-angle approximations (for θ in radians)

- $\sin\theta \approx \theta$
- $\tan\theta \approx \theta$
- $\cos\theta \approx 1 - \dfrac{\theta^2}{2}$
- $\lim\limits_{\theta\to 0} \dfrac{\theta}{\sin\theta} = \lim\limits_{\theta\to 0} \dfrac{\sin\theta}{\theta} = 1$

e Factor formulae

- $\sin\alpha + \sin\beta = 2\sin\left(\dfrac{\alpha + \beta}{2}\right)\cos\left(\dfrac{\alpha - \beta}{2}\right)$
- $\sin\alpha - \sin\beta = 2\cos\left(\dfrac{\alpha + \beta}{2}\right)\sin\left(\dfrac{\alpha - \beta}{2}\right)$
- $\cos\alpha + \cos\beta = 2\cos\left(\dfrac{\alpha + \beta}{2}\right)\cos\left(\dfrac{\alpha - \beta}{2}\right)$
- $\cos\alpha - \cos\beta = -2\sin\left(\dfrac{\alpha + \beta}{2}\right)\sin\left(\dfrac{\alpha - \beta}{2}\right)$

Note the minus sign here.

9 Parametric equations

A mathematician, like a painter or poet, is a maker of patterns. If his patterns are more permanent than theirs it is because they are made with ideas.

G.H. Hardy

When you go on a ride like the one in the picture, your body follows a very unnatural path and this gives rise to sensations which you may find exhilarating or frightening.

You are accustomed to expressing curves as mathematical equations. How would you do so in a case like this?

Figure 9.1 shows a simplified version of such a ride.

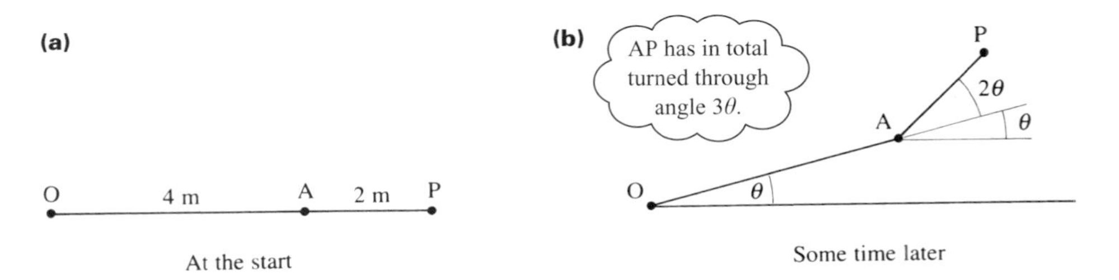

Figure 9.1

The passenger's chair is on the end of a rod AP of length 2 m which is rotating about A. The rod OA is 4 m long and is itself rotating about O. The gearing of the mechanism ensures that the rod AP rotates twice as fast relative to OA as the rod OA does. This is illustrated by the angles marked on figure 9.1(b), at a time when OA has rotated through an angle θ.

At this time, the co-ordinates of the point P, taking O as the origin, are given by

$$x = 4\cos\theta + 2\cos 3\theta$$

$$y = 4\sin\theta + 2\sin 3\theta$$

(see figure 9.2).

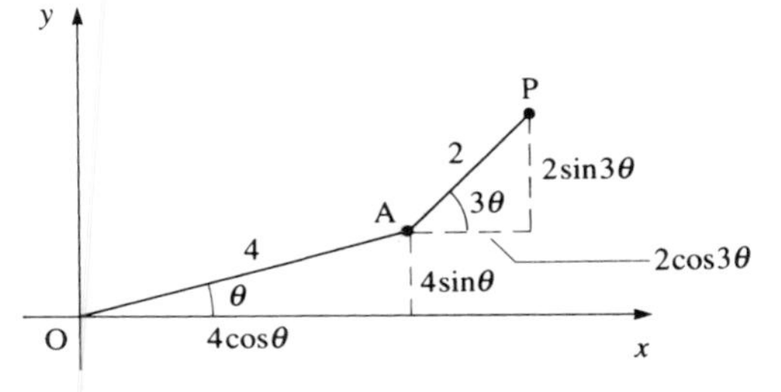

Figure 9.2

These two equations are called *parametric equations* of the curve. They do not give the relationship between x and y directly in the form $y = f(x)$ but use a third variable, θ, to do so. This third variable is called the *parameter*.

To plot the curve, you need to substitute values of θ and find the corresponding values of x and y.

Thus $\theta = 0° \Rightarrow x = 4 + 2 = 6$

$y = 0 + 0 = 0$ Point (6, 0)

$\theta = 30° \Rightarrow x = 4 \times 0.866 + 0 = 3.464$

$y = 4 \times 0.5 + 2 \times 1 = 4$ Point (3.46, 4)

and so on.

Joining points found in this way reveals the curve to have the shape shown in figure 9.3.

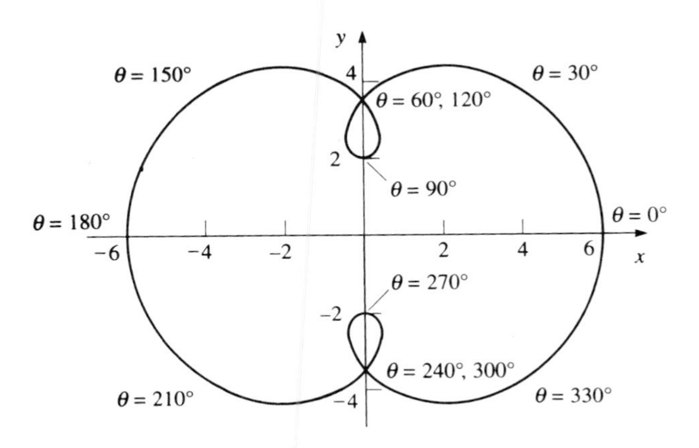

Figure 9.3

At what points of the curve would you feel the greatest sensations?

Graphs from parametric equations

Parametric equations are very useful in situations such as this, where an otherwise complicated equation may be expressed reasonably simply in terms of a parameter. Indeed, there are some curves which can be given by parametric equations but cannot be written as cartesian equations (in terms of x and y only).

The next example is based on a simpler curve. Make sure that you can follow the solution completely before going on to the rest of the chapter.

EXAMPLE 9.1

A curve has the parametric equations $x = 2t$, $y = \frac{36}{t^2}$.

(i) Find the co-ordinates of the points corresponding to $t = 1, 2, 3, -1, -2$ and -3.

(ii) Plot the points you have found and join them to give the curve.

(iii) Explain what happens as $t \to 0$.

SOLUTION

(i)

t	−3	−2	−1	1	2	3
x	−6	−4	−2	2	4	6
y	4	9	36	36	9	4

The points required are (−6, 4), (−4, 9), (−2, 36), (2, 36), (4, 9) and (6, 4).

(ii) The curve is shown in figure 9.4.

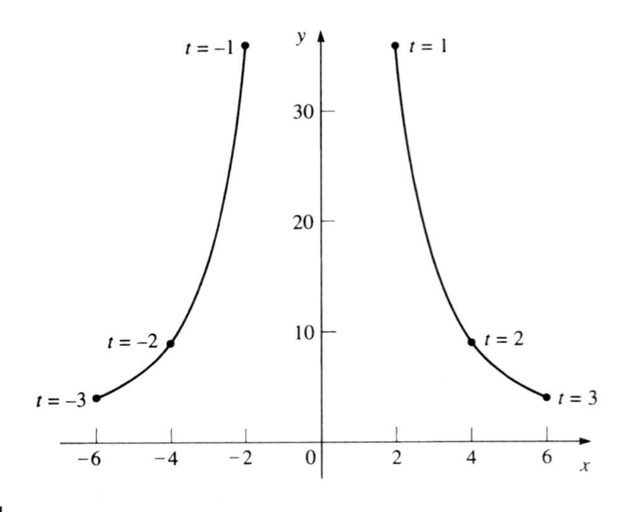

Figure 9.4

(iii) As $t \to 0$, $x \to 0$ and $y \to \infty$. The y axis is an asymptote for the curve.

EXAMPLE 9.2

A curve has the parametric equations $x = t^2$, $y = t^3 - t$.

(i) Find the co-ordinates of the points corresponding to values of t from -2 to $+2$ at half-unit intervals.

(ii) Sketch the curve for $-2 \leqslant t \leqslant 2$.

(iii) Are there any values of x for which the curve is undefined?

SOLUTION

(i)

t	-2	-1.5	-1	-0.5	0	0.5	1	1.5	2
x	4	2.25	1	0.25	0	0.25	1	2.25	4
y	-6	-1.875	0	0.375	0	-0.375	0	1.875	6

(ii)

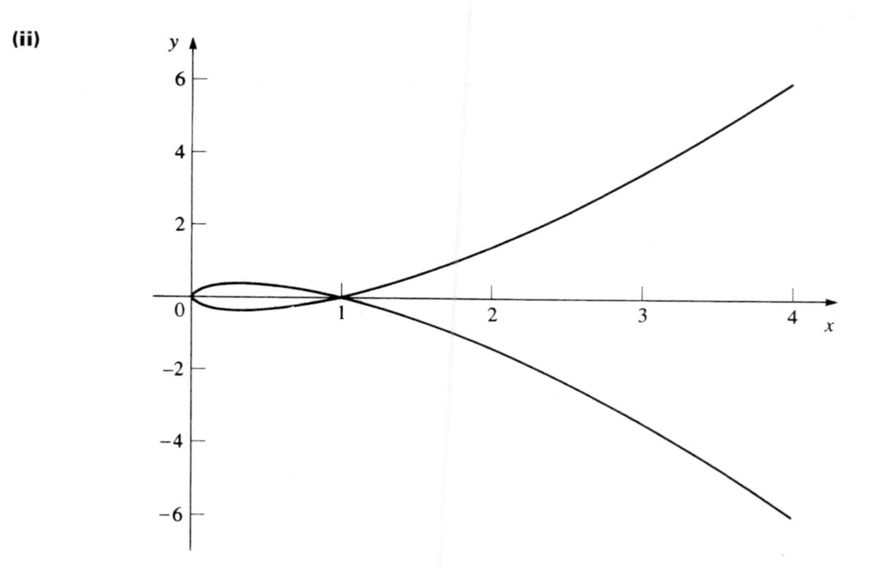

Figure 9.5

(iii) The curve in figure 9.5 is undefined for $x < 0$.

Graphic calculators

Graphic calculators can be used to sketch parametric curves but, as with cartesian curves, you need to be careful when choosing the range.

Finding the equation by eliminating the parameter

For some pairs of parametric equations, it is possible to eliminate the parameter and obtain the cartesian equation for the curve. This is usually done by making the parameter the subject of one of the equations, and substituting this expression into the other.

EXAMPLE 9.3

Eliminate t from the equations $x = t^3 - 2t^2$, $y = \frac{t}{2}$.

SOLUTION

$$y = \frac{t}{2} \quad \Rightarrow \quad t = 2y.$$

Substituting this in the equation $x = t^3 - 2t^2$ gives

$$x = (2y)^3 - 2(2y)^2 \quad \text{or} \quad x = 8y^3 - 8y^2.$$

Sometimes you need to consider the parametric equations simultaneously. There is often more than one way in which you can do this, and the next example gives two different options.

EXAMPLE 9.4

The parametric equations of a curve are

$$x = t + \frac{1}{t} \qquad y = t - \frac{1}{t}.$$

(i) Find the co-ordinates of the points corresponding to $t = -2, -1, -0.5, 0, 0.5, 1, 2$.

(ii) Sketch the curve for $-2 \leqslant t \leqslant 2$.

(iii) For what values of x is the curve undefined?

(iv) Eliminate the parameter by

(a) first finding $x + y$

(b) first squaring x and y.

SOLUTION

(i)

t	–2	–1	–0.5	0	0.5	1	2
x	–2.5	–2	–2.5	undefined	2.5	2	2.5
y	–1.5	0	1.5	undefined	–1.5	0	1.5

(ii)

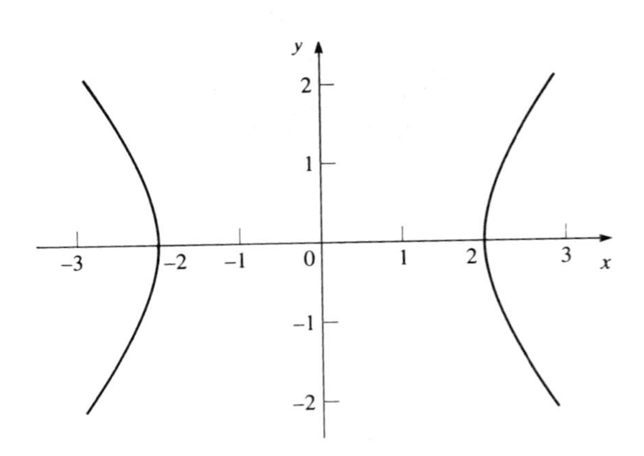

Figure 9.6

(iii) The curve is undefined for $-2 < x < 2$.

(iv) (a) Adding the two equations gives

$$x + y = 2t \quad \text{or} \quad t = \frac{x+y}{2}.$$

Substituting for t in the first equation (it could be either one) gives

$$x = \frac{x+y}{2} + \frac{2}{x+y}.$$

At this point the parameter t has been eliminated, but the equation is not in its neatest form.

Multiplying by $2(x + y)$ to eliminate the fractions:

$$2x(x+y) = (x+y)^2 + 4$$

$$\Rightarrow \quad 2x^2 + 2xy = x^2 + 2xy + y^2 + 4$$

$$\Rightarrow \quad x^2 - y^2 = 4.$$

(b) Squaring gives

$$x^2 = t^2 + 2 + \frac{1}{t^2}$$

$$y^2 = t^2 - 2 + \frac{1}{t^2}.$$

Subtracting gives

$$x^2 - y^2 = 4.$$

Note

Figure 9.7 shows that the curve is the rectangular hyperbola $xy = 2$ rotated clockwise through 45°.

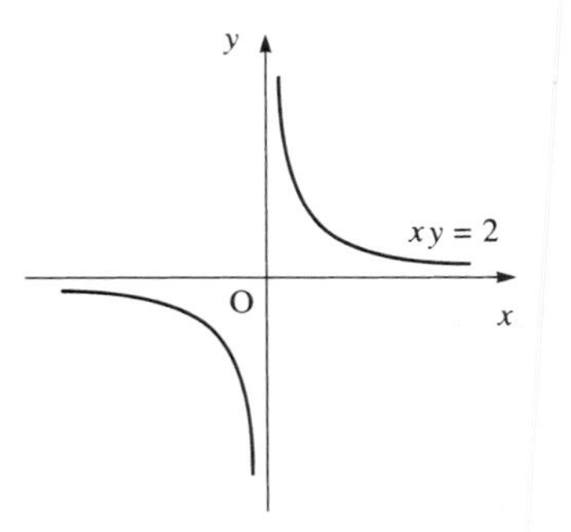

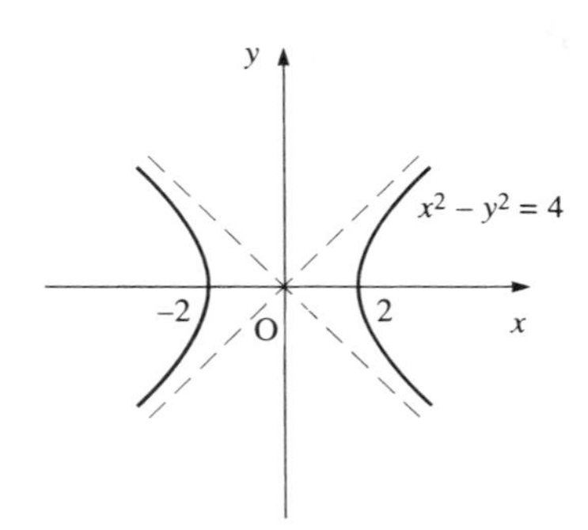

Figure 9.7

Trigonometrical parametric equations

When trigonometrical functions are used in parametric equations, a particular trigonometrical identity may help you to eliminate the parameter. The next example illustrates this.

EXAMPLE 9.5

Eliminate θ from $x = 4\cos\theta$, $y = 3\sin\theta$.

SOLUTION

The identity which connects $\cos\theta$ and $\sin\theta$ is

$$\cos^2\theta + \sin^2\theta = 1 \quad ①$$

$$x = 4\cos\theta \quad \Rightarrow \quad \cos\theta = \frac{x}{4}$$

$$y = 3\sin\theta \quad \Rightarrow \quad \sin\theta = \frac{y}{3}.$$

Substituting these in ① gives

$$\left(\frac{x}{4}\right)^2 + \left(\frac{y}{3}\right)^2 = 1.$$

This is usually written as

$$\frac{x^2}{16} + \frac{y^2}{9} = 1$$

and is the equation of the ellipse shown in figure 9.8.

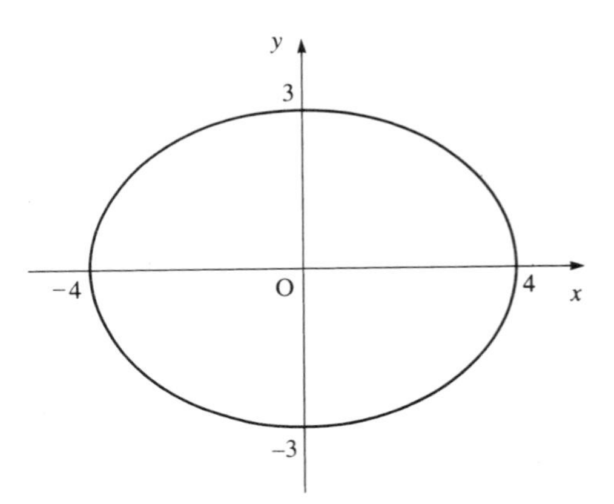

Figure 9.8

Note

The standard equation of the ellipse is $\frac{x^2}{a^2} + \frac{y^2}{b^2} = 1$ and this crosses the x axis at $(-a, 0)$ and $(a, 0)$ and the y axis at $(0, b)$ and $(0, -b)$.

The expansions of $\cos 2\theta$ in terms of either $\sin\theta$ or $\cos\theta$ are also useful in this context.

EXAMPLE 9.6

Eliminate θ from $x = \cos 2\theta$, $y = \sin\theta + 2$.

SOLUTION

The relationship between $\cos 2\theta$ and $\sin\theta$ is

$$\cos 2\theta = 1 - 2\sin^2\theta.$$

Now $\quad y - 2 = \sin\theta$

so $\quad x = 1 - 2(y - 2)^2.$

The parametric equation of a circle

The circle with centre (0, 0)

The circle with centre (0, 0) and radius 4 units has the equation $x^2 + y^2 = 16$. Alternatively, using the triangle OAB and the angle θ in figure 9.9, you can write the equations

$$x = 4\cos\theta$$

$$y = 4\sin\theta.$$

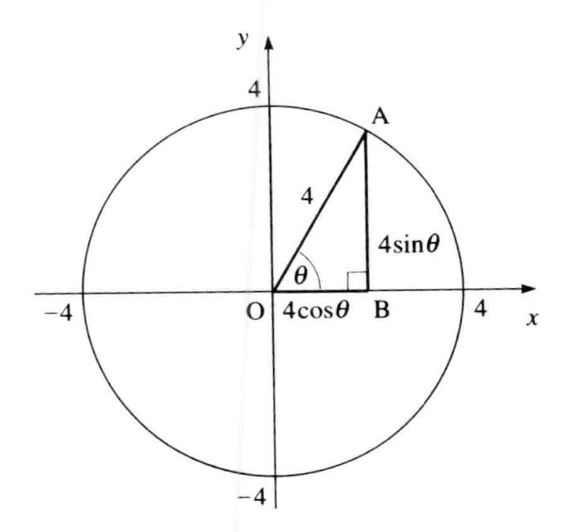

Figure 9.9

Generalising, a circle with centre (0, 0) and radius r has the parametric equations

$$x = r\cos\theta$$

$$y = r\sin\theta.$$

The circle with centre (*a*, *b*)

Translating the centre of the circle to the point (a, b) gives the circle in figure 9.10 with the parametric equations

$$x = a + r\cos\theta$$

$$y = b + r\sin\theta$$

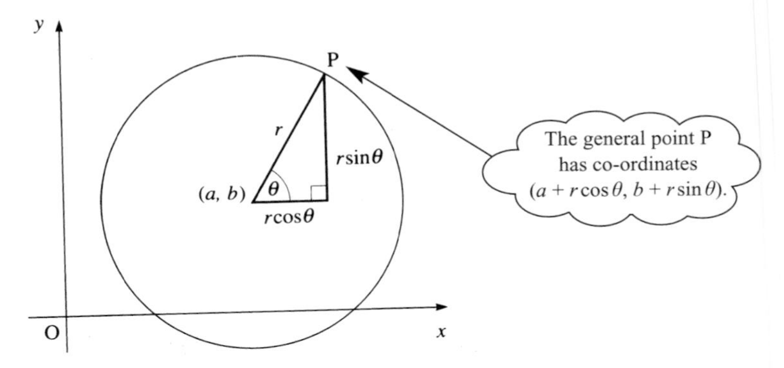

Figure 9.10

e The parametric equations of other standard curves

Ellipse

In Example 9.5, you saw that the parametric equations

$$x = 4\cos\theta$$

$$y = 3\sin\theta$$

were equivalent to the cartesian equation

$$\frac{x^2}{16} + \frac{y^2}{9} = 1.$$

In general the equations

$$x = a\cos\theta \qquad y = b\sin\theta$$

correspond to the ellipse

$$\frac{x^2}{a^2} + \frac{y^2}{b^2} = 1$$

(see figure 9.11).

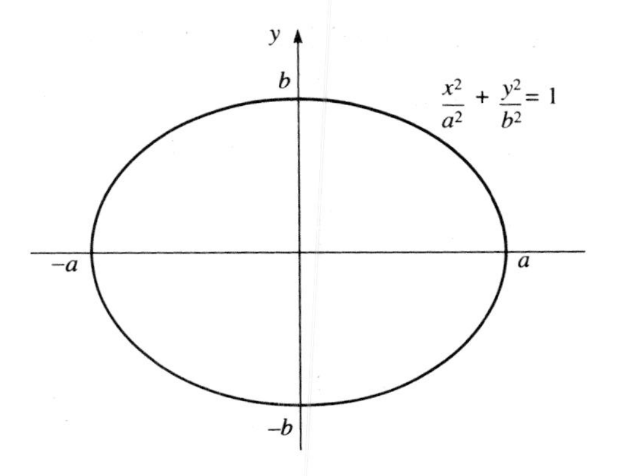

Figure 9.11

---

p How do you prove this result?

Here the parameter θ is not an angle in the ellipse, as it was in the circle. It does, however, have a physical interpretation as an angle in the circumscribing circle.

Parabola

The parabola in figure 9.12 with the x axis as its line of symmetry and the point $(a, 0)$ as its focus, has the cartesian equation $y^2 = 4ax$. The corresponding parametric equations are

$$x = at^2 \qquad y = 2at.$$

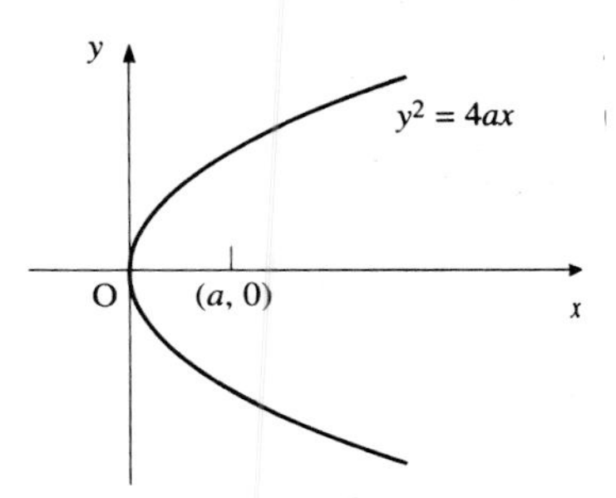

Figure 9.12

Rectangular hyperbola

The rectangular hyperbola $xy = c^2$ shown in figure 9.13(a) has the parametric equations

$$x = ct \qquad y = \frac{c}{t}.$$

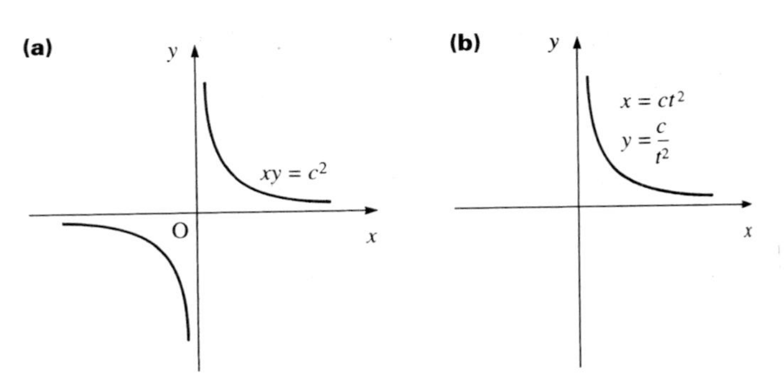

Figure 9.13

When you convert the equation of a curve from parametric to cartesian form, you must take care that there are no restrictions on the values of x and y. For example, in figure 9.13(b), the curve $x = ct^2$, $y = \frac{c}{t^2}$ $(c > 0)$ is restricted to positive values of x and y (since $t^2 > 0$). However, its cartesian form, $xy = c^2$, would appear to allow negative values of x and y.

Note

When the parametric equations can be recognised as those of a standard curve, the curve can be sketched immediately without the need for further investigation.

EXERCISE 9A

In this exercise you should sketch the curves by hand. If you have access to a graphic calculator, you can use it to check your results.

1 In each of the following

(a) find the co-ordinates of the points corresponding to values of t from –2 to +2 at half-unit intervals, or values of θ from 0° to 360° in 30° intervals

(b) sketch the curve

(c) find the cartesian equation of the curve.

(i) $x = 2t$, $y = t^2$

(ii) $x = \cos 2\theta$, $y = \sin^2\theta$

(iii) $x = t^2$, $y = t^3$

(iv) $x = \sin^2\theta$, $y = 1 + 2\sin\theta$

(v) $x = 2\,\text{cosec}\,\theta$, $y = 2\cot\theta$

(vi) $x = 2\sin^2\theta$, $y = 3\cos\theta$

(vii) $x = \tan\theta$, $y = \tan 2\theta$

(viii) $x = t^2$, $y = t^2 - t$

(ix) $x = \dfrac{t}{1+t}$, $y = \dfrac{t}{1-t}$

2 Sketch the standard curves given by the following equations.

(i) $x = 5\cos\theta$
$y = 5\sin\theta$

(ii) $x = 3\cos\theta$
$y = 3\sin\theta$

(iii) $x = 4 + 3\cos\theta$
$y = 1 + 3\sin\theta$

(iv) $x = 2\cos\theta - 1$
$y = 3 + 2\sin\theta$

3 **(i)** Sketch both of these curves on the same axes.

(a) $x = t \quad y = \frac{1}{t}$ **(b)** $x = 4t \quad y = \frac{4}{t}$

(ii) Comment on the relationship between them.

4 A curve has the parametric equations $x = t^2$, $y = t^4$.

(i) Find the co-ordinates of the points corresponding to $t = -2$ to $t = 2$ at half-unit intervals.

(ii) Sketch the curve for $-2 \leqslant t \leqslant 2$.

(iii) Why is it not quite accurate to say this curve has equation $y = x^2$?

5 When a tennis ball is served in still air, its trajectory (path) may be modelled by the parametric equations $x = 20t$, $y = 10t - 5t^2$, where t is the time in seconds after the service.

(i) Find the cartesian equation of its trajectory.

(ii) Sketch its trajectory.

6 A student is investigating the trajectory of a golf ball being hit over level ground. At first she ignores air resistance and this leads her to an initial model given by $x = 40t$, $y = 30t - 5t^2$, where x and y are the horizontal and vertical distances in metres from where the ball is hit, and t is the time in seconds.

(i) Plot the trajectory on graph paper for $t = 0, 1, 2, \ldots$, until the ball hits the ground again.

(ii) How far does the ball travel horizontally before bouncing, according to this model?

The student then decides to make an allowance for air resistance to the horizontal motion and proposes the model $x = 40t - t^2$, $y = 30t - 5t^2$.

(iii) Plot the trajectory according to this model using the same axes as you did in part **(i)**.

(iv) By how much does this model reduce the horizontal distance the ball travels before bouncing?

7 A curve has parametric equations $x = (t + 1)^2$, $y = t - 1$.

(i) Find the co-ordinates of the points corresponding to $t = -4$ to $t = 4$ at intervals of one unit.

(ii) Sketch the curve for $-4 \leqslant t \leqslant 4$.

(iii) State the equation of the line of symmetry of the curve.

(iv) By eliminating the parameter, find the cartesian equation of the curve.

8 A curve has parametric equations $x = e^t$, $y = \sin t$, where t is in radians.

(i) Find, to 2 decimal places, the co-ordinates of the points corresponding to values of t from -2 to $+2$ at half-unit intervals.

(ii) What can you say about the values of x for which the curve is defined?

(iii) Sketch the curve for $-2 \leqslant t \leqslant 2$.

(iv) Predict how this graph would continue if all values of t were considered (that is, $t < -2$ and $t > 2$).

9 ☆ The path traced out by a marked point on the rim of a wheel of radius a when the wheel is rolled along a flat surface is called a cycloid.

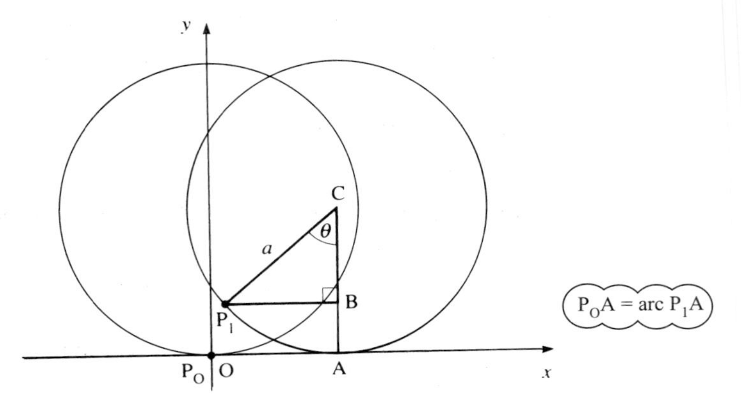

The diagram shows the wheel in its initial position when the lowest point on the rim is P_O, and when it has rotated through an angle θ (radians). In this position, the point P_O has moved to P_1 with parametric equations given by

$$x = OA - P_1B = a\theta - a\sin\theta$$

$$y = AC - BC = a - a\cos\theta.$$

(i) Find the co-ordinates of the points corresponding to values of θ from 0 to 6π at intervals of $\frac{\pi}{3}$.

(ii) Sketch the curve for $0 \leqslant \theta \leqslant 6\pi$.

(iii) What do you notice about the curve?

10 ☆ The curve with parametric equations

$$x = a\cos^3\theta \qquad y = a\sin^3\theta$$

is called an astroid.

(i) Sketch the curve.

(ii) On the same diagram sketch the curve

$$x = a\cos^n\theta \qquad y = a\sin^n\theta$$

for $n = 1, 2, 3, 4, 5, 6$. What happens if $n = 0$?

(iii) What can you say regarding the shape and position of the curve when $n \geqslant 7$ and

(a) n is even **(b)** n is odd?

Cutting out patterns

A soft ball is to be made from felt, as in figure 9.14. The surface of the finished ball is composed of 16 equal sections, and is approximately spherical with a radius of 8 cm.

Investigate the shape needed for each of the sections and draw out a pattern that you can use to cut them out from flat pieces of felt.

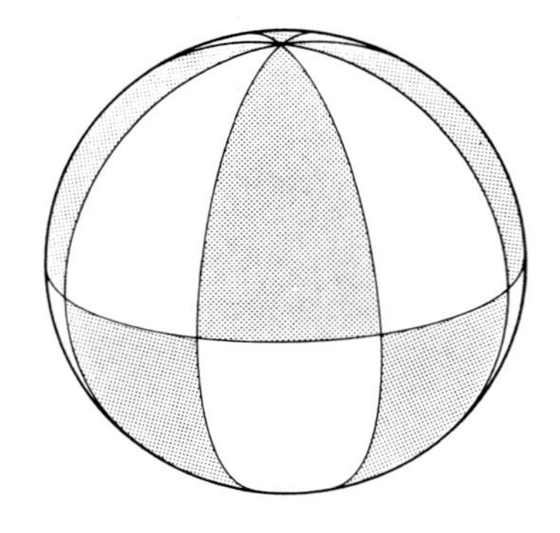

Figure 9.14

The apparent motion of planets

Most of the planets go round the Sun in elliptical (but nearly circular) orbits, and lie in very nearly the same plane. In this investigation you should assume the orbits are circular and you will find it helpful to work, at least to start with, with the suggested approximate data given in the table.

Planet	Mean radius of orbit (km)		Length of year: time for one rotation of the Sun (Earth days)	
	Accurate	Approximate	Accurate	Approximate
Mercury	5.79×10^7	6×10^7	87.97	90
Earth	14.96×10^7	15×10^7	365.26	360
Mars	22.79×10^7	23×10^7	686.98	720

As seen from the Earth, it appears that the Sun is moving in a circle with the other planets circling around it.

(i) Find parametric equations for the paths of Mercury and Mars as seen from Earth, and so sketch their paths.

(ii) What is the effect of taking approximate values for the radius of the orbit and the length of the year?

(iii) If you observe a planet at night over a period of weeks or months you will see that it appears to move across the pattern of background stars. However, at times it will stop and move backwards (retrograde) before resuming its forward motion. How do your sketches of the planets' paths allow you to explain this phenomenon?

(iv) Some astronomy books will tell you that only the superior planets (those further from the Sun than Earth) are retrograde. Is this true, and if not how could such a mistake be made?

Parametric differentiation

To differentiate a function which is defined in terms of a parameter t, you need to use the chain rule:

$$\frac{dy}{dx} = \frac{dy}{dt} \times \frac{dt}{dx}.$$

Since

$$\frac{dt}{dx} = \frac{1}{\frac{dx}{dt}}$$

it follows :hat

$$\frac{dy}{dx} = \frac{\frac{dy}{dt}}{\frac{dx}{dt}}$$

provided that $\frac{dx}{dt} \neq 0$.

EXAMPLE 9.7

A curve has the parametric equations $x = t^2$, $y = 2t$.

(i) Find $\frac{dy}{dx}$ in terms of the parameter t.

(ii) Find the equation of the tangent to the curve at the general point $(t^2, 2t)$.

(iii) Find the equation of the tangent at the point where $t = 3$.

(iv) Eliminate the parameter, and hence sketch the curve and the tangent at the point where $t = 3$.

SOLUTION

(i) $x = t^2 \quad \Rightarrow \quad \frac{dx}{dt} = 2t$

$y = 2t \quad \Rightarrow \quad \frac{dy}{dt} = 2$

$$\frac{dy}{dx} = \frac{\frac{dy}{dt}}{\frac{dx}{dt}} = \frac{2}{2t} = \frac{1}{t}.$$

The gradient of the curve at $(t^2, 2t)$.

(ii) Using $y - y_1 = m(x - x_1)$ and taking the point (x_1, y_1) as $(t^2, 2t)$, the equation of the tangent at the point $(t^2, 2t)$ is

$$y - 2t = \frac{1}{t}(x - t^2)$$

$$\Rightarrow \quad ty - 2t^2 = x - t^2$$

$$\Rightarrow \quad x - ty + t^2 = 0.$$

This equation still contains the parameter, and is called the equation of the tangent at the general point.

(iii) Substituting $t = 3$ into this equation gives the equation of the tangent at the point where $t = 3$.

The tangent is $x - 3y + 9 = 0$.

(iv) Eliminating t from $x = t^2$, $y = 2t$ gives

$$x = \left(\frac{y}{2}\right)^2 \quad \text{or} \quad y^2 = 4x.$$

This a parabola with the x axis as its line of symmetry.

The point where $t = 3$ has co-ordinates (9, 6).

The tangent $x - 3y + 9 = 0$ crosses the axes at (0, 3) and (−9, 0).

The curve is shown in figure 9.15.

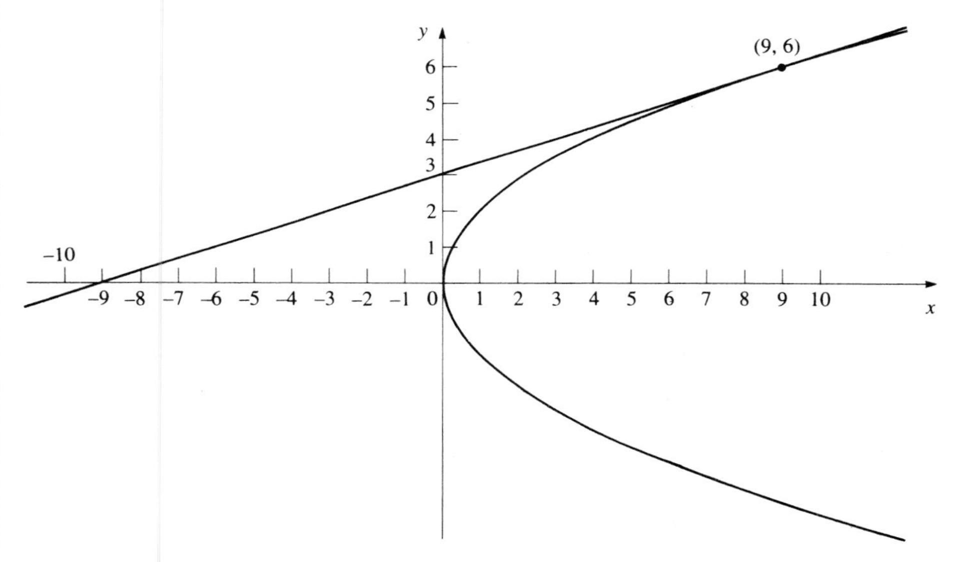

Figure 9.15

EXAMPLE 9.8

An ellipse has parametric equations $x = 4\cos\theta$, $y = 3\sin\theta$.

(i) Find $\frac{dy}{dx}$ at the point with parameter θ.

(ii) Find the equation of the normal at the general point $(4\cos\theta, 3\sin\theta)$.

(iii) Find the equation of the normal at the point where $\theta = \frac{\pi}{4}$.

(iv) Find the co-ordinates of the point where $\theta = \frac{\pi}{4}$.

(v) Show the ellipse and the normal on a sketch.

SOLUTION

(i) $x = 4\cos\theta \quad \Rightarrow \quad \frac{dx}{d\theta} = -4\sin\theta$

$y = 3\sin\theta \quad \Rightarrow \quad \frac{dy}{d\theta} = 3\cos\theta$

$$\frac{dy}{dx} = \frac{\frac{dy}{d\theta}}{\frac{dx}{d\theta}} = \frac{3\cos\theta}{-4\sin\theta}$$

$$= -\frac{3\cos\theta}{4\sin\theta}$$

(ii) The tangent and normal are perpendicular, so the gradient of the normal is

$$-\frac{1}{\frac{dy}{dx}} \quad \text{which is} \quad +\frac{4\sin\theta}{3\cos\theta}.$$

$m_1 m_2 = -1$ for perpendicular lines.

Using $y - y_1 = m(x - x_1)$ and taking the point (x_1, y_1) as $(4\cos\theta, 3\sin\theta)$, the equation of the normal at the point $(4\cos\theta, 3\sin\theta)$ is

$$y - 3\sin\theta = \frac{4\sin\theta}{3\cos\theta}(x - 4\cos\theta)$$

$$\Rightarrow \quad 3y\cos\theta - 9\sin\theta\cos\theta = 4x\sin\theta - 16\sin\theta\cos\theta$$

$$\Rightarrow \quad 4x\sin\theta - 3y\cos\theta - 7\sin\theta\cos\theta = 0.$$

(iii) When $\theta = \frac{\pi}{4}$, $\cos\theta = \frac{1}{\sqrt{2}}$ and $\sin\theta = \frac{1}{\sqrt{2}}$, so the equation of the normal is

$$4x \times \frac{1}{\sqrt{2}} - 3y \times \frac{1}{\sqrt{2}} - 7 \times \frac{1}{\sqrt{2}} \times \frac{1}{\sqrt{2}} = 0$$

$$\Rightarrow \quad 4\sqrt{2}x - 3\sqrt{2}y - 7 = 0$$

$$\Rightarrow \quad 4x - 3y - 4.95 = 0 \text{ (to 2 decimal places).}$$

(iv) The co-ordinates of the point where $\theta = \frac{\pi}{4}$ are

$$\left(4\cos\frac{\pi}{4}, 3\sin\frac{\pi}{4}\right) = \left(4 \times \frac{1}{\sqrt{2}}, 3 \times \frac{1}{\sqrt{2}}\right)$$

$$\approx (2.83, 2.12).$$

(v)

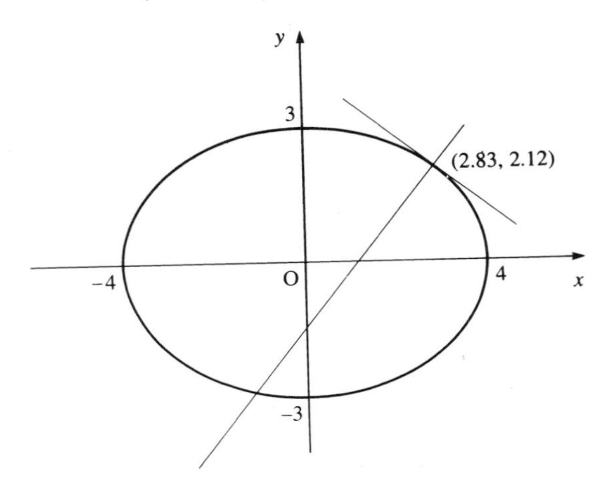

Figure 9.16

Turning points

When the equation of a curve is given parametrically, the easiest way to distinguish between turning points is usually to consider the sign of $\frac{dy}{dx}$. If you use this method, you must be careful to ensure that you take points which are to the left and right of the turning point, i.e. have x co-ordinates smaller and larger than those at the turning point. These will not necessarily be points whose parameters are smaller and larger than those at the turning point.

EXAMPLE 9.9

Find the turning points of the curve with parametric equations $x = 2t + 1$, $y = 3t - t^3$, and distinguish between them.

SOLUTION

$$x = 2t + 1 \quad \Rightarrow \quad \frac{dx}{dt} = 2$$

$$y = 3t - t^3 \quad \Rightarrow \quad \frac{dy}{dt} = 3 - 3t^2$$

$$\frac{dy}{dx} = \frac{\frac{dy}{dt}}{\frac{dx}{dt}} = \frac{3 - 3t^2}{2} = \frac{3(1 - t^2)}{2}$$

Turning points occur when $\frac{dy}{dx} = 0$:

$$\Rightarrow \quad t^2 = 1 \quad \Rightarrow \quad t = 1 \quad \text{or} \quad t = -1.$$

At $t = 1$: $x = 3$, $y = 2$.

At $t = 0.9$: $x = 2.8$ (to the left); $\frac{dy}{dx} = 0.285$ (positive).

At $t = 1.1$: $x = 3.2$ (to the right); $\frac{dy}{dx} = -0.315$ (negative).

There is a maximum at (3, 2).

At $t = -1$: $x = -1$, $y = 2$.

At $t = -1.1$: $x = -1.2$ (to the left); $\frac{dy}{dx} = -0.315$ (negative).

At $t = -0.9$: $x = -0.8$ (to the right); $\frac{dy}{dx} = 0.285$ (positive).

There is a minimum at (–1, –2).

e *An alternative method*

Alternatively, to find $\frac{d^2y}{dx^2}$ when $\frac{dy}{dx}$ is expressed in terms of a parameter requires a further use of the chain rule:

$$\frac{d^2y}{dx^2} = \frac{d}{dx}\left(\frac{dy}{dx}\right) = \frac{d}{dt}\left(\frac{dy}{dx}\right) \times \frac{dt}{dx}.$$

EXERCISE 9B

1 For each of the following curves, find $\frac{dy}{dx}$ in terms of the parameter.

(i) $x = 3t^2$
$y = 2t^3$

(ii) $x = \theta - \cos\theta$
$y = \theta + \sin\theta$

(iii) $x = t + \frac{1}{t}$
$y = t - \frac{1}{t}$

(iv) $x = 3\cos\theta$
$y = 2\sin\theta$

(v) $x = (t+1)^2$
$y = (t-1)^2$

(vi) $x = \theta\sin\theta + \cos\theta$
$y = \theta\cos\theta - \sin\theta$

(vii) $x = e^{2t} + 1$
$y = e^t$

(viii) $x = \frac{t}{1+t}$
$y = \frac{t}{1-t}$

2 A curve has the parametric equations $x = \tan\theta$, $y = \tan 2\theta$. Find

(i) the value of $\frac{dy}{dx}$ when $\theta = \frac{\pi}{6}$

(ii) the equation of the tangent to the curve at the point where $\theta = \frac{\pi}{6}$

(iii) the equation of the normal to the curve at the point where $\theta = \frac{\pi}{6}$.

3 A curve has the parametric equations $x = t^2$, $y = 1 - \frac{1}{2t}$ for $t > 0$. Find

(i) the co-ordinates of the point P where the curve cuts the x axis

(ii) the gradient of the curve at this point

(iii) the equation of the tangent to the curve at P

(iv) the co-ordinates of the point where the tangent cuts the y axis.

4 A curve has parametric equations $x = at^2$, $y = 2at$, where a is constant. Find

(i) the equation of the tangent to the curve at the point with parameter t

(ii) the equation of the normal to the curve at the point with parameter t

(iii) the co-ordinates of the points where the normal cuts the x and y axes.

5 A curve has parametric equations $x = \cos\theta$, $y = \cos 2\theta$.

(i) Show that $\frac{dy}{dx} = 4\cos\theta$.

(ii) By writing $\frac{dy}{dx}$ in terms of x, show that $\frac{d^2y}{dx^2} - 4 = 0$.

6 The parametric equations of a curve are $x = at$, $y = \frac{b}{t}$, where a and b are constant. Find in terms of a, b and t

(i) $\frac{dy}{dx}$

(ii) the equation of the tangent to the curve at the general point $\left(at, \frac{b}{t}\right)$

(iii) the co-ordinates of the points X and Y where the tangent cuts the x and y axes.

(iv) Show that the area of triangle OXY is constant, where O is the origin.

7 The diagram shows a sketch of the curve given parametrically in terms of t by the equations $x = 4t$ and $y = 2t^2$ where t takes positive and negative values.

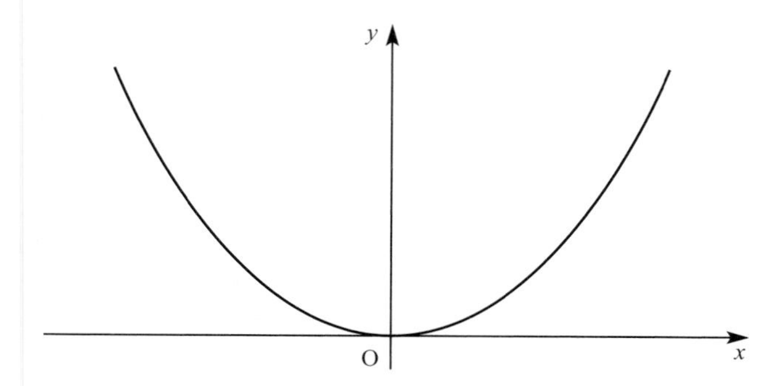

P is the point on the curve with parameter t.

(i) Show that the gradient at P is t.

(ii) Find and simplify the equation of the tangent at P.

The tangents at two points Q (with parameter t_1) and R (with parameter t_2) meet at S.

(iii) Find the co-ordinates of S.

(iv) In the case when $t_1 + t_2 = 2$ show that S lies on a straight line. Give the equation of the line.

[MEI, *adapted*]

8 The diagram shows a sketch of the curve given parametrically in terms of t by the equations $x = 1 - t^2$, $y = 2t + 1$.

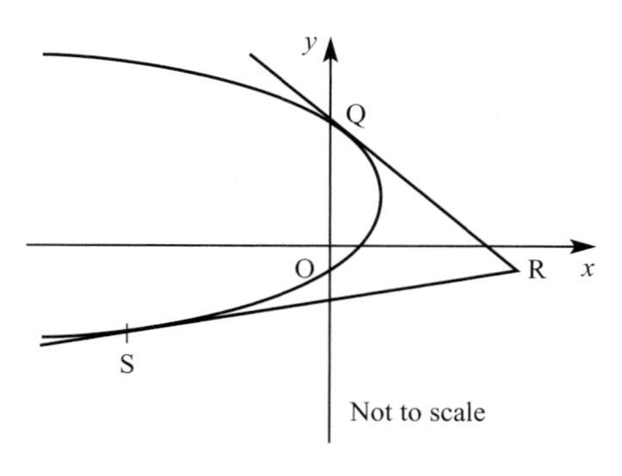

(i) Show that the point Q(0, 3) lies on the curve, stating the value of t corresponding to this point.

(ii) Show that, at the point with parameter t,

$$\frac{dy}{dx} = -\frac{1}{t}.$$

(iii) Find the equation of the tangent at Q.

(iv) Verify that the tangent at Q passes through the point R(4, –1).

(v) The other tangent from R to the curve touches the curve at the point S and has equation $3y - x + 7 = 0$. Find the co-ordinates of S.

[MEI]

9 The diagram shows a sketch of the curve with parametric equations $x = 1 - 2t$, $y = t^2$. The tangent and normal at P are also shown.

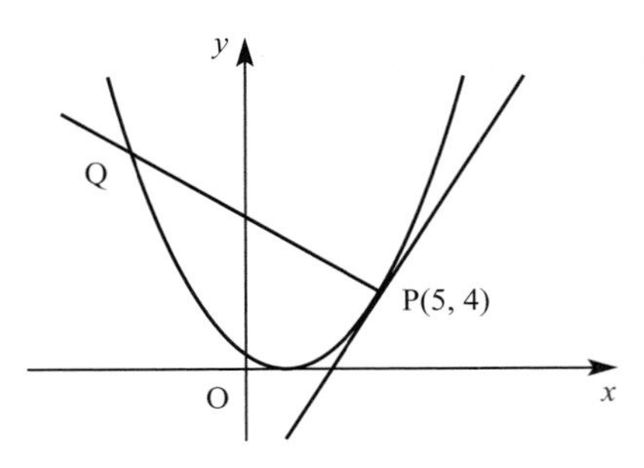

(i) Show that the point P(5, 4) lies on the curve by stating the value of t corresponding to this point.

(ii) Show that, at the point with parameter t, $\dfrac{dy}{dx} = -t$.

(iii) Find the equation of the tangent at P.

(iv) The normal at P cuts the curve again at Q. Find the co-ordinates of Q.

[MEI]

10 A particle P moves in a plane so that at time t its co-ordinates are given by $x = 4\cos t$, $y = 3\sin t$. Find

(i) $\dfrac{dy}{dx}$ in terms of t

(ii) the equation of the tangent to its path at time t

(iii) the values of t for which the particle is travelling parallel to the line $x + y = 0$.

11 A circle has parametric equations $x = 3 + 2\cos\theta$, $y = 3 + 2\sin\theta$.

(i) Find the equation of the tangent at the point with parameter θ.

(ii) Show that this tangent will pass through the origin provided that $\sin\theta + \cos\theta = -\frac{2}{3}$.

(iii) By writing $\sin\theta + \cos\theta$ in the form $R\sin(\theta + \alpha)$, solve the equation $\sin\theta + \cos\theta = -\frac{2}{3}$ for $0 \leqslant \theta \leqslant 2\pi$.

(iv) Illustrate the circle and tangents on a sketch, showing clearly the values of θ which you found in part **(iii)**.

12 The parametric equations of the circle with centre (2, 5) and radius 3 units are $x = 2 + 3\cos\theta$, $y = 5 + 3\sin\theta$.

(i) Find the gradient of the circle at the point with parameter θ.

(ii) Find the equation of the normal to the circle at this point.

(iii) Show that the normal at any point on the circle passes through the centre. (This is an alternative proof of the result 'the tangent and radius are perpendicular'.)

13 The parametric equations of a curve are

$$x = 3\cos\theta, \quad y = 2\sin\theta \quad \text{for } 0 \leqslant \theta < 2\pi.$$

(i) By eliminating θ between these two equations, find the cartesian equation of the curve.

(ii) The diagram shows a sketch of the curve. On a copy of the diagram show the pair of tangents which pass through the point (6, 2).

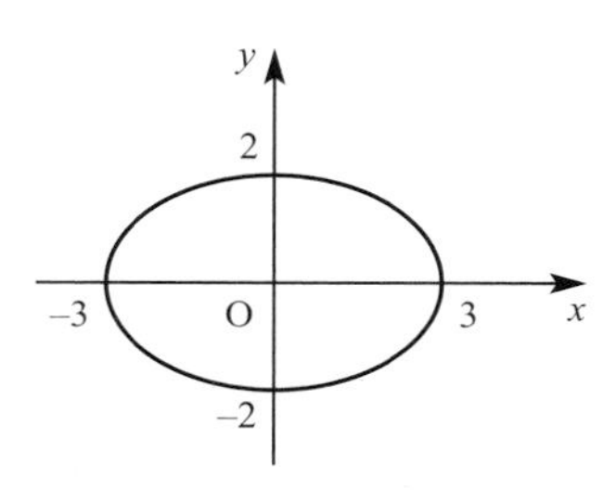

(iii) Use the parametric equations to calculate $\frac{dy}{dx}$ in terms of θ.

You are given that the equation of the tangent to the curve at $(3\cos\theta, 2\sin\theta)$ is

$$2x\cos\theta + 3y\sin\theta = 6.$$

(iv) Show that, for tangents to the curve which pass through the point (6, 2),

$$2\cos\theta + \sin\theta = 1.$$

(v) Solve the equation in part **(iv)** to find the two values of θ (in radians correct to 2 decimal places) corresponding to the two tangents.

[MEI, *adapted*]

14 An ellipse has equation given in parametric form by $x = 4\cos\theta$, $y = 3\sin\theta$, $0 \leqslant \theta < 2\pi$.

The sketch illustrates this ellipse and point $P(4\cos\theta, 3\sin\theta)$, $0 \leqslant \theta \leqslant \frac{\pi}{2}$.

Rectangle PQRS has PQ parallel to the x axis and PS parallel to the y axis, with Q, R and S also on the ellipse.

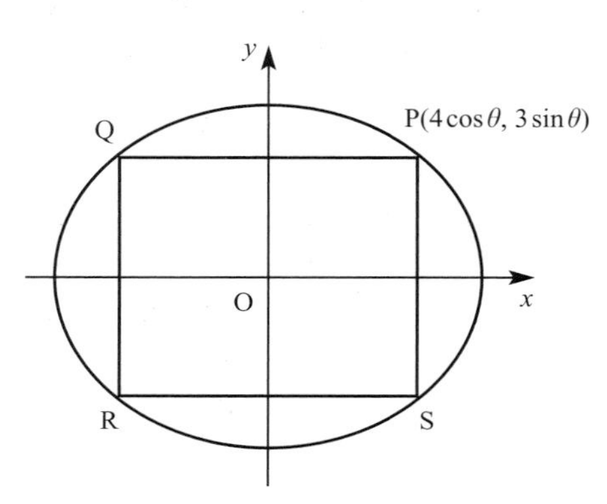

(i) **(a)** Express the equation of the ellipse in cartesian form.

(b) The length, L, of the perimeter of PQRS is given by $L = 12\sin\theta + 16\cos\theta$. Express L in the form $r\sin(\theta + \alpha)$, where r and α are constants to be determined.

(c) Find the maximum value of L and the value of θ, $0 \leqslant \theta \leqslant \frac{\pi}{2}$, for which it occurs.

(ii) The line PS produced meets the line $y = -8$ at the point U with co-ordinates $(4\cos\theta, -8)$, where $0 \leqslant \theta \leqslant \frac{\pi}{2}$.

(a) Write down the gradient of OU.

(b) Calculate the gradient of the tangent at P.

(c) Find the value of θ for which OU is parallel to the tangent at P. Give your answer correct to 2 decimal places.

[MEI]

15 The curve shown in the diagram has parametric equations

$$x = \frac{1}{1+t}, \qquad y = \frac{1}{(1+t)(1-t)}, \qquad (t \neq \pm 1).$$

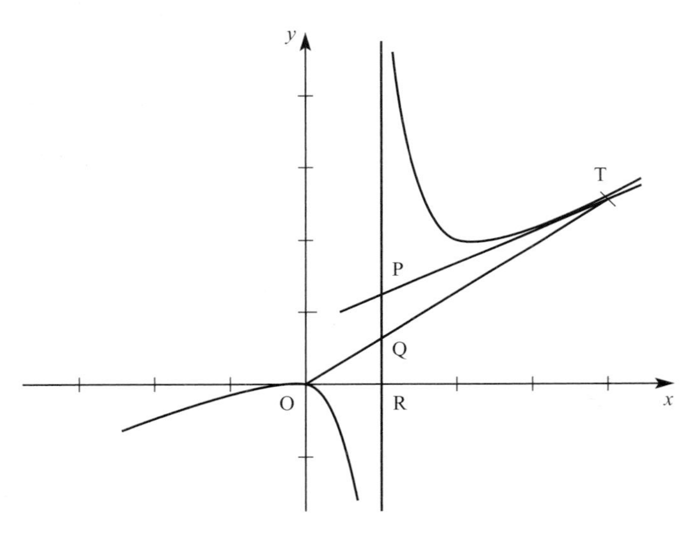

(i) Express t in terms of x.

Hence show that the cartesian equation of the curve is $y = \dfrac{x^2}{2x-1}$.

(ii) Find $\dfrac{dy}{dt}$ and $\dfrac{dx}{dt}$ and hence show that

$$\frac{dy}{dx} = -\frac{2t}{(1-t)^2}.$$

(iii) You are given that the equation of the tangent at the point T having parameter t is $2tx + (1-t)^2 y = 1$.

Find the y co-ordinate of the point P where this tangent cuts the line $x = \frac{1}{2}$.

(iv) The point Q is the intersection of the line $x = \frac{1}{2}$ and the straight line joining the origin to the point T. Point R has co-ordinates $\left(\frac{1}{2}, 0\right)$.

Show that RQ = QP.

[MEI]

16 The diagram shows the curve with parametric equations

$$x = \cos t, \qquad y = \frac{1}{2}\sin 2t$$

for $0 \leqslant t \leqslant 2\pi$. The curve is symmetrical about both axes.

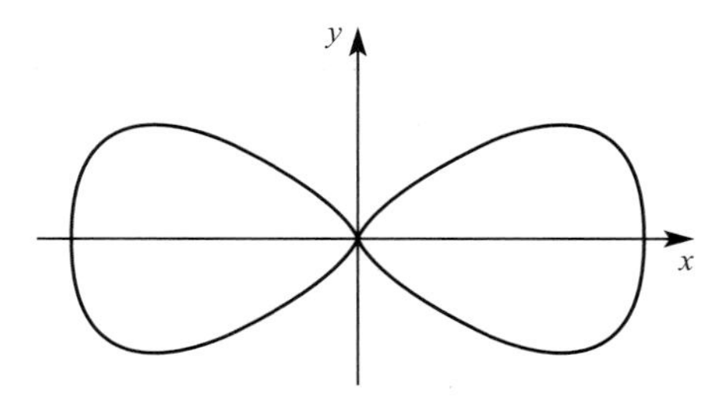

(i) Copy the diagram. Locate and label on your sketch the points having parameters

$$t = 0, \quad t = \frac{\pi}{2}, \quad t = \pi \text{ and } t = \frac{3\pi}{2}.$$

(ii) Find an expression for $\frac{dy}{dx}$ in terms of the parameter t.

Hence show that, at the origin, the curve crosses itself at right angles.

(iii) Show that the cartesian equation of the curve is $y^2 = x^2(1 - x^2)$.

(iv) Show that the parameters of the points where the gradient of the curve is $-\frac{7}{2}$ satisfy the equation $4\sin^2 t + 7\sin t - 2 = 0$.

Find the parameters of these points.

[MEI]

17 The curve in the diagram is given by the parametric equations

$$x = 2\cos\theta + \sin\theta, \qquad y = \cos\theta + 2\sin\theta \qquad \text{for } 0 \leqslant \theta < 2\pi.$$

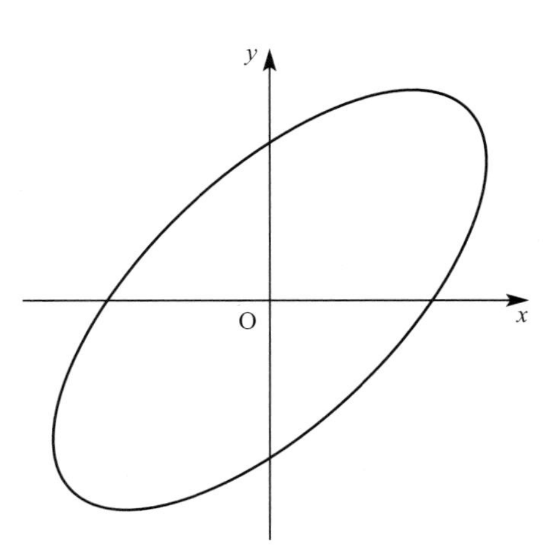

(i) Express x in the form $R\cos(\theta - \alpha)$, where $R > 0$.
Between what values must x lie?

(ii) Find the gradient of the curve at the point where $\theta = \frac{\pi}{2}$.

(iii) Show that, for any point on the curve,

$$x^2 + y^2 = 5 + 4\sin 2\theta.$$

(iv) Find the greatest and least distances of a point on the curve from the origin.

[MEI]

18 The diagram shows a sketch of the curve given by the parametric equations $x = \sin t$, $y = t\sin t$ for $0 \leqslant t \leqslant \pi$.

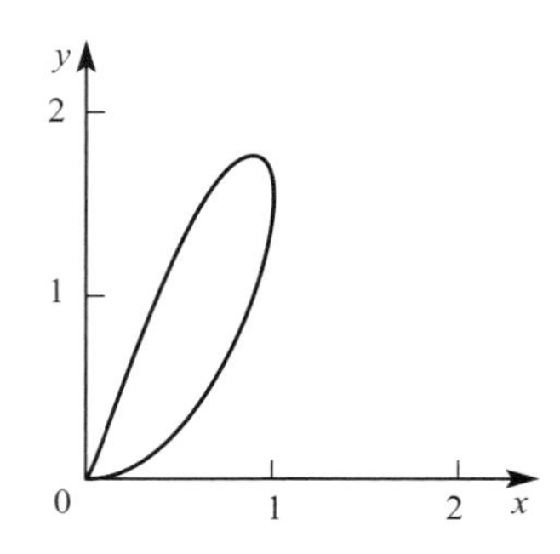

(i) On a copy of the diagram mark the points having parameters $t = 0$, $\frac{1}{2}\pi$ and π.

(ii) Show that $\dfrac{dy}{dx} = t + \tan t$.
Find the gradients of the curve at the origin.

(iii) Find $\int t\sin 2t \, dt$.
Hence show that $\int_0^\pi t\sin 2t \, dt = -\frac{1}{2}\pi$.

(iv) You are given that the area of the region enclosed by this curve is

$$\left| \int_0^\pi y \frac{dx}{dt} dt \right|.$$

Evaluate this area.

[MEI]

19 (i) Given that $\tan\alpha = 2$ and $0 < \alpha < \frac{1}{2}\pi$, find the exact values of $\sin\alpha$, $\cos\alpha$ and $\sin 2\alpha$.

The diagram shows a sketch of the curve given by the parametric equations

$$x = \cos t + 2\sin t, \; y = \sin 2t \quad (0 \leqslant t \leqslant \pi).$$

The curve cuts the x axis at the points A, B and D. The point on the curve where the x co-ordinate attains its maximum value is C.

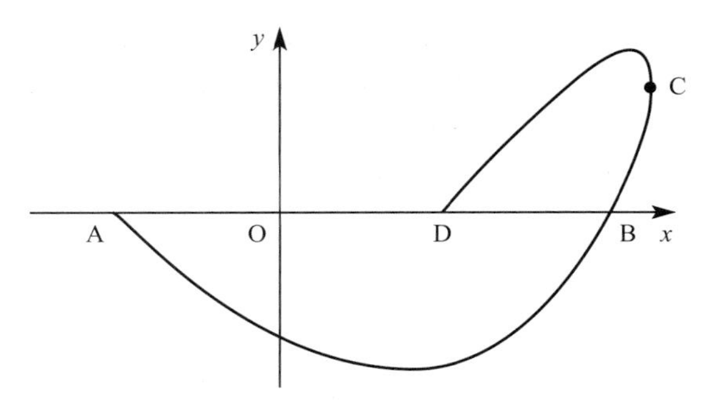

(ii) Find the x co-ordinates of the points A, B and D.

(iii) Show that $\cos t + 2\sin t$ can be expressed in the form $R\cos(t - \alpha)$, where α is the angle given in part **(i)** and R is to determined.

Hence or otherwise find the *exact* co-ordinates of C.

(iv) Find $\frac{dy}{dx}$ in terms of t.

Deduce the value of the gradient of the curve at the point A.

[MEI]

20 The curve with parametric equations

$$x = \theta - \sin\theta, \quad y = 1 - \cos\theta, \quad 0 \leqslant \theta \leqslant 2\pi,$$

is a cycloid. Its graph is shown in the diagram.

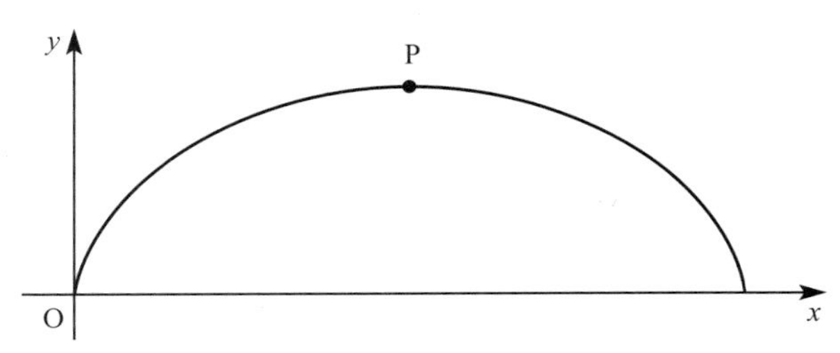

(i) Find $\frac{dy}{dx}$ in terms of θ.

Deduce the co-ordinates of the stationary point P.

(ii) At the point on the curve with parameter α, the gradient is $\frac{1}{2}$. Show that

$$2\sin\alpha + \cos\alpha = 1$$

By expressing the left-hand side of the equation in the form $R\cos(\alpha - \beta)$, solve this equation for α, giving your answer in radians correct to 3 decimal places.

(iii) The area of the region enclosed by the curve and the x axis is A, where

$$A = \int_0^{2\pi} y\frac{dx}{d\theta}\,d\theta.$$

Show that $A = \int_0^{2\pi} (1 - \cos\theta)^2\,d\theta$.

Hence find A, giving your answer as a multiple of π.

$\left(\textbf{Hint: } \cos^2\theta = \frac{1 + \cos 2\theta}{2}\right)$

[MEI]

21 The diagram shows a sketch of the curve with equation $y^2 = (1 - 2x)^3$.
The curve meets the x axis at A and crosses the y axis at the points B and C.

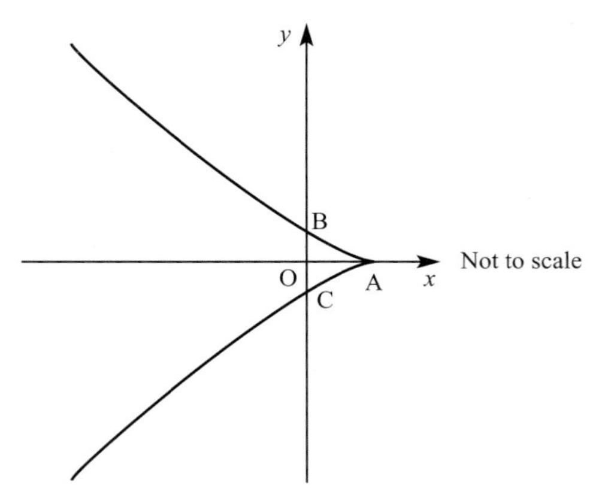

(i) Find the co-ordinates of the points A, B and C.

(ii) Show that the gradient of the curve at the point B is –3.

(iii) Verify that

$$x = \tfrac{1}{2}(1 - t^2), \quad y = t^3$$

are parametric equations for the curve.

Find $\dfrac{dy}{dx}$ in terms of t, and show that the equation of the tangent to the curve at the point with parameter t is

$$6tx + 2y + t^3 - 3t = 0.$$

[MEI]

22 The ellipse shown in the diagram has parametric equations

$$x = 2\cos\theta, \quad y = \sin\theta \quad (0 \leqslant \theta \leqslant 2\pi).$$

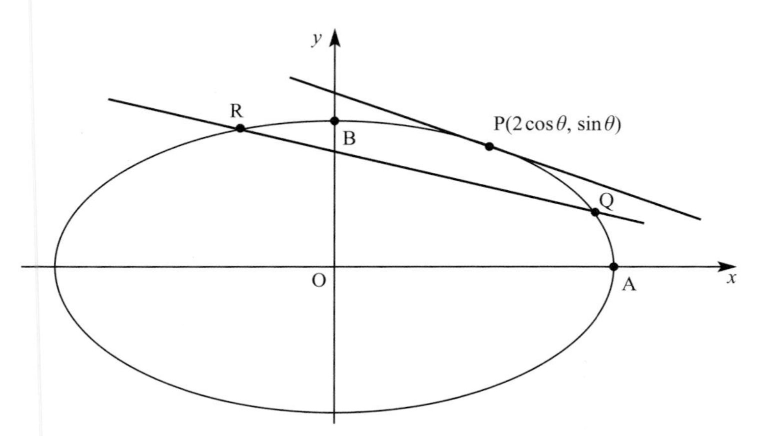

The ellipse crosses the positive co-ordinate axes at A and B.

(i) Write down the parameters and co-ordinates of each of the points A and B.

(ii) Find the cartesian equation of the ellipse.

(iii) Find an expression in terms of θ for the gradient of the tangent to the ellipse at the point P with parameter θ.

The points Q and R have parameters α and $\alpha + \frac{1}{2}\pi$ respectively, where $0 < \alpha < \frac{1}{2}\pi$.

(iv) Find the co-ordinates of R in terms of α.
Hence write down an expression in terms of α for the gradient of the chord QR.

(v) Show that

$$\frac{\cos\left(\alpha + \frac{1}{4}\pi\right)}{\sin\left(\alpha + \frac{1}{4}\pi\right)} = \frac{\cos\alpha - \sin\alpha}{\cos\alpha + \sin\alpha}.$$

Hence or otherwise deduce that the tangent at P is parallel to the chord QR when $\theta = \alpha + \frac{1}{4}\pi$ or $\theta = \alpha + \frac{5}{4}\pi$.

[MEI]

KEY POINTS

1. In parametric equations the relationship between two variables is expressed by writing both of them in terms of a third variable or *parameter*.

2. To draw a graph from parametric equations, plot the points on the curve given by different values of the parameter.

3. Eliminating the parameter gives the cartesian equation of the curve.

4. The parametric equations of circles:

   - **Circle** centre (0, 0) and radius r

     $x = r\cos\theta \qquad y = r\sin\theta$

   - **Circle** centre (a, b) and radius r

     $x = a + r\cos\theta \qquad y = b + r\sin\theta$

5. $\dfrac{dy}{dx} = \dfrac{\frac{dy}{dt}}{\frac{dx}{dt}}$ provided that $\dfrac{dx}{dt} \neq 0$.

e $\dfrac{d^2y}{dx^2} = \dfrac{d}{dx}\left(\dfrac{dy}{dx}\right) = \dfrac{d}{dt}\left(\dfrac{dy}{dx}\right) \times \dfrac{dt}{dx}$

e The parametric equations of some other standard curves:

- **Ellipse** centre (0, 0) with major axis $2a$ and minor axis $2b$

  $x = a\cos\theta \qquad y = b\sin\theta$

- **Parabola** with line of symmetry the x axis

  $x = at^2 \qquad y = 2at$

- **Rectangular hyperbola** $xy = c^2$

  $x = ct \qquad y = \dfrac{c}{t}$

10 Further techniques for integration

A mind once stretched by a new idea never regains its original dimensions.

Oliver Wendell Holmes

These photographs show spiral galaxies. One is taken from near its axis of rotation, the other from a point in its plane. Our own galaxy is a spiral of radius 100 000 light years. At its thickest it is 1000 light years across.

❓ How would you estimate the volume of our galaxy?

Finding volumes by integration

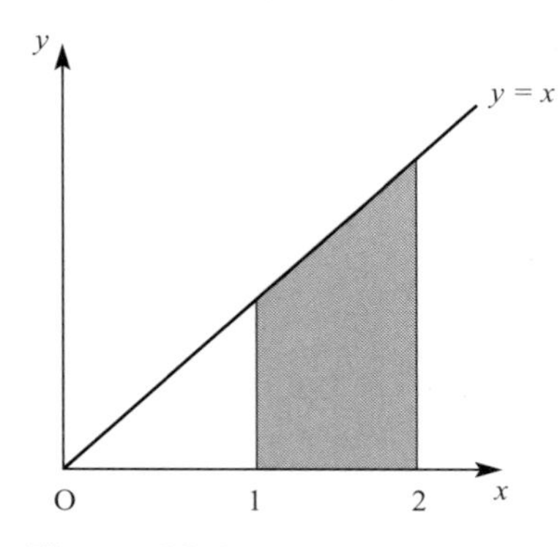

Figure 10.1

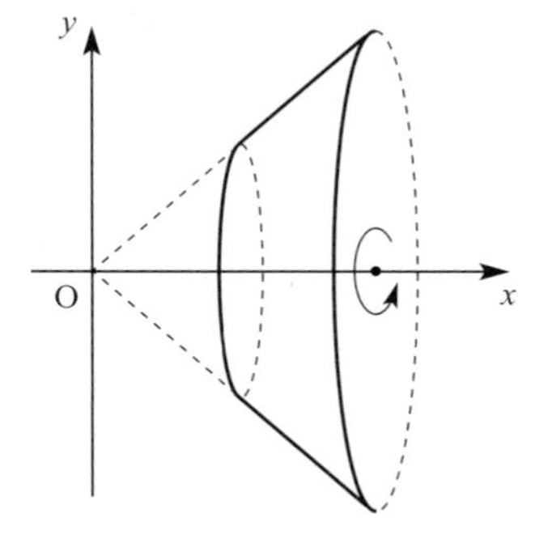

Figure 10.2

When the shaded region in figure 10.1 is rotated through 360° about the x axis, the solid obtained, illustrated in figure 10.2 is called a *solid of revolution.* In this particular case, the volume of the solid could be calculated as the difference between the volumes of two cones $\left(\text{using } V = \frac{1}{3}\pi r^2 h\right)$, but if the line $y = x$ in figure 10.1 was replaced by a curve, such a simple calculation would no longer be possible.

1 Describe the solid of revolution obtained by a rotation through 360° of

(i) a rectangle about one side
(ii) a semi-circle about its diameter
(iii) a circle about a line outside the circle.

2 Calculate the volume of the solid obtained in figure 10.2, leaving your answer as a multiple of π.

Solids formed by rotation about the *x* axis

Now look at the solid formed by rotating the shaded region in figure 10.3 through 360° about the x axis.

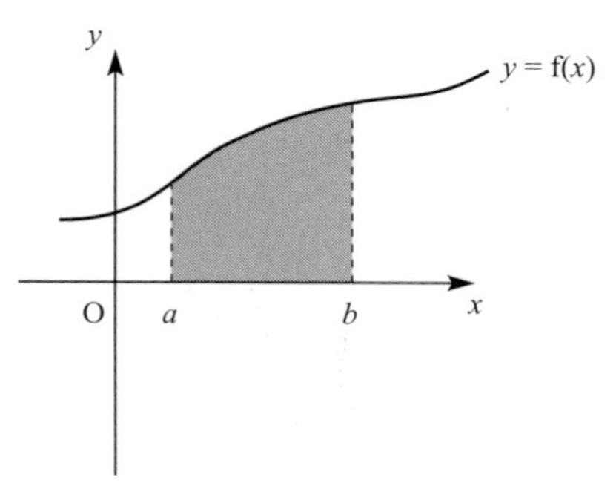

Figure 10.3

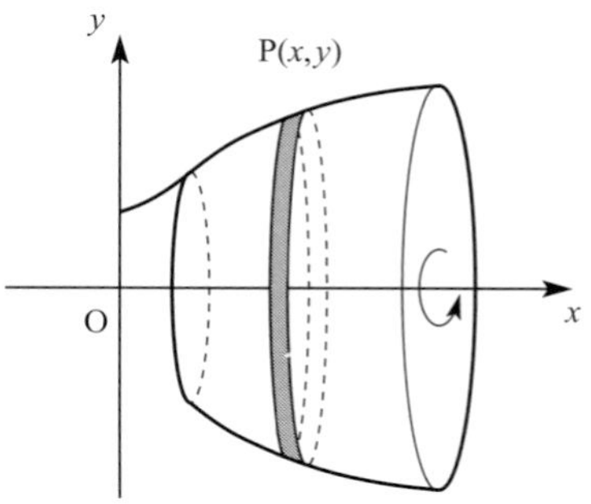

y
P(x, y)
O
x

Figure 10.4

The volume of the solid of revolution (which is usually called the *volume of revolution*) can be found by imagining that the solid can be sliced into thin discs.

The disc shown in figure 10.4 is approximately cylindrical with radius y and thickness δx, so its volume is given by

$$\delta V = \pi y^2 \delta x.$$

The volume of the solid is the limit of the sum of all these elementary discs as $\delta x \to 0$,

i.e. the limit as $\delta x \to 0$ of $\sum_{\substack{\text{over all} \\ \text{discs}}} \delta V$

or the limit as $\delta x \to 0$ of $\sum_{x=a}^{x=b} \pi y^2 \delta x$.

The limiting values of sums such as these are integrals so

$$V = \int_a^b \pi y^2 \mathrm{d}x$$

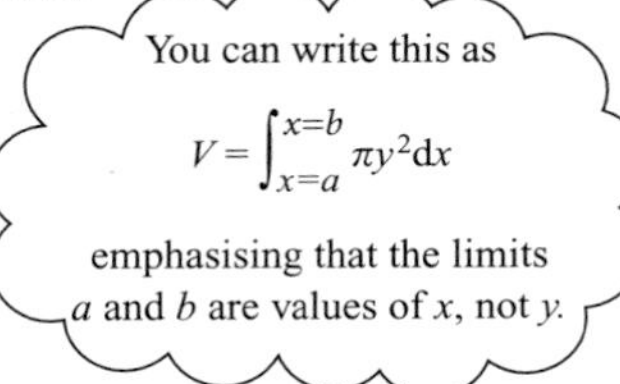

The limits are a and b because x takes values from a to b.

Since the integration is 'with respect to x', indicated by the dx and the fact that the limits a and b are values of x, it cannot be evaluated unless the function y is also written in terms of x.

EXAMPLE 10.1

The region between the curve $y = x^2$, the x axis and the lines $x = 1$ and $x = 3$ is rotated through 360° about the x axis.
Find the volume of revolution which is formed.

SOLUTION

The region is shaded in figure 10.5.

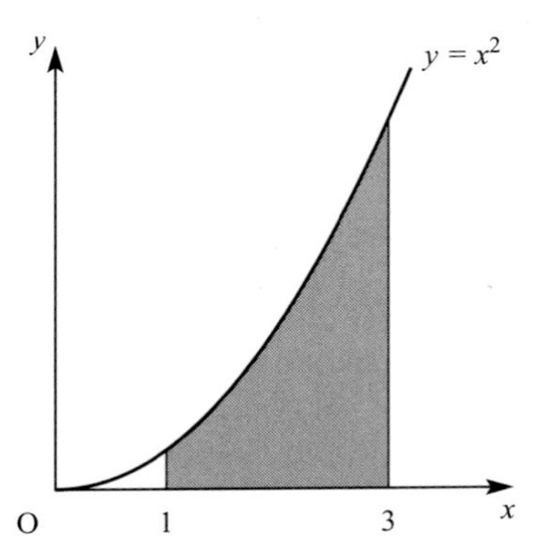

Figure 10.5

Using $V = \int_a^b \pi y^2 \, dx$

$$\text{volume} = \int_1^3 \pi (x^2)^2 \, dx$$

$$= \int_1^3 \pi x^4 \, dx$$

Since in this case $y = x^2$, $y^2 = (x^2)^2 = x^4$.

$$= \left[\frac{\pi x^5}{5} \right]_1^3$$

$$= \frac{\pi}{5}(243 - 1)$$

$$= \frac{242\pi}{5}.$$

The volume is $\frac{242\pi}{5}$ cubic units or 152 cubic units (3 s.f.).

Unless a decimal answer is required, it is usual to leave π in the answer, which is then exact.

EXAMPLE 10.2

(i) Find the volume of a spherical ball of radius 2 cm using integration.

(ii) Verify your result using the formula for the volume of a sphere.

SOLUTION

(i) The volume is obtained by rotating the top half of the circle $x^2 + y^2 = 4$ through 360° about the x axis.

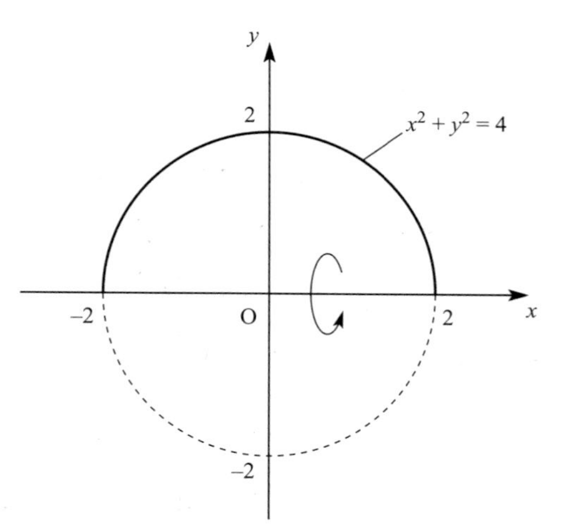

Figure 10.6

(i) Using $V = \int_a^b \pi y^2 \mathrm{d}x$ and $y^2 = 4 - x^2$ from the circle equation

$$\text{volume} = \int_{-2}^{2} \pi(4 - x^2)\mathrm{d}x$$

$$= \pi\left[4x - \frac{x^3}{3}\right]_{-2}^{2}$$

$$= \pi\left[\left(8 - \frac{8}{3}\right) - \left(-8 + \frac{8}{3}\right)\right]$$

$$= \frac{32\pi}{3}\text{cm}^3.$$

(ii) Volume of a sphere $= \frac{4}{3}\pi r^3$

$$= \frac{4}{3}\pi \times 2^3$$

$$= \frac{32\pi}{3}\text{cm}^3.$$

Rotation about the *y* axis

When a region is rotated about the y axis a very different solid is obtained.

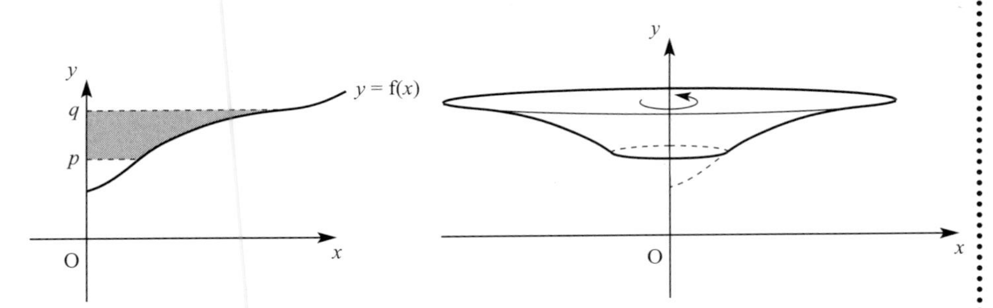

Figure 10.7 **Figure 10.8**

Notice the difference between the solid obtained in figure 10.8 and that in figure 10.4.

For rotation about the x axis you obtained the formula

$$V_{x \text{ axis}} = \int_a^b \pi y^2 \mathrm{d}x.$$

In a similar way, the formula for rotation about the y axis

$V_{y \text{ axis}} = \int_p^q \pi x^2 \mathrm{d}y$ can be obtained.

In this case you will need to substitute for x^2 in terms of y.

How would you prove this result?

EXAMPLE 10.3

The region between the curve $y = x^2$, the y axis and the lines $y = 2$ and $y = 5$ is rotated through 360° about the y axis.
Find the volume of revolution which is formed.

SOLUTION

The region is shaded in figure 10.9.

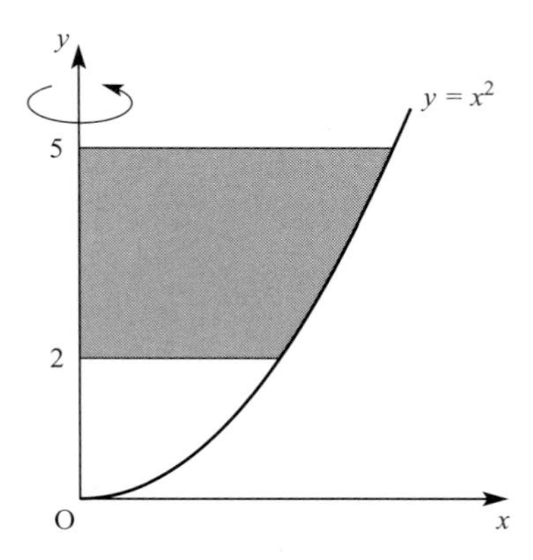

Figure 10.9

Using $V = \int_p^q \pi x^2 \mathrm{d}y$

$$\text{volume} = \int_2^5 \pi y \,\mathrm{d}y \text{ since } x^2 = y$$

$$= \left[\frac{\pi y^2}{2}\right]_2^5$$

$$= \frac{\pi}{2}(25 - 4)$$

$$= \frac{21\pi}{2} \text{ cubic units.}$$

EXERCISE 10A

1 Name six common objects which are solids of revolution.

2 In each part of this question a region is defined in terms of the lines which form its boundaries. Draw a sketch of the region and find the volume of the solid obtained by rotating it through 360° about the x axis.

(i) $y = 2x$, the x axis and the lines $x = 1$ and $x = 3$
(ii) $y = x + 2$, the x axis, the y axis and the line $x = 2$
(iii) $y = x^2 + 1$, the x axis and the lines $x = -1$ and $x = 1$
(iv) $y = \sqrt{x}$, the x axis and the line $x = 4$

3 **(i)** Find the co-ordinates of A and B, the points of intersection of the circle $x^2 + y^2 = 25$ and the line $y = 4$.

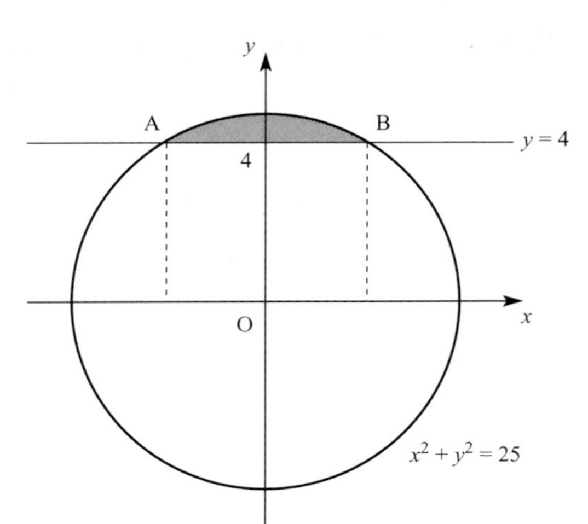

(ii) A napkin ring is formed by rotating the shaded area through 360° about the x axis. By considering the shaded area as the difference between two areas, and hence the volume of the napkin ring as the difference between two volumes, find the volume of the napkin ring.

4 **(i)** Sketch the line $4y = 3x$ for $x \geqslant 0$.

(ii) Identify the area between this line and the x axis which, when rotated through 360° about the x axis, would give a cone of base radius 3 and height 4.

(iii) Calculate the volume of the cone using

(a) integration

(b) a formula.

5 **(i)** Sketch the graph of $y = (x - 2)^2$ for values of x between $x = -1$ and $x = 5$. Shade in the region under the curve, between $x = 0$ and $x = 2$.

(ii) Calculate the area you have shaded.

(iii) Show that $(x - 2)^4 = x^4 - 8x^3 + 24x^2 - 32x + 16$.

(iv) The shaded region is rotated about the x axis to form a volume of revolution. Calculate this volume, using your answer to **(iii)** or otherwise.

[MEI]

6 **(i)** Sketch the graph of $y = (x + 1)^2$ for values of x between $x = -1$ and $x = 4$.

(ii) Shade in the region under the curve between $x = 1$, $x = 3$ and the x axis. Calculate this area.

(iii) Expand $(x + 1)^4$.

(iv) The shaded region in **(ii)** is rotated about the x axis to form a solid of revolution.
Calculate the volume of this solid.

[MEI]

e *The remaining questions relate to enrichment material.*

7 In each part of this question a region is defined in terms of the lines which form its boundaries. Draw a sketch of the region and find the volume of the solid obtained by rotating through 360° about the y axis.

(i) $y = 3x$, the y axis and the lines $y = 3$ and $y = 6$

(ii) $y = x - 3$, the y axis, the x axis and the line $y = 6$

(iii) $y = x^2 - 2$, the y axis and the line $y = 4$

8 A hemispherical bowl is formed by rotating the bottom half of the circle $x^2 + y^2 = 100$ about the y axis as shown in the diagram. (Units are in centimetres.)

(i) Find the volume of the bowl.

(ii) The bowl is filled with water to a depth of 8 cm. Find the volume of water in the bowl.

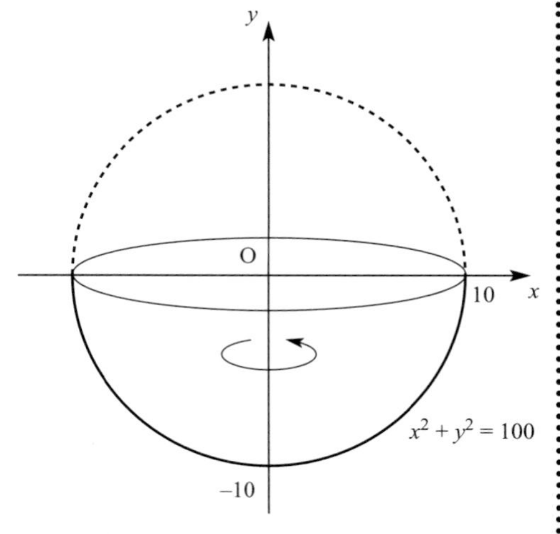

9 A mathematical model for a large garden pot is obtained by rotating through 360° about the y axis the part of the curve $y = 0.1x^2$ which is between $x = 10$ and $x = 25$ and then adding a flat base. Units are in centimetres.

(i) Draw a sketch of the curve and shade in the cross-section of the pot, indicating which line will form its base.

(ii) Garden compost is sold in litres. How many litres will be required to fill the pot to a depth of 45 cm? (Ignore the thickness of the pot.)

10 The graph shows the curve $y = x^2 - 4$.

The region R is formed by the line $y = 12$, the x axis, the y axis and the curve $y = x^2 - 4$ for positive values of x.

(i) Copy the sketch graph and shade the region R.

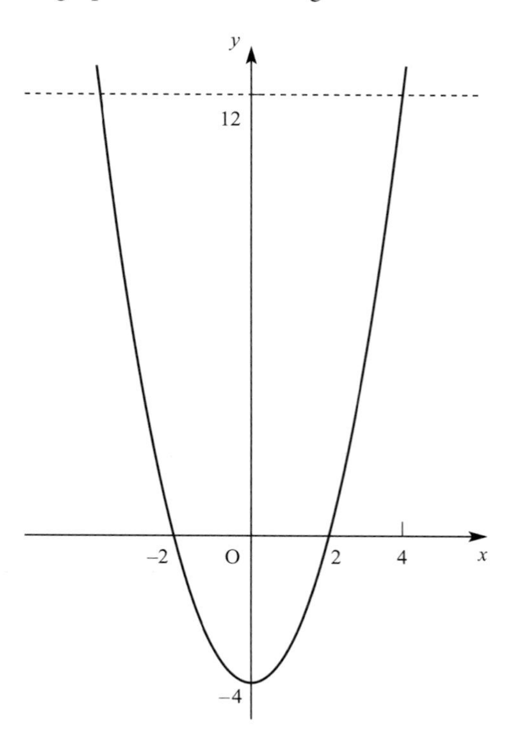

The inside of a vase is formed by rotating the region R through 360° about the y axis. Each unit of x and y represents 2 cm.

(ii) Write down an expression for the volume of revolution of the region R about the y axis.

(iii) Find the capacity of the vase in litres.

(iv) Show that when the vase is filled to $\frac{5}{6}$ of its internal height it is three-quarters full.

[MEI]

The use of partial fractions in integration

Why is it not possible to use any of the integration techniques you have learnt so far to find $\int \frac{2}{x^2 - 1}\,dx$?

Partial fractions

Since $x^2 - 1$ can be factorised to give $(x + 1)(x - 1)$, you can put the function to be integrated into partial fractions.

$$\frac{2}{x^2 - 1} = \frac{A}{x - 1} + \frac{B}{x + 1}$$

$$2 \equiv A(x + 1) + B(x - 1)$$

This is true for all values of x. It is an identity and to emphasise this point we use the identity symbol $\equiv$.

Let $x = 1$ $\quad 2 = 2A \quad \Rightarrow \quad A = 1.$

Let $x = -1$ $\quad 2 = -2B \quad \Rightarrow \quad B = -1.$

Substituting these values for A and B gives

$$\frac{2}{x^2 - 1} = \frac{1}{x - 1} - \frac{1}{x + 1}.$$

The integral then becomes

$$\int \frac{2}{x^2 - 1}\,dx = \int \frac{1}{x - 1}\,dx - \frac{1}{x + 1}\,dx.$$

Now the two integrals on the right can be recognised as logarithms. So

$$\int \frac{2}{x^2 - 1}\,dx = \ln|x - 1| - \ln|x + 1| + c$$

$$= \ln\left|\frac{x - 1}{x + 1}\right| + c.$$

Here you worked with the simplest type of partial fraction, in which there are two different linear factors in the denominator. This type will always result in two functions both of which can be integrated to give logarithmic functions. You will now look at the other types of partial fraction.

A repeated factor in the denominator

EXAMPLE 10.4

Find $\int \frac{x+4}{(2x-1)(x+1)^2} \mathrm{d}x$.

SOLUTION

First put the expression into partial fractions:

$$\frac{x+4}{(2x-1)(x+1)^2} = \frac{A}{(2x-1)} + \frac{B}{(x+1)} + \frac{C}{(x+1)^2}$$

where $\quad x + 4 \equiv A(x+1)^2 + B(2x-1)(x+1) + C(2x-1)$.

Let $x = -1 \quad 3 = -3C \quad \Rightarrow \quad C = -1$.

Let $x = \frac{1}{2} \quad \frac{9}{2} = A\left(\frac{3}{2}\right)^2 \quad \Rightarrow \quad \frac{9}{2} = \frac{9}{4}A \quad \Rightarrow \quad A = 2$.

Let $x = 0 \quad 4 = A - B - C \quad \Rightarrow \quad B = A - C - 4 = 2 + 1 - 4 = -1$.

Substituting these values for A, B and C gives

$$\frac{x+4}{(2x-1)(x+1)^2} = \frac{2}{(2x-1)} - \frac{1}{(x+1)} - \frac{1}{(x+1)^2}.$$

Now that the function is in partial fractions, each part can be integrated separately.

$$\int \frac{x+4}{(2x-1)(x+1)^2} \mathrm{d}x = \int \frac{2}{(2x-1)} \mathrm{d}x - \int \frac{1}{(x+1)} \mathrm{d}x - \int \frac{1}{(x+1)^2} \mathrm{d}x.$$

The first two integrals give logarithmic functions as you saw above. The third, however, is of the form u^{-2} and therefore can be integrated by using the substitution $u = x + 1$, or by inspection (i.e. in your head). So

$$\int \frac{x+4}{(2x-1)(x+1)^2} \mathrm{d}x = \ln|2x-1| - \ln|x+1| + \frac{1}{x+1} + c$$

$$= \ln\left|\frac{2x-1}{x+1}\right| + \frac{1}{x+1} + c.$$

A quadratic factor in the denominator

EXAMPLE 10.5

Find $\displaystyle\int \frac{x-2}{(x^2+2)(x+1)}\,\mathrm{d}x$.

SOLUTION

First put the expression into partial fractions:

$$\frac{x-2}{(x^2+2)(x+1)} = \frac{Ax+B}{(x^2+2)} + \frac{C}{(x+1)}$$

where $\quad x-2 \equiv (Ax+B)(x+1) + C(x^2+2)$.

Rearranging gives

$$x-2 \equiv (A+C)x^2 + (A+B)x + (B+2C).$$

Equating coefficients:

$$\begin{aligned} x^2 \quad &\Rightarrow \quad A + C = 0 \\ x \quad &\Rightarrow \quad A + B = 1 \\ \text{constant terms} \quad &\Rightarrow \quad B + 2C = -2. \end{aligned}$$

Solving these gives $A = 1$, $B = 0$, $C = -1$. Hence

$$\frac{x-2}{(x^2+2)(x+1)} = \frac{x}{(x^2+2)} - \frac{1}{(x+1)}$$

$$\begin{aligned} \int \frac{x-2}{(x^2+2)(x+1)}\,\mathrm{d}x &= \int \frac{x}{(x^2+2)}\,\mathrm{d}x - \int \frac{1}{(x+1)}\,\mathrm{d}x \\ &= \frac{1}{2}\int \frac{2x}{x^2+2}\,\mathrm{d}x - \int \frac{1}{x+1}\,\mathrm{d}x \\ &= \tfrac{1}{2}\ln|x^2+2| - \ln|x+1| + c \\ &= \ln\left|\frac{\sqrt{x^2+2}}{x+1}\right| + c. \end{aligned}$$

$\frac{1}{2}\ln|x^2+2| = \ln\sqrt{x^2+2}$
Notice that (x^2+2) is positive for all values of x.

Note

If B had not been zero, you would have had an expression of the form $\dfrac{Ax+B}{x^2+2}$ to integrate. This can be split into

$$\frac{Ax}{x^2+2} + \frac{B}{x^2+2}$$

The first part of this can be integrated as in Example 10.5, but the second part cannot be integrated by any method you have met so far. If you go on to study the FP2 unit, you will meet integrals of this form then. If in the meantime you come across a case (for example in modelling a situation) where you need to find such an integral, you may choose to use the standard result that

$$\int \frac{1}{(x^2+a^2)}\,\mathrm{d}x = \frac{1}{a}\arctan\left(\frac{x}{a}\right) + c.$$

EXERCISE 10B

1 Express the functions in each of the following integrals in partial fractions, and hence perform the integration.

(i) $\displaystyle\int \frac{1}{(1-x)(3x-2)}\,dx$ **(ii)** $\displaystyle\int \frac{7x-2}{(x-1)^2(2x+3)}\,dx$

(iii) $\displaystyle\int \frac{x+1}{(x^2+1)(x-1)}\,dx$ **(iv)** $\displaystyle\int \frac{3x+3}{(x-1)(2x+1)}\,dx$

(v) $\displaystyle\int \frac{1}{x^2(1-x)}\,dx$ **(vi)** $\displaystyle\int \frac{1}{(x+1)(x+3)}\,dx$

(vii) $\displaystyle\int \frac{2x-4}{(x^2+4)(x+2)}\,dx$ **(viii)** $\displaystyle\int \frac{5x+1}{(x+2)(2x+1)^2}\,dx$

2 Express in partial fractions the function

$$f(x) = \frac{3x+4}{(x^2+4)(x-3)}$$

and hence find $\int_0^2 f(x)\,dx$.

[MEI]

3 Express $\dfrac{1}{x^2(2x+1)}$ in partial fractions. Hence show that

$$\int_1^2 \frac{dx}{x^2(2x+1)} = \tfrac{1}{2} + 2\ln\tfrac{5}{6}.$$

[MEI]

4 (i) (a) Express $\dfrac{3}{(1+x)(1-2x)}$ in partial fractions.

(b) Hence find

$$\int_0^{0.1} \frac{3}{(1+x)(1-2x)}\,dx$$

giving your answer to 5 decimal places.

(ii) (a) Find the first three terms in the binomial expansion of

$$3(1+x)^{-1}(1-2x)^{-1}.$$

(b) Use the first three terms of this expansion to find an approximation for

$$\int_0^{0.1} \frac{3}{(1+x)(1-2x)}\,dx$$

(c) What is the percentage error in your answer to part **(b)**?

5 (i) Given that

$$\frac{x^2-x-24}{(x+2)(x-4)} \equiv A + \frac{B}{(x+2)} + \frac{C}{(x-4)},$$

find the values of the constants A, B and C.

(ii) Find $\displaystyle\int_1^3 \frac{x^2-x-24}{(x+2)(x-4)}\,dx.$

[MEI]

6 **(i)** Find $\int xe^{2x}\,dx$.

(ii) Find the exact value of $\int_{\frac{1}{4}\pi}^{\pi} \sin^2 3x\,dx$.

(iii) The expression $\dfrac{x^2}{(x-4)^2(x-2)}$ is to be written in partial fractions of the form

$$\frac{A}{(x-4)^2} + \frac{B}{x-4} + \frac{C}{x-2}.$$

Show that $B = 0$ and find A and C.

Hence show that $\displaystyle\int_5^8 \frac{x^2}{(x-4)^2(x-2)}\,dx = 6 + \ln 2$.

[MEI]

7 **(i)** Express the function $f(x) = \dfrac{1-3x}{(1+2x)(1+x^2)}$ in the form $\dfrac{A}{1+2x} + \dfrac{Bx+C}{1+x^2}$.

(ii) Use the binomial series to show that, for suitably small values of x,

$$f(x) \approx 1 - 5x + 9x^2.$$

State the range of values of x for which the binomial series expansion is valid.

(iii) By using a small-angle approximation for $\sin\theta$, together with the result in part **(ii)** above, find an approximation for

$$\int_0^{0.1} \frac{1-3\sin\theta}{(1+2\sin\theta)(1+\theta^2)}\,d\theta.$$

[MEI]

8 **(i)** Given that $f(x) = \dfrac{16+2x+15x^2}{(1+x^2)(2-x)} \equiv \dfrac{A+Bx}{1+x^2} + \dfrac{C}{2-x}$, find the values of B and C and show that $A = 0$.

(ii) Find $\int_0^1 f(x)\,dx$ in an exact form.

(iii) Express $f(x)$ as a sum of powers of x up to and including the term in x^4. Determine the range of values of x for which this expansion of $f(x)$ is valid.

[MEI]

9 **(i)** Show that $\dfrac{2u^2}{u^2-1} = 2 + \dfrac{2}{u^2-1}$. Hence express $\dfrac{2u^2}{u^2-1}$ in partial fractions.

(ii) Using the substitution $u = \sqrt{x}$, show that

$$\int_4^9 \frac{\sqrt{x}}{x-1}\,dx = \int_2^3 \frac{2u^2}{u^2-1}\,du.$$

Deduce that $\displaystyle\int_4^9 \frac{\sqrt{x}}{x-1}\,dx = \ln 3 - \ln 2 + 2$.

(iii) Use integration by parts, and the result of part **(ii)**, to show that

$$\int_4^9 \frac{\ln(x-1)}{\sqrt{x}}\,dx = 20\ln 2 - 6\ln 3 - 4.$$

[MEI]

General integration

You now know several techniques for integration which can be used to integrate a wide variety of functions. One of the difficulties which you may now experience when faced with an integration is deciding which technique is appropriate! This section gives you some guidelines on this, as well as revising all the work on integration that you have done so far.

❓ Look at the integrals below and try to decide which technique you would use and, in the case of a substitution, what function you would write as u. Do not attempt actually to carry out the integrations. Make a note of your decisions – you will return to these integrals later.

(i) $\displaystyle\int \frac{x-5}{x^2+2x-3}\,dx$ **(ii)** $\displaystyle\int \frac{x+1}{x^2+2x-3}\,dx$

(iii) $\int xe^x\,dx$ **(iv)** $\int xe^{x^2}\,dx$

(v) $\displaystyle\int \frac{2x+\cos x}{x^2+\sin x}\,dx$ **(vi)** $\int \cos x \sin^2 x\,dx$

Choosing an appropriate method of integration

You have now met the following standard integrals.

$f(x)$	$\int f(x)\,dx$
$x^n \quad (n \neq -1)$	$\dfrac{x^{n+1}}{n+1}$
$\dfrac{1}{x}$	$\ln\lvert x\rvert$
e^x	e^x
$\sin x$	$-\cos x$
$\cos x$	$\sin x$

If you are asked to integrate any of these standard functions, you may simply write down the answer.

For other integrations, the following table may help.

Type of function to be integrated	Examples	Method of integration
Simple variations of any of the standard functions	$\cos(2x+1)$ e^{3x}	Substitution may be used, but it should be possible to do these by inspection.
Product of two functions of the form $f'(x)g[f(x)]$ Note that $f'(x)$ means $\frac{d}{dx}[f(x)]$	$2xe^{x^2}$ $x^2(x^3+1)^6$	Substitution $u = f(x)$
Other products, particularly when one function is a small positive integral power of x or a polynomial in x	xe^x $x^2 \sin x$	Integration by parts
Quotients of the form $\frac{f'(x)}{f(x)}$ or functions which can easily be converted to this form	$\frac{x}{x^2+1}$ $\frac{\sin x}{\cos x}$	Substitution $u = f(x)$ or, better, by inspection: $k \ln\lvert f(x)\rvert + c$, where k is known
Polynomial quotients which may be split into partial fractions	$\frac{x+1}{x(x-1)}$ $\frac{x-4}{x^2-x-2}$	Split into partial fractions and integrate term by term
Odd powers of $\sin x$ or $\cos x$	$\cos^3 x$	Use $\cos^2 x + \sin^2 x = 1$ and write in form $f'(x)g[f(x)]$
e Even powers of $\sin x$ or $\cos x$	$\sin^2 x$ $\cos^4 x$	Use the double-angle formulae to transform the function before integrating.

It is impossible to give an exhaustive list of possible types of integration, but the table above and that on the previous page cover the most common situations that you will meet.

ACTIVITY 10.1 Now look back at the integrals in the discussion point on the previous page and the decisions you made about which method of integration should be used for each one.

(i) $\displaystyle\int \frac{x-5}{x^2+2x-3}\,dx$ **(ii)** $\displaystyle\int \frac{x+1}{x^2+2x-3}\,dx$

(iii) $\displaystyle\int xe^x\,dx$ **(iv)** $\displaystyle\int xe^{x^2}\,dx$

(v) $\displaystyle\int \frac{2x-\cos x}{x^2+\sin x}\,dx$ **(vi)** $\displaystyle\int \cos x \sin^2 x\,dx$

EXERCISE 10C

1 Choose an appropriate method and integrate the following functions. You may find it helpful first to discuss in class which method to use.

(i) $\int \cos(3x - 1)\,dx$ **(ii)** $\int \frac{2x + 1}{(x^2 + x - 1)^2}\,dx$

(iii) $\int e^{1-x}\,dx$ **(iv)** $\int \cos 2x\,dx$

(v) $\int \ln 2x\,dx$ **(vi)** $\int \frac{x}{(x^2 - 1)^3}\,dx$

(vii) $\int \sqrt{2x - 3}\,dx$ **(viii)** $\int \frac{4x - 1}{(x - 1)^2(x + 2)}\,dx$

(ix) $\int x^3 \ln x\,dx$ **(x)** $\int \frac{5}{2x^2 - 7x + 3}\,dx$

(xi) $\int (x + 1)e^{x^2 + 2x}\,dx$ **(xii)** $\int \frac{\sin x - \cos x}{\sin x + \cos x}\,dx$

e *The remaining parts of this question relate to enrichment material.*

(xiii) $\int x^2 \sin 2x\,dx$ **(xiv)** $\int \sin^3 2x\,dx$

2 Evaluate the following definite integrals.

(i) $\int_8^{24} \frac{dx}{\sqrt{3x - 8}}$ **(ii)** $\int_8^{24} \frac{dx}{3x - 8}$ **(iii)** $\int_8^{24} \frac{9x}{3x - 8}\,dx$

(iv) $\int_0^{\frac{\pi}{4}} \sin^3 x\,dx$ **(v)** $\int_1^2 x^2 \ln x\,dx$

3 Evaluate $\int_0^2 \frac{x^2}{\sqrt{1 + x^3}}\,dx$, using the substitution $u = 1 + x^3$, or otherwise.

[MEI]

4 Find $\int_0^{\frac{\pi}{4}} \frac{\sin\theta}{\cos^4\theta}\,d\theta$ in terms of $\sqrt{2}$.

[MEI]

5 Using the substitution $u = \ln x$, or otherwise, find $\int_1^2 \frac{\ln x}{x}\,dx$, giving your answer to 2 decimal places.

[MEI, *part*]

6 Find $\int_0^{\frac{\pi}{4}} x\cos 2x\,dx$, expressing your answer in terms of π.

[MEI]

7 (i) Find $\int xe^{-2x}\,dx$.

(ii) Evaluate $\int_0^1 \frac{x}{(4 + x^2)}\,dx$, giving your answer correct to 3 significant figures.

[MEI]

8 (i) Find $\int \sin(2x - 3)\,dx$.

(ii) Use the method of integration by parts to evaluate $\int_0^2 xe^{2x}\,dx$.

(iii) Using the substitution $t = x^2 - 9$, or otherwise, find $\int \frac{x}{x^2 - 9}\,dx$.

[MEI]

9 Evaluate

(i) $\int_0^1 (2x^2 + 1)(2x^3 + 3x + 4)^{\frac{1}{2}}\,dx$

(ii) $\int_1^e \frac{\ln x}{x^3}\,dx.$

[MEI]

10 Find $\int_0^{\frac{\pi}{2}} \sin x \cos^3 x\,dx$ and $\int_0^1 te^{-2t}\,dt.$

[MEI]

Integrals you cannot do

Sometimes you will need to evaluate a definite integral that you cannot do. It may be that it can be done but you do not know how, or it may be that it just cannot be done algebraically.

Think of a function that cannot be integrated algebraically.

Can you find a function that cannot be differentiated?

When you need to find the value of such a definite integral you can use a numerical method, like the trapezium rule which you met in *AS Pure Mathematics*, Chapter 9.

$$A \approx \tfrac{1}{2} \times h \times [y_0 + y_n + 2(y_1 + y_2 + \dots + y_{n-1})]$$

to work out an approximate value for the area between a curve and the x axis. The formula uses n strips, each of width h, as shown in figure 10.10.

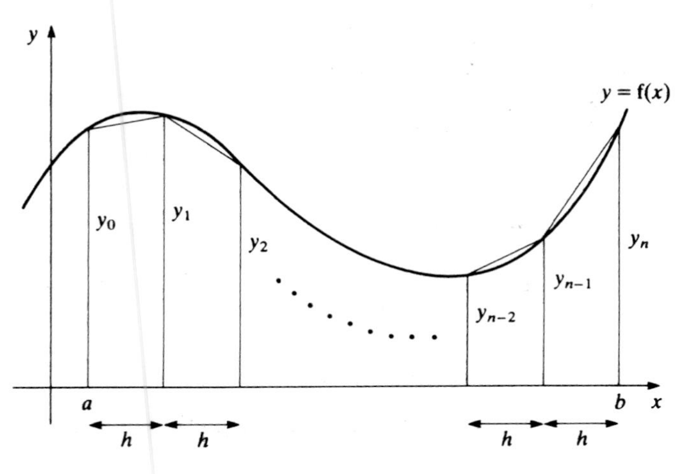

Figure 10.10

Look at the three graphs in figure 10.11 and, in each case, state

(a) whether the trapezium rule would underestimate or overestimate the area, or whether you cannot tell

(b) whether taking a greater number of strips would improve the estimate, or whether you cannot tell.

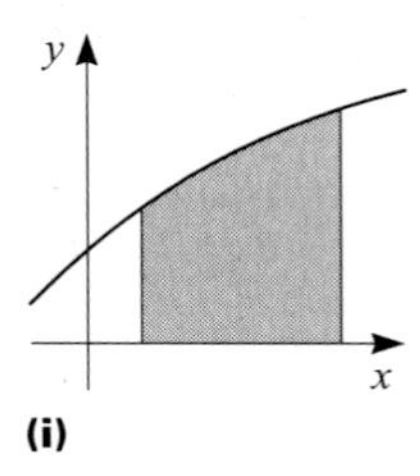

(i)

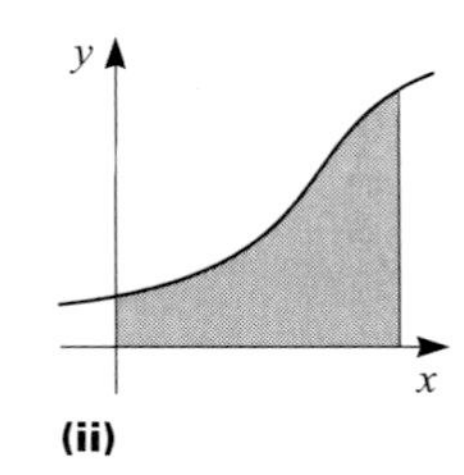

(ii)

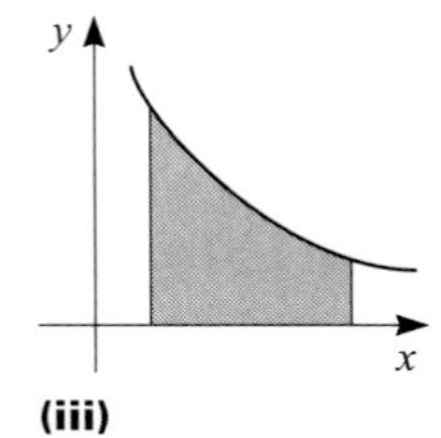

(iii)

Figure 10.11

A numerical method does not give you an exact answer but, by using it repeatedly, you can find the correct answer to whatever level of accuracy you require.

To see how to do this, do Activity 10.2.

ACTIVITY 10.2

1 The trapezium rule is to be used to approximate $I = \int_2^6 \frac{1}{1 + x^2}\,dx$, using n strips.

Figure 10.12 shows the graph of $y = \frac{1}{1 + x^2}$ over the interval [0, 6].

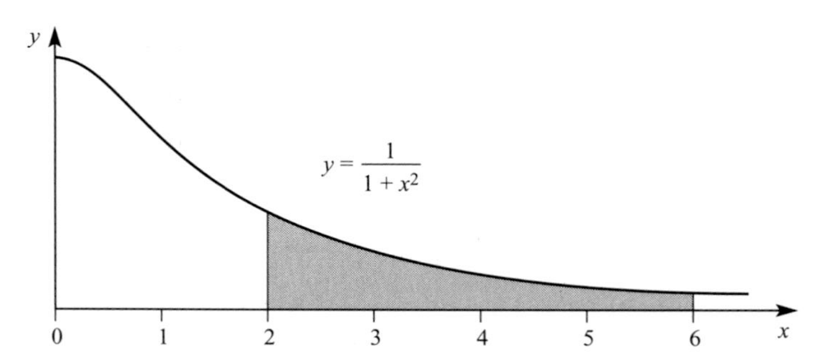

Figure 10.12

Using a computer package, or otherwise, complete the following table, where n is the number of strips used and h is the width of each strip. Give your answers to the number of figures on your computer or calculator.

n	h	**Approximation to I**
1	4	
2	2	
4		
8		
16		

2 Use your table of results to predict the accurate answer to as many decimal places as you feel are justified.

Notice how the answers converge. Applying a numerical method repeatedly does two important things.

- It gives you a more accurate answer.
- It allows you to judge the likely error in your answer.

You apply the trapezium rule just once to estimate the area under a curve. What can you say about the possible error in your answer?

Now do Activity 10.3. This looks at how quickly the error decreases and the answer converges.

ACTIVITY 10.3

1 You can actually evaluate the integral in Activity 10.2 exactly since

$$\int \frac{1}{1+x^2}\,dx = \arctan x + c.$$

(Note that x is measured in radians.)

Find the value of the area to calculator accuracy.

2 Add two further columns to your table from Activity 10.2 to show the values of the absolute error, ε, to the accuracy of your other figures and the value of $\frac{\varepsilon}{h^2}$ to 3 decimal places.

Comment on your results.

This activity should have convinced you that the error in a trapezium rule approximation is approximately proportional to the square of the step length, h. Another way of saying the same thing is that, if you double the number of strips, the error goes down to about one quarter of what it was before.

In the early stages of a set of trapezium rule calculations the error may not be quite as predictable as this, particularly if the curve is partly concave and partly convex, i.e. if the function has a point of inflection in the region in question.

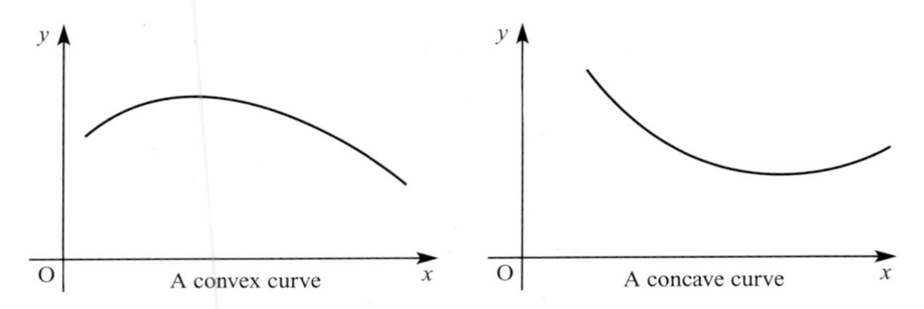

Figure 10.13

e Two applications of the trapezium rule

You can use two applications of the trapezium rule to give you an estimate of the true value of the integral. This is how it is done.

Let T_n be the approximate value obtained using a strip width of h_n for $n = 1, 2$.

$\Rightarrow \quad T_1 - I \approx kh_1^2$ and $T_2 - I \approx kh_2^2$ where I is the true value of the integral

$$\Rightarrow \quad T_1 - T_2 \approx k(h_1^2 - h_2^2)$$

$$\Rightarrow \quad k \approx \frac{T_1 - T_2}{h_1^2 - h_2^2}$$

$$I \approx T_2 - kh_2^2$$

$$\Rightarrow \quad I \approx T_2 - \frac{T_1 - T_2}{h_1^2 - h_2^2} \times h_2^2$$

k will be positive if the curve is concave and negative if it is convex.

---

p Explain each step of the derivation of this result.

EXAMPLE 10.6

(i) Use the trapezium rule with $h = 0.4$, 0.2 and 0.1 to give successive approximations for $\int_0^{0.8} \frac{1}{\sqrt{1-x^2}}\,dx$ to 6 decimal places.

(ii) Use the last two of these approximations to improve your estimate for the true value of $\int_0^{0.8} \frac{1}{\sqrt{1-x^2}}\,dx$ to 6 decimal places.

(iii) You are given that $\int \frac{1}{\sqrt{1-x^2}}\,dx = \arcsin x$ where x is measured in radians.

Find the true value of $\int_0^{0.8} \frac{1}{\sqrt{1-x^2}}\,dx$ to 6 decimal places and the percentage error obtained using the estimate in part **(ii)**.

SOLUTION

(i) Using $A \approx \frac{1}{2} \times h \times [y_0 + y_n + 2(y_1 + y_2 + \ldots + y_{n-1})]$ gives the following results.

$$h_1 = 0.4 \Rightarrow \text{approximation } T_1 = 0.969\,769$$
$$h_2 = 0.2 \Rightarrow \text{approximation } T_2 = 0.939\,009$$
$$h_3 = 0.1 \Rightarrow \text{approximation } T_3 = 0.930\,335$$

(ii) Using $I \approx T_3 - \frac{T_2 - T_3}{h_2^2 - h_3^2} \times h_3^2 \quad \Rightarrow \quad I \approx 0.927\,444$ (6 d.p.)

(iii) $\int_0^{0.8} \frac{1}{\sqrt{1-x^2}}\,dx = \left[\arcsin x\right]_0^{0.8} = 0.927\,295$ (6 d.p.)

Percentage error $= \frac{0.927\,444 - 0.927\,295}{0.927\,295} = 0.016\%$.

EXERCISE 10D

You may find it helpful to use a spreadsheet with this exercise.

1 The trapezium rule is used to estimate the value of $I = \int_0^{1.6} \sqrt{1 + x^2}\,dx$.

(i) Draw the graph of $y = \sqrt{1 + x^2}$ for $0 \leqslant x \leqslant 1.6$.

(ii) Use strip widths of 0.8, 0.4, 0.2 and 0.1 to find approximations to the value of the integral.

(iii) State the value of the integral to as many decimal places as you can justify.

2 The trapezium rule is used to estimate the value of $\int_0^1 \sqrt{\sin x}\,dx$.

(i) Draw the graph of $y = \sqrt{\sin x}$ for $0 \leqslant x \leqslant 1$.

(ii) Use 1, 2, 4, 8 and 16 strips to find approximations to the value of the integral.

(iii) State the value of the integral to as many decimal places as you can justify.

3 The trapezium rule is used to estimate the value of $\int_0^1 \frac{4}{1 + x^2}\,dx$.

(i) Draw the graph of $y = \frac{4}{1 + x^2}$ for $0 \leqslant x \leqslant 1$.

(ii) Use strip widths of 1, 0.5, 0.25 and 0.125 to find approximations to the value of the integral.

(iii) State the value of the integral to as many decimal places as you can justify.

4 A student uses the trapezium rule to estimate the value of $\int_0^2 (2 - \cos 2\pi x)\,dx$.

(i) Find approximations to the value of the integral by applying the trapezium rule using strip widths of

(a) 2 **(b)** 1 **(c)** 0.5 **(d)** 0.25.

(ii) Sketch the graph of $y = 2 - \cos 2\pi x$ for $0 \leqslant x \leqslant 2$.
On copies of your graph shade the areas you have found in part **(i)(a)** to **(d)**.

(iii) Use integration to find the exact value of this integral.

5 In statistics the curve of the normal distribution is given by $f(z) = \frac{1}{\sqrt{2\pi}} e^{-\frac{z^2}{2}}$.

Use the trapezium rule to estimate the value of $\int_0^1 f(z)\,dz$.

(This is denoted by $\Phi(1)$ in statistics.)
Repeated with progressively more strips until you are certain that the answer is correct to 2 decimal places.

INVESTIGATION

This investigation relates to enrichment material.

(i) Sketch the graphs of $y = e^{-x}$, $y = \sin x$ and $y = e^{-x} \sin x$ for $0 \leqslant x \leqslant 2\pi$.

(ii) Find the trapezium rule estimates for the area between the curve $y = e^{-x} \sin x$ and the x axis, using 4 strips and 8 strips, for $0 \leqslant x \leqslant \pi$.

(ii) Use your answers to part **(ii)** to give a better estimate for the area.

KEY POINTS

1 Volumes of revolution

About the x axis $V = \int_a^b \pi y^2 \, dx$

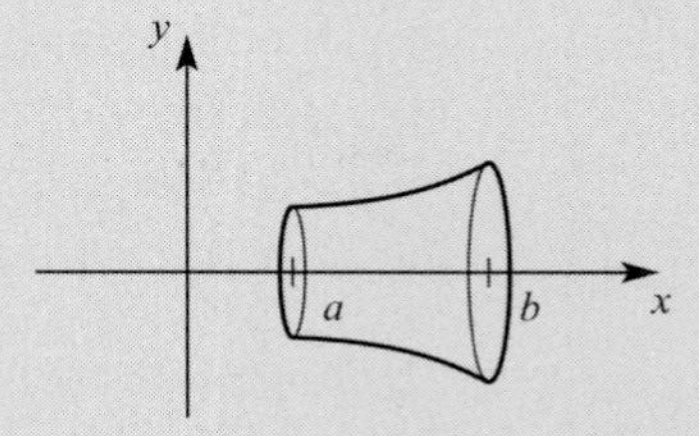

About the y axis $V = \int_p^q \pi x^2 \, dy$

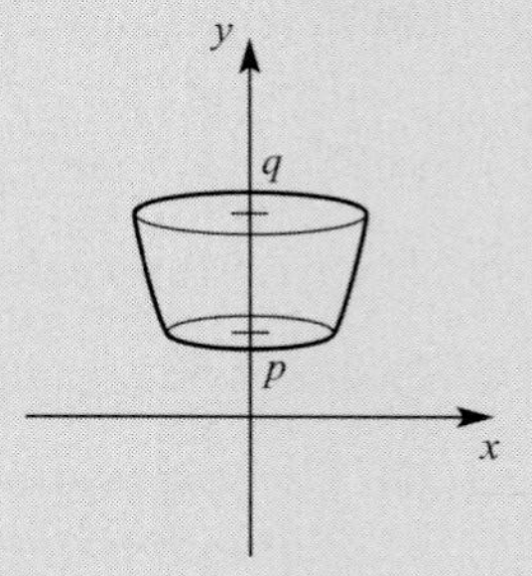

2 Some fractional expressions may be integrated by first splitting them into partial fractions.

3 You can use the trapezium rule, with n strips of width h, to find an approximate value for a definite integral as

$$A = \frac{h}{2}\left[y_0 + 2(y_1 + y_2 + \ldots + y_{n-1}) + y_n\right]$$

Increasing the number of strips used usually gives a more accurate result.

11 Vectors

We drove into the future looking into a rear view mirror.

Herbert Marshall McLuhan

? What information do you need to decide how close the two aircraft which left these vapour trails passed to each other?

Vectors

A quantity which has both size and direction is called a *vector*. The velocity of an aircraft through the sky is an example of a vector, having size (e.g. 600 mph) and direction (on a course of 254°). By contrast the mass of the aircraft (100 tonnes) is completely described by its size and no direction is associated with it; such a quantity is called a *scalar*.

Vectors are used extensively in mechanics to represent quantities such as force, velocity and momentum, and in geometry to represent displacements. They are an essential tool in three-dimensional co-ordinate geometry and it is this application of vectors which is the subject of this chapter. However, before coming on to this, you need to be familiar with the associated vocabulary and notation, in two and three dimensions.

Terminology

In two dimensions, it is common to represent a vector by a drawing of a straight line with an arrowhead. The length represents the size, or magnitude, of the vector and the direction is indicated by the line and the arrowhead. Direction is usually given as the angle the vector makes with the positive x axis, with the anticlockwise direction taken to be positive.

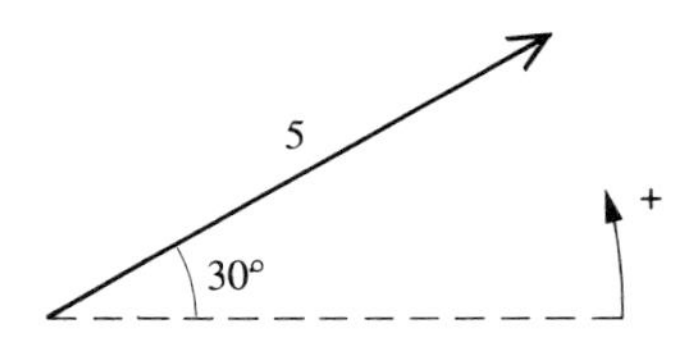

Figure 11.1

The vector in figure 11.1 has magnitude 5, direction +30°. This is written (5, 30°) and said to be in *magnitude–direction form* or in *polar form*. The general form of a vector written in this way is (r, θ) where r is its magnitude and θ its direction.

Note

In the special case when the vector is representing real travel, as in the case of the velocity of an aircraft, the direction may be described by a compass bearing with the angle measured from north, clockwise. However, this is not done in this chapter, where directions are all taken to be measured anticlockwise from the positive x direction.

An alternative way of describing a vector is in terms of *components* in given directions. The vector in figure 11.2 is 4 units in the x direction, and 2 in the y direction, and this is denoted by $\begin{pmatrix} 4 \\ 2 \end{pmatrix}$.

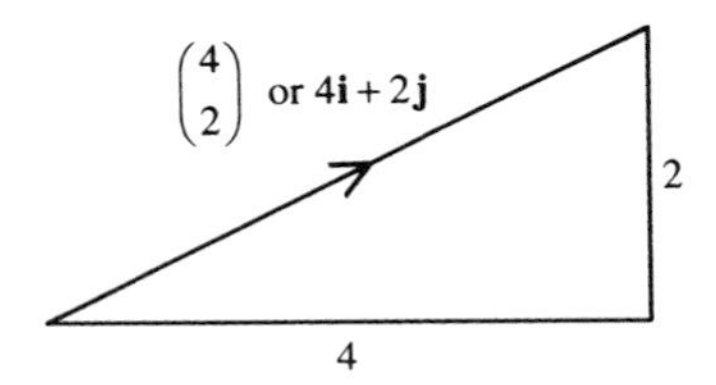

Figure 11.2

This may also be written as $4\mathbf{i} + 2\mathbf{j}$, where **i** is a vector of magnitude 1, a *unit vector*, in the x direction and **j** is a unit vector in the y direction (figure 11.3).

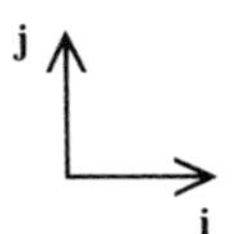

Figure 11.3

In a book, a vector may be printed in bold, for example **p** or **OP**, or as a line between two points with an arrow above it to indicate its direction, such as $\overrightarrow{OP}$. When you write a vector by hand, it is usual to underline it, for example, $\underline{p}$ or $\underline{OP}$, or to put an arrow above it, as in $\overrightarrow{OP}$.

To convert a vector from component form to magnitude–direction form, or vice versa, is just a matter of applying trigonometry to a right-angled triangle.

EXAMPLE 11.1

Write the vector $\mathbf{a} = 4\mathbf{i} + 2\mathbf{j}$ in magnitude–direction form.

SOLUTION

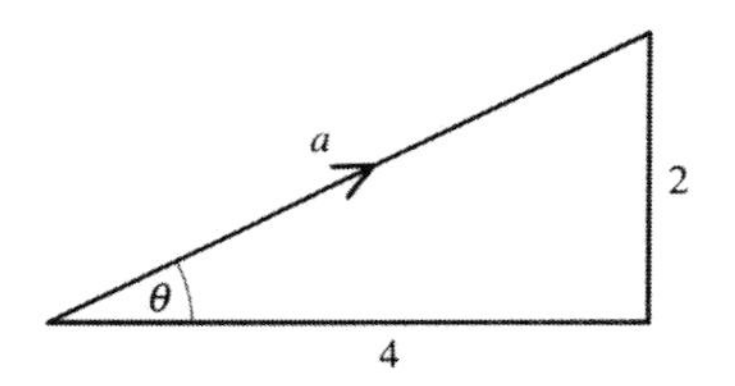

Figure 11.4

The magnitude of $\mathbf{a}$ is given by the length a in figure 11.4.

$$a = \sqrt{4^2 + 2^2} \quad \text{(using Pythagoras' theorem)}$$

$$= 4.47 \quad \text{(to 3 significant figures)}$$

The direction is given by the angle θ.

$$\tan\theta = \frac{2}{4} = 0.5$$

$$\theta = 26.6° \quad \text{(to 3 significant figures)}$$

The vector $\mathbf{a}$ is (4.47, 26.6°).

The magnitude of a vector is also called its *modulus* and denoted by the symbols $|\ |$. In the example $\mathbf{a} = 4\mathbf{i} + 2\mathbf{j}$, the modulus of $\mathbf{a}$, written $|\mathbf{a}|$, is 4.47. Another convention for writing the magnitude of a vector is to use the same letter, but in italics and not bold type; thus the magnitude of $\mathbf{a}$ may be written a.

EXAMPLE 11.2

Write the vector (5, 60°) in component form.

SOLUTION

In the right-angled triangle OPX

$$\text{OX} = 5\cos 60° = 2.5$$

$$\text{XP} = 5\sin 60° = 4.33$$
(to 2 decimal places)

$$\overrightarrow{\text{OP}} \text{ is } \begin{pmatrix} 2.5 \\ 4.33 \end{pmatrix} \quad \text{or} \quad 2.5\mathbf{i} + 4.33\mathbf{j}.$$

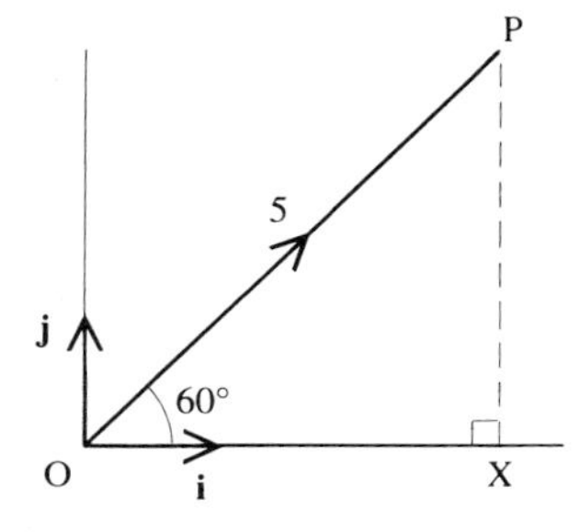

Figure 11.5

This technique can be written as a general rule, for all values of θ.

$$(r, \theta) \rightarrow \begin{pmatrix} r\cos\theta \\ r\sin\theta \end{pmatrix} = (r\cos\theta)\mathbf{i} + (r\sin\theta)\mathbf{j}$$

EXAMPLE 11.3

Write the vector (10, 290°) in component form.

SOLUTION

In this case $r = 10$ and $\theta = 290°$.

$(10, 290°) \rightarrow \begin{pmatrix} 10\cos 290° \\ 10\sin 290° \end{pmatrix} = \begin{pmatrix} 3.42 \\ -9.40 \end{pmatrix}$ to 2 decimal places.

This may also be written $3.42\mathbf{i} - 9.40\mathbf{j}$.

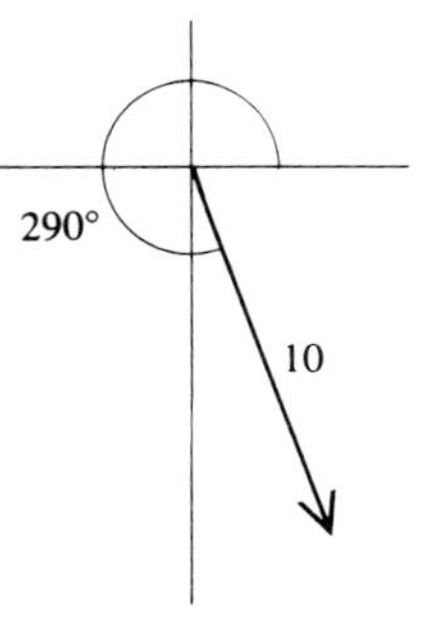

Figure 11.6

In Example 11.3 the signs looked after themselves. The component in the **i** direction came out positive, that in the **j** direction negative, as must be the case for a direction in the fourth quadrant ($270° < \theta < 360°$). This will always be the case when the conversion is from magnitude–direction form into component form.

The situation is not quite so straightforward when the conversion is carried out the other way, from component form to magnitude–direction form. In that case, it is best to draw a diagram and use it to see the approximate size of the angle required. This is shown in the next example.

EXAMPLE 11.4

Write $-5\mathbf{i} + 4\mathbf{j}$ in magnitude–direction form.

SOLUTION

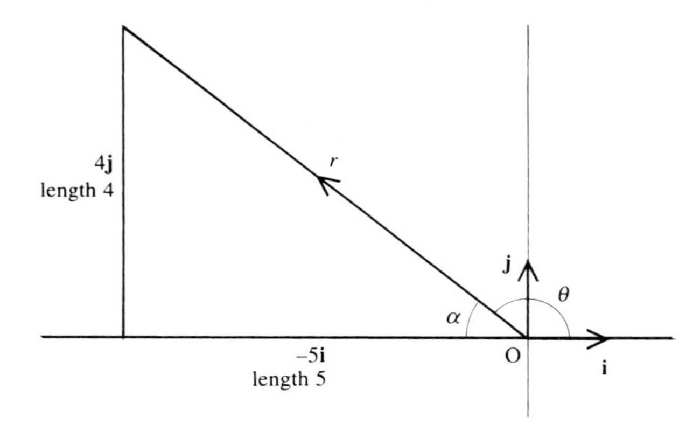

Figure 11.7

In this case, the magnitude $r = \sqrt{5^2 + 4^2} = \sqrt{41}$

$= 6.40$ (to 2 decimal places).

The direction is given by the angle θ in figure 11.7, but first find the angle α.

$$\tan\alpha = \frac{4}{5} \quad \Rightarrow \quad \alpha = 38.7° \qquad \text{(to nearest 0.1°)}$$

so $\quad \theta = 180 - \alpha = 141.3°$

The vector is (6.40, 141.3°) in magnitude–direction form.

Using your calculator

Most graphic calculators include the facility to convert from polar co-ordinates (r, θ) to rectangular co-ordinates (x, y), and vice versa. This is the same as converting one form of a vector into the other. Once you are clear what is involved, you will probably prefer to do such conversions on your calculator.

Equal vectors

The statement that two vectors **a** and **b** are equal means two things.

- The direction of **a** is the same as the direction of **b**.
- The magnitude of **a** is the same as the magnitude of **b**.

If the vectors are given in component form, each component of **a** equals the corresponding component of **b**.

Position vectors

Saying the vector **a** is given by $4\mathbf{i} + 2\mathbf{j}$ tells you the components of the vector, or equivalently its magnitude and direction. It does not tell you where the vector is situated; indeed it could be anywhere.

All of the lines in figure 11.8 represent the vector **a**.

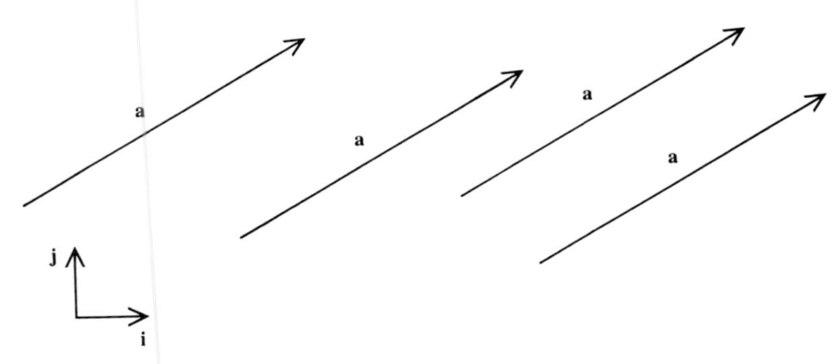

Figure 11.8

There is, however, one special case which is an exception to the rule, that of a vector which starts at the origin. This is called a *position vector*. Thus the line joining the origin to the point (3, 5) is the position vector $\begin{pmatrix} 3 \\ 5 \end{pmatrix}$ or $3\mathbf{i} + 5\mathbf{j}$. Another way of expressing this is to say that the point (3, 5) has the position vector $\begin{pmatrix} 3 \\ 5 \end{pmatrix}$.

EXAMPLE 11.5

Points L, M and N have co-ordinates (4, 3), (–2, –1) and (2, 2).

(i) Write down, in component form, the position vector of L and the vector $\overrightarrow{MN}$.

(ii) What do your answers to part **(i)** tell you about the lines OL and MN?

SOLUTION

(i) The position vector of L is $\overrightarrow{OL} = \begin{pmatrix} 4 \\ 3 \end{pmatrix}$.

The vector $\overrightarrow{MN}$ is also $\begin{pmatrix} 4 \\ 3 \end{pmatrix}$ (see figure 11.9).

(ii) Since $\overrightarrow{OL} = \overrightarrow{MN}$, lines OL and MN are parallel and equal in length.

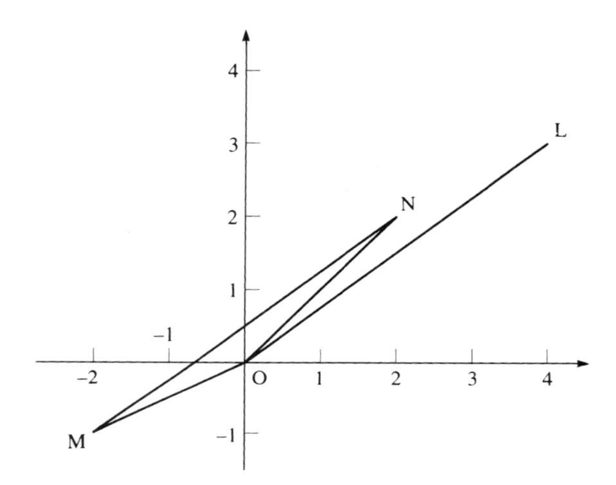

Figure 11.9

Note

A line joining two points, like MN in figure 11.9, is often called a *line segment*, meaning that it is just that particular part of the infinite straight line that passes through those two points.

EXERCISE 11A

1 Express the following vectors in component form.

(i)

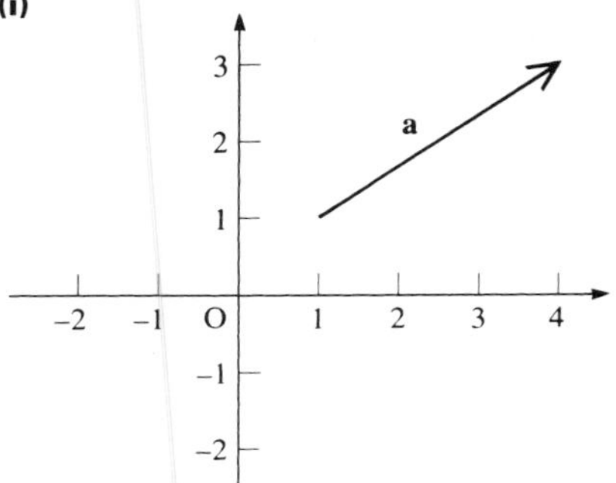

(ii)

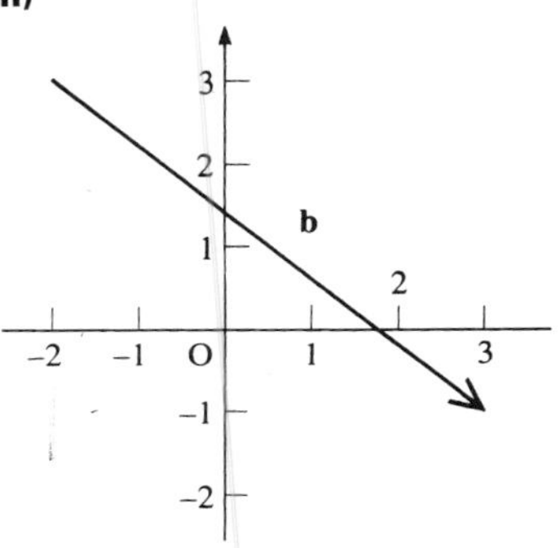

(iii)

(iv)

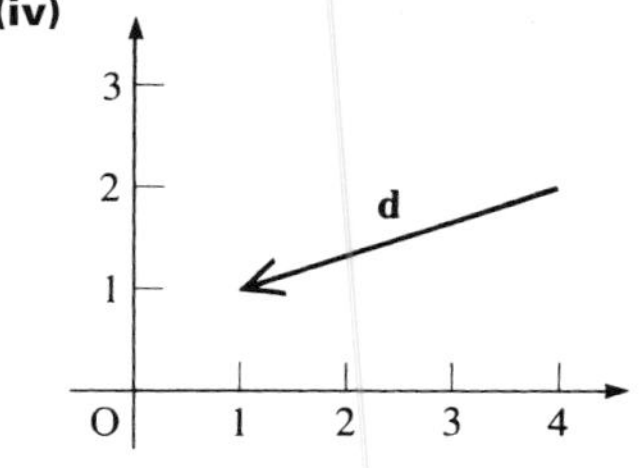

(v)

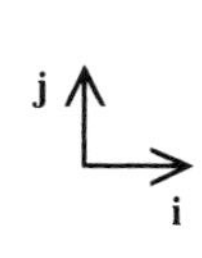

2 Draw diagrams to show these vectors and then write them in magnitude–direction form. You may find it helpful to use your calculator to check your answers.

(i) $2\mathbf{i} + 3\mathbf{j}$ **(ii)** $\begin{pmatrix} 3 \\ -2 \end{pmatrix}$ **(iii)** $\begin{pmatrix} -4 \\ -4 \end{pmatrix}$

(iv) $-\mathbf{i} + 2\mathbf{j}$ **(v)** $3\mathbf{i} - 4\mathbf{j}$

3 Draw diagrams to show these vectors and then write them in component form. You may find it helpful to use your calculator to check your answers.

(i) $(5, 45°)$ **(ii)** $(10, 210°)$ **(iii)** $\left(4, \frac{\pi}{2}\right)$

(iv) $(8, 2\pi)$ **(v)** $\left(4, \frac{5\pi}{4}\right)$

4 Write, in component form, the vectors represented by the line segments joining the following points.

(i) $(2, 3)$ to $(4, 1)$ **(ii)** $(4, 0)$ to $(6, 0)$

(iii) $(0, 0)$ to $(0, -4)$ **(iv)** $(0, -4)$ to $(0, 0)$

(v) $(-3, -4)$ to $(-4, -3)$ **(vi)** $(-4, -3)$ to $(-3, -4)$

(vii) $(0, 0)$ to $(8, 0)$ **(viii)** $(8, 0)$ to $(0, 0)$

(ix) $(3, 1)$ to $(5, -3)$ **(x)** $(3, -1)$ to $(7, 3)$

5 The points A, B and C have co-ordinates $(2, 3)$, $(0, 4)$ and $(-2, 1)$.

(i) Write down the position vectors of A and C.

(ii) Write down the vectors of the line segments joining AB and CB.

(iii) What do your answers to parts **(i)** and **(ii)** tell you about

(a) AB and OC

(b) CB and OA?

(iv) Describe the quadrilateral OABC.

Multiplying a vector by a scalar

When a vector is multiplied by a number (a scalar) its length is altered but its direction remains the same.

The vector $2\mathbf{a}$ in figure 11.10 is twice as long as the vector $\mathbf{a}$ but in the same direction.

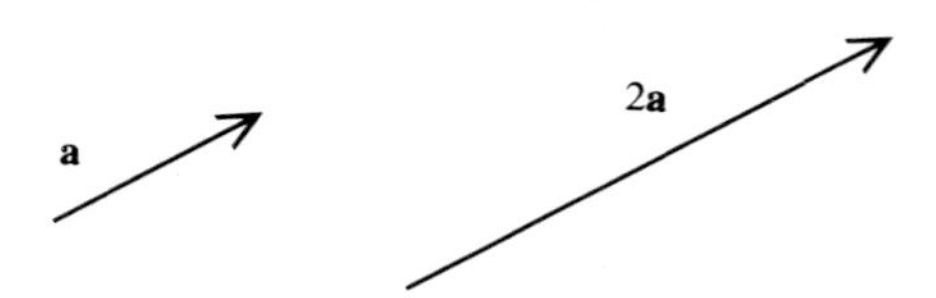

Figure 11.10

When the vector is in component form, each component is multiplied by the number. For example:

$$2 \times (3\mathbf{i} - 5\mathbf{j}) = 6\mathbf{i} - 10\mathbf{j}$$

$$2 \times \begin{pmatrix} 3 \\ -5 \end{pmatrix} = \begin{pmatrix} 6 \\ -10 \end{pmatrix}.$$

The negative of a vector

In figure 11.11 the vector **–a** has the same length as the vector **a** but the opposite direction.

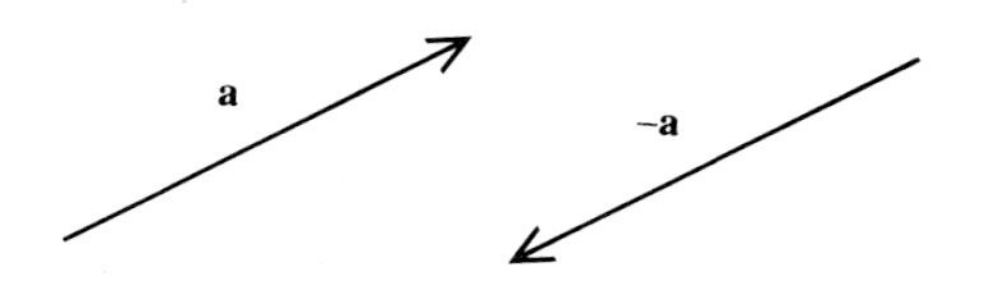

Figure 11.11

When **a** is given in component form, the components of **–a** are the same as those for **a** but with their signs reversed. So

$$-\begin{pmatrix} 23 \\ -11 \end{pmatrix} = \begin{pmatrix} -23 \\ +11 \end{pmatrix}.$$

Adding vectors

When vectors are given in component form, they can be added component by component. This process can be seen geometrically by drawing them on graph paper, as in the example below.

EXAMPLE 11.6

Add the vectors $2\mathbf{i} - 3\mathbf{j}$ and $3\mathbf{i} + 5\mathbf{j}$.

SOLUTION

$2\mathbf{i} - 3\mathbf{j} + 3\mathbf{i} + 5\mathbf{j} = 5\mathbf{i} + 2\mathbf{j}$

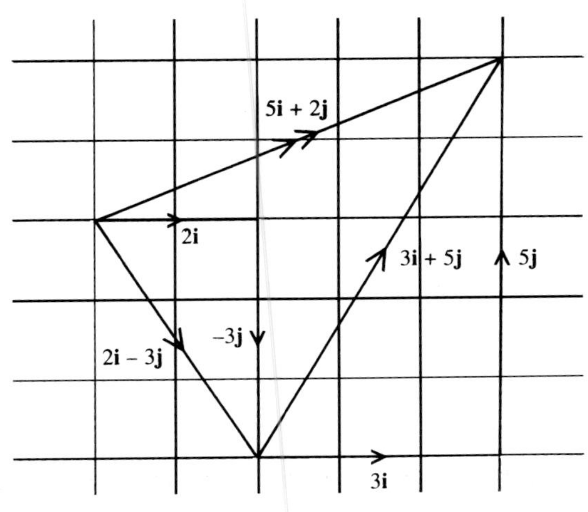

Figure 11.12

The sum of two (or more) vectors is called the *resultant* and is usually indicated by being marked with two arrowheads.

Adding vectors is like adding the legs of a journey to find its overall outcome (see figure 11.13).

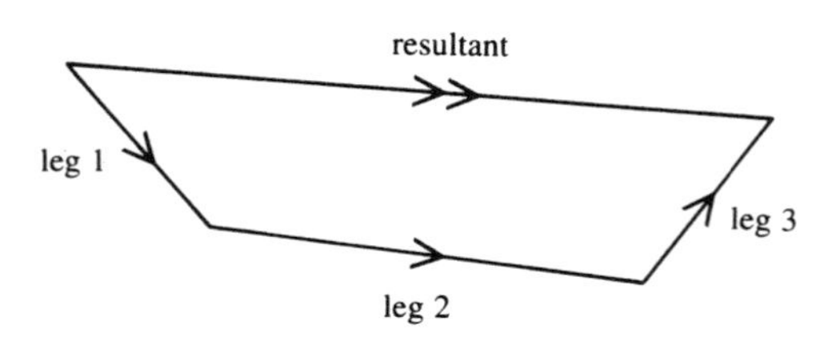

Figure 11.13

When vectors are given in magnitude–direction form, you can find their resultant by making a scale drawing, as in figure 11.13. If, however, you need to calculate their resultant, it is usually easiest to convert the vectors into component form, add component by component, and then convert the answer back to magnitude–direction form.

Subtracting vectors

Subtracting one vector from another is the same as adding the negative of the vector.

EXAMPLE 11.7

Two vectors **a** and **b** are given by

$$\mathbf{a} = 2\mathbf{i} + 3\mathbf{j} \qquad \mathbf{b} = -\mathbf{i} + 2\mathbf{j}.$$

(i) Find **a** – **b**.

(ii) Draw diagrams showing **a**, **b**, **a** – **b**.

SOLUTION

(i) $\mathbf{a} - \mathbf{b} = (2\mathbf{i} + 3\mathbf{j}) - (-\mathbf{i} + 2\mathbf{j})$
$= 3\mathbf{i} + \mathbf{j}$

(ii)

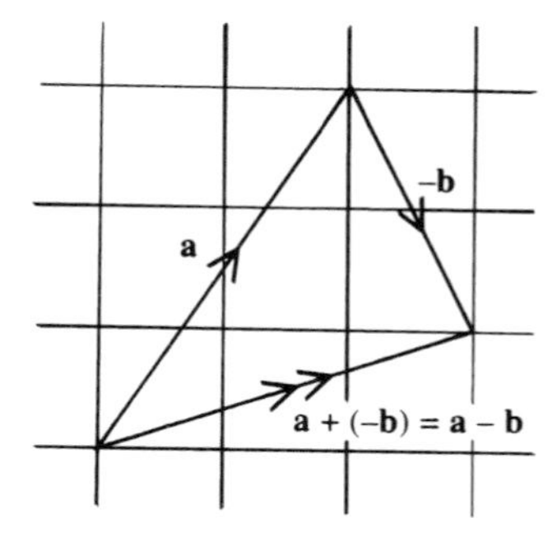

Figure 11.14

When you find the vector represented by the line segment joining two points, you are in effect subtracting their position vectors. If, for example, P is the point (2, 1) and Q is the point (3, 5), $\overrightarrow{PQ}$ is $\begin{pmatrix}1\\4\end{pmatrix}$, as figure 11.15 shows.

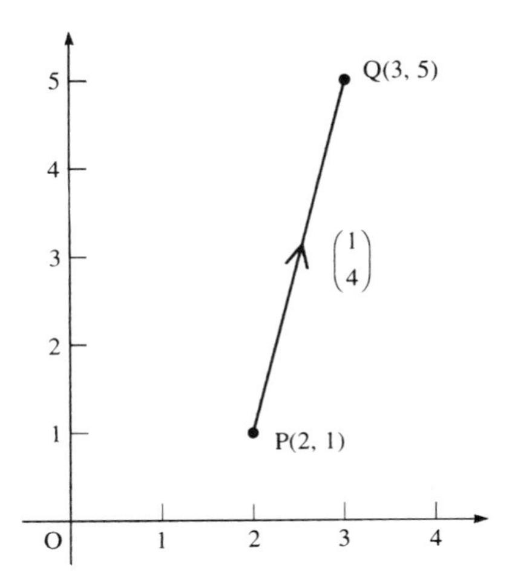

Figure 11.15

You find this by saying

$$\overrightarrow{PQ} = \overrightarrow{PO} + \overrightarrow{OQ} = -\mathbf{p} + \mathbf{q}.$$

In this case, this gives

$$\overrightarrow{PQ} = -\begin{pmatrix}2\\1\end{pmatrix} + \begin{pmatrix}3\\5\end{pmatrix} = \begin{pmatrix}1\\4\end{pmatrix}$$

as expected.

This is an important result, that

$$\overrightarrow{PQ} = \mathbf{q} - \mathbf{p}$$

where $\mathbf{p}$ and $\mathbf{q}$ are the position vectors of P and Q.

Geometrical figures

It is often useful to be able to express lines in a geometrical figure in terms of given vectors, as in the next example.

EXAMPLE 11.8

Figure 11.16 shows a hexagon ABCDEF.

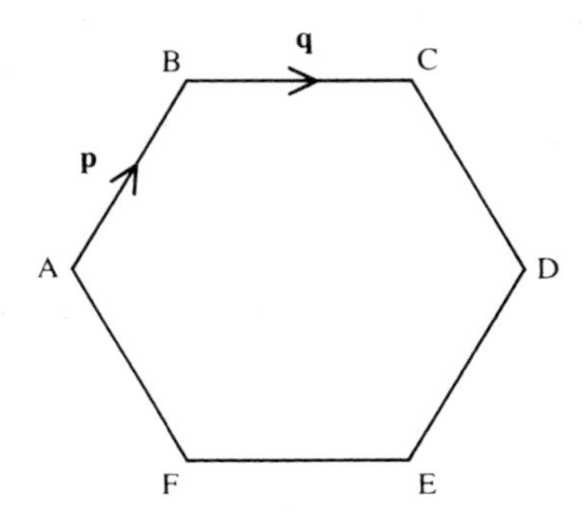

Figure 11.16

The hexagon is regular and consequently $\overrightarrow{AD} = 2\overrightarrow{BC}$.
$\overrightarrow{AB} = \mathbf{p}$ and $\overrightarrow{BC} = \mathbf{q}$. Express the following in terms of $\mathbf{p}$ and $\mathbf{q}$.

(i) $\overrightarrow{AC}$ **(ii)** $\overrightarrow{AD}$ **(iii)** $\overrightarrow{CD}$
(iv) $\overrightarrow{DE}$ **(v)** $\overrightarrow{EF}$ **(vi)** $\overrightarrow{BE}$

SOLUTION

(i) $\overrightarrow{AC} = \overrightarrow{AB} + \overrightarrow{BC}$
$= \mathbf{p} + \mathbf{q}$

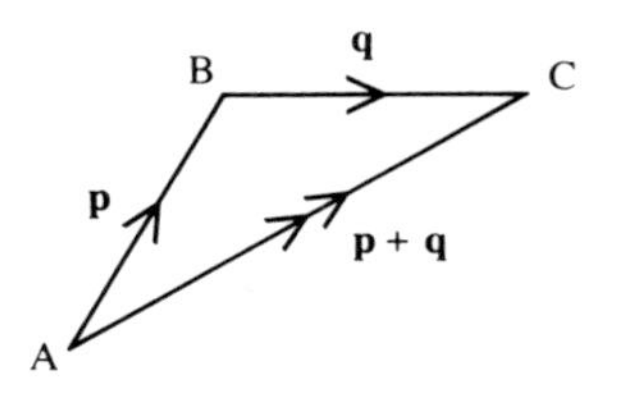

(ii) $\overrightarrow{AD} = 2\overrightarrow{BC}$
$= 2\mathbf{q}$

(iii) Since $\overrightarrow{AC} + \overrightarrow{CD} = \overrightarrow{AD}$

$\mathbf{p} + \mathbf{q} + \overrightarrow{CD} = 2\mathbf{q}$

and so $\overrightarrow{CD} = \mathbf{q} - \mathbf{p}$

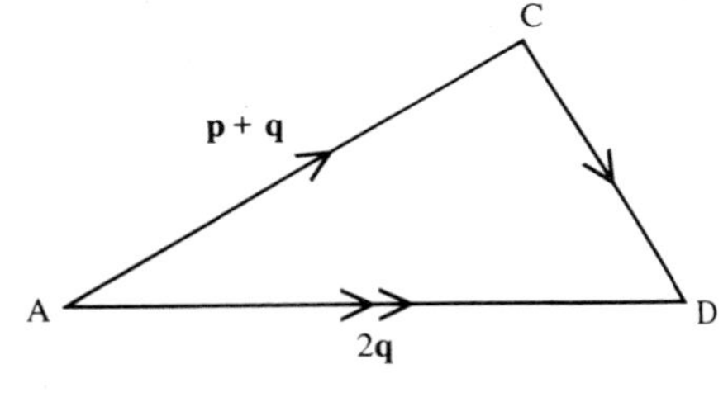

(iv) $\overrightarrow{DE} = -\overrightarrow{AB}$
$= -\mathbf{p}$

(v) $\overrightarrow{EF} = -\overrightarrow{BC}$
$= -\mathbf{q}$

(vi) $\overrightarrow{BE} = \overrightarrow{BC} + \overrightarrow{CD} + \overrightarrow{DE}$
$= \mathbf{q} + (\mathbf{q} - \mathbf{p}) + -\mathbf{p}$
$= 2\mathbf{q} - 2\mathbf{p}$

Notice that $\overrightarrow{BE} = 2\overrightarrow{CD}$.

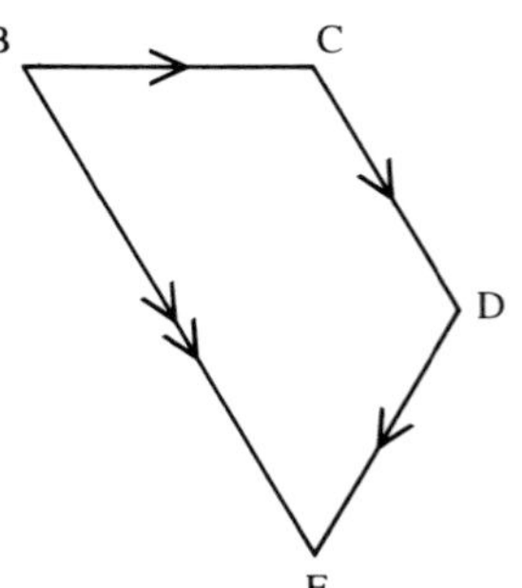

Figure 11.17

Unit vectors

A unit vector is a vector with a magnitude of 1, like **i** and **j**. To find the unit vector in the same direction as a given vector, divide that vector by its magnitude.
Thus the vector $3\mathbf{i} + 5\mathbf{j}$ (in figure 11.18) has magnitude $\sqrt{3^2 + 5^2} = \sqrt{34}$, and so the vector $\frac{3}{\sqrt{34}}\mathbf{i} + \frac{5}{\sqrt{34}}\mathbf{j}$ is a unit vector. It has magnitude 1.

The unit vector in the direction of vector **a** is written as $\hat{\mathbf{a}}$ and read as 'a hat'.

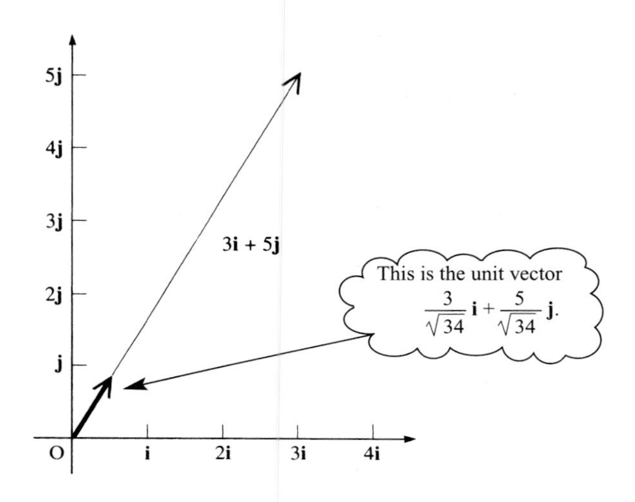

Figure 11.18

EXERCISE 11B

1 Simplify the following.

(i) $\begin{pmatrix} 2 \\ 3 \end{pmatrix} + \begin{pmatrix} 4 \\ 5 \end{pmatrix}$

(ii) $\begin{pmatrix} 2 \\ -1 \end{pmatrix} + \begin{pmatrix} -1 \\ 2 \end{pmatrix}$

(iii) $\begin{pmatrix} 3 \\ 4 \end{pmatrix} + \begin{pmatrix} -3 \\ -4 \end{pmatrix}$

(iv) $3\begin{pmatrix} 2 \\ 1 \end{pmatrix} + 2\begin{pmatrix} 1 \\ -2 \end{pmatrix}$

(v) $6(3\mathbf{i} - 2\mathbf{j}) - 9(2\mathbf{i} - \mathbf{j})$

2 The vectors **p**, **q** and **r** are given by

$$\mathbf{p} = 3\mathbf{i} + 2\mathbf{j} \qquad \mathbf{q} = 2\mathbf{i} + 2\mathbf{j} \qquad \mathbf{r} = -3\mathbf{i} - \mathbf{j}.$$

Find, in component form, the following vectors.

(i) $\mathbf{p} + \mathbf{q} + \mathbf{r}$

(ii) $\mathbf{p} - \mathbf{q}$

(iii) $\mathbf{p} + \mathbf{r}$

(iv) $3(\mathbf{p} - \mathbf{q}) + 2(\mathbf{p} + \mathbf{r})$

(v) $4\mathbf{p} - 3\mathbf{q} + 2\mathbf{r}$

3 In the diagram, PQRS is a parallelogram and $\overrightarrow{PQ} = \mathbf{a}$, $\overrightarrow{PS} = \mathbf{b}$.

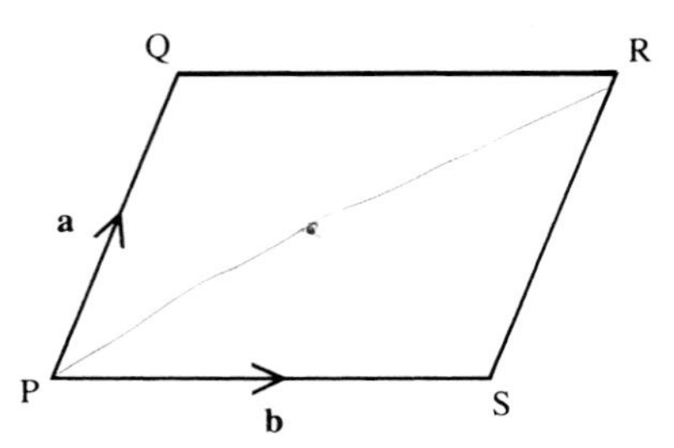

(i) Write, in terms of **a** and **b**, the following vectors.

(a) $\overrightarrow{QR}$ **(b)** $\overrightarrow{PR}$ **(c)** $\overrightarrow{QS}$

(ii) The mid-point of PR is M. Find

(a) $\overrightarrow{PM}$ **(b)** $\overrightarrow{QM}$.

(iii) Explain why this shows you that the diagonals of a parallelogram bisect each other.

4 In the diagram, ABCD is a kite. AC and BD meet at M.

$\overrightarrow{AB} = \mathbf{i} + \mathbf{j}$ and $\overrightarrow{AD} = \mathbf{i} - 2\mathbf{j}$

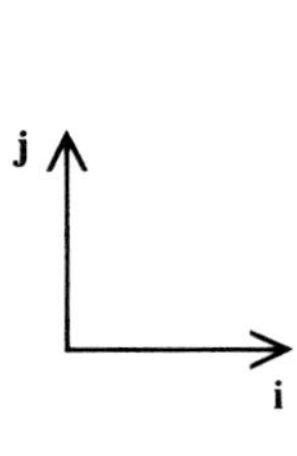

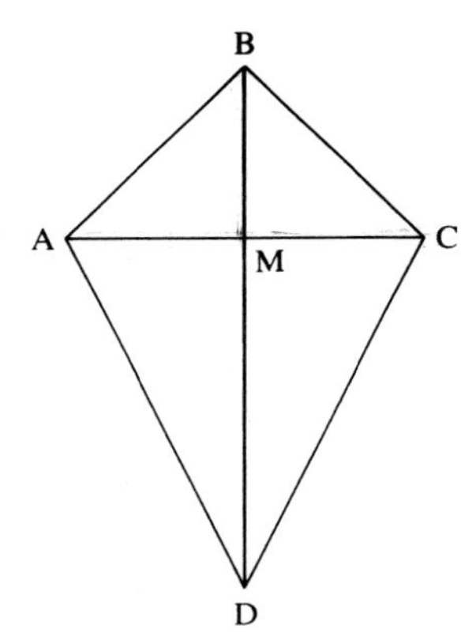

(i) Use the facts that the diagonals of a kite meet at right angles and that M is the mid-point of AC to find, in terms of **i** and **j**,

(a) $\overrightarrow{AM}$ **(b)** $\overrightarrow{AC}$ **(c)** $\overrightarrow{BC}$ **(d)** $\overrightarrow{CD}$.

(ii) Verify that $|\overrightarrow{AB}| = |\overrightarrow{BC}|$ and $|\overrightarrow{AD}| = |\overrightarrow{CD}|$.

5 In the diagram, ABC is a triangle. L, M and N are the mid-points of the sides BC, CA and AB.

$$\overrightarrow{AB} = \mathbf{p} \qquad \text{and} \qquad \overrightarrow{AC} = \mathbf{q}$$

A

N M

B L C

(i) Find, in terms of $\mathbf{p}$ and $\mathbf{q}$, $\overrightarrow{BC}$, $\overrightarrow{MN}$, $\overrightarrow{LM}$ and $\overrightarrow{LN}$.

(ii) Explain how your results from part **(i)** show you that the sides of triangle LMN are parallel to those of triangle ABC, and half their lengths.

6 Find unit vectors in the same directions as the following vectors.

(i) $\begin{pmatrix} 2 \\ 3 \end{pmatrix}$ **(ii)** $3\mathbf{i} + 4\mathbf{j}$ **(iii)** $\begin{pmatrix} -2 \\ -2 \end{pmatrix}$ **(iv)** $5\mathbf{i} - 12\mathbf{j}$

(v) $6\mathbf{i}$ **(vi)** $\begin{pmatrix} -2 \\ 4 \end{pmatrix}$ **(vii)** $\begin{pmatrix} -1 \\ 2 \end{pmatrix}$ **(viii)** $\begin{pmatrix} 3 \\ 6 \end{pmatrix}$

(ix) $\begin{pmatrix} r\cos\alpha \\ r\sin\alpha \end{pmatrix}$ **(x)** $\begin{pmatrix} 1 \\ \tan\beta \end{pmatrix}$

Co-ordinate geometry using vectors: two dimensions

Two-dimensional co-ordinate geometry involves the study of points, given as co-ordinates, and lines, given as cartesian equations. The same work may also be treated using vectors.

The co-ordinates of a point, say (3, 4), are replaced by its position vector $\begin{pmatrix} 3 \\ 4 \end{pmatrix}$ or $3\mathbf{i} + 4\mathbf{j}$. The cartesian equation of a line is replaced by its vector form, and this is introduced on page 291.

Since most two-dimensional problems are readily solved using the methods of cartesian co-ordinate geometry, as introduced in *AS Pure Mathematics*, Chapter 2, why go to the trouble of relearning it all in vectors? The answer is that vector methods are very much easier to use in many three-dimensional situations than cartesian methods are. In preparation for that, we review some familiar two-dimensional work in this section, comparing cartesian and vector methods.

The vector joining two points

In figure 11.19, start by looking at two points A(2, –1) and B(4, 3); that is the points with position vectors $\overrightarrow{OA} = \begin{pmatrix} 2 \\ -1 \end{pmatrix}$ and $\overrightarrow{OB} = \begin{pmatrix} 4 \\ 3 \end{pmatrix}$, alternatively $2\mathbf{i} - \mathbf{j}$ and $4\mathbf{i} + 3\mathbf{j}$.

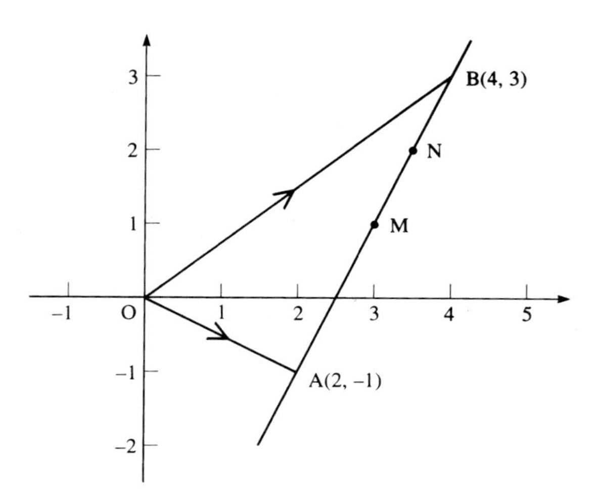

Figure 11.19

The vector joining A to B is $\overrightarrow{AB}$ and this is given by

$$\begin{aligned}\overrightarrow{AB} &= \overrightarrow{AO} + \overrightarrow{OB} \\ &= -\overrightarrow{OA} + \overrightarrow{OB} \\ &= \overrightarrow{OB} - \overrightarrow{OA} \\ &= \begin{pmatrix} 4 \\ 3 \end{pmatrix} - \begin{pmatrix} 2 \\ -1 \end{pmatrix} = \begin{pmatrix} 2 \\ 4 \end{pmatrix}.\end{aligned}$$

Since $\overrightarrow{AB} = \begin{pmatrix} 2 \\ 4 \end{pmatrix}$, then it follows that the length of AB is given by

$$\begin{aligned}|\overrightarrow{AB}| &= \sqrt{2^2 + 4^2} \\ &= \sqrt{20}.\end{aligned}$$

You can find the position vectors of points along AB as follows.

The mid-point, M, has position vector $\overrightarrow{OM}$, given by

$$\begin{aligned}\overrightarrow{OM} &= \overrightarrow{OA} + \tfrac{1}{2}\overrightarrow{AB} \\ &= \begin{pmatrix} 2 \\ -1 \end{pmatrix} + \frac{1}{2}\begin{pmatrix} 2 \\ 4 \end{pmatrix} \\ &= \begin{pmatrix} 3 \\ 1 \end{pmatrix}.\end{aligned}$$

In the same way, the position vector of the point N, three-quarters of the distance from A to B, is given by

$$\overrightarrow{ON} = \begin{pmatrix} 2 \\ -1 \end{pmatrix} + \frac{3}{4}\begin{pmatrix} 2 \\ 4 \end{pmatrix}$$

$$= \begin{pmatrix} 3\frac{1}{2} \\ 2 \end{pmatrix}$$

and it is possible to find the position vector of any other point of subdivision of the line AB in the same way.

---

p A point P has position vector $\overrightarrow{OP} = \overrightarrow{OA} + \lambda\overrightarrow{AB}$ where λ is a fraction.

Show that this can be expressed as

$$\overrightarrow{OP} = (1 - \lambda)\,\overrightarrow{OA} + \lambda\overrightarrow{OB}.$$

The vector equation of a line

It is now a small step to go from finding the position vector of any point on the line AB to finding the vector form of the equation of the line AB. To take this step, you will find it helpful to carry out the following activity.

ACTIVITY 11.1 The position vectors of a set of points are given by

$$\mathbf{r} = \begin{pmatrix} 2 \\ -1 \end{pmatrix} + \lambda\begin{pmatrix} 2 \\ 4 \end{pmatrix}$$

where λ is a parameter which may take any value.

(i) Show that $\lambda = 2$ corresponds to the point with position vector $\begin{pmatrix} 6 \\ 7 \end{pmatrix}$.

(ii) Find the position vectors of points corresponding to values of λ of -2, -1, 0, $\frac{1}{2}$, $\frac{3}{4}$, 1, 3.

(iii) Mark all your points on a sheet of graph paper and show that when they are joined up they give the line AB in figure 11.19.

(iv) State what values of λ correspond to the points A, B, M and N.

(v) What can you say about the position of the point if

(a) $0 < \lambda < 1$?

(b) $\lambda > 1$?

(c) $\lambda < 0$?

Conclusions from the activity

This activity should have convinced you that

$$\mathbf{r} = \begin{pmatrix} 2 \\ -1 \end{pmatrix} + \lambda\begin{pmatrix} 2 \\ 4 \end{pmatrix}$$

is the equation of the line passing through $(2, -1)$ and $(4, 3)$, written in vector form.

You may find it helpful to think of this in these terms.

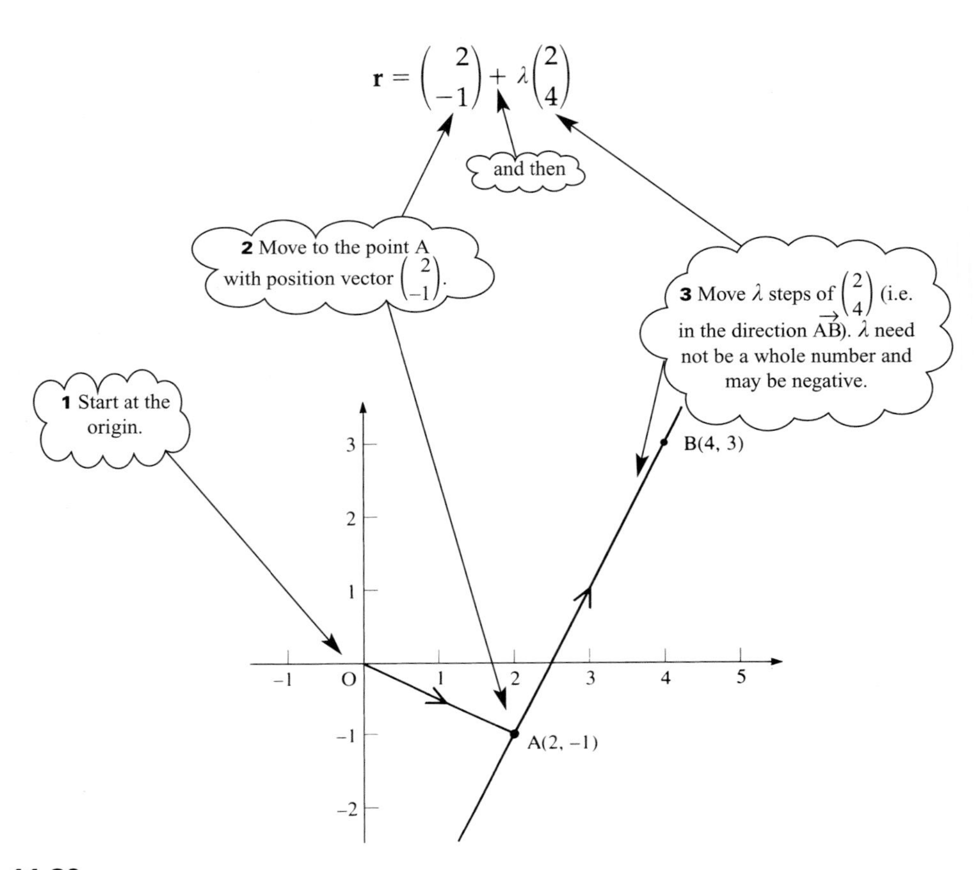

Figure 11.20

You should also have noticed that when:

$\lambda = 0$	the point corresponds to the point A
$\lambda = 1$	the point corresponds to the point B
$0 < \lambda < 1$	the point lies between A and B
$\lambda > 1$	the point lies beyond B
$\lambda < 0$	the point lies beyond A.

The vector form of the equation is not unique; there are many (in fact infinitely many) different ways in which the equation of any particular line may be expressed. There are two reasons for this: direction and location.

Direction

The direction of the line in the example is $\begin{pmatrix} 2 \\ 4 \end{pmatrix}$. That means that for every 2 units along (in the **i** direction), the line goes up 4 units (in the **j** direction). This is equivalent to stating that for every 1 unit along, the line goes up 2 units, corresponding to the equation

$$\mathbf{r} = \begin{pmatrix} 2 \\ -1 \end{pmatrix} + \lambda \begin{pmatrix} 1 \\ 2 \end{pmatrix}.$$

The only difference is that the two equations have different values of λ for particular points. In the first equation, point B, with position vector $\begin{pmatrix} 4 \\ 3 \end{pmatrix}$, corresponds to a value of λ of 1. In the second equation, the value of λ for B is 2.

The direction $\begin{pmatrix} 2 \\ 4 \end{pmatrix}$ is the same as $\begin{pmatrix} 1 \\ 2 \end{pmatrix}$, or as any multiple of $\begin{pmatrix} 1 \\ 2 \end{pmatrix}$ such as $\begin{pmatrix} 3 \\ 6 \end{pmatrix}$, $\begin{pmatrix} -5 \\ -10 \end{pmatrix}$ or $\begin{pmatrix} 100.5 \\ 201 \end{pmatrix}$. Any of these could be used in the vector equation of the line.

Location

In the equation

$$\mathbf{r} = \begin{pmatrix} 2 \\ -1 \end{pmatrix} + \lambda \begin{pmatrix} 2 \\ 4 \end{pmatrix}$$

$\begin{pmatrix} 2 \\ -1 \end{pmatrix}$ is the position vector of the point A on the line, and represents the point at which the line was joined. However, this could have been any other point on the line, such as M(3, 1), B(4, 3) etc. Consequently

$$\mathbf{r} = \begin{pmatrix} 3 \\ 1 \end{pmatrix} + \lambda \begin{pmatrix} 2 \\ 4 \end{pmatrix}$$

and

$$\mathbf{r} = \begin{pmatrix} 4 \\ 3 \end{pmatrix} + \lambda \begin{pmatrix} 2 \\ 4 \end{pmatrix}$$

are also equations of the same line, and there are infinitely many other possibilities, one corresponding to each point on the line.

Notes

1 It is usual to refer to any valid vector form of the equation as *the* vector equation of the line even though it is not unique.

2 It is often a good idea to give the direction vector in its simplest integer form: for example, replacing $\begin{pmatrix} 2 \\ 4 \end{pmatrix}$ with $\begin{pmatrix} 1 \\ 2 \end{pmatrix}$.

The general vector form of the equation of a line

If A and B are points with position **a** and **b**, then the equation

$$\mathbf{r} = \overrightarrow{OA} + \lambda\overrightarrow{AB}$$

may be written as $\mathbf{r} = \mathbf{a} + \lambda(\mathbf{b} - \mathbf{a})$

which implies $\mathbf{r} = (1 - \lambda)\mathbf{a} + \lambda\mathbf{b}.$

This is the general vector form of the equation of the line joining two points.

ACTIVITY 11.2 Plot the following lines on the same sheet of graph paper. When you have done so, explain why certain among them are the same as each other, others are parallel to each other, and others are in different directions.

(i) $\mathbf{r} = \begin{pmatrix} 2 \\ -1 \end{pmatrix} + \lambda\begin{pmatrix} 1 \\ 2 \end{pmatrix}$ **(ii)** $\mathbf{r} = \begin{pmatrix} 2 \\ -1 \end{pmatrix} + \lambda\begin{pmatrix} -1 \\ 2 \end{pmatrix}$ **(iii)** $\mathbf{r} = \begin{pmatrix} 0 \\ 2 \end{pmatrix} + \lambda\begin{pmatrix} 1 \\ 2 \end{pmatrix}$

(iv) $\mathbf{r} = \begin{pmatrix} 1 \\ -3 \end{pmatrix} + \lambda\begin{pmatrix} 3 \\ 6 \end{pmatrix}$ **(v)** $\mathbf{r} = \begin{pmatrix} 4 \\ 3 \end{pmatrix} + \lambda\begin{pmatrix} 1 \\ -2 \end{pmatrix}$

Cartesian and vector forms of the equation of a line

To find the cartesian form of the equation of a line which is given in vector form

$$\mathbf{r} = \begin{pmatrix} 2 \\ -1 \end{pmatrix} + \lambda\begin{pmatrix} 2 \\ 4 \end{pmatrix}$$

write **r** as $\begin{pmatrix} x \\ y \end{pmatrix}$, so the equation of the line becomes

$$\begin{pmatrix} x \\ y \end{pmatrix} = \begin{pmatrix} 2 \\ -1 \end{pmatrix} + \lambda\begin{pmatrix} 2 \\ 4 \end{pmatrix}$$

or $x = 2 + 2\lambda$

$y = -1 + 4\lambda$

The last two equations can be rewritten as

$$\frac{x-2}{2} = \lambda \quad \text{and} \quad \frac{y+1}{4} = \lambda$$

$$\Rightarrow \quad \frac{x-2}{2} = \frac{y+1}{4} \ (= \lambda).$$

The equation is now in cartesian form and may be tidied up to give $y = 2x - 5$.

When converting from cartesian form to vector form, you need to find any point on the line, and to convert the gradient into a vector with the same direction, as shown in the following example.

EXAMPLE 11.9

Write $y = \frac{1}{3}x + 2$ in vector form.

SOLUTION

First find any point on the line. For example, when $x = 0$, $y = 2$ and so the point (0, 2) with position vector $\begin{pmatrix} 0 \\ 2 \end{pmatrix}$ is on the line.

Then convert the gradient into a vector with the same direction. The equation of the line is of the form $y = mx + c$ and so its gradient m is $\frac{1}{3}$.

The vector $\begin{pmatrix} 3 \\ 1 \end{pmatrix}$ has gradient $\frac{1}{3}$.

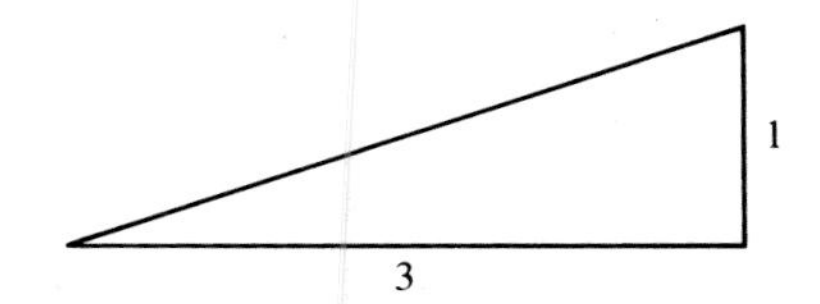

Figure 11.21

So the vector equation of the line is

$$\mathbf{r} = \begin{pmatrix} 0 \\ 2 \end{pmatrix} + \lambda \begin{pmatrix} 3 \\ 1 \end{pmatrix}.$$

Remember that there are other ways of writing this vector equation.

The intersection of two lines

EXAMPLE 11.10

Find the position vector of the point where the following lines intersect.

$$\mathbf{r} = \begin{pmatrix} 2 \\ 3 \end{pmatrix} + \lambda \begin{pmatrix} 1 \\ 2 \end{pmatrix} \quad \text{and} \quad \mathbf{r} = \begin{pmatrix} 6 \\ 1 \end{pmatrix} + \mu \begin{pmatrix} 1 \\ -3 \end{pmatrix}$$

Note here that different letters are used for the parameters in the two equations to avoid confusion.

SOLUTION

When the lines intersect, the position vector is the same for each of them.

$$\mathbf{r} = \begin{pmatrix} x \\ y \end{pmatrix} = \begin{pmatrix} 2 \\ 3 \end{pmatrix} + \lambda \begin{pmatrix} 1 \\ 2 \end{pmatrix} = \begin{pmatrix} 6 \\ 1 \end{pmatrix} + \mu \begin{pmatrix} 1 \\ -3 \end{pmatrix}$$

This gives two simultaneous equations for λ and μ.

$$x: \quad 2 + \lambda = 6 + \mu \quad \Rightarrow \quad \lambda - \mu = 4$$

$$y: \quad 3 + 2\lambda = 1 - 3\mu \quad \Rightarrow \quad 2\lambda + 3\mu = -2$$

Solving these gives $\lambda = 2$ and $\mu = -2$. Substituting in either equation gives

$$\mathbf{r} = \begin{pmatrix} 4 \\ 7 \end{pmatrix}$$

which is the position vector of the point of intersection.

EXAMPLE 11.11

Find the co-ordinates of the point of intersection of the lines joining A(1, 6) to B(4, 0), and C(1, 1) to D(5, 3).

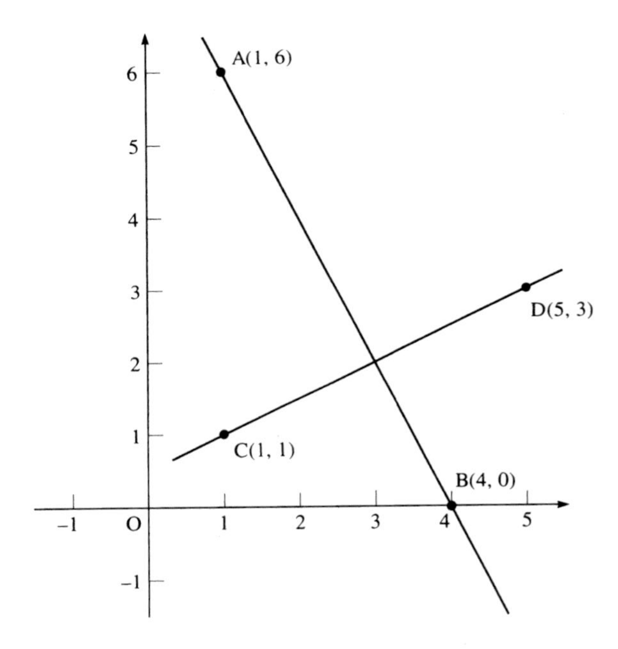

Figure 11.22

SOLUTION

$$\overrightarrow{AB} = \begin{pmatrix} 4 \\ 0 \end{pmatrix} - \begin{pmatrix} 1 \\ 6 \end{pmatrix} = \begin{pmatrix} 3 \\ -6 \end{pmatrix}$$

and so the vector equation of line AB is

$$\mathbf{r} = \overrightarrow{OA} + \lambda\overrightarrow{AB}$$

$$\mathbf{r} = \begin{pmatrix} 1 \\ 6 \end{pmatrix} + \lambda\begin{pmatrix} 3 \\ -6 \end{pmatrix}$$

$$\overrightarrow{CD} = \begin{pmatrix} 5 \\ 3 \end{pmatrix} - \begin{pmatrix} 1 \\ 1 \end{pmatrix} = \begin{pmatrix} 4 \\ 2 \end{pmatrix}$$

and so the vector equation of line CD is

$$\mathbf{r} = \overrightarrow{OC} + \mu\overrightarrow{CD}$$

$$\mathbf{r} = \begin{pmatrix}1\\1\end{pmatrix} + \mu\begin{pmatrix}4\\2\end{pmatrix}.$$

The intersection of these lines is at

$$\mathbf{r} = \begin{pmatrix}1\\6\end{pmatrix} + \lambda\begin{pmatrix}3\\-6\end{pmatrix} = \begin{pmatrix}1\\1\end{pmatrix} + \mu\begin{pmatrix}4\\2\end{pmatrix}.$$

x: $1 + 3\lambda = 1 + 4\mu \Rightarrow 3\lambda - 4\mu = 0$ ①

y: $6 - 6\lambda = 1 + 2\mu \Rightarrow 6\lambda + 2\mu = 5$ ②

Solve ① and ② simultaneously:

$$\begin{aligned} &①: & 3\lambda - 4\mu &= 0 \\ &② \times 2: & 12\lambda + 4\mu &= 10 \\ &\text{Add:} & 15\lambda &= 10 \\ &\Rightarrow & \lambda &= \tfrac{2}{3}. \end{aligned}$$

Substitute $\lambda = \frac{2}{3}$ in the equation for AB:

$$\Rightarrow \quad \mathbf{r} = \begin{pmatrix}1\\6\end{pmatrix} + \frac{2}{3}\begin{pmatrix}3\\-6\end{pmatrix}$$

$$\Rightarrow \quad \mathbf{r} = \begin{pmatrix}3\\2\end{pmatrix}.$$

The point of intersection has co-ordinates (3, 2).

Note

Alternatively, you could have found $\mu = \frac{1}{2}$ and substituted in the equation for CD.

EXERCISE 11C

1 For each of these pairs of points, A and B, write down:

(a) the vector $\overrightarrow{AB}$

(b) $|\overrightarrow{AB}|$

(c) the position vector of the mid-point of AB.

(i) A is (2, 3), B is (4, 11).

(ii) A is (4, 3), B is (0, 0).

(iii) A is (–2, –1), B is (4, 7).

(iv) A is (–3, 4), B is (3, –4).

(v) A is (–10, –8), B is (–5, 4).

2 Find the equation of each of these lines in vector form.

(i) Joining (2, 1) to (4, 5).
(ii) Joining (3, 5) to (0, 8).
(iii) Joining (–6, –6) to (4, 4).
(iv) Through (5, 3) in the same direction as $\mathbf{i} + \mathbf{j}$.
(v) Through (2, 1) parallel to $6\mathbf{i} + 3\mathbf{j}$.
(vi) Through (0, 0) parallel to $\begin{pmatrix} -1 \\ 4 \end{pmatrix}$.
(vii) Joining (0, 0) to (–2, 8).
(viii) Joining (3, –12) to (–1, 4).

3 Write these lines in cartesian form.

(i) $\mathbf{r} = \begin{pmatrix} 1 \\ 2 \end{pmatrix} + \lambda\begin{pmatrix} 1 \\ 3 \end{pmatrix}$ **(ii)** $\mathbf{r} = \begin{pmatrix} -2 \\ 0 \end{pmatrix} + \lambda\begin{pmatrix} -2 \\ -1 \end{pmatrix}$
(iii) $\mathbf{r} = \begin{pmatrix} 1 \\ 0 \end{pmatrix} + \lambda\begin{pmatrix} 4 \\ 4 \end{pmatrix}$ **(iv)** $\mathbf{r} = \begin{pmatrix} 4 \\ 3 \end{pmatrix} + \lambda\begin{pmatrix} 1 \\ 1 \end{pmatrix}$
(v) $\mathbf{r} = \begin{pmatrix} 2 \\ 5 \end{pmatrix} + \lambda\begin{pmatrix} 4 \\ 0 \end{pmatrix}$

4 Write these lines in vector form.

(i) $y = 2x + 3$ **(ii)** $y = x - 4$
(iii) $y = \frac{1}{2}x - 1$ **(iv)** $y = -\frac{1}{4}x$
(v) $x + 2y = 8$

5 Find the position vector of the point of intersection of each of these pairs of lines.

(i) $\mathbf{r} = \begin{pmatrix} 2 \\ 1 \end{pmatrix} + \lambda\begin{pmatrix} 1 \\ 0 \end{pmatrix} \quad : \quad \mathbf{r} = \begin{pmatrix} 3 \\ 0 \end{pmatrix} + \mu\begin{pmatrix} 1 \\ 1 \end{pmatrix}$
(ii) $\mathbf{r} = \begin{pmatrix} 2 \\ -1 \end{pmatrix} + \lambda\begin{pmatrix} 1 \\ 2 \end{pmatrix} \quad : \quad \mathbf{r} = \mu\begin{pmatrix} 1 \\ 1 \end{pmatrix}$
(iii) $\mathbf{r} = \begin{pmatrix} 0 \\ 5 \end{pmatrix} + \lambda\begin{pmatrix} -2 \\ -2 \end{pmatrix} \quad : \quad \mathbf{r} = \begin{pmatrix} 0 \\ -7 \end{pmatrix} + \mu\begin{pmatrix} 1 \\ 2 \end{pmatrix}$
(iv) $\mathbf{r} = \begin{pmatrix} -2 \\ -3 \end{pmatrix} + \lambda\begin{pmatrix} -1 \\ 3 \end{pmatrix} \quad : \quad \mathbf{r} = \begin{pmatrix} 1 \\ 3 \end{pmatrix} + \mu\begin{pmatrix} 2 \\ -1 \end{pmatrix}$
(v) $\mathbf{r} = \begin{pmatrix} 2 \\ 7 \end{pmatrix} + \lambda\begin{pmatrix} 1 \\ -1 \end{pmatrix} \quad : \quad \mathbf{r} = \begin{pmatrix} 5 \\ 1 \end{pmatrix} + \mu\begin{pmatrix} 1 \\ 2 \end{pmatrix}$

6 In this question the origin is taken to be at a harbour and the unit vectors $\mathbf{i}$ and $\mathbf{j}$ to have lengths of 1 km in the directions E and N.

A cargo vessel leaves the harbour and its position vector t hours later is given by

$$\mathbf{r}_1 = 12t\mathbf{i} + 16t\mathbf{j}.$$

A fishing boat is trawling nearby and its position at time t is given by

$$\mathbf{r}_2 = (10 - 3t)\mathbf{i} + (8 + 4t)\mathbf{j}.$$

(i) How far apart are the two boats when the cargo vessel leaves harbour?
(ii) How fast is each boat travelling?
(iii) What happens?

7 The points A(1, 0), B(7, 2) and C(13, 7) are the vertices of a triangle. The mid-points of the sides BC, CA and AB are L, M and N.

(i) Write down the position vectors of L, M and N.

(ii) Find the vector equations of the lines AL, BM and CN.

(iii) Find the intersections of these pairs of lines.

(a) AL and BM **(b)** BM and CN

(iv) What do you notice?

The angle between two vectors

P As you work through the proof in this section, make a list of all the results that you are assuming.

To find the angle θ between the two vectors

$$\overrightarrow{OA} = \mathbf{a} = a_1\mathbf{i} + a_2\mathbf{j} \quad \text{and} \quad \overrightarrow{OB} = \mathbf{b} = b_1\mathbf{i} + b_2\mathbf{j}$$

start by applying the cosine rule to triangle OAB in figure 11.23.

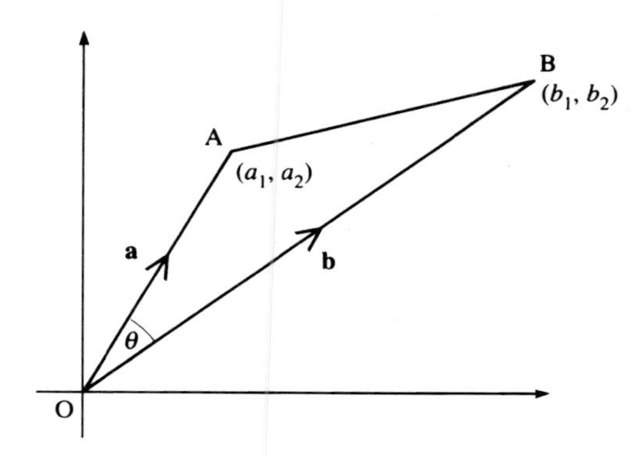

Figure 11.23

$$\cos\theta = \frac{OA^2 + OB^2 - AB^2}{2OA \times OB}$$

In this, OA, OB and AB are the lengths of the vectors $\overrightarrow{OA}$, $\overrightarrow{OB}$ and $\overrightarrow{AB}$, and so

$$OA = |\mathbf{a}| = \sqrt{a_1^2 + a_2^2} \quad \text{and} \quad OB = |\mathbf{b}| = \sqrt{b_1^2 + b_2^2}.$$

The vector $\overrightarrow{AB} = \mathbf{b} - \mathbf{a}$

$$= (b_1\mathbf{i} + b_2\mathbf{j}) - (a_1\mathbf{i} + a_2\mathbf{j})$$

$$= (b_1 - a_1)\mathbf{i} + (b_2 - a_2)\mathbf{j}$$

and so its length is given by

$$AB = |\mathbf{b} - \mathbf{a}| = \sqrt{(b_1 - a_1)^2 + (b_2 - a_2)^2}.$$

Substituting for OA, OB and AB in the cosine rule gives

$$\cos\theta = \frac{(a_1^2 + a_2^2) + (b_1^2 + b_2^2) - [(b_1 - a_1)^2 + (b_2 - a_2)^2]}{2\sqrt{a_1^2 + a_2^2} \times \sqrt{b_1^2 + b_2^2}}$$

$$= \frac{a_1^2 + a_2^2 + b_1^2 + b_2^2 - (b_1^2 - 2a_1b_1 + a_1^2 + b_2^2 - 2a_2b_2 + a_2^2)}{2\,|\mathbf{a}|\,|\mathbf{b}|}.$$

This simplifies to

$$\cos\theta = \frac{2a_1b_1 + 2a_2b_2}{2\,|\mathbf{a}|\,|\mathbf{b}|}$$

$$= \frac{a_1b_1 + a_2b_2}{|\mathbf{a}|\,|\mathbf{b}|}.$$

The expression on the top line, $a_1b_1 + a_2b_2$, is called the *scalar product* (or *dot product*) of the vectors **a** and **b** and is written **a.b**. Thus

$$\cos\theta = \frac{\mathbf{a}.\mathbf{b}}{|\mathbf{a}|\,|\mathbf{b}|}.$$

This result is usually written in the form

$$\mathbf{a}.\mathbf{b} = |\mathbf{a}|\,|\mathbf{b}|\cos\theta.$$

The next example shows you how to use it to find the angle between two vectors given numerically.

EXAMPLE 11.12

Find the angle between the vectors $\begin{pmatrix} 3 \\ 4 \end{pmatrix}$ and $\begin{pmatrix} 5 \\ -12 \end{pmatrix}$.

SOLUTION

Let $\mathbf{a} = \begin{pmatrix} 3 \\ 4 \end{pmatrix} \Rightarrow |\mathbf{a}| = \sqrt{3^2 + 4^2} = 5$

and $\mathbf{b} = \begin{pmatrix} 5 \\ -12 \end{pmatrix} \Rightarrow |\mathbf{b}| = \sqrt{5^2 + (-12)^2} = 13.$

The scalar product

$$\begin{pmatrix} 3 \\ 4 \end{pmatrix}.\begin{pmatrix} 5 \\ -12 \end{pmatrix} = 3 \times 5 + 4 \times (-12)$$

$$= 15 - 48$$

$$= -33.$$

Substituting in $\mathbf{a}.\mathbf{b} = |\mathbf{a}|\,|\mathbf{b}|\cos\theta$ gives

$$-33 = 5 \times 13 \times \cos\theta$$

$$\cos\theta = \frac{-33}{65}$$

$$\Rightarrow \quad \theta = 120.5°.$$

Perpendicular vectors

Since $\cos 90° = 0$, it follows that if vectors **a** and **b** are perpendicular then $\mathbf{a.b} = 0$.

Conversely, if the scalar product of two non-zero vectors is zero, they are perpendicular.

EXAMPLE 11.13

Show that the vectors $\mathbf{a} = \begin{pmatrix} 2 \\ 4 \end{pmatrix}$ and $\mathbf{b} = \begin{pmatrix} 6 \\ -3 \end{pmatrix}$ are perpendicular.

SOLUTION

The scalar product of the vectors is

$$\begin{aligned} \mathbf{a.b} &= \begin{pmatrix} 2 \\ 4 \end{pmatrix} \cdot \begin{pmatrix} 6 \\ -3 \end{pmatrix} \\ &= 2 \times 6 + 4 \times (-3) \\ &= 12 - 12 = 0. \end{aligned}$$

Therefore the vectors are perpendicular.

Further points concerning the scalar product

- You will notice that the scalar product of two vectors is an ordinary number. It has size but no direction and so is a scalar, rather than a vector. It is for this reason that it is called the scalar product. There is another way of multiplying vectors that gives a vector as the answer; it is called the *vector product.* This is covered in FP3.

- The scalar product is calculated in the same way for three-dimensional vectors. For example:

$$\begin{pmatrix} 2 \\ 3 \\ 4 \end{pmatrix} \cdot \begin{pmatrix} 5 \\ 6 \\ 7 \end{pmatrix} = 2 \times 5 + 3 \times 6 + 4 \times 7 = 56.$$

  In general

$$\begin{pmatrix} a_1 \\ a_2 \\ a_3 \end{pmatrix} \cdot \begin{pmatrix} b_1 \\ b_2 \\ b_3 \end{pmatrix} = a_1 b_1 + a_2 b_2 + a_3 b_3.$$

- The scalar product of two vectors is commutative. It has the same value whichever of them is on the left-hand side or right-hand side. Thus $\mathbf{a.b} = \mathbf{b.a}$, as in the following example.

$$\begin{pmatrix} 2 \\ 3 \end{pmatrix} \cdot \begin{pmatrix} 6 \\ 7 \end{pmatrix} = 2 \times 6 + 3 \times 7 = 33 \qquad \begin{pmatrix} 6 \\ 7 \end{pmatrix} \cdot \begin{pmatrix} 2 \\ 3 \end{pmatrix} = 6 \times 2 + 7 \times 3 = 33.$$

---

p How would you prove this result?

EXERCISE 11D

1 Find the angles between these vectors.

(i) $2\mathbf{i} + 3\mathbf{j}$ and $4\mathbf{i} + \mathbf{j}$ **(ii)** $2\mathbf{i} - \mathbf{j}$ and $\mathbf{i} + 2\mathbf{j}$

(iii) $\begin{pmatrix} -1 \\ -1 \end{pmatrix}$ and $\begin{pmatrix} -1 \\ -2 \end{pmatrix}$ **(iv)** $4\mathbf{i} + \mathbf{j}$ and $\mathbf{i} + \mathbf{j}$

(v) $\begin{pmatrix} 2 \\ 3 \end{pmatrix}$ and $\begin{pmatrix} -6 \\ 4 \end{pmatrix}$ **(vi)** $\begin{pmatrix} 3 \\ -1 \end{pmatrix}$ and $\begin{pmatrix} -6 \\ 2 \end{pmatrix}$

2 Points A, B, C and D are (1, 0), (9, 4), (6, 1) and (9, 7), respectively.

(i) Write down the vector equation of line AB.

(ii) Write down the vector equation of line CD.

(iii) Find the position vector of the point of intersection.

(iv) Find the angle between the lines AB and CD.

3 The equations of the four sides AB, BC, CD, DA of a quadrilateral are:

AB: $\mathbf{r} = \begin{pmatrix} 1 \\ 1 \end{pmatrix} + \lambda_1 \begin{pmatrix} 4 \\ 1 \end{pmatrix}$ BC: $\mathbf{r} = \begin{pmatrix} 1 \\ 1 \end{pmatrix} + \lambda_2 \begin{pmatrix} 1 \\ 3 \end{pmatrix}$

CD: $\mathbf{r} = \begin{pmatrix} 6 \\ 5 \end{pmatrix} + \lambda_3 \begin{pmatrix} 4 \\ 1 \end{pmatrix}$ DA: $\mathbf{r} = \begin{pmatrix} 6 \\ 5 \end{pmatrix} + \lambda_4 \begin{pmatrix} 1 \\ 3 \end{pmatrix}$.

(i) Look carefully at the equations of the four lines and state, with reasons, what sort of quadrilateral ABCD is.

(ii) Find the co-ordinates of the four vertices of the quadrilateral.

(iii) Find the internal angles of the quadrilateral.

4 The points A, B and C have co-ordinates (3, 2), (6, 3) and (5, 6), respectively.

(i) Write down the vectors $\overrightarrow{AB}$ and $\overrightarrow{BC}$.

(ii) Show that the angle ABC is 90°.

(iii) Show that $|\overrightarrow{AB}| = |\overrightarrow{BC}|$.

The figure ABCD is a square.

(iv) Find the co-ordinates of the point D.

5 Three points P, Q and R have position vectors, $\mathbf{p}$, $\mathbf{q}$ and $\mathbf{r}$ respectively, where

$$\mathbf{p} = 7\mathbf{i} + 10\mathbf{j}, \quad \mathbf{q} = 3\mathbf{i} + 12\mathbf{j}, \quad \mathbf{r} = -\mathbf{i} + 4\mathbf{j}.$$

(i) Write down the vectors $\overrightarrow{PQ}$ and $\overrightarrow{RQ}$, and show that they are perpendicular.

(ii) Using a scalar product, or otherwise, find the angle PRQ.

(iii) Find the position vector of S, the mid-point of PR.

(iv) Show that $|\overrightarrow{QS}| = |\overrightarrow{RS}|$.

Using your previous results, or otherwise, find the angle PSQ.

[MEI]

Co-ordinate geometry using vectors: three dimensions

Points

In three dimensions, a point has three co-ordinates, usually called x, y and z.

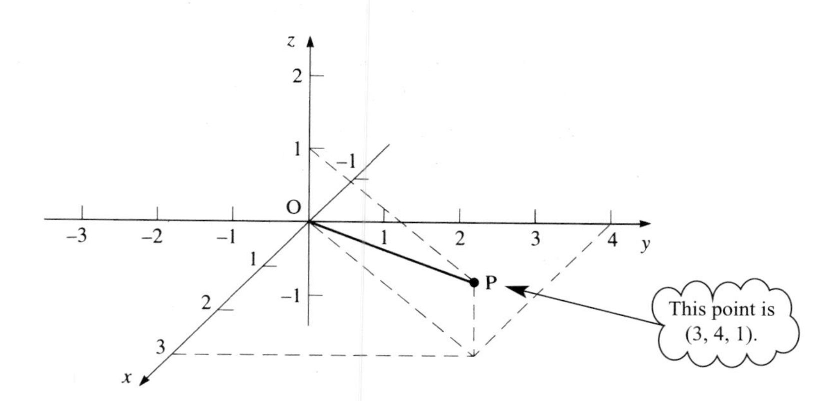

Figure 11.24

The axes are conventionally arranged as shown in figure 11.24, where the point P is (3, 4, 1). Even on correctly drawn three-dimensional grids, it is often hard to see the relationship between the points, lines and planes, so it is seldom worth your while trying to plot points accurately.

There are many important results that can be extended from two dimensions into three dimensions. Here you are asked to prove two of these.

The length of a vector

In two dimensions, the use of Pythagoras' theorem leads to the result that a vector $a_1\mathbf{i} + a_2\mathbf{j}$ has length $|\mathbf{a}|$ given by

$$|\mathbf{a}| = \sqrt{a_1^2 + a_2^2}.$$

---

p Show that the length of the three-dimensional vector $a_1\mathbf{i} + a_2\mathbf{j} + a_3\mathbf{k}$ is given by

$$|\mathbf{a}| = \sqrt{a_1^2 + a_2^2 + a_3^2}.$$

The angle between two vectors

The angle θ between the vectors $\mathbf{a} = a_1\mathbf{i} + a_2\mathbf{j}$ and $b_1\mathbf{i} + b_2\mathbf{j}$ in two dimensions is given by

$$\cos\theta = \frac{a_1b_1 + a_2b_2}{\sqrt{a_1^2 + a_2^2} \times \sqrt{b_1^2 + b_2^2}} = \frac{\mathbf{a}.\mathbf{b}}{|\mathbf{a}|\,|\mathbf{b}|}$$

where **a.b** is the scalar product of **a** and **b**. This result was proved by using the cosine rule on pages 299–300.

---

p Show that the angle between the three-dimensional vectors

$$\mathbf{a} = a_1\mathbf{i} + a_2\mathbf{j} + a_3\mathbf{k} \quad \text{and} \quad \mathbf{b} = b_1\mathbf{i} + b_2\mathbf{j} + b_3\mathbf{k}$$

is also given by

$$\cos\theta = \frac{\mathbf{a}.\mathbf{b}}{|\mathbf{a}|\,|\mathbf{b}|}$$

but that the scalar product **a.b** is now

$$\mathbf{a}.\mathbf{b} = a_1b_1 + a_2b_2 + a_3b_3.$$

Vectors

The position vector of the point P in figure 11.24 is given by

$$3\mathbf{i} + 4\mathbf{j} + \mathbf{k} \quad \text{or} \quad \begin{pmatrix} 3 \\ 4 \\ 1 \end{pmatrix}$$

and other vectors are given in the same style, with **k** the unit vector in the z direction.

The vector equation of a line is just like that in two dimensions. For example:

$$\mathrm{r} = \begin{pmatrix} 3 \\ 4 \\ 1 \end{pmatrix} + \lambda \begin{pmatrix} 2 \\ 3 \\ 6 \end{pmatrix}$$

represents a line through the point with position vector $\begin{pmatrix} 3 \\ 4 \\ 1 \end{pmatrix}$, in the direction $\begin{pmatrix} 2 \\ 3 \\ 6 \end{pmatrix}$.

By contrast the cartesian form of a line in three dimensions is rather more complicated. The equation

$$\mathbf{r} = \begin{pmatrix} x \\ y \\ z \end{pmatrix} = \begin{pmatrix} 3 \\ 4 \\ 1 \end{pmatrix} + \lambda \begin{pmatrix} 2 \\ 3 \\ 6 \end{pmatrix}$$

contains three relationships, which are parametric equations for the line.

$$x = 3 + 2\lambda \qquad y = 4 + 3\lambda \qquad z = 1 + 6\lambda$$

Making λ the subject of each of these gives

$$\lambda = \frac{x-3}{2} \qquad \lambda = \frac{y-4}{3} \quad \text{and} \quad \lambda = \frac{z-1}{6}$$

which leads to

$$\frac{x-3}{2} = \frac{y-4}{3} = \frac{z-1}{6}.$$

This is the cartesian form of the equation of the line.

Note

The line's direction vector $\begin{pmatrix} 2 \\ 3 \\ 6 \end{pmatrix}$ can be read from the denominators of the three expressions in this equation, and a point through which it passes (3,4,1) from the three numerators.

The procedure may be generalised to write the equation of a straight line passing in direction **u** through a given point A with position vector **a**, as in figure 11.25.

$$\mathbf{a} = \begin{pmatrix} a_1 \\ a_2 \\ a_3 \end{pmatrix} \qquad \mathbf{u} = \begin{pmatrix} u_1 \\ u_2 \\ u_3 \end{pmatrix}$$

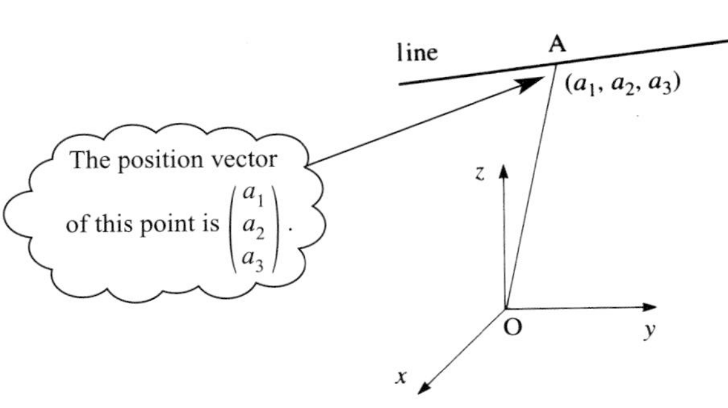

Figure 11.25

In vector form this is given by $\mathbf{r} = \overrightarrow{OA} + \lambda\mathbf{u}$

which may be written as $\mathbf{r} = \mathbf{a} + \lambda\mathbf{u}$

or in component form as

$$\mathbf{r} = \begin{pmatrix} x \\ y \\ z \end{pmatrix} = \begin{pmatrix} a_1 \\ a_2 \\ a_3 \end{pmatrix} + \lambda \begin{pmatrix} u_1 \\ u_2 \\ u_3 \end{pmatrix}.$$

This may then be written as the cartesian form of the equation.

$$\frac{x - a_1}{u_1} = \frac{y - a_2}{u_2} = \frac{z - a_3}{u_3}$$

The cartesian form involves two = symbols rather than one.

Special cases of the cartesian form

In the general cartesian form of the equation of the straight line

$$\frac{x - a_1}{u_1} = \frac{y - a_2}{u_2} = \frac{z - a_3}{u_3}$$

the vector $\begin{pmatrix} u_1 \\ u_2 \\ u_3 \end{pmatrix}$ gives the direction of the line.

In this vector, at least one of u_1, u_2 and u_3 must be non-zero (otherwise the line would not be going anywhere and so would not be a line). However, there is no reason why more than one should be non-zero.

$\begin{pmatrix} 1 \\ 0 \\ 0 \end{pmatrix}$ and $\begin{pmatrix} 4 \\ 1 \\ 0 \end{pmatrix}$ are both valid directions.

In such cases, the equation of the line needs to be written differently, as in the following examples.

EXAMPLE 11.14

Find the cartesian form of the equation of the line through (7, 2, 3) in the direction $\begin{pmatrix} 0 \\ 5 \\ 2 \end{pmatrix}$.

SOLUTION

Substituting in the general form

$$\frac{x - a_1}{u_1} = \frac{y - a_2}{u_2} = \frac{z - a_2}{u_3}$$

gives

$$\frac{x - 7}{0} = \frac{y - 2}{5} = \frac{z - 3}{2}.$$

There is clearly a problem here since the first fraction involves division by zero. This difficulty is explained by the fact that for every point on the line $x - 7 = 0$, or $x = 7$. What was $\frac{x-7}{0}$ is now $\frac{0}{0}$; this is still undefined and so it is not equated to the other two expressions in the equation. Instead, the equation of the line is written

$$x = 7 \quad \text{and} \quad \frac{y - 2}{5} = \frac{z - 3}{2}.$$

EXAMPLE 11.15

Find the cartesian form of the equation of the line through (4, 2, 3) in the direction $\begin{pmatrix} 1 \\ 0 \\ 0 \end{pmatrix}$.

SOLUTION

Substituting in the general form

$$\frac{x - a_1}{u_1} = \frac{y - a_2}{u_2} = \frac{z - a_3}{u_3}$$

gives

$$\frac{x - 4}{1} = \frac{y - 2}{0} = \frac{z - 3}{0}.$$

The last two expressions tell you that $y = 2$ and $z = 3$.

The first part $\frac{x-4}{1}$ does not really give any further information: x may take any value, and this is understood when the equation of the line is written as

$$y = 2 \quad \text{and} \quad z = 3.$$

The line is shown in figure 11.26.

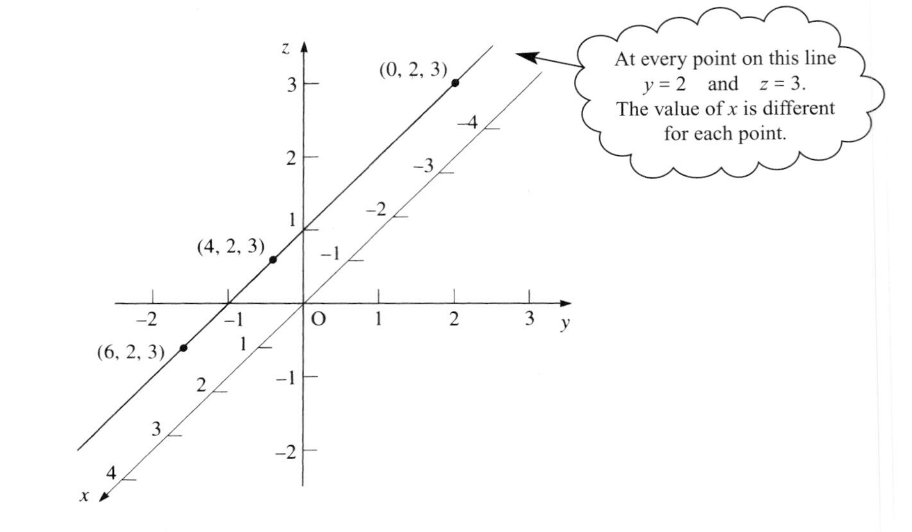

Figure 11.26

The vector forms of the equations of the lines given in the last two examples are

$$\mathbf{r} = \begin{pmatrix} x \\ y \\ z \end{pmatrix} = \begin{pmatrix} 7 \\ 2 \\ 3 \end{pmatrix} + \lambda \begin{pmatrix} 0 \\ 5 \\ 2 \end{pmatrix} \text{ and } \quad \mathbf{r} = \begin{pmatrix} x \\ y \\ z \end{pmatrix} = \begin{pmatrix} 4 \\ 2 \\ 3 \end{pmatrix} + \lambda \begin{pmatrix} 1 \\ 0 \\ 0 \end{pmatrix}.$$

These are considerably simpler than the equivalent cartesian forms. You will usually find it much easier to work with the equation of the line in vector form.

To convert from cartesian to vector form, you can reverse the procedure as in the following example. Usually, however, you would just write down the answer by looking at the numbers in the three numerators and denominators.

EXAMPLE 11.16

Write the equation of this line in vector form.

$$\frac{x-5}{2} = \frac{y+1}{1} = \frac{z+3}{6}$$

SOLUTION

$$\frac{x-5}{2} = \frac{y+1}{1} = \frac{z+3}{6} = \lambda$$

$$\frac{x-5}{2} = \lambda \quad \Rightarrow \quad x = 5 + 2\lambda$$

$$\frac{y+1}{1} = \lambda \quad \Rightarrow \quad y = -1 + \lambda$$

$$\frac{z+3}{6} = \lambda \quad \Rightarrow \quad z = -3 + 6\lambda$$

So

$$\mathbf{r} = \begin{pmatrix} x \\ y \\ z \end{pmatrix} = \begin{pmatrix} 5 + 2\lambda \\ -1 + \lambda \\ -3 + 6\lambda \end{pmatrix}$$

which is written

$$\mathbf{r} = \begin{pmatrix} 5 \\ -1 \\ -3 \end{pmatrix} + \lambda \begin{pmatrix} 2 \\ 1 \\ 6 \end{pmatrix}.$$

This line passes through (5, –1, –3) in the direction $\begin{pmatrix} 2 \\ 1 \\ 6 \end{pmatrix}$.

The angle between two directions

When working in two dimensions you found the angle between two lines by using the scalar product. On page 304 you proved that this method can be extended into three dimensions, and its use is shown in the following example.

EXAMPLE 11.17

The points P, Q and R are (1, 0, –1), (2, 4, 1) and (3, 5, 6). Find ∠QPR.

SOLUTION

The angle between $\overrightarrow{PQ}$ and $\overrightarrow{PR}$ is given by θ in

$$\cos\theta = \frac{\overrightarrow{PQ}.\overrightarrow{PR}}{|\overrightarrow{PQ}|\,|\overrightarrow{PR}|}$$

In this

$$\overrightarrow{PQ} = \begin{pmatrix} 2 \\ 4 \\ 1 \end{pmatrix} - \begin{pmatrix} 1 \\ 0 \\ -1 \end{pmatrix} = \begin{pmatrix} 1 \\ 4 \\ 2 \end{pmatrix} \qquad |\overrightarrow{PQ}| = \sqrt{1^2 + 4^2 + 2^2} = \sqrt{21}$$

Similarly

$$\overrightarrow{PR} = \begin{pmatrix} 3 \\ 5 \\ 6 \end{pmatrix} - \begin{pmatrix} 1 \\ 0 \\ -1 \end{pmatrix} = \begin{pmatrix} 2 \\ 5 \\ 7 \end{pmatrix} \qquad |\overrightarrow{PR}| = \sqrt{2^2 + 5^2 + 7^2} = \sqrt{78}$$

Therefore

$$\overrightarrow{PQ}.\overrightarrow{PR} = \begin{pmatrix} 1 \\ 4 \\ 2 \end{pmatrix}.\begin{pmatrix} 2 \\ 5 \\ 7 \end{pmatrix}$$

$$= 1 \times 2 + 4 \times 5 + 2 \times 7$$
$$= 36$$

Substituting gives

$$\cos\theta = \frac{36}{\sqrt{21}\times\sqrt{78}}$$

$$\Rightarrow\ \theta = 27.2°$$

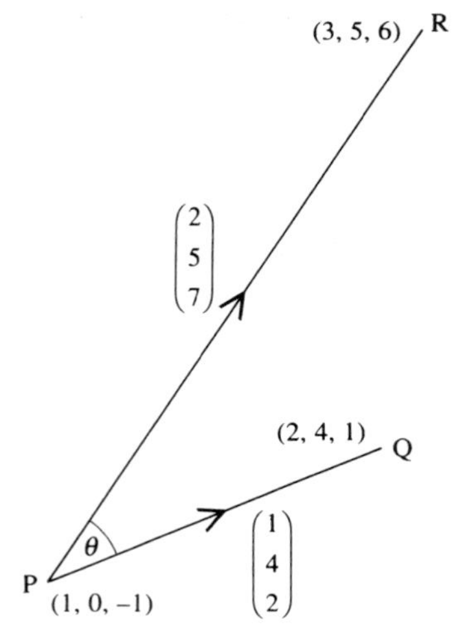

Figure 11.27

You must be careful to find the correct angle. To find $\angle$QPR (see figure 11.28), you need the scalar product $\overrightarrow{PQ}.\overrightarrow{PR}$. If you take $\overrightarrow{QP}.\overrightarrow{PR}$, you will obtain $\angle$Q′PR, which is $180° - \angle$QPR.

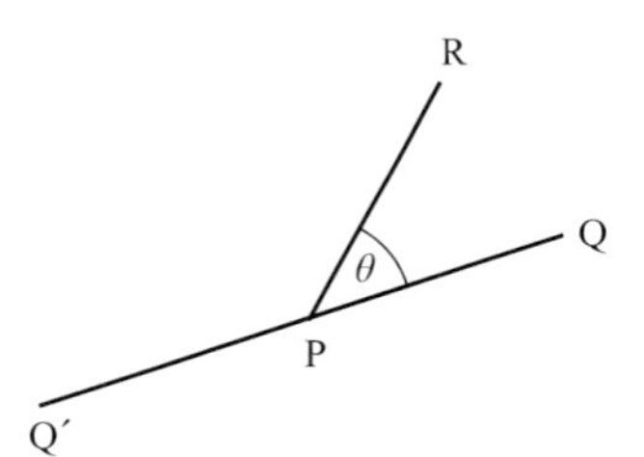

Figure 11.28

Even if two lines do not meet, it is still possible to specify the angle between them. The lines l and m shown in figure 11.29 do not meet; they are described as *skew*. The angle between them is that between their directions; it is shown in figure 11.29 as the angle θ between the lines l and m', where m' is a translation of the line m to a position where it does intersect the line l.

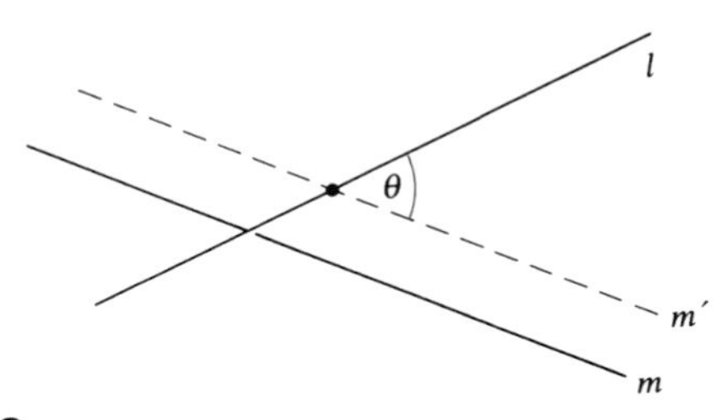

Figure 11.29

EXAMPLE 11.18 Find the angle between the lines

$$\mathbf{r} = \begin{pmatrix} 1 \\ 0 \\ 4 \end{pmatrix} + \lambda \begin{pmatrix} 2 \\ -1 \\ -1 \end{pmatrix} \quad \text{and} \quad \mathbf{r} = \begin{pmatrix} 2 \\ -1 \\ 3 \end{pmatrix} + \mu \begin{pmatrix} 3 \\ 0 \\ 1 \end{pmatrix}.$$

SOLUTION

The angle between the lines is the angle between their directions $\begin{pmatrix} 2 \\ -1 \\ -1 \end{pmatrix}$ and $\begin{pmatrix} 3 \\ 0 \\ 1 \end{pmatrix}$.

Using $\cos\theta = \dfrac{\mathbf{a}.\mathbf{b}}{|\mathbf{a}|\,|\mathbf{b}|}$

$$\cos\theta = \frac{2 \times 3 + (-1) \times 0 + (-1) \times 1}{\sqrt{2^2 + (-1)^2 + (-1)^2} \times \sqrt{3^2 + 0^2 + 1^2}}$$

$$\cos\theta = \frac{5}{\sqrt{6} \times \sqrt{10}}$$

$$\Rightarrow \qquad \theta = 49.8°.$$

EXERCISE 11E

1 Find the equations of the following lines in vector form.

(i) Through (2, 4, –1) in the direction $\begin{pmatrix} 3 \\ 6 \\ 4 \end{pmatrix}$

(ii) Through (1, 0, –1) in the direction $\begin{pmatrix} 1 \\ 0 \\ 0 \end{pmatrix}$

(iii) Through (1, 0, 4) and (6, 3, –2)

(iv) Through (0, 0, 1) and (2, 1, 4)

(v) Through (1, 2, 3) and (–2, –4, –6)

2 Write the equations of the following lines in cartesian form.

(i) $\mathbf{r} = \begin{pmatrix} 2 \\ 4 \\ -1 \end{pmatrix} + \lambda \begin{pmatrix} 3 \\ 6 \\ 4 \end{pmatrix}$

(ii) $\mathbf{r} = \begin{pmatrix} 1 \\ 0 \\ -1 \end{pmatrix} + \lambda \begin{pmatrix} 1 \\ 3 \\ 4 \end{pmatrix}$

(iii) $\mathbf{r} = \begin{pmatrix} 3 \\ 0 \\ 4 \end{pmatrix} + \lambda \begin{pmatrix} 1 \\ 0 \\ 2 \end{pmatrix}$

(iv) $\mathbf{r} = \begin{pmatrix} 0 \\ 4 \\ 1 \end{pmatrix} + \lambda \begin{pmatrix} 2 \\ 0 \\ 4 \end{pmatrix}$

(v) $\mathbf{r} = \begin{pmatrix} -2 \\ -7 \\ 3 \end{pmatrix} + \lambda \begin{pmatrix} 0 \\ 1 \\ 0 \end{pmatrix}$

3 Write the equations of the following lines in vector form.

(i) $\dfrac{x-3}{5} = \dfrac{y+2}{3} = \dfrac{z-1}{4}$

(ii) $\dfrac{x+6}{6} = \dfrac{y}{2} = \dfrac{z+4}{3}$

(iii) $x = \dfrac{y}{2} = \dfrac{z+1}{3}$

(iv) $x = y = z$

(v) $x = 2$ and $y = z$

4 Find the angles between these pairs of vectors.

(i) $\begin{pmatrix} 2 \\ 1 \\ 3 \end{pmatrix}$ and $\begin{pmatrix} 2 \\ -1 \\ 4 \end{pmatrix}$

(ii) $\begin{pmatrix} 1 \\ -1 \\ 0 \end{pmatrix}$ and $\begin{pmatrix} 3 \\ 1 \\ 5 \end{pmatrix}$

(iii) $3\mathbf{i} + 2\mathbf{j} - 2\mathbf{k}$ and $-4\mathbf{i} - \mathbf{j} + 3\mathbf{k}$

5 Find the angles between these pairs of lines.

(i) $\mathbf{r} = \begin{pmatrix} 2 \\ 1 \\ 3 \end{pmatrix} + \lambda\begin{pmatrix} 1 \\ 4 \\ 0 \end{pmatrix}$ and $\mathbf{r} = \begin{pmatrix} 6 \\ 10 \\ 4 \end{pmatrix} + \lambda\begin{pmatrix} 2 \\ 1 \\ 1 \end{pmatrix}$

(ii) $\mathbf{r} = \lambda\begin{pmatrix} 4 \\ 1 \\ 4 \end{pmatrix}$ and $\mathbf{r} = \begin{pmatrix} 7 \\ 0 \\ -3 \end{pmatrix} + \lambda\begin{pmatrix} 1 \\ 2 \\ -1 \end{pmatrix}$

(iii) $\dfrac{x-4}{3} = \dfrac{y-2}{7} = \dfrac{z+1}{-4}$ and $\dfrac{x-5}{2} = \dfrac{y-1}{8} = \dfrac{z}{-5}$

6 The room illustrated in the diagram has rectangular walls, floor and ceiling. A string has been stretched in a straight line between the corners A and G.

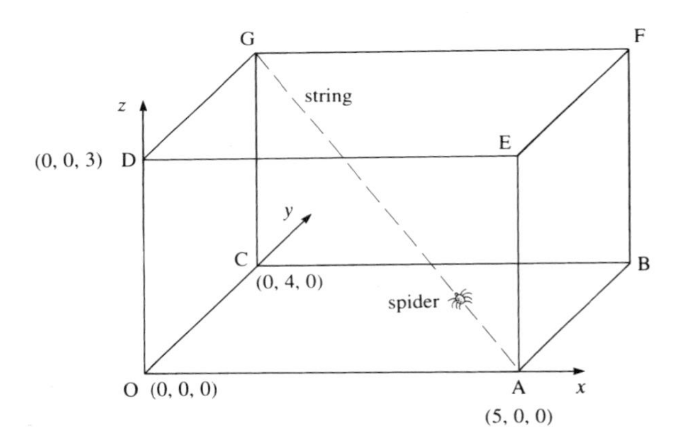

The corner O is taken as the origin. A is (5, 0, 0), C is (0, 4, 0) and D is (0, 0, 3), where the lengths are in metres.

(i) Write down the co-ordinates of G.

(ii) Find the vector $\overrightarrow{AG}$ and the length of the string $|\overrightarrow{AG}|$.

(iii) Write down the equation of the line AG in vector form.

A spider walks up the string, starting from A.

(iv) Find the position vector of the spider when it is at Q, one quarter of the way from A to G, and find the angle OQG.

(v) Show that when the spider is 1.5 m above the floor it is at its closest point to O, and find how far it is then from O.

[MEI]

7 The diagram shows an extension to a house. Its base and walls are rectangular and the end of its roof, EPF, is sloping, as illustrated.

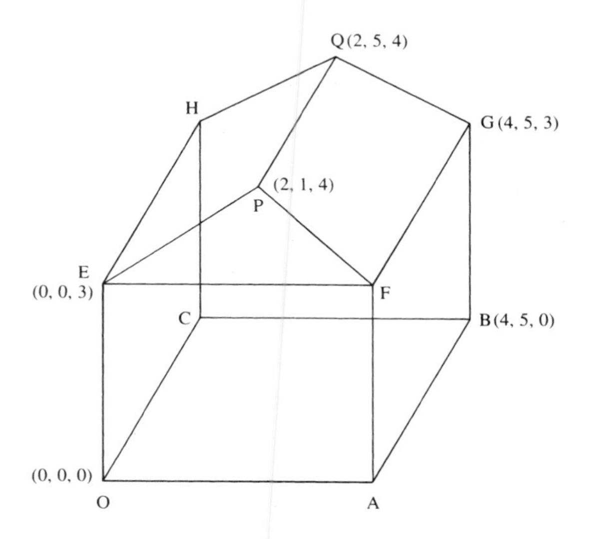

(i) Write down the co-ordinates of A and F.

(ii) Find, using vector methods, the angles FPQ and EPF.

The owner decorates the room with two streamers which are pulled taut. One goes from O to G, the other from A to H. She says that they touch each other and that they are perpendicular to each other.

(iii) Is she right?

8 The drawing shows an ordinary music stand, which consists of a rectangle DEFG with a vertical support OA.

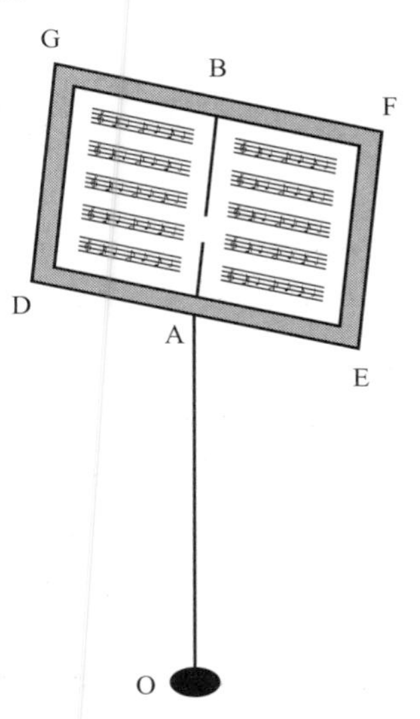

Relative to axes through the origin O, which is on the floor, the co-ordinates of various points are given (with dimensions in metres) as:

A is $(0, 0, 1)$ D is $(-0.25, 0, 1)$ F is $(0.25, 0.15, 1.3)$.

DE and GF are horizontal, A is the mid-point of DE and B is the mid-point of GF.

C is on AB so that $AC = \frac{1}{3}AB$.

(i) Write down the vector $\overrightarrow{AD}$ and show that $\overrightarrow{EF}$ is $\begin{pmatrix} 0 \\ 0.15 \\ 0.3 \end{pmatrix}$.

(ii) Calculate the co-ordinates of C.

(iii) Find the equations of the lines DE and EF in vector form.

[MEI, *part*]

9 The diagram illustrates the flight path of a helicopter H taking off from an airport.
Co-ordinate axes Oxyz are set up with the origin O at the base of the airport control tower. The x axis is due east, the y axis due north, and the z axis vertical. The units of distance are kilometres throughout.

The helicopter takes off from the point G.
The position vector **r** of the helicopter t minutes after take-off is given by

$$\mathbf{r} = (1 + t)\mathbf{i} + (0.5 + 2t)\mathbf{j} + 2t\mathbf{k}.$$

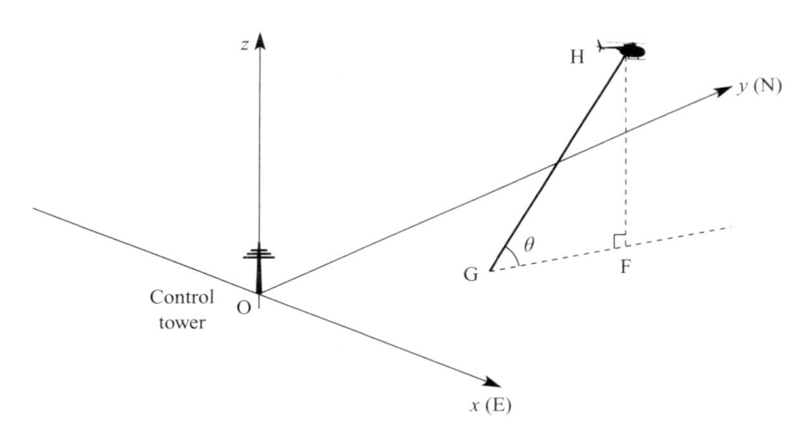

(i) Write down the co-ordinates of G.

(ii) Find the angle the flight path makes with the horizontal.
(This angle is shown as θ in the diagram.)

(iii) Find the bearing of the flight path.
(This is the bearing of the line GF shown in the diagram.)

(iv) The helicopter enters a cloud at a height of 2 km.
Find the co-ordinates of the point where the helicopter enters the cloud.

(v) A mountain top is situated at M(5, 4.5, 3).
Find the value of t when HM is perpendicular to the flight path GH.
Find the distance from the helicopter to the mountain top at this time.

[MEI]

Which balances better, a three-legged stool or a four-legged stool? Why? What information do you need to specify a particular plane?

There are various ways of finding the equation of a plane. Two of these are given in this book. Your choice of which one to use will depend on the information you are given.

The equation of a plane, given three points on it

There are several methods used to find the equation of a plane through three given points. The shortest method involves the use of vector product which is beyond the scope of this book but is covered in FP3. The method given here develops the same ideas as were used for the equation of a line. It will help you to understand the extra concepts involved, but it is not a requirement of the MEI Core 4 subject criteria.

To find the vector form of the equation of the plane through the points A, B and C (with position vectors $\overrightarrow{OA} = \mathbf{a}$, $\overrightarrow{OB} = \mathbf{b}$, $\overrightarrow{OC} = \mathbf{c}$), think of starting at the origin, travelling along OA to join the plane at A, and then any distance in each of the directions $\overrightarrow{AB}$ and $\overrightarrow{AC}$ to reach a general point R with position vector $\mathbf{r}$, where

$$\mathbf{r} = \overrightarrow{OA} + \lambda\overrightarrow{AB} + \mu\overrightarrow{AC}.$$

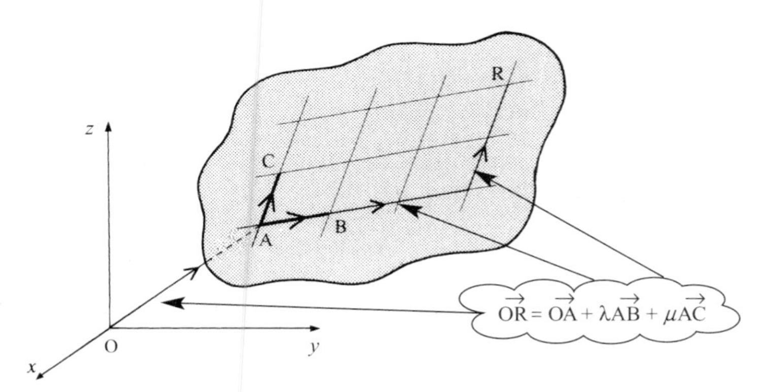

Figure 11.30

This is a vector form of the equation of the plane. Since $\overrightarrow{OA} = \mathbf{a}$, $\overrightarrow{AB} = \mathbf{b} - \mathbf{a}$ and $\overrightarrow{AC} = \mathbf{c} - \mathbf{a}$, it may also be written as

$$\mathbf{r} = \mathbf{a} + \lambda(\mathbf{b} - \mathbf{a}) + \mu(\mathbf{c} - \mathbf{a}).$$

EXAMPLE 11.19

Find the equation of the plane through A(4, 2, 0), B(3, 1, 1) and C(4, –1, 1).

SOLUTION

$$\overrightarrow{OA} = \begin{pmatrix} 4 \\ 2 \\ 0 \end{pmatrix}$$

$$\overrightarrow{AB} = \overrightarrow{OB} - \overrightarrow{OA} = \begin{pmatrix} 3 \\ 1 \\ 1 \end{pmatrix} - \begin{pmatrix} 4 \\ 2 \\ 0 \end{pmatrix} = \begin{pmatrix} -1 \\ -1 \\ 1 \end{pmatrix}$$

$$\overrightarrow{AC} = \overrightarrow{OC} - \overrightarrow{OA} = \begin{pmatrix} 4 \\ -1 \\ 1 \end{pmatrix} - \begin{pmatrix} 4 \\ 2 \\ 0 \end{pmatrix} = \begin{pmatrix} 0 \\ -3 \\ 1 \end{pmatrix}$$

So the equation $\mathbf{r} = \overrightarrow{OA} + \lambda\overrightarrow{AB} + \mu\overrightarrow{AC}$ becomes

$$\mathbf{r} = \begin{pmatrix} 4 \\ 2 \\ 0 \end{pmatrix} + \lambda\begin{pmatrix} -1 \\ -1 \\ 1 \end{pmatrix} + \mu\begin{pmatrix} 0 \\ -3 \\ 1 \end{pmatrix}.$$

This is the vector form of the equation, written using components.

Cartesian form

You can convert this equation into cartesian form by writing it as

$$\begin{pmatrix} x \\ y \\ z \end{pmatrix} = \begin{pmatrix} 4 \\ 2 \\ 0 \end{pmatrix} + \lambda\begin{pmatrix} -1 \\ -1 \\ 1 \end{pmatrix} + \mu\begin{pmatrix} 0 \\ -3 \\ 1 \end{pmatrix}$$

and eliminating λ and μ. The three equations contained in this vector equation may be simplified to give

$$\lambda = -x + 4 \quad ①$$

$$\lambda + 3\mu = -y + 2 \quad ②$$

$$\lambda + \mu = z. \quad ③$$

Substituting ① into ② gives

$$-x + 4 + 3\mu = -y + 2$$

$$3\mu = x - y - 2$$

$$\mu = \tfrac{1}{3}(x - y - 2).$$

Substituting this and ① into ③ gives

$$-x + 4 + \tfrac{1}{3}(x - y - 2) = z$$

$$-3x + 12 + x - y - 2 = 3z$$

$$2x + y + 3z = 10$$

and this is the cartesian equation of the plane through A, B and C.

Note

In contrast to the equation of a line, the equation of a plane is more neatly expressed in cartesian form. The general cartesian equation of a plane is often written as either

$$ax + by + cz + d = 0 \quad \text{or} \quad n_1x + n_2y + n_3z + d = 0.$$

The direction perpendicular to a plane

? Lay a sheet of paper on a flat horizontal table and mark several straight lines on it. Now take a pencil and stand it upright on the sheet of paper (see figure 11.31).

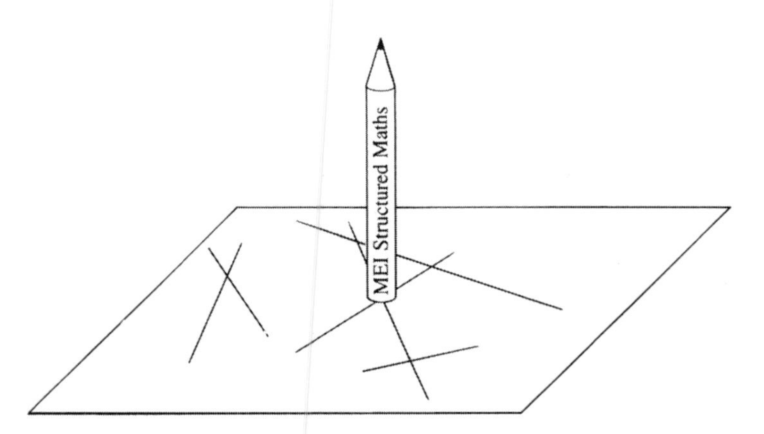

Figure 11.31

(i) What angle does the pencil make with any individual line?

(ii) Would it make any difference if the table were tilted at an angle (apart from the fact that you could no longer balance the pencil)?

The discussion on the previous page shows you that there is a direction (that of the pencil) which is at right angles to every straight line in the plane. A line in that direction is said to be perpendicular to the plane or normal to the plane.

This allows you to find a different vector form of the equation of a plane which you use when you know the position vector **a** of one point A in the plane and the direction $\mathbf{n} = n_1\mathbf{i} + n_2\mathbf{j} + n_3\mathbf{k}$ perpendicular to the plane.

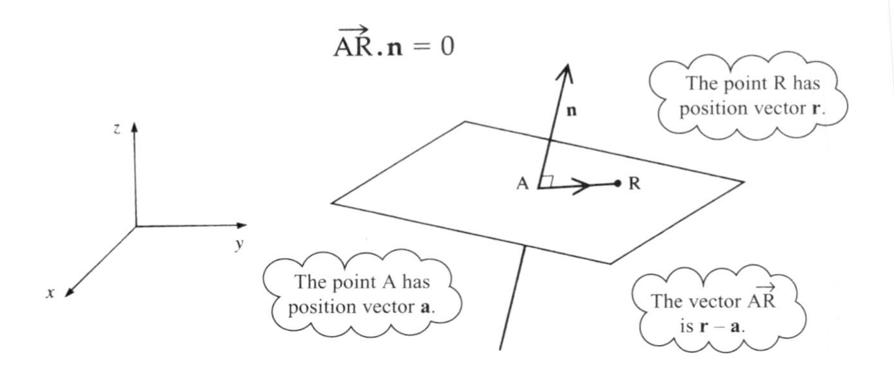

Figure 11.32

What you want to find is an expression for the position vector **r** of a general point R in the plane (see figure 11.32). Since AR is a line in the plane, it follows that AR is at right angles to the direction **n**.

$$\overrightarrow{AR}.\mathbf{n} = 0$$

The vector $\overrightarrow{AR}$ is given by

$$\overrightarrow{AR} = \mathbf{r} - \mathbf{a}$$

and so $\quad (\mathbf{r} - \mathbf{a}).\mathbf{n} = 0.$

This can also be written as

$$\mathbf{r}.\mathbf{n} - \mathbf{a}.\mathbf{n} = 0$$

or $\quad \begin{pmatrix} x \\ y \\ z \end{pmatrix} . \begin{pmatrix} n_1 \\ n_2 \\ n_3 \end{pmatrix} - \mathbf{a}.\mathbf{n} = 0$

$$\Rightarrow \; n_1x + n_2y + n_3z + d = 0$$

where $d = -\mathbf{a}.\mathbf{n}$.

Notice that d is a constant scalar.

EXAMPLE 11.20 Write down the equation of the plane through the point (2, 1, 3) given that the vector $\begin{pmatrix} 4 \\ 5 \\ 6 \end{pmatrix}$ is perpendicular to the plane.

SOLUTION

In this case, the position vector $\mathbf{a}$ of the point (2, 1, 3) is given by $\mathbf{a} = \begin{pmatrix} 2 \\ 1 \\ 3 \end{pmatrix}$.

The vector perpendicular to the plane is

$$\mathbf{n} = \begin{pmatrix} n_1 \\ n_2 \\ n_3 \end{pmatrix} = \begin{pmatrix} 4 \\ 5 \\ 6 \end{pmatrix}.$$

The equation of the plane is

$$n_1x + n_2y + n_3z - \mathbf{a}.\mathbf{n} = 0$$

$$4x + 5y + 6z - (2 \times 4 + 1 \times 5 + 3 \times 6) = 0$$

$$4x + 5y + 6z - 31 = 0.$$

Look carefully at the equation of the plane in Example 11.20. You can see at once that the vector $\begin{pmatrix} 4 \\ 5 \\ 6 \end{pmatrix}$, formed from the coefficients of x, y and z, is perpendicular to the plane.

The vector $\begin{pmatrix} n_1 \\ n_2 \\ n_3 \end{pmatrix}$ is perpendicular to all planes of the form

$$n_1x + n_2y + n_3z + d = 0$$

whatever the value of d (see figure 11.33). Consequently, all planes of that form are parallel; the coefficients of x, y and z determine the direction of the plane, the value of d its location.

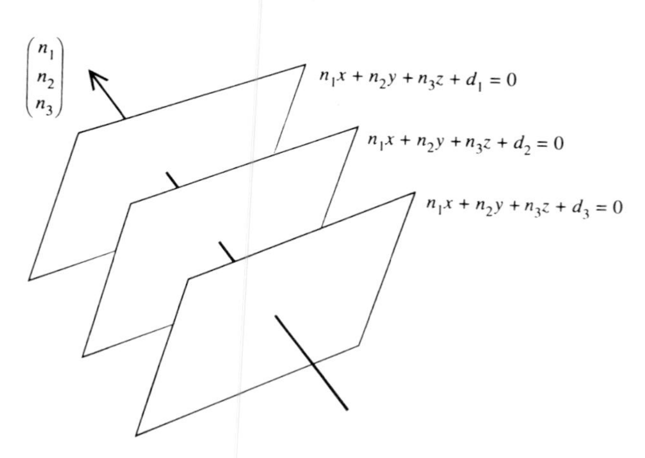

Figure 11.33

The intersection of a line and a plane

The point of intersection of a line and a plane is found by following the procedure in the next example.

EXAMPLE 11.21

Find the point of intersection of the line

$$\mathbf{r} = \begin{pmatrix} 2 \\ 3 \\ 4 \end{pmatrix} + \lambda \begin{pmatrix} 1 \\ 2 \\ -1 \end{pmatrix}$$

with the plane $5x + y - z = 1$.

SOLUTION

The line is

$$\mathbf{r} = \begin{pmatrix} x \\ y \\ z \end{pmatrix} = \begin{pmatrix} 2 \\ 3 \\ 4 \end{pmatrix} + \lambda \begin{pmatrix} 1 \\ 2 \\ -1 \end{pmatrix}$$

and so for any point on the line

$$x = 2 + \lambda \qquad y = 3 + 2\lambda \qquad \text{and} \qquad z = 4 - \lambda.$$

Substituting these into the equation of the plane $5x + y - z = 1$ gives

$$\begin{aligned} 5(2 + \lambda) + (3 + 2\lambda) - (4 - \lambda) &= 1 \\ 8\lambda &= -8 \\ \lambda &= -1. \end{aligned}$$

Substituting $\lambda = -1$ in the equation of the line gives

$$\mathbf{r} = \begin{pmatrix} x \\ y \\ z \end{pmatrix} = \begin{pmatrix} 2 \\ 3 \\ 4 \end{pmatrix} - \begin{pmatrix} 1 \\ 2 \\ -1 \end{pmatrix} = \begin{pmatrix} 1 \\ 1 \\ 5 \end{pmatrix}$$

so the point of intersection is $(1, 1, 5)$.

As a check, substitute $(1, 1, 5)$ into the equation of the plane:

$$\begin{aligned} 5x + y - z &= 5 + 1 - 5 \\ &= 1 \qquad \text{as required.} \end{aligned}$$

The distance of a point from a plane

The shortest distance of a point, A, from a plane is the distance AP, where P is the point where the line through A perpendicular to the plane intersects the plane (see figure 11.34). This is usually just called the distance of the point from the plane. The process of finding this distance is shown in the next example.

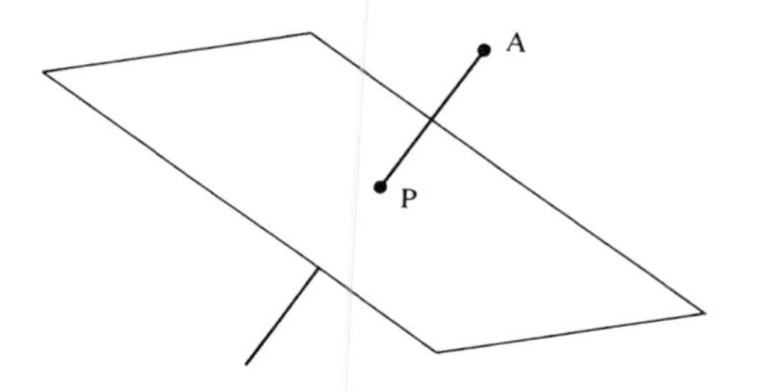

Figure 11.34

EXAMPLE 11.22

A is the point (7, 5, 3) and the plane π has the equation $3x + 2y + z = 6$. Find

(i) the equation of the line through A perpendicular to the plane π

(ii) the point of intersection, P, of this line with the plane

(iii) the distance AP.

SOLUTION

(i) The direction perpendicular to the plane $3x + 2y + z = 6$ is $\begin{pmatrix} 3 \\ 2 \\ 1 \end{pmatrix}$ so the line through (7, 5, 3) perpendicular to the plane is given by

$$\mathbf{r} = \begin{pmatrix} 7 \\ 5 \\ 3 \end{pmatrix} + \lambda \begin{pmatrix} 3 \\ 2 \\ 1 \end{pmatrix}.$$

(ii) For any point on the line

$$x = 7 + 3\lambda \qquad y = 5 + 2\lambda \qquad \text{and} \qquad z = 3 + \lambda.$$

Substituting these expressions into the equation of the plane $3x + 2y + z = 6$ gives

$$3(7 + 3\lambda) + 2(5 + 2\lambda) + (3 + \lambda) = 6$$

$$14\lambda = -28$$

$$\lambda = -2.$$

So the point P has co-ordinates (1, 1, 1).

(iii) The vector $\overrightarrow{AP}$ is given by

$$\begin{pmatrix} 1 \\ 1 \\ 1 \end{pmatrix} - \begin{pmatrix} 7 \\ 5 \\ 3 \end{pmatrix} = \begin{pmatrix} -6 \\ -4 \\ -2 \end{pmatrix}$$

and so the length AP is $\sqrt{(-6)^2 + (-4)^2 + (-2)^2} = \sqrt{56}$.

Note

In practice, you would usually not follow the procedure in Example 11.22 because there is a well-known formula for the distance of a point from a plane. You are invited to derive this in the following activity.

ACTIVITY 11.3 Generalise the work in Example 11.22 to show that the distance of the point (α, β, γ) from the plane $n_1x + n_2y + n_3z + d = 0$ is given by

$$\frac{|n_1\alpha + n_2\beta + n_3\gamma + d|}{\sqrt{n_1^2 + n_2^2 + n_3^2}}.$$

EXERCISE 11F

1 The points A, B and C have co-ordinates (0, 1, 1), (–2, –1, –5) and (1, –1, 0).

(i) Find the vectors $\overrightarrow{AB}$ and $\overrightarrow{AC}$.

(ii) Find the equation of the plane ABC in the form

$$\mathbf{r} = \overrightarrow{OA} + \lambda\overrightarrow{AB} + \mu\overrightarrow{AC}.$$

(iii) Verify that A, B and C lie in the plane $5x + 4y - 3z = 1$.

(iv) Show that

$$\overrightarrow{AB}.\begin{pmatrix}5\\4\\-3\end{pmatrix} = \overrightarrow{BC}.\begin{pmatrix}5\\4\\-3\end{pmatrix} = 0$$

and explain the significance of these results.

2 The points L, M and N have co-ordinates (0, –1, 2), (2, 1, 0) and (5, 1, 1).

(i) Write down the vectors $\overrightarrow{LM}$ and $\overrightarrow{LN}$.

(ii) Show that

$$\overrightarrow{LM}.\begin{pmatrix}1\\-4\\-3\end{pmatrix} = \overrightarrow{LN}.\begin{pmatrix}1\\-4\\-3\end{pmatrix} = 0.$$

(iii) Find the equation of the plane LMN.

3 The points A, B and C have co-ordinates (3, 0, 0), (3, 1, 2) and (3, 4, –2).

(i) Show that the equation of the plane ABC may be written as

$$\mathbf{r} = \begin{pmatrix}3\\0\\0\end{pmatrix} + \lambda\begin{pmatrix}0\\1\\2\end{pmatrix} + \mu\begin{pmatrix}0\\2\\-1\end{pmatrix}.$$

(ii) Show that the equation of the plane may also be written in the form $x = 3$.

(iii) Describe this plane.

4 **(i)** Show that the points A(1, 1, 1), B(3, 0, 0) and C(2, 0, 2) all lie in the plane $2x + 3y + z = 6$.

(ii) Show that

$$\overrightarrow{AB}.\begin{pmatrix}2\\3\\1\end{pmatrix} = \overrightarrow{AC}.\begin{pmatrix}2\\3\\1\end{pmatrix} = 0.$$

(iii) The point D has co-ordinates (7, 6, 2). D lies on a line perpendicular to the plane through one of the points A, B or C.
Through which of these points does the line pass?

5 The lines l, $\mathbf{r} = \begin{pmatrix}2\\1\\0\end{pmatrix} + \lambda\begin{pmatrix}1\\1\\1\end{pmatrix}$, and m, $\mathbf{r} = \begin{pmatrix}4\\0\\2\end{pmatrix} + \mu\begin{pmatrix}1\\0\\1\end{pmatrix}$, lie in the same plane π.

(i) Find the co-ordinates of any two points on each of the lines.

(ii) Show that all the four points you found in part **(i)** lie on the plane $x - z = 2$.

(iii) Explain why you now have more than sufficient evidence to show that the plane π has equation $x - z = 2$.

(iv) Find the co-ordinates of the point where the lines l and m intersect.

6 Find the points of intersection of the following planes and lines.

(i) $x + 2y + 3z = 11$ and $\mathbf{r} = \begin{pmatrix}1\\2\\4\end{pmatrix} + \lambda\begin{pmatrix}1\\1\\1\end{pmatrix}$

(ii) $2x + 3y - 4z = 1$ and $\dfrac{x+2}{3} = \dfrac{y+3}{4} = \dfrac{z+4}{5}$

(iii) $3x - 2y - z = 14$ and $\mathbf{r} = \begin{pmatrix}8\\4\\2\end{pmatrix} + \lambda\begin{pmatrix}1\\2\\1\end{pmatrix}$

(iv) $x + y + z = 0$ and $\mathbf{r} = \lambda\begin{pmatrix}1\\1\\2\end{pmatrix}$

(v) $5x - 4y - 7z = 49$ and $\dfrac{x-3}{2} = \dfrac{y+1}{5} = \dfrac{z-2}{-3}$

7 In each of the following examples you are given a point A and a plane π. Find

(a) the equation of the line through A perpendicular to π

(b) the point of intersection, P, of this line with π

(c) the distance AP.

(i) A is (2, 2, 3); π is $x - y + 2z = 0$

(ii) A is (2, 3, 0); π is $2x + 5y + 3z = 0$

(iii) A is (3, 1, 3); π is $x = 0$

(iv) A is (2, 1, 0); π is $3x - 4y + z = 2$

(v) A is (0, 0, 0); π is $x + y + z = 6$

8 The points U and V have co-ordinates (4, 0, 7) and (6, 4, 13).
The line UV is perpendicular to a plane and the point U lies in the plane.

(i) Find the equation of the plane in cartesian form.

(ii) The point W has co-ordinates (–1, 10, 2).
Show that $WV^2 = WU^2 + UV^2$.

(iii) What information does this give you about the position of W?
Confirm this information by a different method.

9 (i) Find the equation of the line through (13, 5, 0) parallel to the line

$$\mathbf{r} = \begin{pmatrix} 2 \\ -1 \\ 4 \end{pmatrix} + \lambda \begin{pmatrix} 3 \\ 1 \\ -2 \end{pmatrix}.$$

(ii) Where does this line meet the plane $3x + y - 2z = 2$?

(iii) How far is the point of intersection from (13, 5, 0)?

10 A is the point (1, 2, 0), B is (0, 4, 1) and C is (9, –2, 1).

(i) Show that A, B and C lie in the plane $2x + 3y - 4z = 8$.

(ii) Write down the vectors $\overrightarrow{AB}$ and $\overrightarrow{AC}$ and verify that they are at right angles to $\begin{pmatrix} 2 \\ 3 \\ -4 \end{pmatrix}$.

(iii) Find the angle BAC.

(iv) Find the area of triangle ABC (using area $= \frac{1}{2}bc\sin A$).

11 P is the point (2, –1, 3), Q is (5, –5, 3) and R is (7, 2, –3). Find

(i) the lengths of **(a)** PQ **(b)** QR

(ii) the angle PQR

(iii) the area of triangle PQR

(iv) the point S such that PQRS is a parallelogram.

12 P is the point (2, 2, 4), Q is (0, 6, 8), X is (–2, –2, –3) and Y is (2, 6, 9).

(i) Write in vector form the equations of the lines PQ and XY.

(ii) Verify that the equation of the plane PQX is $2x + 5y - 4z = -2$.

(iii) Does the point Y lie in the plane PQX?

(iv) Does any point on PQ lie on XY? (That is, do the lines intersect?)

13 (i) Find, in vector or cartesian form, the equation of a line passing through the two points A(4, 1, 3) and B(6, 4, 8).

(ii) Find the co-ordinates of the point P where the line which you have found in part **(i)** meets the plane $x + 2y - z + 3 = 0$.

A line is drawn through A perpendicular to the plane.

(iii) Find the co-ordinates of the point Q where this line cuts the plane and also the co-ordinates of the point A_1, the mirror image of the point A in the plane.

(iv) Use scalar products to calculate the angles PAQ and PA_1Q.

[MEI]

14 You are given the four points O(0, 0, 0), A(5, –12, 16), B(8, 3, 19) and C(–23, –80, 12).

(i) Show that the three points A, B and C all lie in the plane with equation $2x - y + 3z = 70$.

(ii) Write down a vector which is normal to this plane.

(iii) The line from the origin O perpendicular to this plane meets the plane at D. Find the co-ordinates of D.

(iv) Write down the equations of the two lines OA and AB in vector form.

(v) Hence find the angle OAB, correct to the nearest degree.

[MEI]

15 (i) Write down in vector or cartesian form the equation of the line joining A(8, 0, –4) to B(12, 2, –6).

(ii) This line meets the plane $2x + y - z = 2$ at C. Find the co-ordinates of C.

(iii) Find the length of the line joining C to B.

(iv) Find the ratio in which the point A divides CB.

(v) Find the angle AOB where O is the origin.

[MEI]

16 In bad weather, the roof of a barn begins to sag. It is decided to support it as shown in the diagram.

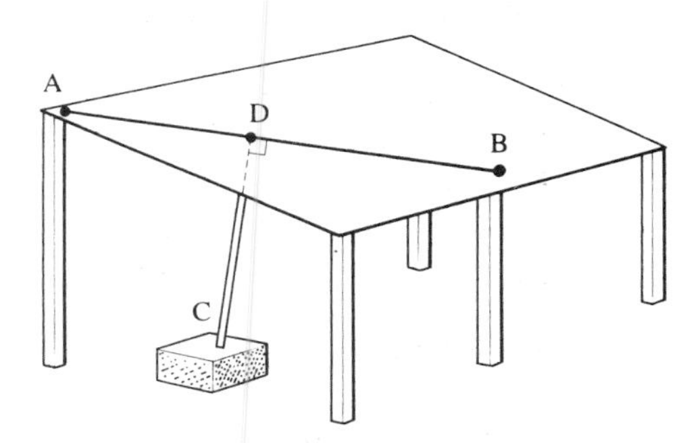

When the roof is supported, ADB is a straight line. Two points on the roof are A(2, 0, 15) and B(14, 9, 9) relative to an arbitrary origin.

(i) Find the equation of the line AB in vector form.

The support CD, resting on concrete blocks at C, is perpendicular to the line AB. C is the point (3, –1, 1).

(ii) Write down the vector $\overrightarrow{CP}$, where P is a general point on the line AB. Hence, using a scalar product, find the co-ordinates of D on AB such that CD is perpendicular to AB.

(iii) Calculate the length of the support CD.

(iv) Calculate the ratio AD : DB.

[MEI]

17 A pyramid in the shape of a tetrahedron has base ABC and vertex P as shown in the diagram. The vertices A, B, C, P have position vectors

$\mathbf{a} = -4\mathbf{j} + 2\mathbf{k}$,

$\mathbf{b} = 2\mathbf{i} + 4\mathbf{k}$,

$\mathbf{c} = -5\mathbf{i} - 2\mathbf{j} + 6\mathbf{k}$,

$\mathbf{p} = 3\mathbf{i} - 8\mathbf{j} + 12\mathbf{k}$

respectively.

The equation of the plane of the base is

$$\mathbf{r}.\begin{pmatrix} 2 \\ -3 \\ 4 \end{pmatrix} = 20.$$

(i) Write down a vector which is normal to the base ABC.

The line through P, perpendicular to the base, cuts the base at L.

(ii) Find the equation of the line PL in vector form and use it to find the co-ordinates of L.

(iii) Find the co-ordinates of the point N on LP, such that $\overrightarrow{LN} = \frac{1}{4}\overrightarrow{LP}$.

(iv) Find the angle between PA and PL.

[MEI]

18 The diagram shows an arrow embedded in a target. The line of the arrow passes through the point A(2, 3, 5) and has direction vector $3\mathbf{i} + \mathbf{j} - 2\mathbf{k}$. The arrow intersects the target at the point B. The plane of the target has equation $x + 2y - 3z = 4$. The units are metres.

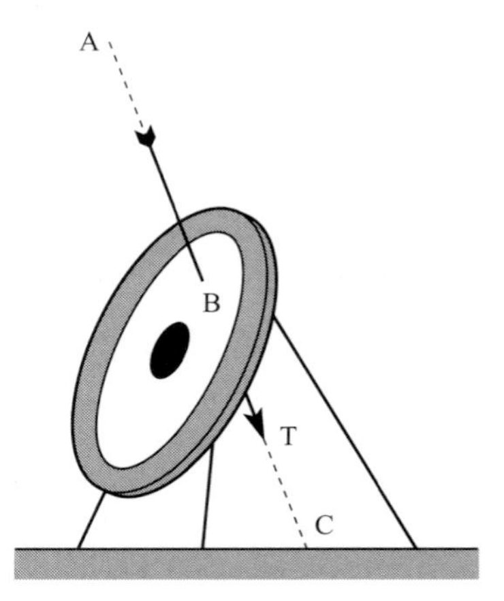

(i) Write down the vector equation of the line of the arrow in the form

$$\mathbf{r} = \mathbf{p} + \lambda\mathbf{q}.$$

(ii) Find the value of λ which corresponds to B.
Hence write down the co-ordinates of B.

(iii) The point C is where the line of the arrow meets the ground, which is the plane $z = 0$. Find the co-ordinates of C.

(iv) The tip, T, of the arrow is one-third of the way from B to C. Find the co-ordinates of T and the length of BT.

(v) Write down a normal vector to the plane of the target. Find the acute angle between the arrow and this normal.

[MEI]

19 The position vectors of three points A, B, C on a plane ski-slope are

$$\mathbf{a} = 4\mathbf{i} + 2\mathbf{j} - \mathbf{k}, \quad \mathbf{b} = -2\mathbf{i} + 26\mathbf{j} + 11\mathbf{k}, \quad \mathbf{c} = 16\mathbf{i} + 17\mathbf{j} + 2\mathbf{k},$$

where the units are metres.

(i) Show that the vector $2\mathbf{i} - 3\mathbf{j} + 7\mathbf{k}$ is perpendicular to $\overrightarrow{AB}$ and also perpendicular to $\overrightarrow{AC}$.
Hence find the equation of the plane of the ski-slope.

The track for an overhead railway lies along DEF, where D and E have position vectors $\mathbf{d} = 130\mathbf{i} - 40\mathbf{j} + 20\mathbf{k}$ and $\mathbf{e} = 90\mathbf{i} - 20\mathbf{j} + 15\mathbf{k}$, and F is a point on the ski-slope.

(ii) Find the equation of the straight line DE.

(iii) Find the position vector of the point F.

(iv) Find the length of the track DF.

[MEI]

20 A plane π has equation $ax + by + z = d$.

(i) Write down, in terms of a and b, a vector which is perpendicular to π.

Points A(2, –1, 2), B(4, –4, 2), C(5, –6, 3) lie on π.

(ii) Write down the vectors $\overrightarrow{AB}$ and $\overrightarrow{AC}$.

(iii) Use scalar products to obtain two equations for a and b.

(iv) Find the equation of the plane π.

(v) Find the angle which the plane π makes with the plane $x = 0$.

(vi) Point D is the mid-point of AC. Point E is on the line between D and B such that DE : EB = 1 : 2. Find the co-ordinates of E.

[MEI]

21 ABCD is a parallelogram. The co-ordinates of A, B and D are (4, 2, 3), (18, 4, 8) and (–1, 12, 13) respectively. The origin of co-ordinates is O.

(i) Find the vectors $\overrightarrow{AB}$ and $\overrightarrow{AD}$. Find the co-ordinates of C.

(ii) Show that ABCD is a square of side 15 units.

(iii) Show that $\overrightarrow{OA}$ can be expressed in the form $\lambda\overrightarrow{AB} + \mu\overrightarrow{AD}$, stating the values of λ and μ. What does this tell you about the plane ABCD?

(iv) Find the cartesian equation of the plane ABCD.

[MEI]

22 The diagram, which is not to scale, illustrates part of the roof of a building. Lines OA and OD are horizontal and at right angles. Lines BC and BE are also horizontal and at right angles. Line BC is parallel to OA and BE is parallel to OD.

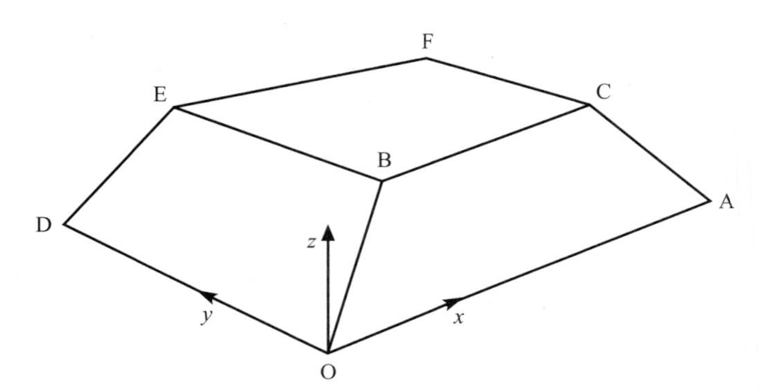

Axes are taken with O as origin, the x axis along OA, the y axis along OD and the z axis vertically upwards. The units are metres.

Point A has the co-ordinates (50, 0, 0) and point D has the co-ordinates (0, 20, 0). The equation of line OB is $\frac{x}{4} = \frac{y}{3} = \frac{z}{2}$. The equation of plane CBEF is $z = 3$.

(i) Find the co-ordinates of B.

(ii) Verify that the equation of plane AOBC is $2y - 3z = 0$.

(iii) Find the equation of plane DOBE.

(iv) Write down normal vectors for planes AOBC and DOBE. Find the angle between these normal vectors. Hence write down the internal angle between the two roof surfaces AOBC and DOBE.

[MEI]

23 A tunnel is to be excavated through a hill. In order to define position, co-ordinates (x, y, z) are taken relative to an origin O such that x is the distance east from O, y is the distance north and z is the vertical distance upwards, with one unit equal to 100 m.

The tunnel starts at point A(2, 3, 5) and runs in the direction $\begin{pmatrix} 1 \\ 1 \\ -0.5 \end{pmatrix}$.

It meets the hillside again at B. At B the side of the hill forms a plane with equation $x + 5y + 2z = 77$.

(i) Write down the equation of the line AB in the form $\mathbf{r} = \mathbf{u} + \lambda\mathbf{t}$.

(ii) Find the co-ordinates of B.

(iii) Find the angle which AB makes with the upward vertical.

(iv) An old tunnel through the hill has equation $\mathbf{r} = \begin{pmatrix} 4 \\ 1 \\ 2 \end{pmatrix} + \mu\begin{pmatrix} 7 \\ 15 \\ 0 \end{pmatrix}$.

Show that the point P on AB where $x = 7\frac{1}{2}$ is directly above a point Q in the old tunnel. Find the vertical separation PQ of the tunnels at this point.

[MEI]

24 Point A has co-ordinates $(2, -1, 3)$ and point B has co-ordinates $(1, 0, 5)$.

(i) Write down the equation of the line AB in the form $\mathbf{r} = \mathbf{a} + t\mathbf{u}$.
Find the point of intersection of AB with the plane $x - 2y + 3z - 7 = 0$.

(ii) Find the cartesian equation of the plane which passes through the points $(3, 0, 0)$, $(2, 0, 5)$ and $(4, -3, 1)$.

(iii) Show that, for any value of λ, a point (x, y, z) on the line

$$\begin{pmatrix} x \\ y \\ z \end{pmatrix} = \begin{pmatrix} 1 \\ 3 \\ 4 \end{pmatrix} + \lambda \begin{pmatrix} -4 \\ 7 \\ 6 \end{pmatrix}$$

lies in the plane $x - 2y + 3z - 7 = 0$ and also in the plane in part **(ii)**.

(iv) Find the angle between the line AB and the line in part **(iii)**, giving your answer to the nearest degree.

[MEI]

25 ABCD is a parallelogram. The co-ordinates of A, B and D are $(-1, 1, 2)$, $(1, 2, 0)$ and $(1, 0, 2)$ respectively.

(i) Find the co-ordinates of C.

(ii) Use a scalar product to find the size of angle BAD.

(iii) Show that the vector $\mathbf{i} + 2\mathbf{j} + 2\mathbf{k}$ is perpendicular to the plane ABCD.

(iv) The diagonals AC and BD intersect at the point E.
Find a vector equation of the straight line l through E perpendicular to the plane ABCD.

(v) A point F lies on l and is 3 units from A.
Find the co-ordinates of the two possible positions of F.

[MEI]

26 The position vectors of four points are as follows.

A: $\mathbf{i} + 2\mathbf{j} + 3\mathbf{k}$
B: $3\mathbf{i} + 2\mathbf{j} + \mathbf{k}$
C: $3\mathbf{j}$
V: $\mathbf{i} + \mathbf{j} - 2\mathbf{k}$

(i) Find the length of the line VA.

(ii) Show that the vector $\mathbf{i} + 4\mathbf{j} + \mathbf{k}$ is perpendicular to each of the lines AB and AC.

(iii) Deduce the cartesian equation of the plane ABC.

The line through V perpendicular to the plane ABC meets the plane at D.

(iv) Find a vector equation of the line VD.
Deduce the co-ordinates of D.

(v) Find the angle AVD.

[MEI]

27 With respect to co-ordinate axes Oxyz, A is the point (2, 0, 0), B is (0, 0, 1) and C is (3, 1, 3).

(i) Find the vectors $\overrightarrow{CA}$ and $\overrightarrow{CB}$.
Hence find angle ACB.

(ii) Write down the cartesian equation of the plane p through A with normal vector $\mathbf{i} - \mathbf{j} + 2\mathbf{k}$.
Verify that B also lies in this plane.

(iii) Write down the vector equation of the line through C perpendicular to the plane p.
Find the point of intersection of this line with the plane, and the distance from C to the plane.

[MEI]

28 With respect to co-ordinate axes Oxyz, A is the point (3, 0, 1), B is (1, 0, 3), C is (3, 2, 3) and D is (2, –1, 1).

(i) Show that triangle ABC is equilateral.

(ii) Show that the vector $\overrightarrow{AD}$ can be expressed as $\lambda\overrightarrow{AB} + \mu\overrightarrow{AC}$, where λ and μ are constants to be determined.
What can you deduce about the points A, B, C and D?

(iii) Verify that the vector $\mathbf{n} = \mathbf{i} - \mathbf{j} + \mathbf{k}$ is perpendicular to the plane ABC.
Hence or otherwise find the cartesian equation of the plane ABC.

(iv) Find the angle between the lines AB and DC.

[MEI]

29 In the diagram, ABCDPQ represents a tent, held up by vertical poles OP and RQ.
The axes Ox and Oy are horizontal at ground level, and Oz is vertically upwards.

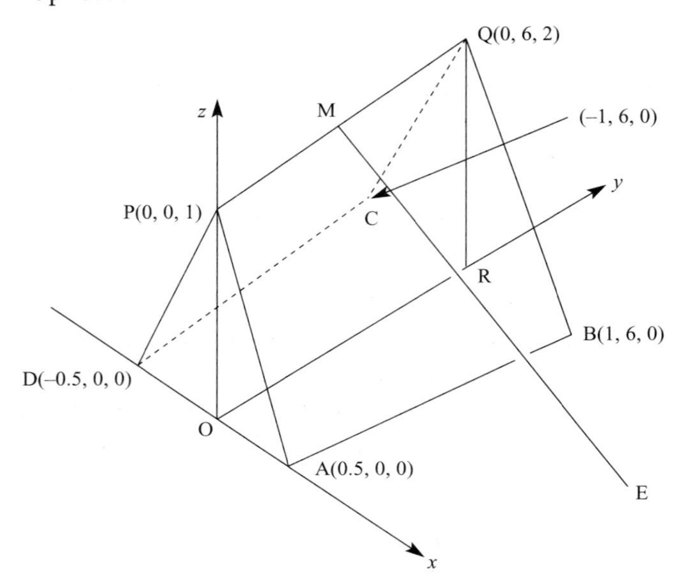

The co-ordinates of A, B, C, D, P and Q are as shown in the diagram. Lengths are in metres.

(i) Find the length of PQ.

(ii) Show that the vector $\mathbf{n}_1 = 12\mathbf{i} - \mathbf{j} + 6\mathbf{k}$ is perpendicular to each of the lines AP and PQ.
Hence find that cartesian equation of the plane APQ.
Verify that the point B lies in this plane.

(iii) The vector $\mathbf{n}_2 = -12\mathbf{i} - \mathbf{j} + 6\mathbf{k}$ is a normal to the plane DCQP.
Find the angle between the vectors $\mathbf{n}_1$ and $\mathbf{n}_2$.
Deduce the acute angle in degrees between the planes ABQP and DCQP.

(iv) A rope ME of length 2 metres is stretched from the mid-point M of PQ to the ground.
Given that the rope is perpendicular to PQ, find the co-ordinates of E.

[MEI]

30 An explorer comes across a hollow pyramid with a square base of side 100 m and with height 100 m.

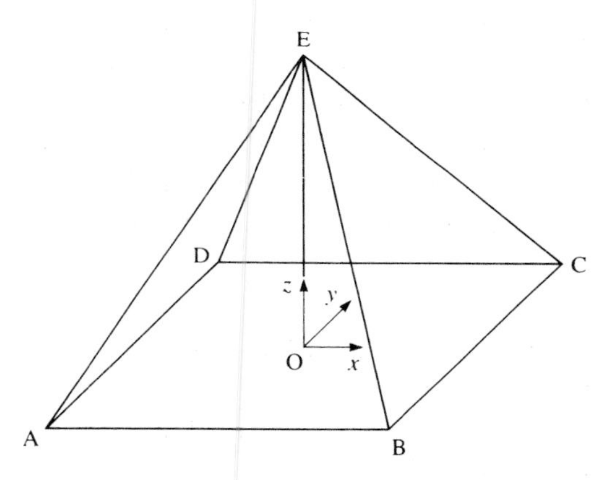

Take the origin to be the middle point of the base and 1 unit to be 1 m.

(i) Write down the co-ordinates of the vertices of the pyramid.

(ii) Show that the face BCE has equation $2x + z = 100$ and write down the equations of the other three sloping faces.

The explorer finds that inside the pyramid a rope is hanging from vertex E, and begins to climb it.

(iii) When he has climbed 20 m, he shines his torch directly on to the face BCE. Find the equation of the line of the torch beam, in vector form, and hence find how far the explorer is from the face.

(iv) When the explorer has climbed to a height h metres, he is the same distance from the ground as he is from each of the sloping faces. Show that

$$h = \frac{100}{1 + \sqrt{5}}.$$

Magic eye

You may well have seen other pictures like that in figure 11.35. Although it is nothing more than a collection of marks on a flat sheet of paper, your eyes can be tricked into seeing it as a three-dimensional object at some distance beyond the page.

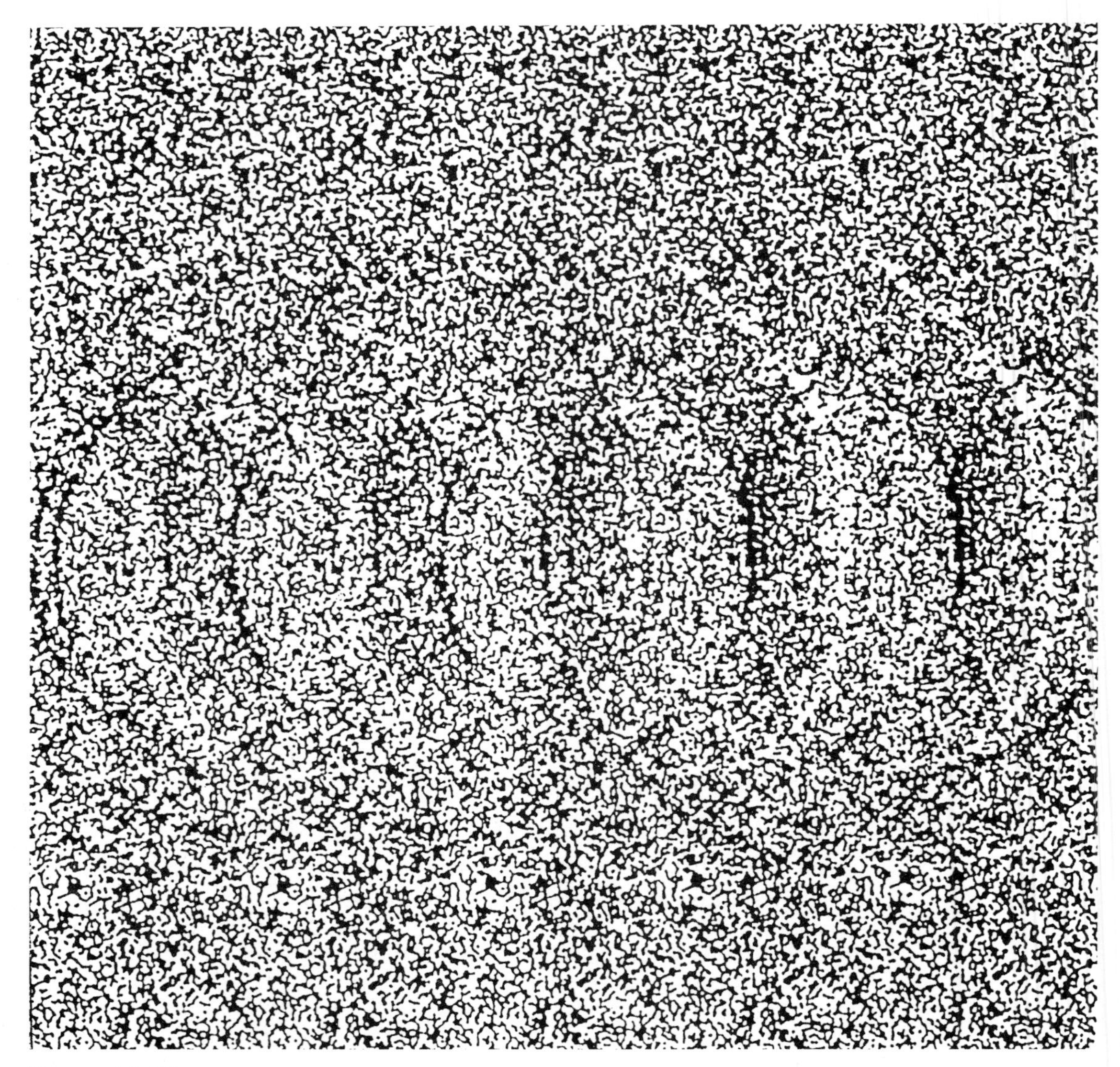

Figure 11.35

As shown in figure 11.36, the principle is very simple.

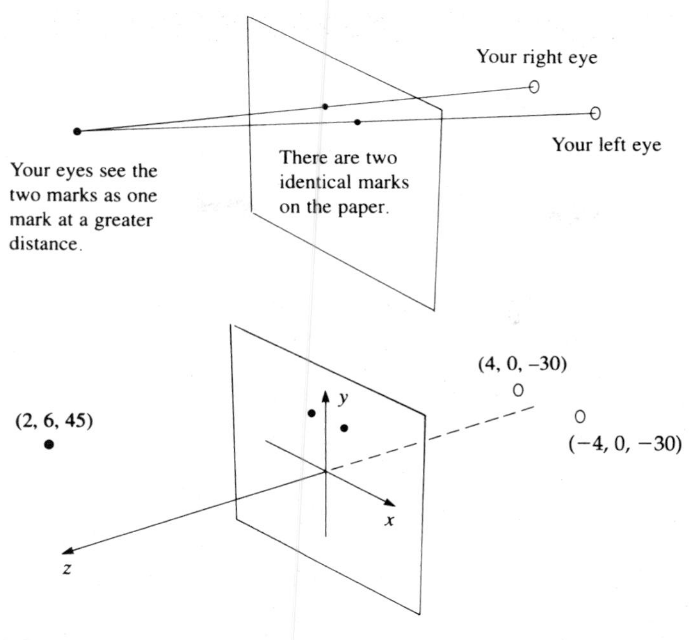

Figure 11.36

Take the paper as the xy plane, that is the plane $z = 0$, with the origin at the centre of the paper and 1 cm to represent 1 unit.

Taking the positions of your eyes to be (4, 0, –30) and (–4, 0, –30), find the positions on the paper of the two points needed to produce a single image at the point (2, 6, 45).

Design a simple 'magic eye' of your own.

KEY POINTS

1. A vector quantity has magnitude and direction.
2. A scalar quantity has magnitude only.
3. Vectors are typeset in bold, **a** or **OA**, or in the form $\overrightarrow{\mathrm{OA}}$. They are handwritten either in the underlined form $\underset{\sim}{a}$, or as $\overrightarrow{OA}$.
4. The length (or modulus or magnitude) of the vector **a** is written as a or as $|\mathbf{a}|$.
5. Unit vectors in the x, y and z directions are denoted by **i**, **j** and **k**, respectively.

6 A vector may be specified in

- magnitude–direction form: (r, θ) (in two dimensions)
- component form: $x\mathbf{i} + y\mathbf{j}$ or $\begin{pmatrix} x \\ y \end{pmatrix}$ (in two dimensions)

$$x\mathbf{i} + y\mathbf{j} + z\mathbf{k} \quad \text{or} \quad \begin{pmatrix} x \\ y \\ z \end{pmatrix} \quad \text{(in three dimensions).}$$

7 The position vector $\overrightarrow{\mathrm{OP}}$ of a point P is the vector joining the origin to P.

8 The vector $\overrightarrow{\mathrm{AB}}$ is $\mathbf{b} - \mathbf{a}$, where $\mathbf{a}$ and $\mathbf{b}$ are the position vectors of A and B.

9 The vector $\mathbf{r}$ often denotes the position vector of a general point.

10 The vector equation of the line through A with direction vector $\mathbf{u}$ is given by

$$\mathbf{r} = \mathbf{a} + \lambda\mathbf{u}.$$

11 The vector equation of the line through points A and B is given by

$$\begin{aligned} \mathbf{r} &= \overrightarrow{\mathrm{OA}} + \lambda\overrightarrow{\mathrm{AB}} \\ &= \mathbf{a} + \lambda(\mathbf{b} - \mathbf{a}) \\ &= (1 - \lambda)\mathbf{a} + \lambda\mathbf{b}. \end{aligned}$$

12 The equation of the line through (a_1, a_2, a_3) in the direction $\begin{pmatrix} u_1 \\ u_2 \\ u_3 \end{pmatrix}$ is given by

$$\mathbf{r} = \begin{pmatrix} a_1 \\ a_2 \\ a_3 \end{pmatrix} + \lambda \begin{pmatrix} u_1 \\ u_2 \\ u_3 \end{pmatrix} \qquad \text{vector form}$$

$$\frac{x - a_1}{u_1} = \frac{y - a_2}{u_2} = \frac{z - a_3}{u_3} \qquad \text{cartesian form.}$$

13 The angle between two vectors, $\mathbf{a}$ and $\mathbf{b}$, is given by θ in

$$\cos\theta = \frac{\mathbf{a}.\mathbf{b}}{|\mathbf{a}|\,|\mathbf{b}|}$$

where $\mathbf{a}.\mathbf{b} = a_1b_1 + a_2b_2$ (in two dimensions)
$= a_1b_1 + a_2b_2 + a_3b_3$ (in three dimensions).

14 The cartesian equation of a plane perpendicular to the vector $\mathbf{n} = \begin{pmatrix} n_1 \\ n_2 \\ n_3 \end{pmatrix}$ is

$$n_1x + n_2y + n_3z + d = 0.$$

15 The equation of the plane through the point with position vector $\mathbf{a}$, and perpendicular to $\mathbf{n}$, is given by $(\mathbf{r} - \mathbf{a}).\mathbf{n} = 0$.

e The vector equation of the plane through the points A, B and C is

$$\mathbf{r} = \overrightarrow{\mathrm{OA}} + \lambda\overrightarrow{\mathrm{AB}} + \mu\overrightarrow{\mathrm{AC}}.$$

12 Differential equations

The greater our knowledge increases, the more our ignorance unfolds.

John F. Kennedy

Suppose you are in a hurry to go out and want to drink a cup of hot tea before you go.

How long will you have to wait until it is cool enough to drink?

To solve this problem, you would need to know something about the rate at which liquids cool at different temperatures. Figure 12.1 shows an example of the temperature of a liquid plotted against time.

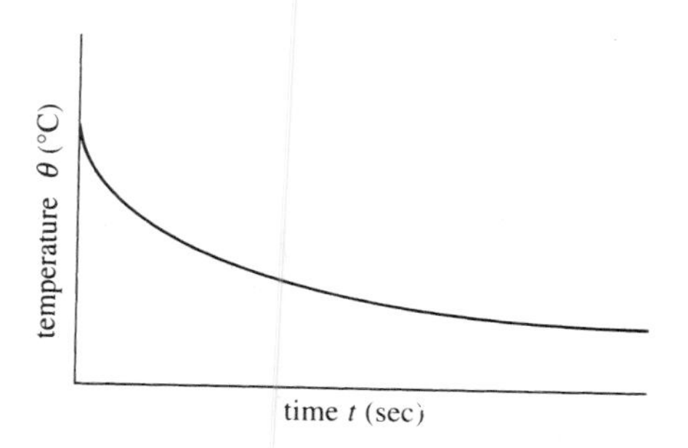

Figure 12.1

Notice that the graph is steepest at high temperatures and becomes less steep as the liquid cools. In other words, the rate of change of temperature is numerically greatest at high temperatures and gets numerically less as the temperature drops. The rate of change is always negative since the temperature is decreasing.

If you study physics, you may have come across Newton's law of cooling: The rate of cooling of a body is proportional to the temperature of the body above that of the surrounding air.

The gradient of the temperature graph may be written as $\frac{d\theta}{dt}$, where θ is the temperature of the liquid, and t is the time. The quantity $\frac{d\theta}{dt}$ tells us the rate at which the temperature of the liquid is increasing. As the liquid is cooling, $\frac{d\theta}{dt}$ will be negative, so the rate of cooling may be written as $-\frac{d\theta}{dt}$.

The temperature of the liquid above that of the surrounding air may be written as $\theta - \theta_0$, where θ_0 is the temperature of the surrounding air. So Newton's law of cooling may be expressed mathematically as:

$$-\frac{d\theta}{dt} \propto (\theta - \theta_0)$$

or $$\frac{d\theta}{dt} = -k(\theta - \theta_0)$$

where k is a positive constant.

Any equation, like this one, which involves a derivative, such as $\frac{d\theta}{dt}$, $\frac{dy}{dx}$ or $\frac{d^2y}{dx^2}$, is known as a *differential equation.* A differential equation which only involves a first derivative such as $\frac{dy}{dx}$ is called a *first-order differential equation.* One which involves a second derivative such as $\frac{d^2y}{dx^2}$ is called a *second-order differential equation.* A third-order differential equation involves a third derivative and so on. In this chapter, you will be looking only at first-order differential equations such as the one above for Newton's law of cooling.

By the end of this chapter, you will be able to solve problems such as the tea cooling problem given at the beginning of this chapter, by using first-order differential equations.

Forming differential equations from rates of change

If you are given sufficient information about the rate of change of a quantity, such as temperature or velocity, you can work out a differential equation to model the situation, like the one above for Newton's law of cooling. It is important to look carefully at the wording of the problem which you are studying in order to write an equivalent mathematical statement. For example, if the altitude of an aircraft is being considered, the phrase 'the rate of change of height' might be used. This actually means 'the rate of change of height *with respect to time*' and could be written as $\frac{dh}{dt}$. However, you might be more interested in how the height of the aircraft changes according to the horizontal distance it has travelled. In this case, you would talk about 'the rate of change of height *with respect to horizontal distance*' and could write this as $\frac{dh}{dx}$, where x is the horizontal distance travelled.

Some of the situations you meet in this chapter involve motion along a straight line, and so you will need to know the meanings of the associated terms.

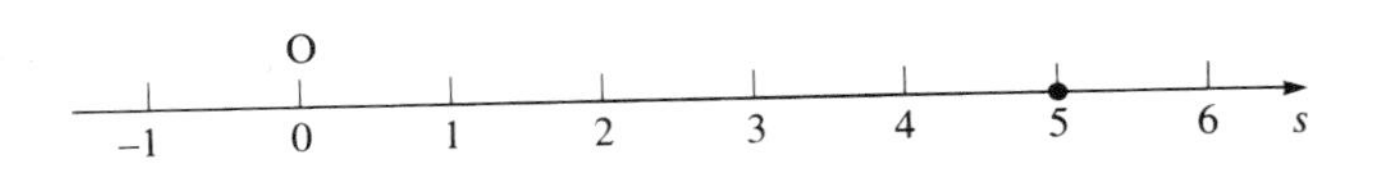

Figure 12.2

The position of an object (+5 in figure 12.2) is its distance from the origin O in the direction you have chosen to define as being positive.

The rate of change of position of the object with respect to time is its velocity, and this can take positive or negative values according to whether the object is moving away from the origin or towards it.

$$v = \frac{ds}{dt}$$

The rate of change of an object's velocity with respect to time is called its acceleration, a.

$$a = \frac{dv}{dt}$$

Velocity and acceleration are vector quantities but in one-dimensional motion there is no choice in direction, only in sense (i.e. whether positive or negative). Consequently, as you may already have noticed, the conventional bold type for vectors is not used in this chapter.

EXAMPLE 12.1

An object is moving through a liquid so that the rate at which its velocity decreases is proportional to its velocity at any given instant. When it enters the liquid, it has a velocity of $5\,\text{ms}^{-1}$ and the velocity is decreasing at a rate of $1\,\text{ms}^{-2}$. Find the differential equation to model this situation.

SOLUTION

The rate of change of velocity means the rate of change of velocity with respect to time and so can be written as $\frac{dv}{dt}$. As it is decreasing, the rate of change must be negative, so

$$-\frac{dv}{dt} \propto v$$

or $$\frac{dv}{dt} = -kv$$

where k is a positive constant.

When the object enters the liquid its velocity is $5\,\text{ms}^{-1}$, so $v = 5$, and the velocity is decreasing at the rate of $1\,\text{ms}^{-2}$, so

$$\frac{dv}{dt} = -1.$$

Putting this information into the equation gives

$$-1 = -k \times 5 \quad \Rightarrow \quad k = \tfrac{1}{5}.$$

So the situation is modelled by the differential equation

$$\frac{dv}{dt} = -\frac{v}{5}.$$

EXAMPLE 12.2

A model is proposed for the temperature gradient within a star, in which the temperature decreases with respect to the distance from the centre of the star at a rate which is inversely proportional to the square of the distance from the centre. Express this model as a differential equation.

SOLUTION

In this example the rate of change of temperature is not with respect to time but with respect to distance. If θ represents the temperature at a point in the star and r the distance from the centre of the star, the rate of change of temperature with respect to distance may be written as $-\frac{\mathrm{d}\theta}{\mathrm{d}r}$, so

$$-\frac{\mathrm{d}\theta}{\mathrm{d}r} \propto \frac{1}{r^2} \text{ or } \frac{\mathrm{d}\theta}{\mathrm{d}r} = -\frac{k}{r^2}$$

where k is a positive constant.

Note

This model must break down near the centre of the star, otherwise it would be infinitely hot there.

EXAMPLE 12.3

The area A of a square is increasing at a rate proportional to the length of its side s. The constant of proportionality is k. Find an expression for $\frac{\mathrm{d}s}{\mathrm{d}t}$.

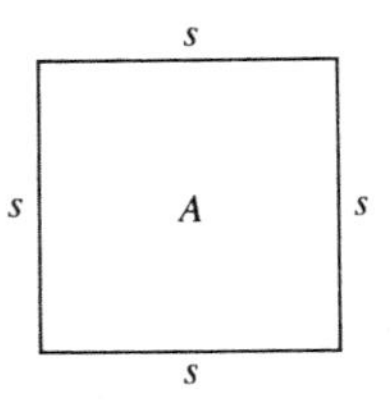

Figure 12.3

SOLUTION

The rate of increase of A with respect to time may be written as $\frac{\mathrm{d}A}{\mathrm{d}t}$.

As this is proportional to s, it may be written as

$$\frac{\mathrm{d}A}{\mathrm{d}t} = ks$$

where k is a positive constant.

You can use the chain rule to write down an expression for $\frac{\mathrm{d}s}{\mathrm{d}t}$ in terms of $\frac{\mathrm{d}A}{\mathrm{d}t}$.

$$\frac{\mathrm{d}s}{\mathrm{d}t} = \frac{\mathrm{d}s}{\mathrm{d}A} \times \frac{\mathrm{d}A}{\mathrm{d}t}$$

You now need an expression for $\frac{ds}{dA}$. Because A is a square

$$A = s^2$$

$$\Rightarrow \quad \frac{dA}{ds} = 2s$$

$$\Rightarrow \quad \frac{ds}{dA} = \frac{1}{2s}.$$

Substituting the expressions for $\frac{ds}{dA}$ and $\frac{dA}{dt}$ into the expression for $\frac{ds}{dt}$

$$\Rightarrow \quad \frac{ds}{dt} = \frac{1}{2s} \times ks$$

$$\Rightarrow \quad \frac{ds}{dt} = \tfrac{1}{2}k.$$

EXERCISE 12A

1 The differential equation

$$\frac{dv}{dt} = 5v^2$$

models the motion of a particle, where v is the velocity of the particle in ms^{-1} and t is the time in seconds. Explain the meaning of $\frac{dv}{dt}$ and what the differential equation tells you about the motion of the particle.

2 A spark from a Roman candle is moving in a straight line at a speed which is inversely proportional to the square of the distance which the spark has travelled from the candle. Find an expression for the speed (i.e. the rate of change of distance travelled) of the spark.

3 The rate at which a sunflower increases in height is proportional to the natural logarithm of the difference between its final height H and its height h at a particular time. Find a differential equation to model this situation.

4 In a chemical reaction in which substance A is converted into substance B, the rate of increase of the mass of substance B is inversely proportional to the mass of substance B present. Find a differential equation to model this situation.

5 After a major advertising campaign, an engineering company finds that its profits are increasing at a rate proportional to the square root of the profits at any given time. Find an expression to model this situation.

6 The coefficient of restitution e of a squash ball increases with respect to the ball's temperature θ at a rate proportional to the temperature, for typical playing temperatures. (The coefficient of restitution is a measure of how elastic, or bouncy, the ball is. Its value lies between zero and one, zero meaning that the ball is not at all elastic and one meaning that it is perfectly elastic.) Find a differential equation to model this situation.

7 A cup of tea cools at a rate proportional to the temperature of the tea above that of the surrounding air. Initially, the tea is at a temperature of 95°C and is cooling at a rate of $0.5°\text{C}\text{s}^{-1}$. The surrounding air is at 15°C.
Find a differential equation to model this situation.

8 The rate of increase of bacteria is modelled as being proportional to the number of bacteria at any time during their initial growth phase.

When the bacteria number 2×10^6 they are increasing at a rate of 10^5 per day. Find a differential equation to model this situation.

9 The acceleration (i.e. the rate of change of velocity) of a moving object under a particular force is inversely proportional to the square root of its velocity. When the speed is $4\,\text{ms}^{-1}$ the acceleration is $2\,\text{ms}^{-2}$. Find a differential equation to model this situation.

10 The radius of a circular ink blot is increasing at a rate inversely proportional to its area A. Find an expression for $\frac{\mathrm{d}A}{\mathrm{d}t}$.

11 A poker, 80 cm long, has one end in a fire. The temperature of the poker decreases with respect to the distance from that end at a rate proportional to that distance. Halfway along the poker, the temperature is decreasing at a rate of $10°\text{C cm}^{-1}$. Find a differential equation to model this situation.

12 A conical egg timer, shown in the diagram, is letting sand through from top to bottom at a rate of $0.02\,\text{cm}^3\,\text{s}^{-1}$.

Find an expression for the rate of change of height $\left(\frac{\mathrm{d}h}{\mathrm{d}t}\right)$ of the sand in the top of the timer.

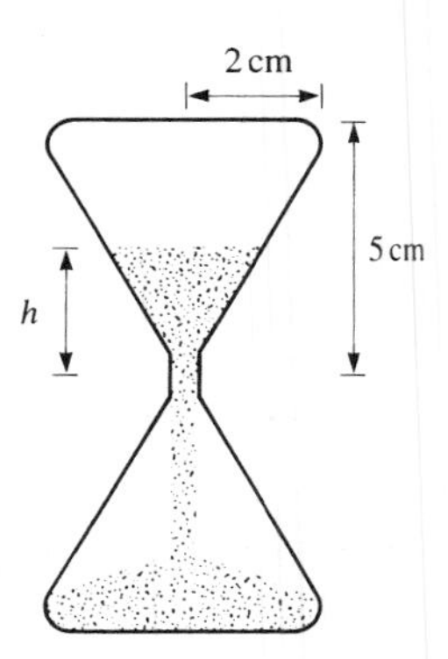

13 A spherical balloon is allowed to deflate. The rate at which air is leaving the balloon is proportional to the volume V of air left in the balloon. When the radius of the balloon is 15 cm, air is leaving at a rate of $8\,\text{cm}^3\text{s}^{-1}$.
Find an expression for $\frac{\mathrm{d}V}{\mathrm{d}t}$.

14 A tank is shaped as a cuboid with a square base of side 10 cm. Water runs out through a hole in the base at a rate proportional to the square root of the height, h cm, of water in the tank. At the same time, water is pumped into the tank at a constant rate of $2\,\text{cm}^3\,\text{s}^{-1}$. Find an expression for $\frac{\mathrm{d}h}{\mathrm{d}t}$.

Figure 12.4 shows the isobars (lines of equal pressure) on a weather map featuring a storm. The wind direction is almost parallel to the isobars and its speed is proportional to the pressure gradient.

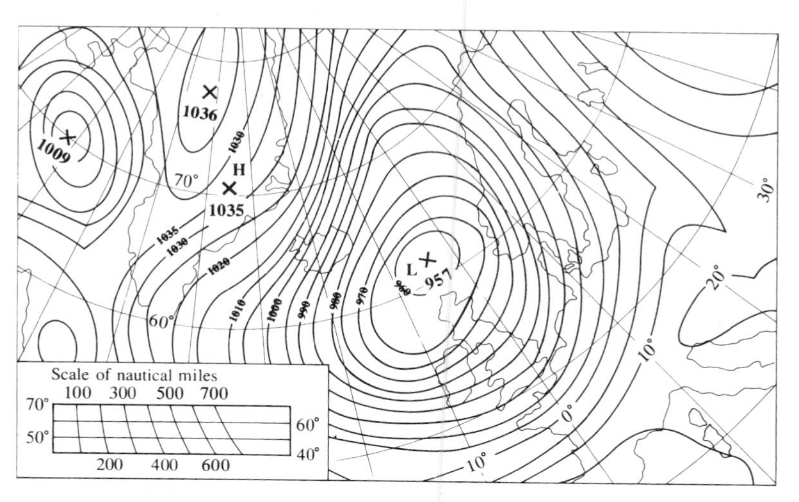

Figure 12.4

Draw a line from the point H to the point L. This runs approximately perpendicular to the isobars. It is suggested that along this line the pressure gradient (and so the wind speed) may be modelled by the differential equation

$$\frac{dp}{dx} = -a \sin bx$$

Suggest values for a and b, and comment on the suitability of this model.

Solving differential equations

Finding an expression for $f(x)$ from a differential equation involving derivatives of $f(x)$ is called solving the equation.

Some differential equations may be solved simply by integration.

EXAMPLE 12.4

Solve the differential equation

$$\frac{dy}{dx} = 3x^2 - 2.$$

SOLUTION

Integrating gives

$$y = \int (3x^2 - 2)\, dx$$

$$y = x^3 - 2x + c.$$

The general solution of the differential equation

Notice that when you solve a differential equation, you get not just one solution, but a whole family of solutions, as c can take any value. This is called the *general solution* of the differential equation. The family of solutions for the differential equation in the example above would be translations in the y direction of the curve $y = x^3 - 2x$. Graphs of members of the family of curves can be found in figure 12.5 on page 345.

The method of separation of variables

It is not difficult to solve a differential equation like the one in Example 12.4, because the right-hand side is a function of x only. So long as the function can be integrated, the equation can be solved.

Now look at the differential equation

$$\frac{dy}{dx} = xy.$$

This cannot be solved directly by integration, because the right-hand side is a function of both x and y. However, as you will see in the next example, you can solve this and similar differential equations where the right-hand side consists of a function of x and a function of y multiplied together.

EXAMPLE 12.5

Find, for $y > 0$, the general solution of the differential equation

$$\frac{dy}{dx} = xy.$$

SOLUTION

The equation may be rewritten as

$$\frac{1}{y}\frac{dy}{dx} = x$$

so that the right-hand side is now a function of x only.

Integrating both sides with respect to x gives

$$\int \frac{1}{y}\frac{dy}{dx}\,dx = \int x\,dx.$$

As $\frac{dy}{dx}\,dx$ can be written as dy

$$\int \frac{1}{y}\,dy = \int x\,dx.$$

Both sides may now be integrated separately.

$$\ln|y| = \tfrac{1}{2}x^2 + c$$

Since you have been told $y > 0$, you may drop the modulus symbol. In this case, $|y| = y$.

Explain why there is no need to put a constant of integration on both sides of the equation.

You now need to rearrange the solution above to give y in terms of x. Making both sides powers of e gives

$$e^{\ln y} = e^{\frac{1}{2}x^2+c}$$

$$\Rightarrow \quad y = e^{\frac{1}{2}x^2+c}$$

$$\Rightarrow \quad y = e^{\frac{1}{2}x^2}e^c.$$

Notice that the right-hand side is $e^{\frac{1}{2}x^2+c}$ and not $e^{\frac{1}{2}x^2} + e^c$.

This expression can be simplified by replacing e^c with a new constant A.

So $\quad y = Ae^{\frac{1}{2}x^2}.$

Note

Usually the first part of this process is carried out in just one step

$$\frac{dy}{dx} = xy$$

can immediately be rewritten as

$$\int \frac{1}{y}\,dy = \int x\,dx.$$

This method is called *separation of variables.* It can be helpful to do this by thinking of the differential equation as though $\frac{dy}{dx}$ were a fraction, and trying to rearrange the equation to obtain all the x terms on one side and all the y terms on the other. Then just insert an integration sign on each side. Remember that dy and dx must both end up on the top line (numerator).

EXAMPLE 12.6

Find the general solution of the differential equation

$$\frac{dy}{dx} = e^{-y}.$$

SOLUTION

Separating the variables gives

$$\int \frac{1}{e^{-y}}\,dy = \int dx$$

$$\Rightarrow \quad \int e^y \, dy = \int dx.$$

The right-hand side can be thought of as integrating 1 with respect to x.

$$e^y = x + c$$

Taking logarithms of both sides gives

$$y = \ln(x + c).$$

$\ln(x + c)$ is not the same as $\ln x + c$.

EXERCISE 12B

1 Solve the following differential equations by integration.

(i) $\dfrac{dy}{dx} = x^2$ **(ii)** $\dfrac{dy}{dx} = \cos x$

(iii) $\dfrac{dy}{dx} = e^x$ **(iv)** $\dfrac{dy}{dx} = \sqrt{x}$

2 Find the general solutions of the following differential equations by separating the variables.

(i) $\dfrac{dy}{dx} = xy^2$ **(ii)** $\dfrac{dy}{dx} = \dfrac{x^2}{y}$

(iii) $\dfrac{dy}{dx} = y$ **(iv)** $\dfrac{dy}{dx} = e^{x-y}$

(v) $\dfrac{dy}{dx} = \dfrac{y}{x}$ **(vi)** $\dfrac{dy}{dx} = x\sqrt{y}$

(vii) $\dfrac{dy}{dx} = y^2 \cos x$ **(viii)** $\dfrac{dy}{dx} = \dfrac{x(y^2 + 1)}{y(x^2 + 1)}$

(ix) $\dfrac{dy}{dx} = xe^y$ **(x)** $\dfrac{dy}{dx} = \dfrac{x \ln x}{y^2}$

Particular solutions

You have already seen that a differential equation has an infinite number of different solutions corresponding to different values of the constant of integration. In Example 12.4, you found that

$$\frac{dy}{dx} = 3x^2 - 2$$

had a general solution of $y = x^3 - 2x + c$.

Figure 12.5 shows the curves of the solutions corresponding to some different values of c.

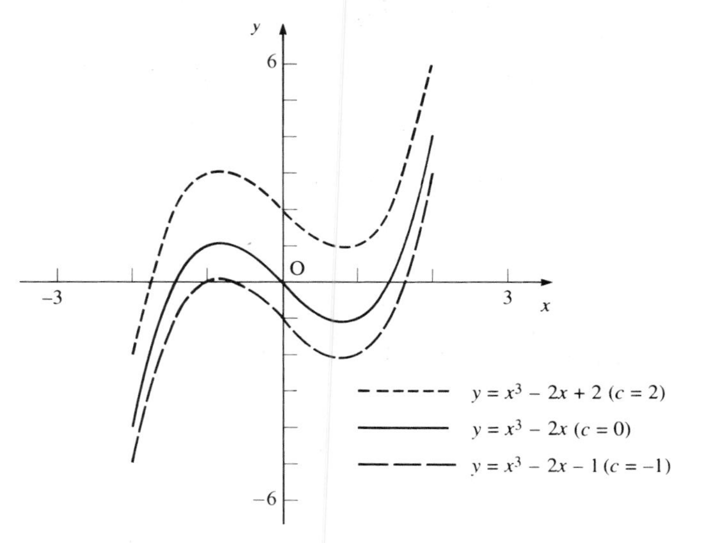

Figure 12.5

If you are given some more information, you can find out which of the possible solutions is the one that matches the situation in question. For example, you might be told that when $x = 1$, $y = 0$. This tells you that the correct solution is the one with the curve that passes through the point $(1, 0)$. You can use this information to find out the value of c for this particular solution by substituting the values $x = 1$ and $y = 0$ into the general solution.

$$y = x^3 - 2x + c$$

$$0 = 1 - 2 + c$$

$$\Rightarrow \quad c = 1$$

So the solution in this case is $y = x^3 - 2x + 1$.

This is called the *particular solution*.

EXAMPLE 12.7

(i) Find the general solution of the differential equation $\frac{dy}{dx} = y^2$.

(ii) Find the particular solution for which $y = 1$ when $x = 0$.

SOLUTION

(i) Separating the variables gives $\int \frac{1}{y^2}\, dy = \int dx$

$$-\frac{1}{y} = x + c.$$

The general solution is $\quad y = -\frac{1}{x + c}.$

Figure 12.6 shows the set of solution curves.

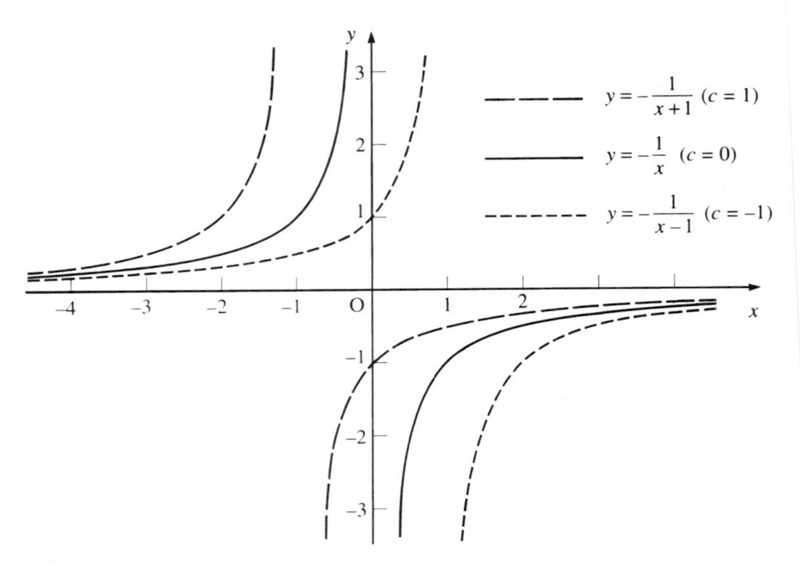

Figure 12.6

(ii) When $x = 0$, $y = 1$, which gives

$$1 = -\frac{1}{c} \qquad \Rightarrow \qquad c = -1.$$

So the particular solution is

$$y = -\frac{1}{x-1} \quad \text{or} \quad y = \frac{1}{1-x}.$$

This is one of the curves illustrated in figure 12.6.

EXAMPLE 12.8

The acceleration of an object is inversely proportional to its velocity at any given time and the direction of motion is taken to be positive.
When the velocity is $1\,\text{ms}^{-1}$, the acceleration is $3\,\text{ms}^{-2}$.

(i) Find a differential equation to model this situation.
(ii) Find the particular solution to this differential equation for which the initial velocity is $2\,\text{ms}^{-1}$.
(iii) In this case, how long does the object take to reach a velocity of $8\,\text{ms}^{-1}$?

SOLUTION

(i) $\frac{\mathrm{d}v}{\mathrm{d}t} = \frac{k}{v}$

When $v = 1$, $\frac{\mathrm{d}v}{\mathrm{d}t} = 3$ so $k = 3$, which gives $\frac{\mathrm{d}v}{\mathrm{d}t} = \frac{3}{v}$.

(ii) Separating the variables:

$$\int v\,\mathrm{d}v = \int 3\,\mathrm{d}t$$

$$\tfrac{1}{2}v^2 = 3t + c.$$

When $t = 0$, $v = 2$ so $c = 2$, which gives

$$\tfrac{1}{2}v^2 = 3t + 2$$

$$v^2 = 6t + 4.$$

Since the direction of motion is positive

$$v = \sqrt{6t + 4}.$$

(iii) When $v = 8$ $\quad 64 = 6t + 4$

$$60 = 6t \quad \Rightarrow \quad t = 10.$$

The object takes 10 seconds.

The graph of the particular solution is shown in figure 12.7.

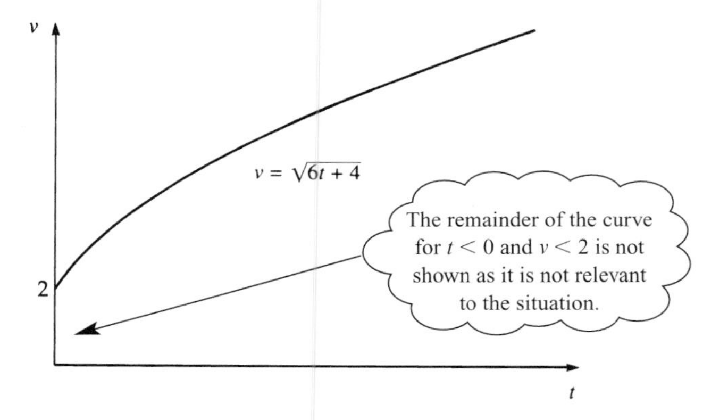

Figure 12.7

Sometimes you will be asked to *verify* the solution of a differential equation. In that case you are expected to do two things:

- substitute the solution in the differential equation and show that it works
- show that the solution fits the conditions you have been given.

EXAMPLE 12.9

Show that $\sin y = x$ is a solution of the differential equation

$$\frac{dy}{dx} = \frac{1}{\sqrt{1-x^2}}$$

given that $y = 0$ when $x = 0$.

SOLUTION

$$\sin y = x$$

$$\Rightarrow \quad \cos y \frac{dy}{dx} = 1$$

$$\Rightarrow \quad \frac{dy}{dx} = \frac{1}{\cos y}$$

Substituting into the differential equation:

L.H.S. $\dfrac{1}{\cos y}$ R.H.S $\dfrac{1}{\sqrt{1-x^2}} = \dfrac{1}{\sqrt{1-\sin^2 y}} = \dfrac{1}{\cos y}$

So the solution fits the differential equation.

Substituting $x = 0$ into the solution $\sin y = x$ gives $\sin y = 0$

and this is satisfied by $y = 0$.

So the solution also fits the particular conditions.

EXERCISE 12C

1 Find the particular solution of each of the following differential equations.

(i) $\dfrac{dy}{dx} = x^2 - 1$ $y = 2$ when $x = 3$

(ii) $\dfrac{dy}{dx} = x^2 y$ $y = 1$ when $x = 0$

(iii) $\dfrac{dy}{dx} = xe^{-y}$ $y = 0$ when $x = 0$

(iv) $\dfrac{dy}{dx} = y^2$ $y = 1$ when $x = 1$

(v) $\dfrac{dy}{dx} = x(y+1)$ $y = 0$ when $x = 1$

(vi) $\dfrac{dy}{dx} = y^2 \sin x$ $y = 1$ when $x = 0$

2 A cold liquid at temperature θ°C, where $\theta < 20$, is standing in a warm room. The temperature of the liquid obeys the differential equation

$$\frac{d\theta}{dt} = 2(20 - \theta)$$

where the time t is measured in hours.

(i) Find the general solution of this differential equation.

(ii) Find the particular solution for which $\theta = 5$ when $t = 0$.

(iii) In this case, how long does the liquid take to reach a temperature of 18°C?

3 A population of rabbits increases so that the number of rabbits N (in hundreds), after t years is modelled by the differential equation

$$\frac{dN}{dt} = N.$$

(i) Find the general solution for N in terms of t.

(ii) Find the particular solution for which $N = 10$ when $t = 0$.

(iii) What will happen to the number of rabbits when t becomes very large? Why is this not a realistic model for an actual population of rabbits?

4 An object is moving so that its velocity $v\left(= \frac{ds}{dt}\right)$ is inversely proportional to its displacement s from a fixed point.
If its velocity is $1\,\text{ms}^{-1}$ when its displacement is 2 m, find a differential equation to model the situation.
Find the general solution of your differential equation.

5 **(i)** Write $\dfrac{1}{y(3 - y)}$ in partial fractions.

(ii) Find $\displaystyle\int \frac{1}{y(3 - y)}\,dy$.

(iii) Solve the differential equation

$$x\frac{dy}{dx} = y(3 - y)$$

where $x = 2$ when $y = 2$, giving y as a function of x.

[MEI]

6 Given that k is a constant, find the solution of the differential equation

$$\frac{dy}{dt} + ky = 2k$$

for which $y = 3$ when $t = 0$.

Sketch the graph of y against $|kt|$, making clear how it behaves for large values of $|kt|$.

[MEI]

7 A colony of bacteria which is initially of size 1500 increases at a rate proportional to its size so that, after t hours, its population N satisfies the equation

$$\frac{dN}{dt} = kN.$$

(i) If the size of the colony increases to 3000 in 20 hours, solve the differential equation to find N in terms of t.

(ii) What size is the colony when $t = 80$?

(iii) How long did it take, to the nearest minute, for the population to increase from 2000 to 3000?

[MEI]

8 (i) Show that

$$\frac{x^2+1}{x^2-1} = 1 + \frac{2}{x^2-1}.$$

(ii) Find the partial fractions for

$$\frac{2}{(x-1)(x+1)}.$$

(iii) Solve the differential equation

$$(x^2-1)\frac{dy}{dx} = -(x^2+1)y \qquad \text{(where } x > 1\text{)}$$

given that $y = 1$ when $x = 3$. Express y as a function of x.

[MEI]

9 A hemispherical bowl of radius a has its axis vertical and is full of water. At time $t = 0$ water starts running out of a small hole in the bottom of the bowl so that the depth of water in the bowl at time t is x. The rate at which the volume of water is decreasing is proportional to x. Given that the volume of water in the bowl when the depth is x is $\pi(ax^2 - \frac{1}{3}x^3)$, show that there is a positive constant k such that

$$\pi(2ax - x^2)\frac{dx}{dt} = -kx.$$

Given that the bowl is empty after a time T, show that

$$k = \frac{3\pi a^2}{2T}.$$

[MEI]

10 The square horizontal cross-section of a container has side 2 m. Water is poured in at the constant rate of $0.08\,\text{m}^3\text{s}^{-1}$ and, at the same time, leaks out of a hole in the base at the rate of $0.12x\,\text{m}^3\text{s}^{-1}$, where x m is the depth of the water in the container at time ts. So the volume, $V\text{m}^3$, of the water in the container at time t is given by $V = 4x$ and the rate of change of volume is given by

$$\frac{\mathrm{d}V}{\mathrm{d}t} = 0.08 - 0.12x.$$

Use these results to find an equation for $\frac{\mathrm{d}x}{\mathrm{d}t}$ in terms of x and solve this to find x in terms of t if the container is empty initially.

Determine to the nearest 0.1 s the time taken for the depth to rise from 0.1 to 0.5 m.

[MEI]

11 To control the pests inside a large greenhouse, 600 ladybirds were introduced. After t days there are P ladybirds in the greenhouse.

In a simple model, P is assumed to be a continuous variable satisfying the differential equation

$$\frac{\mathrm{d}P}{\mathrm{d}t} = kP, \text{ where } k \text{ is a constant.}$$

(i) Solve the differential equation, with initial condition $P = 600$ when $t = 0$, to express P in terms of k and t.

Observations of the number of ladybirds (estimated to the nearest hundred) were made as follows.

t	0	150	250
P	600	1200	3100

(ii) Show that $P = 1200$ when $t = 150$ implies that $k \approx 0.004\,62$.
Show that this is not consistent with the observed value when $t = 250$.

In a refined model, allowing for seasonal variations, it is assumed that P satisfies the differential equation

$$\frac{\mathrm{d}P}{\mathrm{d}t} = P[0.005 - 0.008\cos(0.02t)]$$

with initial condition $P = 600$ when $t = 0$.

(iii) Solve this differential equation to express P in terms of t, and comment on how well this fits with the data given above.

(iv) Show that, according to the refined model, the number of ladybirds will decrease initially, and find the smallest number of ladybirds in the greenhouse.

[MEI]

12 A patch of oil pollution in the sea is approximately circular in shape. When first seen its radius was 100 m and its radius was increasing at a rate of 0.5 m per minute. At a time t minutes later, its radius is r metres. An expert believes that, if the patch is untreated, its radius will increase at a rate which is proportional to $\frac{1}{r^2}$.

(i) Write down a differential equation for this situation, using a constant of proportionality, k.

(ii) Using the initial conditions, find the value of k. Hence calculate the expert's prediction of the radius of the oil patch after 2 hours.

The expert thinks that if the oil patch is treated with chemicals then its radius will increase at a rate which is proportional to $\frac{1}{r^2(2+t)}$.

(iii) Write down a differential equation for this new situation and, using the same initial conditions as before, find the value of the new constant of proportionality.

(iv) Calculate the expert's prediction of the radius of the treated oil patch after 2 hours.

[MEI]

13 (i) Express $\frac{1}{(2-x)(1+x)}$ in partial fractions.

An industrial process creates a chemical C. At time t hours after the start of the process the amount of C produced is x kg. The rate at which C is produced is given by the differential equation

$$\frac{dx}{dt} = k(2-x)(1+x)e^{-t},$$

where k is a constant.

(ii) When $t = 0$, $x = 0$ and the rate of production of C is $\frac{2}{3}$ kg per hour. Calculate the value of k.

(iii) Show that $\ln\left(\frac{1+x}{2-x}\right) = -e^{-t} + 1 - \ln 2$, provided that $x < 2$.

(iv) Find, in hours, the time taken to produce 0.5 kg of C, giving your answer correct to 2 decimal places.

(v) Show that there is a finite limit to the amount of C which this process can produce, however long it runs, and determine the value of this limit.

[MEI]

14 (i) Use integration by parts to evaluate

$$\int 4x \cos 2x \, dx.$$

(ii) Use part **(i)**, together with a suitable expression for $\cos^2 x$, to show that

$$\int 8x \cos^2 x \, dx = 2x^2 + 2x \sin 2x + \cos 2x + c.$$

(iii) Find the solution of the differential equation

$$\frac{dy}{dx} = \frac{8x\cos^2 x}{y}$$

which satisfies $y = \sqrt{3}$ when $x = 0$.

(iv) Show that any point (x, y) on the graph of this solution which satisfies $\sin 2x = 1$ also lies on one of the lines $y = 2x + 1$ or $y = -2x - 1$.

[MEI]

15 A curve C is given by the parametic equations $x = t^2$, $y = 2t$.

(i) Find the cartesian equation of the curve.

(ii) Find $\frac{dy}{dx}$ in terms of t.

Hence, or otherwise, show that $\frac{dy}{dx} = \frac{y}{2x}$ at any point on the curve.

(iii) Another curve D has gradient given by $\frac{dy}{dx} = -\frac{2x}{y}$. Show that, at any point where C and D intersect, the two curves are perpendicular.

(iv) Solve the differential equation $\frac{dy}{dx} = -\frac{2x}{y}$, and hence find the equation of D given that $y = 2$ when $x = 0$.

(v) Draw on the same axes a sketch showing the curves C and D.

[MEI]

16 **(i)** Express $\frac{1}{(3x-1)x}$ in partial fractions.

A model for the way in which a population of animals in a closed environment varies with time is given, for $P > \frac{1}{3}$, by

$$\frac{dP}{dt} = \tfrac{1}{2}(3P^2 - P)\sin t$$

where P is the size of the population in thousands at time t.

(ii) Given that $P = \frac{1}{2}$ when $t = 0$, use the method of separation of variables to show that

$$\ln\left(\frac{3P-1}{P}\right) = \tfrac{1}{2}(1 - \cos t).$$

(iii) Calculate the smallest positive value of t for which $P = 1$.

(iv) Rearrange the equation at the end of part **(ii)** to show that

$$P = \frac{1}{3 - e^{\frac{1}{2}(1-\cos t)}}.$$

Hence find the two values between which the number of animals in the population oscillates.

[MEI]

17 (i) Use integration by parts to show that

$$\int \ln x \, dx = x \ln x - x + c.$$

(ii) Differentiate $\ln(\sin x)$ with respect to x, for $0 < x < \frac{\pi}{2}$.

Hence write down $\int \cot x \, dx$, for $0 < x < \frac{\pi}{2}$.

(iii) For $x > 0$ and $0 < y < \frac{\pi}{2}$, the variables y and x are connected by the differential equation

$$\frac{dy}{dx} = \frac{\ln x}{\cot y},$$

and $y = \frac{\pi}{6}$ when $x = e$.

Find the value of y when $x = 1$, giving your answer correct to 3 significant figures.

Use the differential equation to show that this value of y is a stationary value, and determine its nature.

[MEI]

18 (i) Newton's law of cooling states that the rate at which an object cools is proportional to the difference in temperature between the object and its surroundings.

The temperature, θ°C, of a hot drink, t minutes after it has been poured, satisfies the differential equation

$$\frac{d\theta}{dt} = -a(\theta - b),$$

where a and b are constants. The temperature of the surroundings of the drink is 25°C.

Write down the value of b.

The rate of cooling when $\theta = 65$ is 8°C per minute. Find the value of a.

(ii) The temperature, ϕ°C, of another hot drink, t minutes after being poured, satisfies the differential equation

$$\frac{d\phi}{dt} = -k(\phi - 20),$$

where k is a constant.

(a) Solve this differential equation to show that $\phi = A + Be^{-kt}$, where A and B are constants and the value of A is to be found.

(b) Given that $\phi = 80$ when $t = 0$ and that $\phi = 50$ when $t = 2$, find the values of B and k.

(iii) An object in an industrial oven has temperature T°C at time t, where

$$T = 1000 + 200e^{\sin t}$$

and t is measured in days.

Find a function $f(t)$ and a constant c such that

$$\frac{dT}{dt} = f(t)(T - c).$$

[MEI]

19 The curve C has parametric equations

$$x = 2\cos\theta - \sin\theta + 2, \qquad y = \cos\theta + 2\sin\theta - 1 \qquad (0 \leqslant \theta < 2\pi).$$

(i) Show that the point with parameter $\theta = 0$ has co-ordinates (4, 0).

(ii) Find $\dfrac{dy}{dx}$ in terms of θ.

Deduce that x and y satisfy the differential equation

$$\frac{dy}{dx} = -\frac{x - 2}{y + 1}.$$

(iii) Solve this differential equation, using the condition that $y = 0$ when $x = 4$.

Hence show that the equation of C may be written in the form

$$(x - 2)^2 + (y + 1)^2 = 5.$$

Describe the curve C.

(iv) Express $2\cos\theta - \sin\theta$ in the form $R\cos(\theta + \alpha)$, where R and α are constants to be determined.

Show also that, for the same values of R and α,

$$\cos\theta + 2\sin\theta = R\sin(\theta + \alpha).$$

(v) The equation of C given in part **(iii)** can also be obtained by eliminating θ between the parametric equations for x and y. Use the results of part **(iv)** to carry out this elimination.

[MEI]

20 The population of a city is P millions at time t years. When $t = 0$, $P = 1$.

(i) A simple model is given by the differential equation

$$\frac{\mathrm{d}P}{\mathrm{d}t} = kP,$$

where k is a constant.

(a) Verify that $P = Ae^{kt}$ satisfies this differential equation, and show that $A = 1$.

Given that $P = 1.24$ when $t = 1$, find k.

(b) Why is this model unsatisfactory in the long term?

(ii) An alternative model is given by the differential equation

$$4\frac{\mathrm{d}P}{\mathrm{d}t} = P(2 - P).$$

(a) Express $\dfrac{4}{P(2 - P)}$ in partial fractions.

(b) Hence, by integration, show that

$$\frac{P}{2 - P} = e^{\frac{1}{2}t}.$$

(c) Express P in terms of t. Verify that, when $t = 1$, P is approximately 1.24.

(d) According to this model, what happens to the population of the city in the long term?

[MEI]

21 **(i)** Express $\dfrac{1 - x}{(1 + x)(1 + x^2)}$ in the form $\dfrac{A}{1 + x} + \dfrac{Bx + C}{1 + x^2}$.

(ii) Hence show that the solution of the differential equation

$$\frac{\mathrm{d}y}{\mathrm{d}x} = \frac{y(1 - x)}{(1 + x)(1 + x^2)},$$

given that $y = 1$ when $x = 0$, is

$$y = \frac{1 + x}{\sqrt{1 + x^2}}.$$

(iii) Find the first three terms of the binomial expansion of $\dfrac{1}{\sqrt{1 + x^2}}$.

Hence find a polynomial approximation for $y = \dfrac{1 + x}{\sqrt{1 + x^2}}$ up to the term in x^5.

[MEI]

22 A wind is blowing offshore and so the waves become larger the further from the shore you travel. At the water's edge the waves have zero height. Three models are considered for the rate of increase in wave height h with respect to distance s from the shore.

(i) Rate of increase of h with respect to s is proportional to s.
(ii) Rate of increase of h with respect to s is inversely proportional to $(s + 5)$.
(ii) Rate of increase of h with respect to s is proportional to e^{-cs}, where c is a positive constant.

(a) For each of these models, form and solve a differential equation.
(b) For each model, sketch the graph of h against s.
(c) Discuss which of the models is the most realistic. In particular, consider the behaviour for large values of s.

INVESTIGATION

Investigate the tea cooling problem introduced on page 335. You will need to make some assumptions about the initial temperature of the tea and the temperature of the room.

What difference would it make if you were to add some cold milk to the tea and then leave it to cool?

Would it be better to allow the tea to cool first before adding the milk?

KEY POINTS

1 A differential equation is an equation involving derivatives such as

$$\frac{dy}{dx} \quad \text{and} \quad \frac{d^2y}{dx^2}.$$

2 A first-order differential equation involves a first derivative only.

3 Some first-order differential equations may be solved by separating the variables.

4 A general solution is one in which the constant of integration is left in the solution, and a particular solution is one in which additional information is used to calculate the constant of integration.

5 A general solution may be represented by a family of curves, a particular solution by a particular member of that family.

Answers

Chapter 1

(Page 2)

$$c^2 = (a+b)^2 - 4 \times \tfrac{1}{2}ab$$
$$\Rightarrow \quad c^2 = a^2 + 2ab + b^2 - 2ab$$
$$\Rightarrow \quad c^2 = a^2 + b^2$$

Exercise 1A (Page 6)

1 True – direct proof – remove the brackets

2 True – direct proof using the converse of Pythagoras' theorem

3 True – proof by exhaustion considering the squares of one-digit numbers

4 True – direct proof – let the numbers be n and $n + 1$

5 True – proof by contradiction

6 **(i)** True – direct proof

(ii) True – direct proof

7 **(i)** True – direct proof

(ii) True – direct proof

8 False, e.g. $n = 10$

9 **(i)** True – direct proof

(ii) False, e.g. 1, 2, 3, 4

10 True – direct proof

Chapter 2

? (Page 8)

$\frac{1}{x} = x^{-1}$. This means that $n = -1$ and so $n + 1 = 0$. You cannot divide by zero.

Investigation (Page 8)

(i) 1.099

(ii) 0.693

(iii) 1.792

$$\int_1^3 \frac{1}{x}\,dx + \int_1^2 \frac{1}{x}\,dx = \int_1^6 \frac{1}{x}\,dx$$

Activity 2.1 (Page 9)

(i)

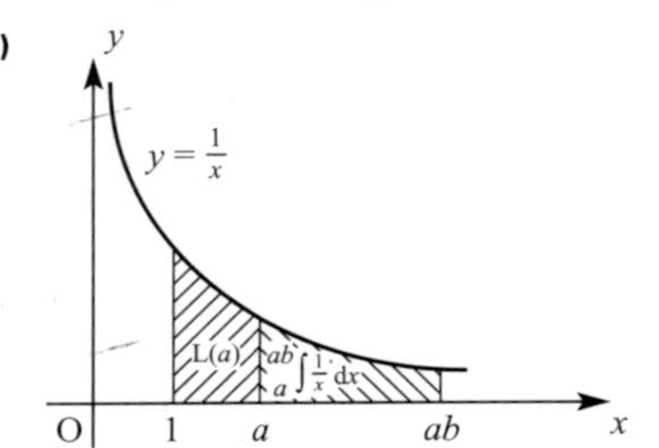

(ii) $\displaystyle\int_a^{ab} \frac{1}{x}\,dx \qquad x = az \Rightarrow dx = a\,dz$

converting the limits:

$\displaystyle= \int_1^b \frac{1}{az} \times a\,dz \qquad x = a \Rightarrow z = 1$

$x = ab \Rightarrow z = b$

$$= \int_1^b \frac{1}{z}\,dz$$

$$\int_1^b \frac{1}{z}\,dz = \int_1^b \frac{1}{x}\,dx = L(b)$$

(iii) $\displaystyle L(a) + \int_a^{ab} \frac{1}{x}\,dx = L(ab) \Rightarrow L(a) + L(b) = L(ab)$

Activity 2.2 (Page 10)

(i) $\displaystyle L(1) = \int_1^1 \frac{1}{x}\,dx = 0$

(ii) $\displaystyle L(a) - L(b) = \int_1^a \frac{1}{x}\,dx - \int_1^b \frac{1}{x}\,dx$

$$= \int_b^a \frac{1}{x}\,dx$$

Let $x = bz$

$$\int_b^a \frac{1}{x}\,dx = \int_1^{\frac{a}{b}} \frac{1}{z}\,dz$$

$$= L\left(\frac{a}{b}\right)$$

(iii) $\displaystyle L(a^n) = \int_1^{a^n} \frac{1}{x}\,dx$

Let $x = z^n$ then $dx = nz^{n-1}\,dz$.

$$\int_1^a \frac{1}{x}\,dx = \int_1^a \frac{1}{z^n} \times nz^{n-1}\,dz$$

$$= n\int_1^a \frac{1}{z}\,dz$$

$$= n\,L(a)$$

Activity 2.3 (Page 10)

e = 2.72 (2 d.p.)

Exercise 2A (Page 15)

1 $x = x_0 e^{kt}$

2 $t = \frac{1}{k} \ln\left(\frac{s_0}{s}\right)$

3 $p = 25e^{-0.02t}$

4 $x = \ln\left(\frac{y-5}{y_0-5}\right)$

5 **(i)**

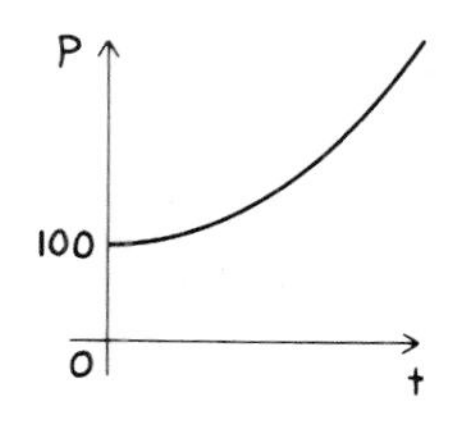

(ii) 100

(iii) 1218

(iv) 184 years

6 **(i)**

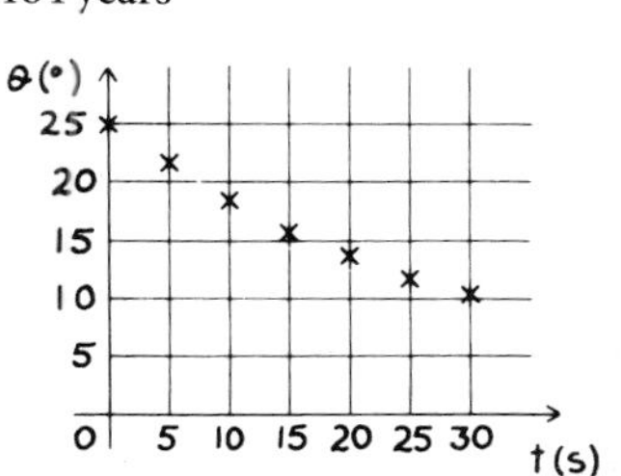

(ii) 25°

(iii) 4.1°

(iv) 22

7 **(i)**

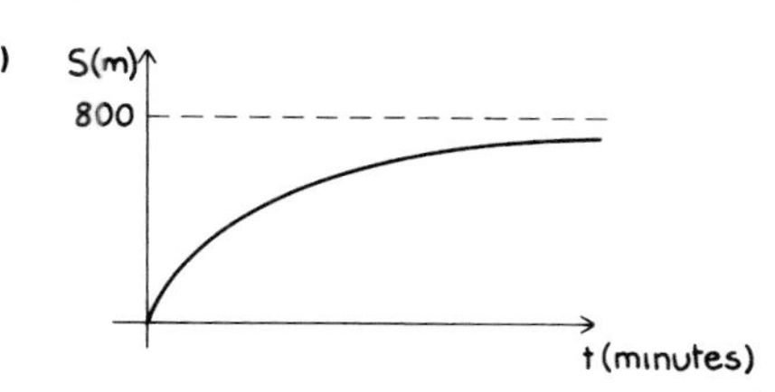

(ii) 621.5 m

(iii) 8.07 am (to the nearest minute)

(iv) Never

8 **(i)**

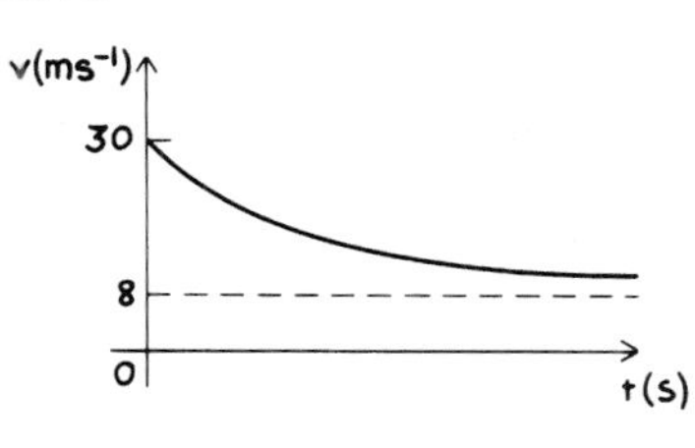

(ii) $30\,\text{ms}^{-1}$, $8\,\text{ms}^{-1}$

(iii) $8.33\,\text{ms}^{-1}$

(iv) 8.7 seconds

9 **(i)** 1 m

(ii) 4.61 m, 6.09 years

(iii) $a = e^{-2} = 0.135$, $b = 2.5$

(iv) 11 years

10 **(ii)** 54.6 mpg, 40.0 mpg

(iii) 63 mpg, 39.4 mpg

(iv) The first model gives the better results overall.

Chapter 3

? (Page 21)

(i) **(a)** One-to-one

(b) One-to-many

(c) Many-to-one

(d) Many-to-many

Exercise 3A (Page 23)

1 **(i)** One-to-one, yes, equal

(ii) Many-to-one, yes, not equal

(iii) Many-to-many, no, equal

(iv) One-to-many, no, equal

(v) Many-to-many, no, not equal

(vi) One-to-one, yes, not equal

(vii) Many-to-many, no, equal

(viii) Many-to-one, yes, not equal

2 **(i)** **(a)** Examples: one $\rightarrow$ 3, word $\rightarrow$ 4

(b) Many-to-one

(c) Domain: words, co-domain: $\mathbb{Z}^+$

(ii) **(a)** Examples: $1 \rightarrow 4$, $2.1 \rightarrow 8.4$

(b) One-to-one

(c) Domain: $\mathbb{R}^+$, co-domain: $\mathbb{R}^+$

(iii) (a) Examples: $1 \rightarrow 1, 6 \rightarrow 4$

(b) Many-to-one

(c) Domain: $\mathbb{Z}^+$,

co-domain: $\mathbb{Z}^+$

(iv) (a) Examples: $1 \rightarrow -3$,

$-4 \rightarrow -13$

(b) One-to-one

(c) Domain: $\mathbb{R}$, co-domain: $\mathbb{R}$

(v) (a) Examples: $4 \rightarrow 2, 9 \rightarrow 3$

(b) One-to-one

(c) Domain: $x \geqslant 0$,

co-domain: $x \geqslant 0$

(vi) (a) Examples: $36\pi \rightarrow 3$,

$\frac{9}{2}\pi \rightarrow 1.5$

(b) One-to-one

(c) Domain: $\mathbb{R}^+$,

co-domain: $\mathbb{R}^+$

(vii) (a) Examples: $12\pi \rightarrow 3$,

$12\pi \rightarrow 12$

(b) Many-to-many

(c) Domain: $\mathbb{R}^+$,

co-domain: $\mathbb{R}^+$

(viii) (a) Examples: $1 \rightarrow \frac{3}{2}\sqrt{3}$,

$4 \rightarrow 24\sqrt{3}$

(b) One-to-one

(c) Domain: $\mathbb{R}^+$,

co-domain: $\mathbb{R}^+$

(ix) (a) Examples: $4 \rightarrow 16$,

$-0.7 \rightarrow 0.49$

(b) Many-to-one

(c) Domain: $\mathbb{R}$,

co-domain: $x \geqslant 0$

3 **(i)** **(a)** -5 **(b)** 9 **(c)** -11

(ii) **(a)** 3 **(b)** 5 **(c)** 10

(iii) **(a)** 32 **(b)** 82.4 **(c)** 14 **(d)** -40

4 **(i)** $f(x) \leqslant 2$

(ii) $0 \leqslant f(\theta) \leqslant 1$

(iii) $y \in \{2, 3, 6, 11, 18\}$

(iv) $y \in \mathbb{R}^+$

(v) $\mathbb{R}$

(vi) $\left\{\frac{1}{2}, 1, 2, 4\right\}$

(vii) $0 \leqslant y \leqslant 1$

(viii) $\mathbb{R}$

(ix) $0 < f(x) \leqslant 1$

(x) $f(x) \geqslant 3$

5 For f, every value of x (including $x = 3$) gives a unique output, whereas g(2) can equal either 4 or 6.

Activity 3.1 (Page 25)

(i) **(a)** Vertices at (6, 0), (8, 3) and (10, 0).

(b) Vertices at (3, 0), (5, 3) and (7, 0).

Different

(ii) **(a)** Vertices at (3, 0), (4, 6) and (5, 0).

(b) Vertices at (3, 0), (4, 6) and (5, 0).

Same

(iii) **(a)** Vertices at (0, 3), (2, 6) and (4, 3).

(b) Vertices at (0, 3), (2, 6) and (4, 3).

Same

(iv) **(a)** Vertices at (0, 6), (1, 12) and (2, 6).

(b) Vertices at (0, 3), (1, 9) and (2, 3).

Different

(v) **(a)** Vertices at (0, 0), (2, 9) and (4, 0).

(b) Vertices at (0, 0), (2, 9) and (4, 0).

Same

p (Page 27)

You can prove it by reference to the graph which has a minimum at $(-a, b)$ and so never crosses the x axis.

Alternatively you can prove it algebraically.

$$(x + a)^2 = -b$$

$$\Rightarrow \quad (x + a) = \pm\sqrt{-b}$$

but there is no real value of $\sqrt{-b}$.

Exercise 3B (Page 28)

1 **(i)** Translation $\begin{pmatrix} 0 \\ -2 \end{pmatrix}$; $x = 0$

(ii) Stretch parallel to the y axis of s.f. 3; $x = 0$

(iii) Translation $\begin{pmatrix} 2 \\ 0 \end{pmatrix}$; $x = 2$

(iv) Stretch parallel to the y axis of s.f. 3 and translation $\begin{pmatrix} 2 \\ 0 \end{pmatrix}$ in either order; $x = 2$

(v) Translation $\begin{pmatrix} 2 \\ 0 \end{pmatrix}$ then stretch s.f. $\frac{1}{3}$ parallel to the x axis; $x = \frac{2}{3}$

(vi) $y = (x - 2)^2 - 4$; translation $\begin{pmatrix} 2 \\ -4 \end{pmatrix}$; $x = 2$

(vii) $y = 2[(x + 1)^2 - 1\frac{1}{2}]$:

translation $\begin{pmatrix} -1 \\ -1\frac{1}{2} \end{pmatrix}$; then stretch parallel to y axis of s.f. 2; $x = -1$

(viii) $y = 3\left[(x - 1)^2 - \frac{5}{3}\right]$:

translation $\begin{pmatrix} 1 \\ -\frac{5}{3} \end{pmatrix}$; then stretch parallel to y axis of s.f. 3; $x = 1$

2 **(i)** **(a)** Translation $\begin{pmatrix} 0 \\ 7 \end{pmatrix}$

(b)

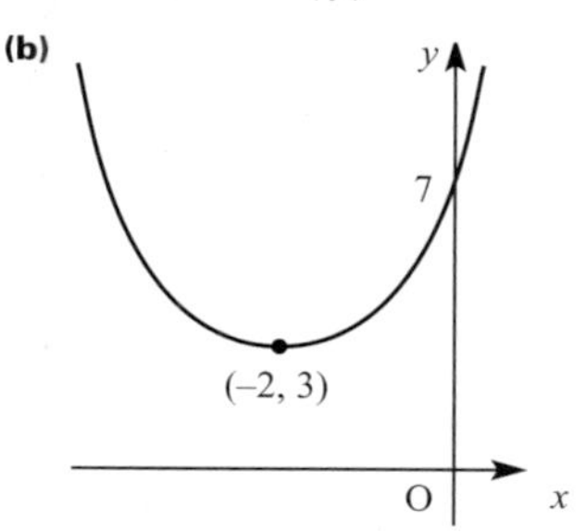

(ii) **(a)** Translation $\begin{pmatrix} 2 \\ 0 \end{pmatrix}$

(b)

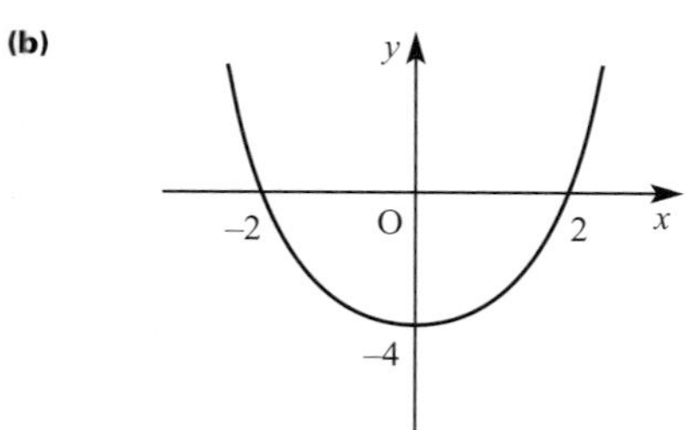

(iii) **(a)** Stretch parallel to the y axis, s.f. 2; then translation $\begin{pmatrix} 0 \\ 3 \end{pmatrix}$

(b)

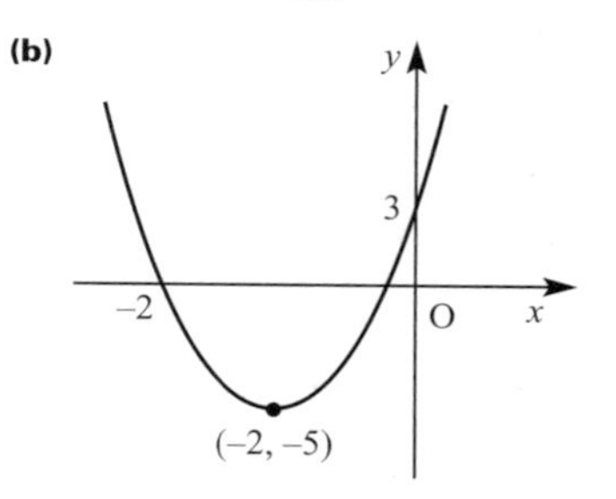

(iv) **(a)** Stretch parallel to the x axis, s.f. $\frac{1}{2}$; then translation $\begin{pmatrix} 0 \\ 3 \end{pmatrix}$

(b)

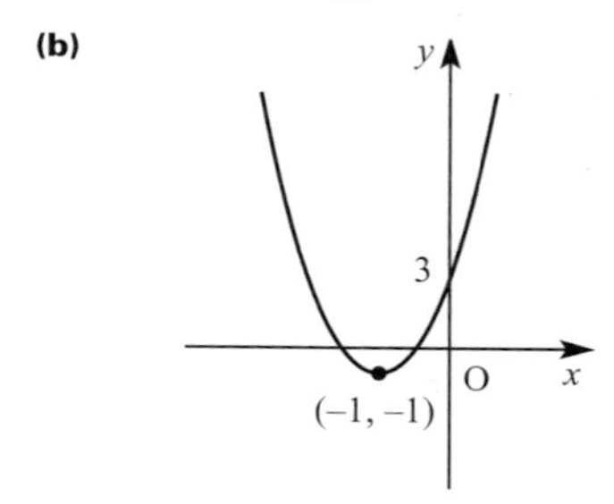

(v) **(a)** Translation $\begin{pmatrix} 2 \\ 0 \end{pmatrix}$; then stretch parallel to the y axis, s.f. 3

(b)

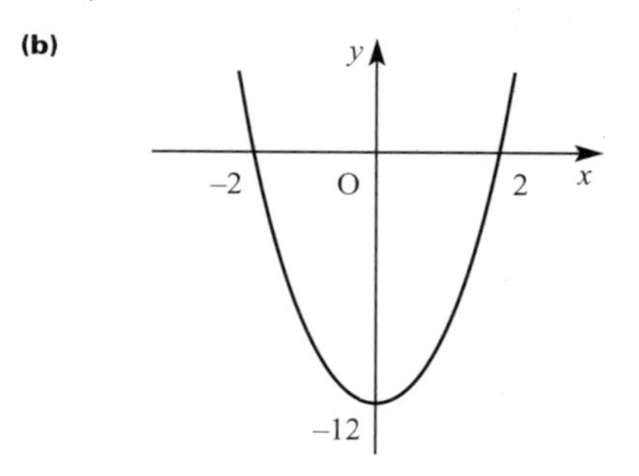

3 **(i)**

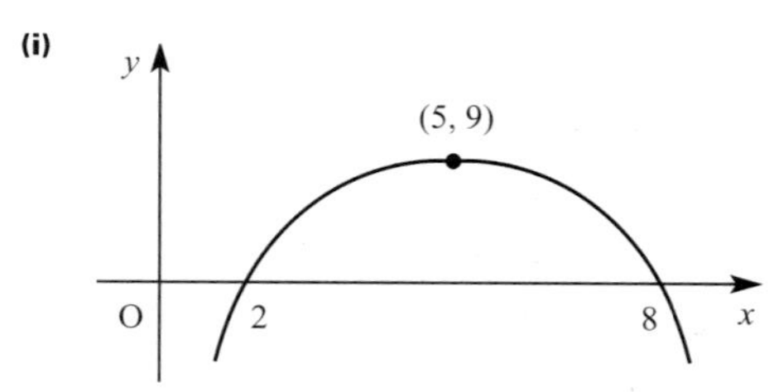

(ii)

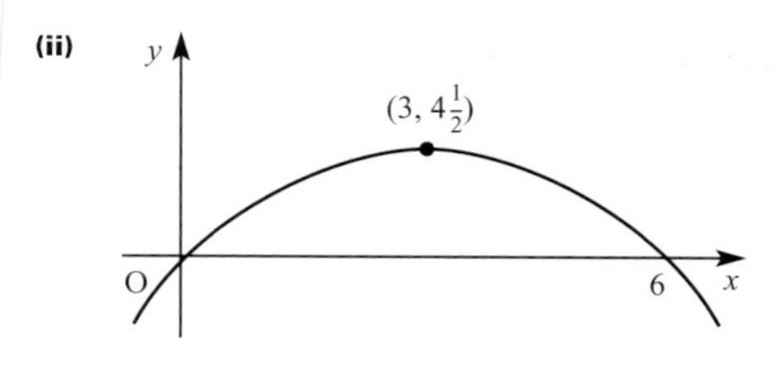

(iii)

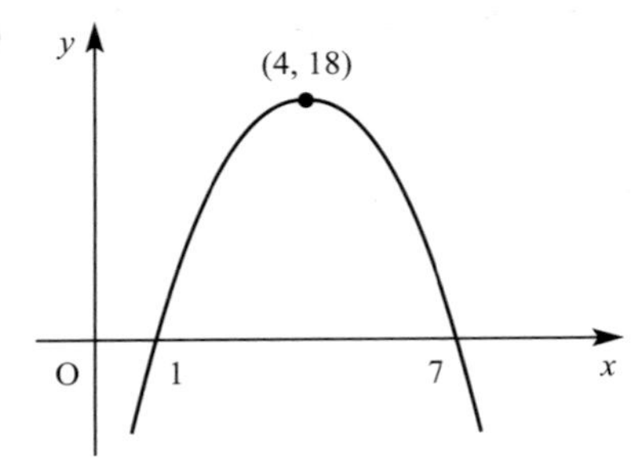

4 **(i)**

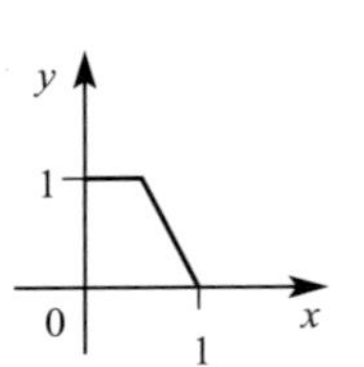

(ii)

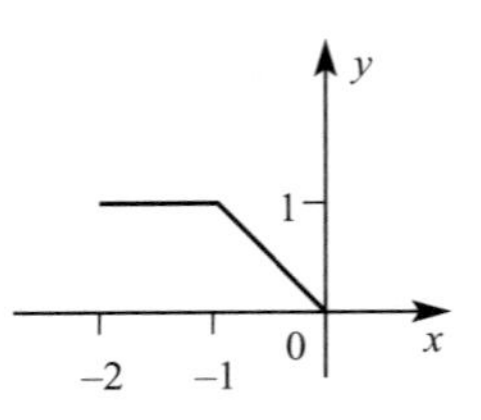

(iii)

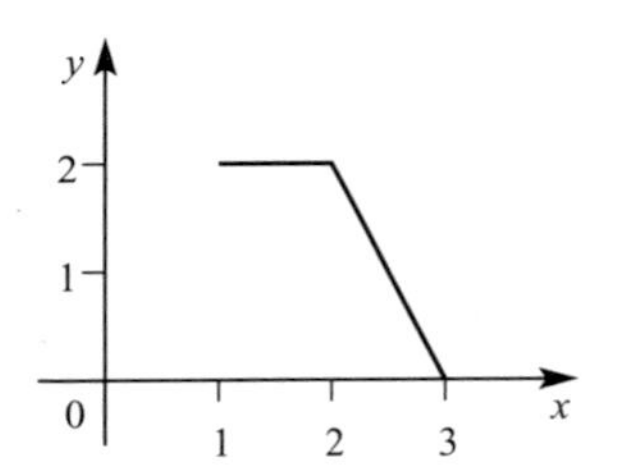

(iv)

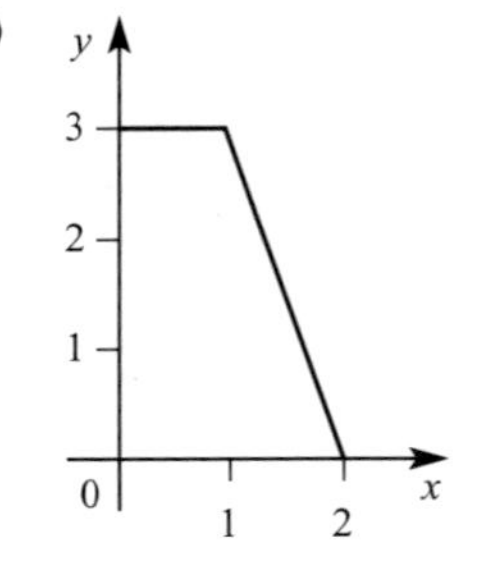

(v)

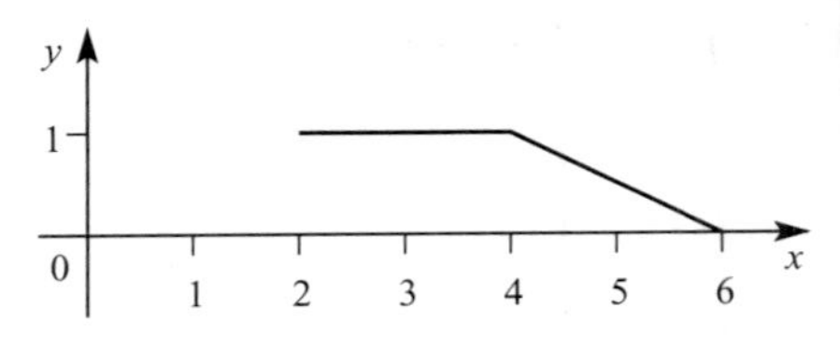

(vi)

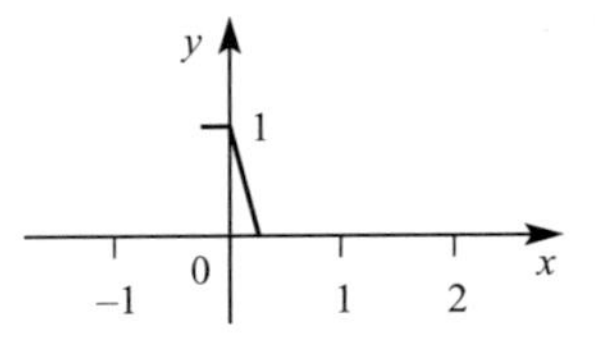

5 **(i)** Stretch s.f. $\frac{1}{2}$ in the x direction and stretch s.f. 3 in the y direction

(ii) Stretch s.f. 3 in the x direction and translation $\begin{pmatrix} 0 \\ -1 \end{pmatrix}$

(iii) Translation $\begin{pmatrix} -30 \\ 0 \end{pmatrix}$ followed by stretch s.f. $\frac{1}{2}$ in the x direction

6 **(i)** **(a)** $f(x) = 3\sin x$

$g(x) = \sin 2x$

$h(x) = 2\sin\frac{x}{2}$

(b) **(A)** $y = \sin x + 2$

(B) $y = \sin(x - 90°)$

(c) 180°

(ii) **(a)** $b - c \leqslant F(x) \leqslant b + c$

(b) (30°, 0), (150°, 0)

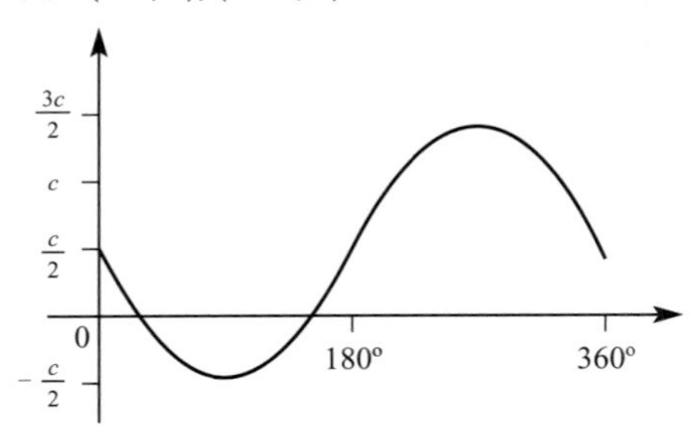

Activity 3.2 (Page 30)

(i)

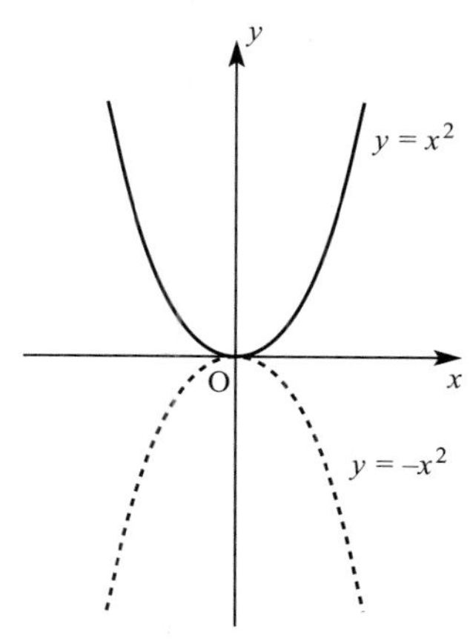

$y = -x^2$ gives a reflection in the x axis.

(ii)

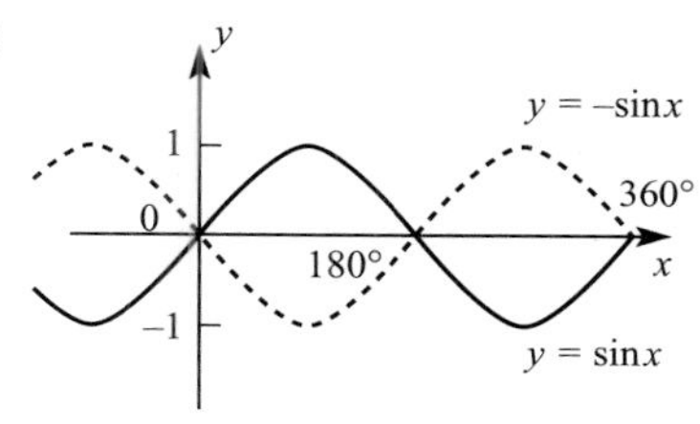

$y = -\sin x$ could be a reflection in the x axis or a translation $\begin{pmatrix} 180° \\ 0 \end{pmatrix}$.

(iii)

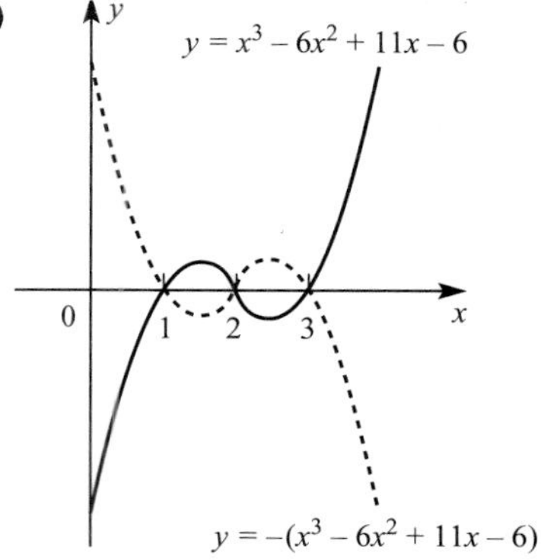

$y = -(x^3 - 6x^2 + 11x - 6)$ could be a reflection in the x axis or a reflection in the line $x = 2$.

The only option in common is a reflection in the x axis.

Activity 3.3 (Page 31)

(i)

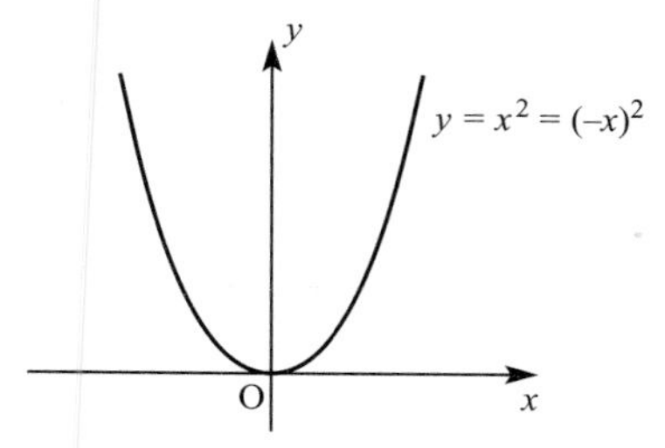

$y = (-x)^2$ seems unchanged but could be a reflection in the y axis.

(ii)

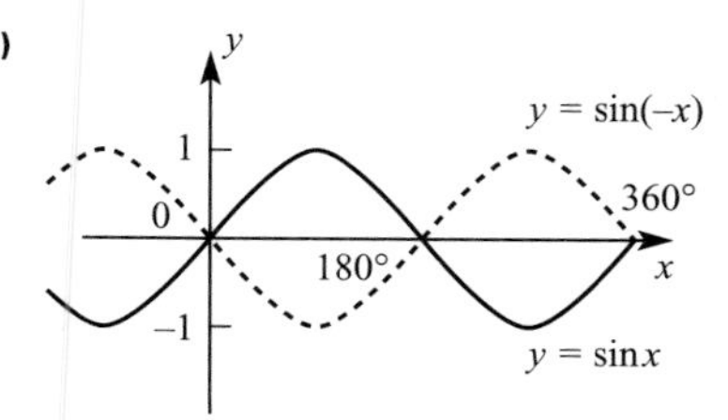

$y = \sin(-x)$ could be a reflection in the y axis or a reflection in the x axis.

(iii)

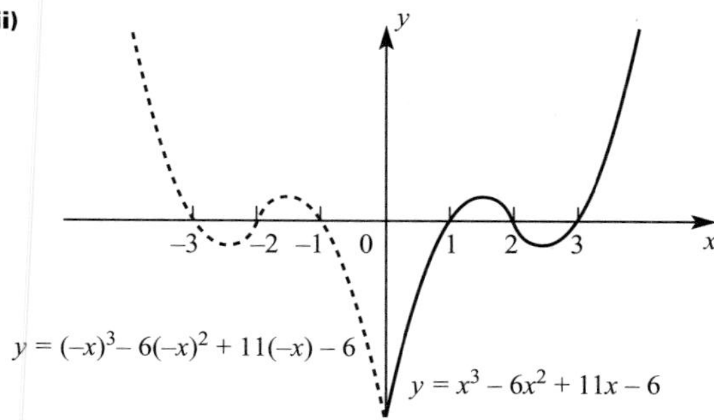

$y = (-x)^3 - 6(-x)^2 + 11(-x) - 6$ is a reflection in the y axis.

The only option in common is a reflection in the y axis.

Exercise 3C (Page 34)

1 **(i)** Stretch parallel to y axis of s.f. 2, and reflection in x axis, either order; $x = 0$

(ii) Reflection in x axis then translation $\begin{pmatrix} 0 \\ 4 \end{pmatrix}$; $x = 0$

(iii) $y = -(x - 1)^2$: translation $\begin{pmatrix} 1 \\ 0 \end{pmatrix}$, and reflection in x axis, either order; $x = 1$

2 **(i)** **(a)**

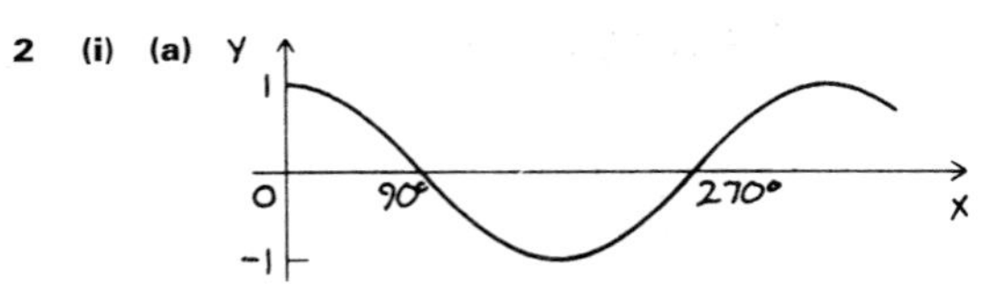

(b) $y = \cos x$

(ii) **(a)**

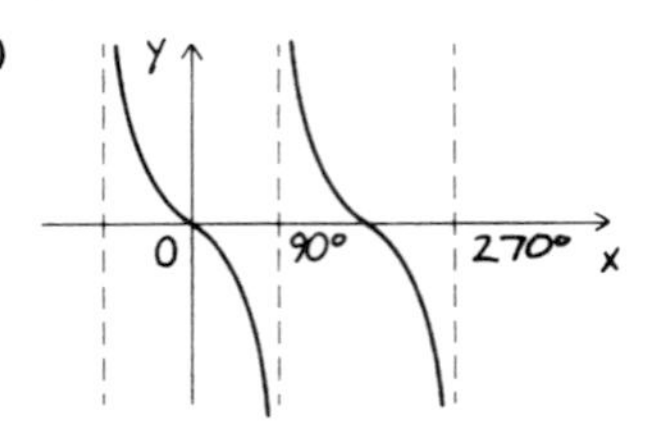

(b) $y = -\tan x$

(iii) **(a)**

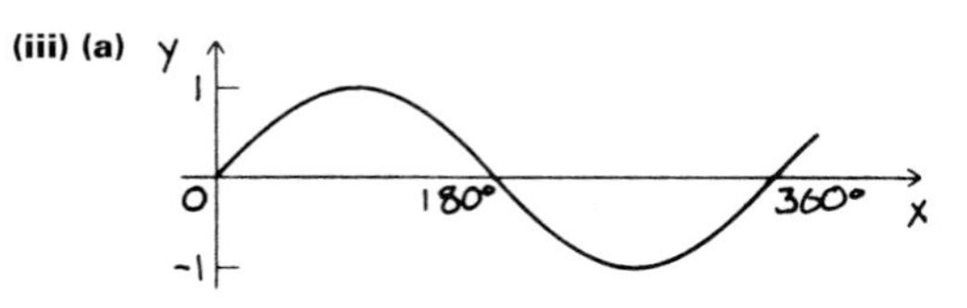

(b) $y = \sin x$

(iv) **(a)**

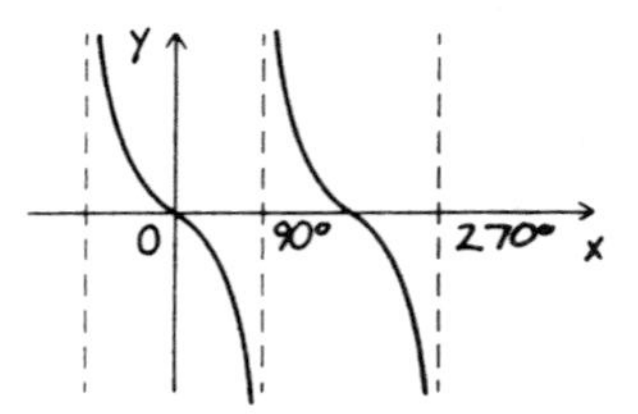

(b) $y = -\tan x$

(v) **(a)**

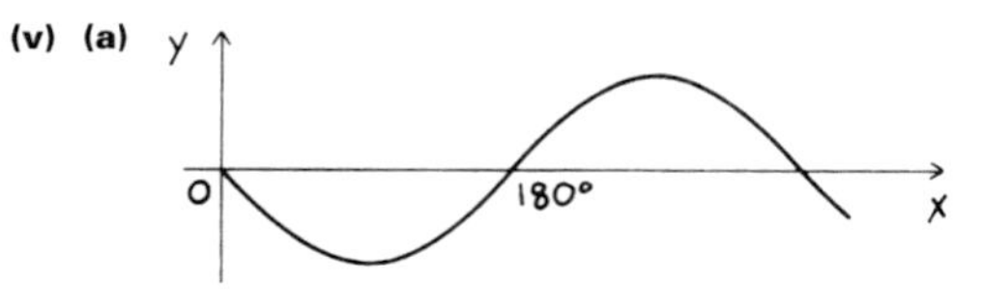

(b) $y = -\sin x$

3 **(i)** $a = 3, b = 5$

(ii) Translation $\begin{pmatrix} 3 \\ 5 \end{pmatrix}$

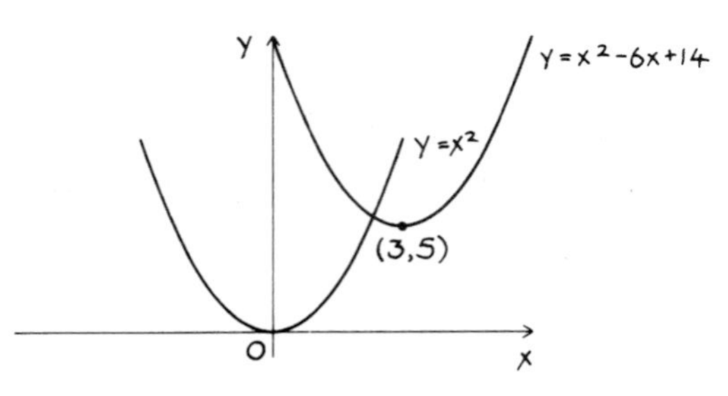

(iii) $y = 6x - x^2 - 14$

4 **(i)**

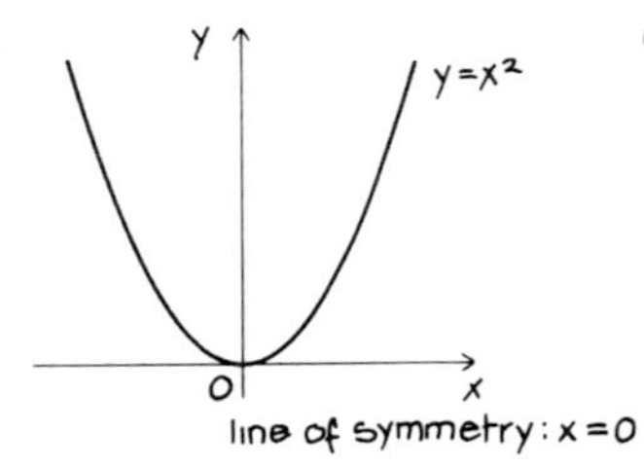

(ii) **(a)**

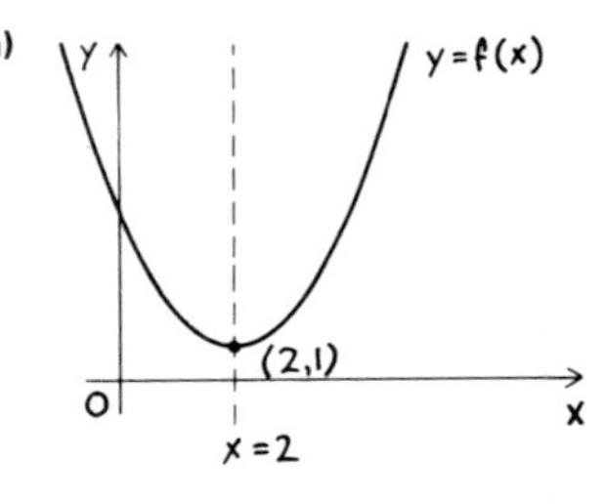

(b)

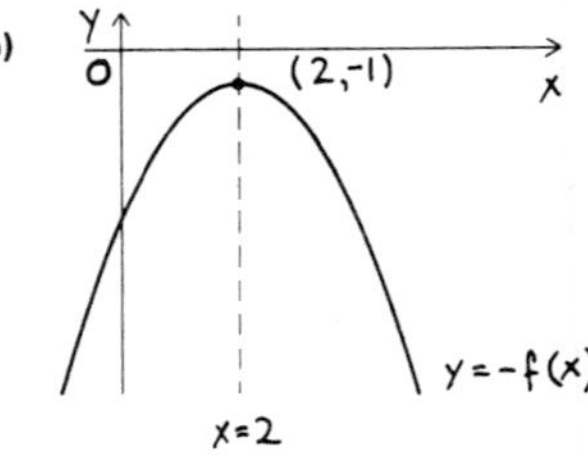

(c)

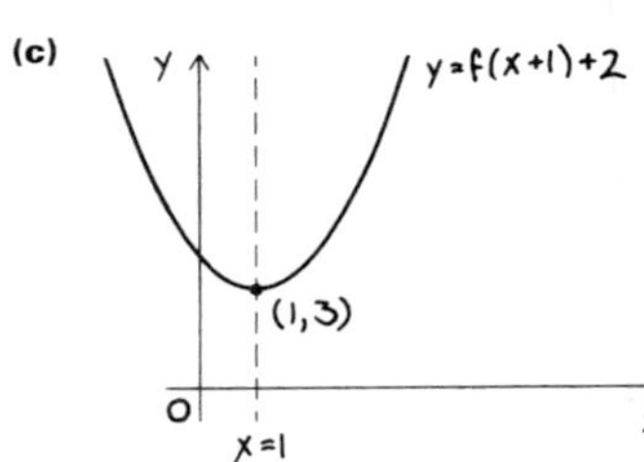

5 $a = 2, b = 1, c = 3; (-1, 3)$

6 $\dfrac{x^2}{9} + \dfrac{y^2}{4} = 1$

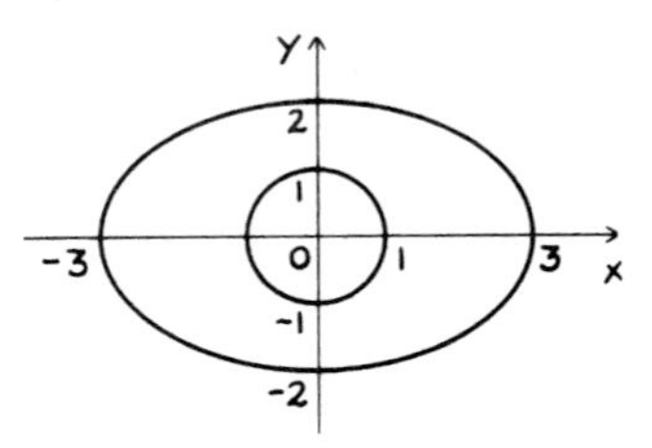

7 **(i)** $y = f(x + 2)$

(ii) $y = -f(x)$

(iii) $y = f\left(\dfrac{x}{2}\right)$

(iv) $y = f(x) - 3$

(v) $y = f(-x)$ (or $y = 2 - f(x)$)

(vi) $y = \frac{3}{2}f(x)$

8 **(i)** $(-1, 5)$; $y = 2$

(ii) $a = -3$, $b = 5$

(iii)

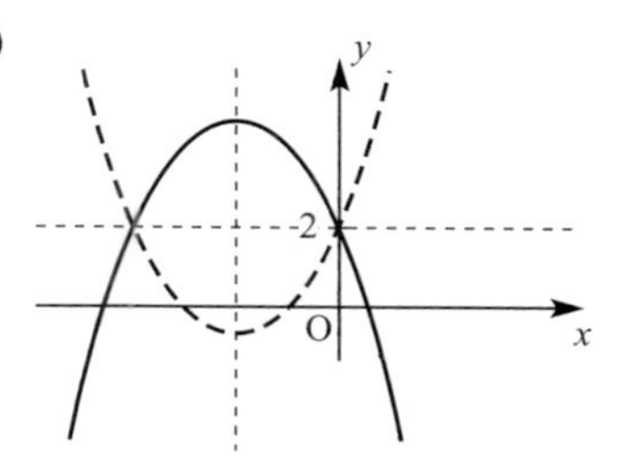

(iv) $y = 3x^2 + 6x + 2$; $(-1, -1)$

9 **(i)**

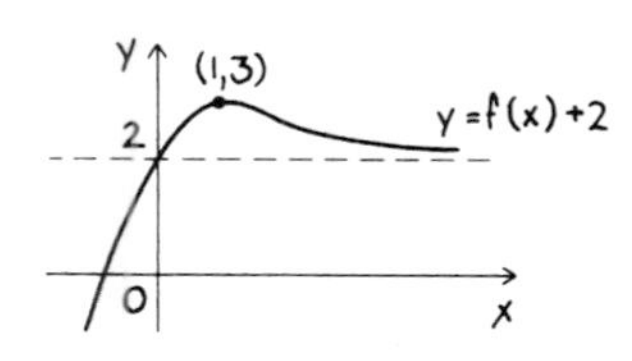

(ii)

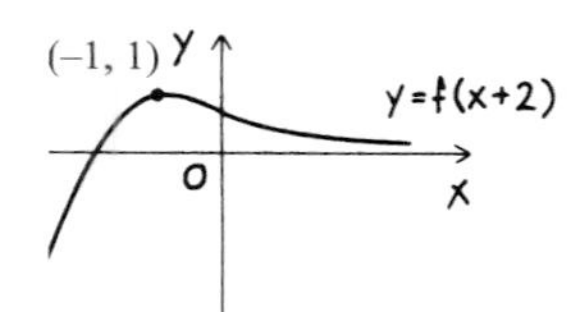

(iii)

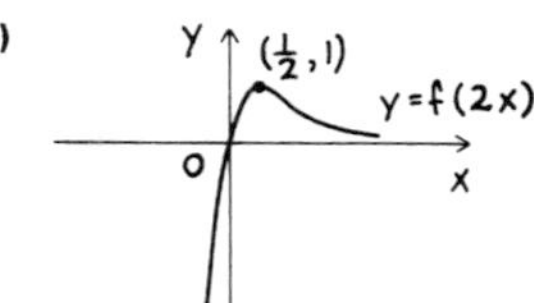

❓ (Page 39)

(i) **(a)** Function with an inverse function.

(b) f: $C \to \frac{9}{5}C + 32$

f^{-1}: $F \to \frac{5}{9}(F - 32)$

(ii) **(a)** Function but no inverse function since one grade corresponds to several marks.

(iii) **(a)** Function with an inverse function.

(b) 1 light year $\approx 6 \times 10^{12}$ miles or almost 10^{16} metres.

f: $x \to 10^{16}x$ (approx.)

f^{-1}: $x \to 10^{-16}x$ (approx.)

(iv) **(a)** Function but no inverse function since fares are banded.

Activity 3.4 (Page 41)

(i)

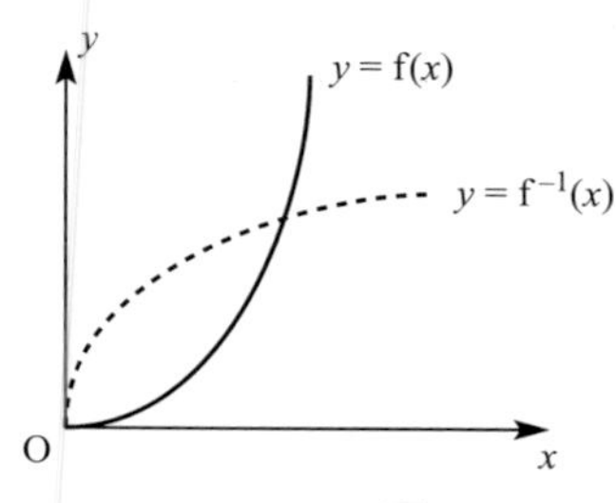

$f(x) = x^2$; $f^{-1}(x) = \sqrt{x}$

(ii)

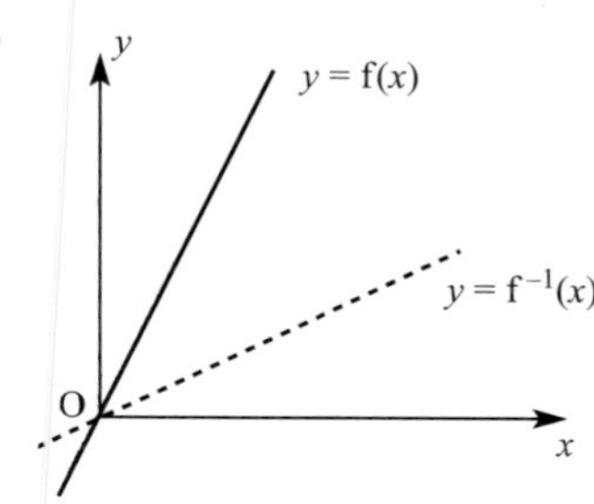

$f(x) = 2x$; $f^{-1}(x) = \frac{1}{2}x$

(iii)

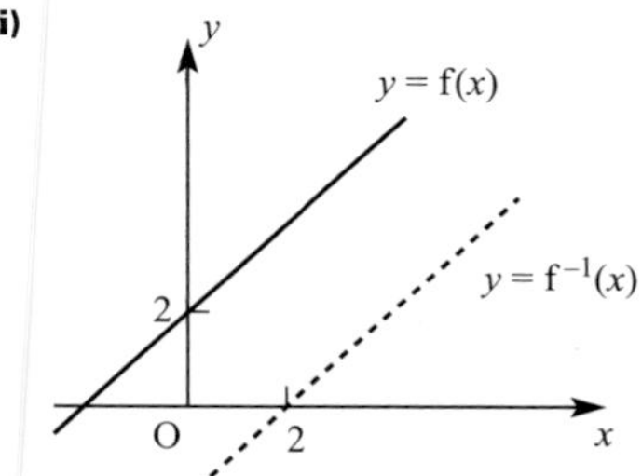

$f(x) = x + 2$; $f^{-1}(x) = x - 2$

(iv)

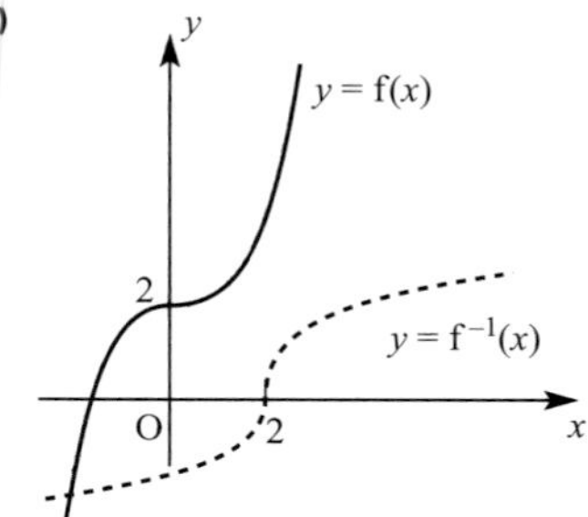

$f(x) = x^3 + 2$; $f^{-1}(x) = \sqrt[3]{x - 2}$

$y = f(x)$ and $y = f^{-1}(x)$ appear to be reflections of each other in $y = x$.

? (Page 45)

(i) Sometimes it depends on the number of significant figures in the original number and in the calculator memory. For example:

$123 \rightarrow 15\,129 \rightarrow 123$ but

$123.456\,789\,12 \rightarrow 15\,241.578\,77 \rightarrow 123.456\,789\,1$

on some calculators.

Also $-2 \rightarrow 4 \rightarrow 2$ since a calculator will give the positive root.

(ii) $\sin 199° = -0.325\ldots$.

$\arcsin(-0.325\ldots) = -19°$ since this is the solution in the range of the inverse function.

P (Page 46)

$\sec\theta = 0.5 \Leftrightarrow \cos\theta = 2$

(i)

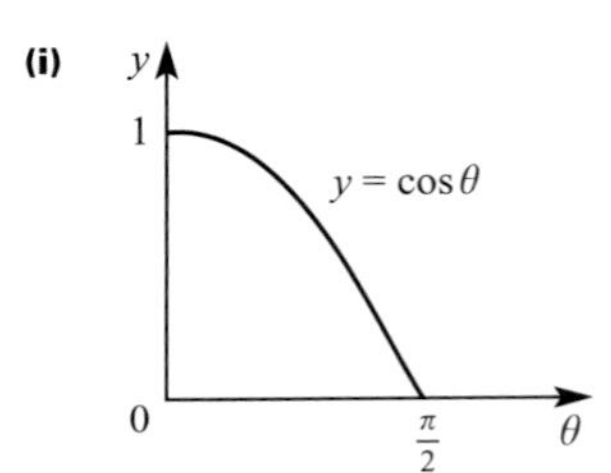

so there is no solution for $0 \leqslant \theta \leqslant \frac{\pi}{2}$

(ii) $\cos\theta$ continues to oscillate between $+1$ and -1 so there is no solution for any value of θ.

Exercise 3D (Page 47)

1 **(i)** $8x^3$

(ii) $2x^3$

(iii) $(x+2)^3$

(iv) x^3+2

(v) $8(x+2)^3$

(vi) $2(x^3+2)$

(vii) $4x$

(viii) $[(x+2)^3+2]^3$

(ix) $x+4$

2 **(i)** $f^{-1}(x) = \dfrac{x-7}{2}$

(ii) $f^{-1}(x) = 4 - x$

(iii) $f^{-1}(x) = \dfrac{2x-4}{x}$

(iv) $f^{-1}(x) = \sqrt{x+3},\ x \geqslant -3$

3 **(i), (ii)**

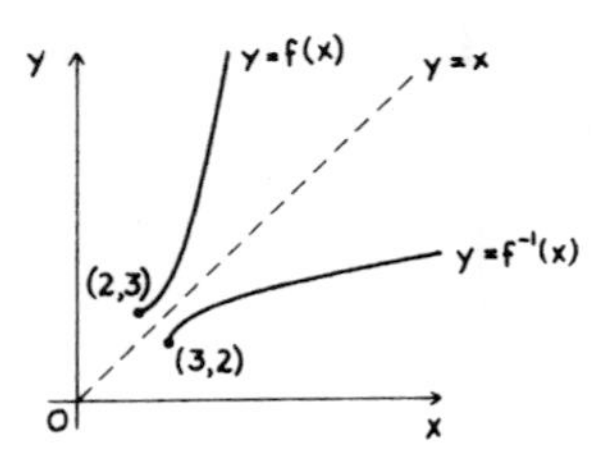

4 **(i)** fg

(ii) g^2

(iii) fg^2

(iv) gf

5 **(i)** $f(x)$ not defined for $x = 4$;

$h(x)$ not defined for $x > 2$

(ii) $f^{-1}(x) = \dfrac{4x+3}{x}$;

$h^{-1}(x) = 2 - x^2,\ x \geqslant 0$

(iii) $g(x)$ is not one-to-one.

(iv) Suitable domain: $x \geqslant 0$

(v) No: $fg(x) = \dfrac{3}{x^2-4}$, not defined for $x = \pm 2$; $gf(x) = \left(\dfrac{3}{x-4}\right)^2$, not defined for $x = 4$.

6 **(i)** x

(ii) $\dfrac{1}{x}$

(iii) $\dfrac{1}{x}$

(iv) $\dfrac{1}{x}$

7 **(i)** $a = 3$

(ii)

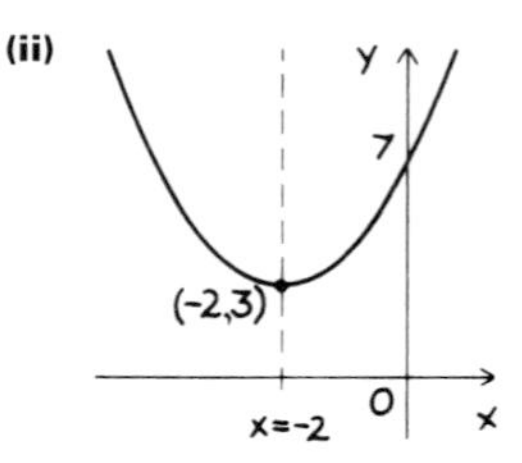

(iii) $f(x) \geqslant 3$

(iv) Function f is not one-to-one when domain is $\mathbb{R}$.

Inverse exists for function with domain $x \geqslant -2$.

8 $f^{-1}: x \rightarrow \sqrt[3]{\dfrac{x-3}{4}},\ x \in \mathbb{R}$.

The graphs are reflections of each other in the line $y = x$.

9 **(i)** $a = 2, b = -5$

(ii) Translation $\begin{pmatrix}-2\\-5\end{pmatrix}$

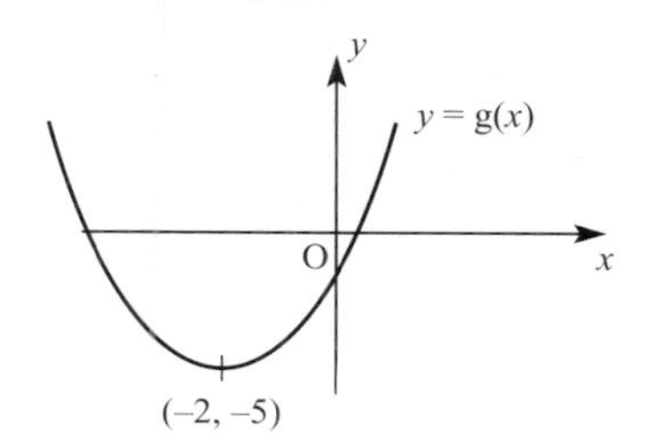

(iii) $y \geqslant -5$

(iv) $c = -2$

(v)

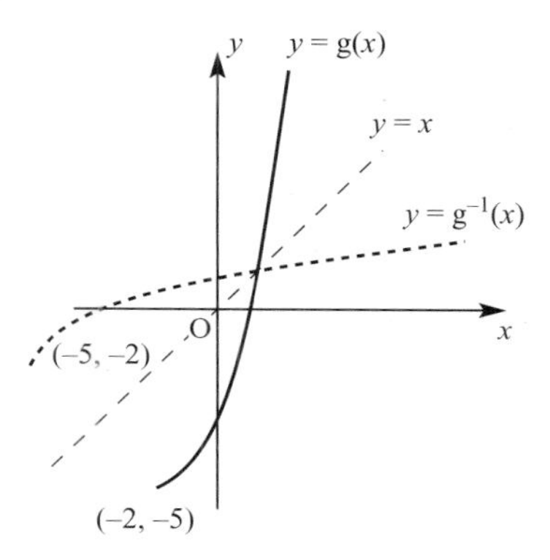

10 **(i)** $P(c, 0)$; $Q\left(\frac{b}{a}, 0\right)$; $R\left(0, \frac{b}{c}\right)$; $S(0, a)$

(ii) $x = \dfrac{cy - b}{y - a}$

(iii) $a = 3$; $b = 4$; $c = 3$

(iv) $a = 3$; $b = 2$; $c = 1$

11 **(i)** $x = 5.35$

(ii) $c = 3, d = 4$

(iii) $g = 4, h = 2$

P (Page 51)

$f(x) = x^2 - 2x \Leftrightarrow f(-x) = (-x)^2 - 2(-x)$

$= x^2 + 2x$

$f(x) \neq f(-x)$ so $f(x)$ is not even.

$-f(x) = -(x^2 - 2x) = -x^2 + 2x$

$f(-x) \neq -f(x)$ so $f(x)$ is not odd.

Exercise 3E (Page 53)

1 **(i)** Even

(ii) Odd

(iii) Neither

(iv) Neither

(v) Odd

(vi) Even

2 **(i)** Even

(ii) Odd, periodic; $\frac{2}{3}\pi$

(iii) None

(iv) Odd

(v) Periodic; 2π

(vi) Odd, periodic; π

3 **(i)**

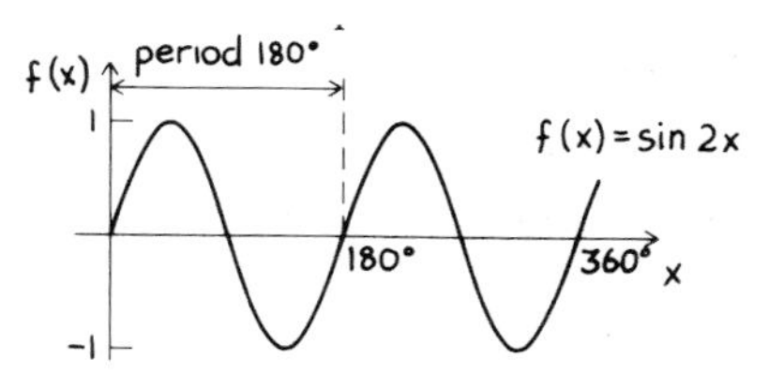

(ii) Half the period of $\sin x$

(iii) **(a)** 90°

(b) 120°

(c) 720°

4

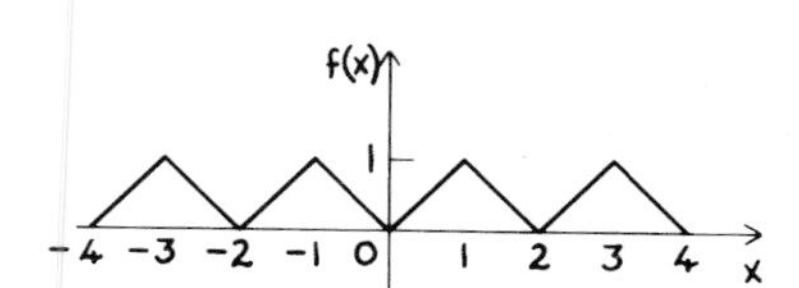

5

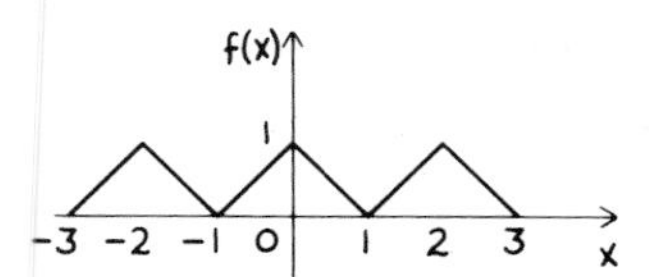

(i) $f(x) = x + 1$

(ii) $f(x) = 3 - x$

6

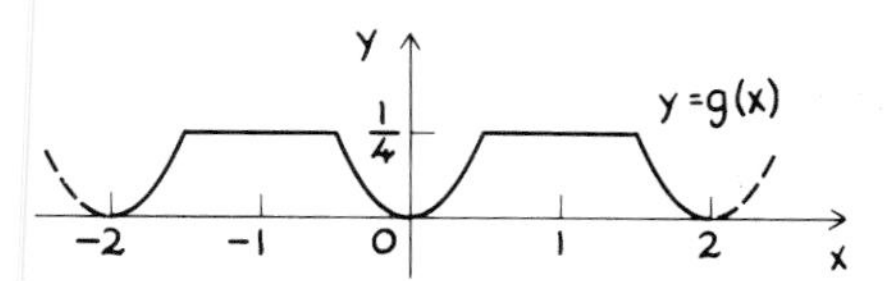

7 **(i)** **(a)** 2

(b) $f(x) = x + 1$ for $-1 \leqslant x \leqslant 0$;

$f(x) = 1 - x$ for $0 \leqslant x \leqslant 1$

(ii) **(a)** $A_1(0, 1)$; $B_1\left(\frac{1}{2}, 0\right)$; $C_1(1, 1)$; $D_1\left(1\frac{1}{2}, 0\right)$

(b) $A_2(-3, 1)$; $B_2(-2, 0)$; $C_2(-1, 1)$; $D_2(0, 0)$.

8

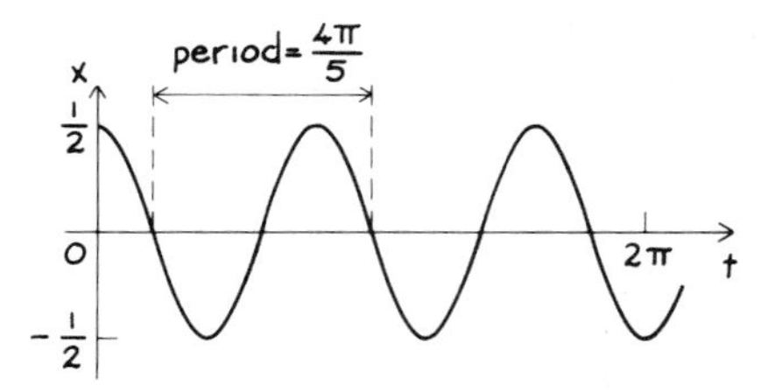

9 **(i)** $f(x) \geqslant 18$; Range of $g(x) = \mathbb{R}$;

$g(x)$ is one-to-one; $g^{-1}(x) = \dfrac{x+1}{2}$

(ii) $gf(x) = 2x^2 + 35$;

$fg(x) = 4x^2 - 4x + 19$

(iii) $x = 4$ or -2

(iv)

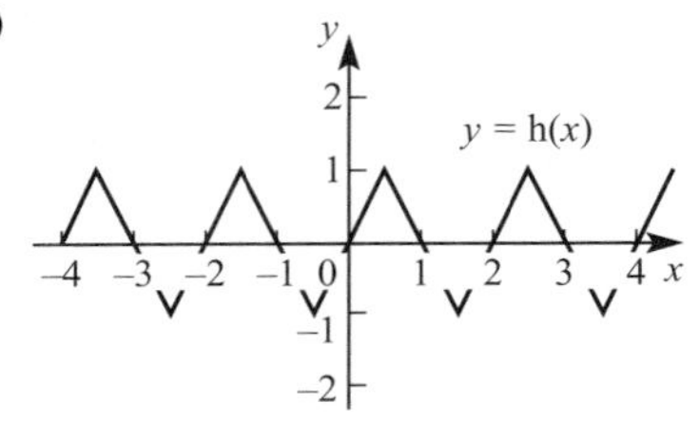

(v)

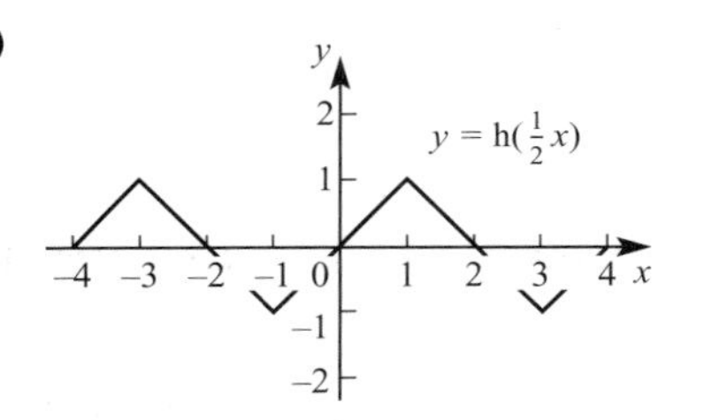

(vi)

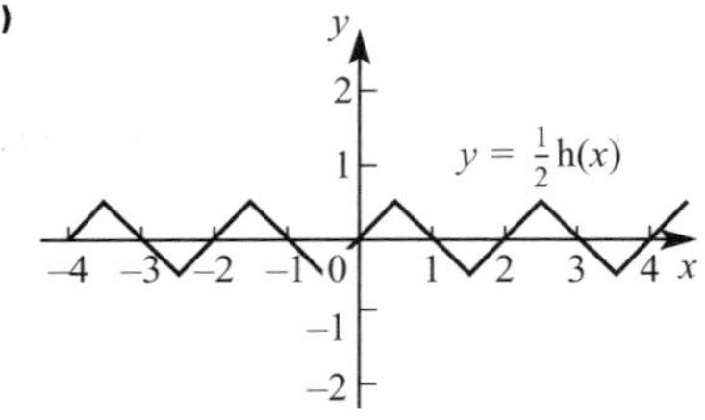

? (Page 57)

$g(3) = 3$, $g(-3) = 3$

$|3 + 3| = 6$, $|3 - 3| = 0$, $|3| + |3| = 6$, $|3| + |-3| = 6$

? (Page 58)

$|x| < 2$ and $x \geqslant 0 \Rightarrow 0 \leqslant x < 2$

$|x| < 2$ and $x < 0 \Rightarrow -2 < x < 0$

Exercise 3F (Page 59)

1 **(i)** $-8 < x < 2$

(ii) $0 \leqslant x \leqslant 4$

(iii) $x < -1$ or $x > 11$

(iv) $x \leqslant -3$ or $x \geqslant 1$

(v) $-2 < x < 5$

(vi) $-\frac{2}{3} \leqslant x \leqslant 2$

2 **(i)** $|x - 1| < 2$

(ii) $|x - 5| < 3$

(iii) $|x - 1| < 3$

(iv) $|x - 2.5| < 3.5$

(v) $|x - 10| < 0.1$

(vi) $|x - 4| < 3.5$

3 **(i)**

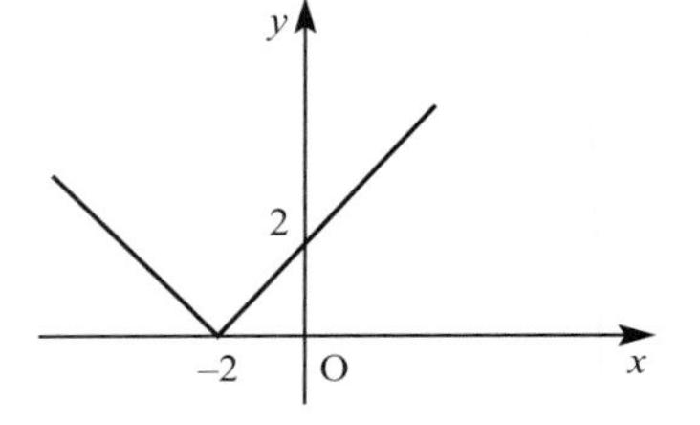

(ii)

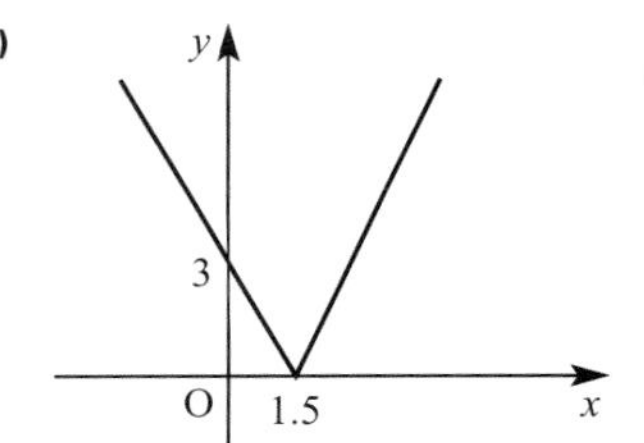

(iii)

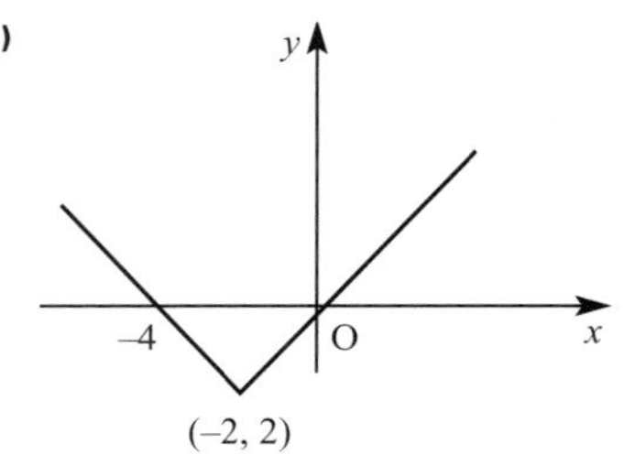

(iv)

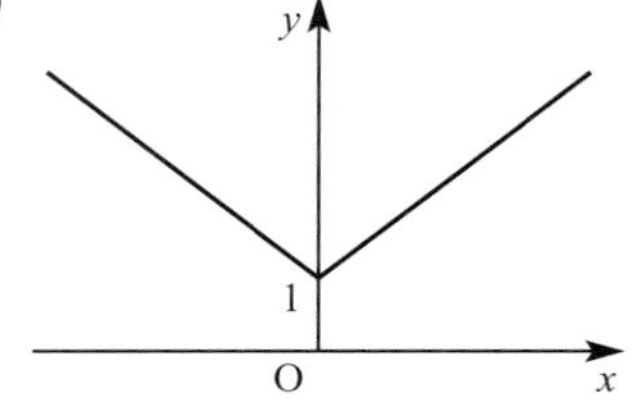

(v)

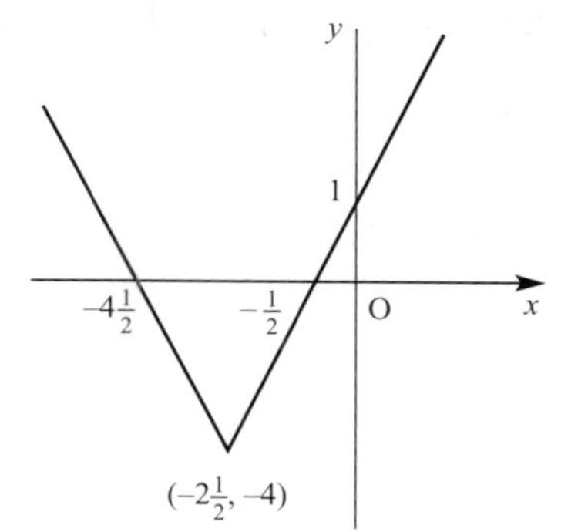

(vi)

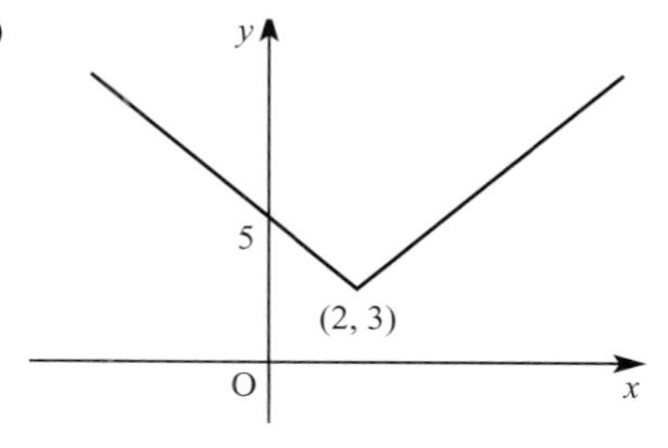

Activity 3.5 (Page 60)

1

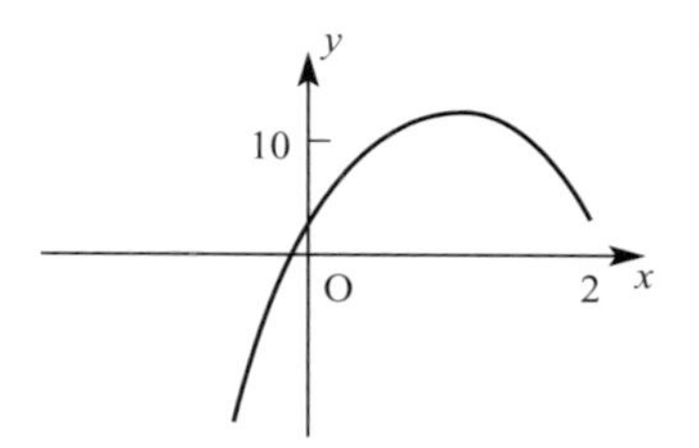

(i) one

(ii) two

(iii)

(iv) Increase x max. to 15

Decrease y min. to -300

2

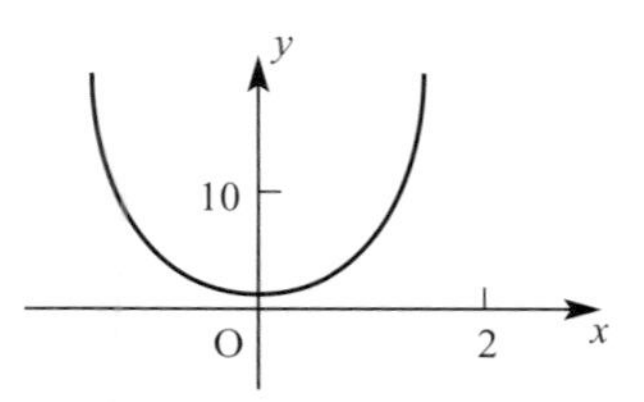

(i) one

(ii) three

(iii)

(iv) x min.: -0.4 $\quad$ x max.: 0.4

y min.: 0.9 $\quad$ y max.: 1.1

3

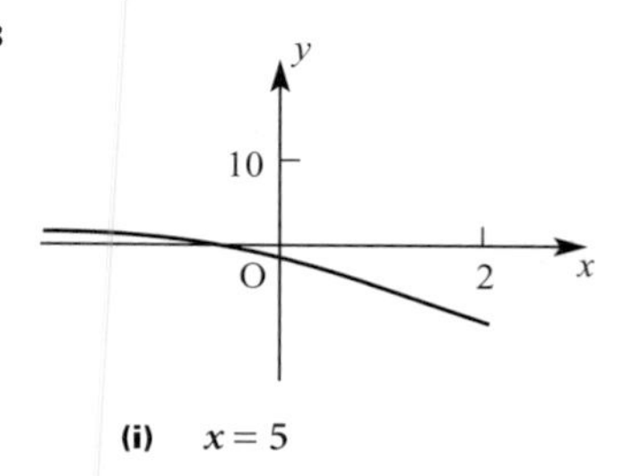

(i) $x = 5$

Investigation (page 61)

$\mathrm{f}(x) = 0 \Leftrightarrow \dfrac{1}{\mathrm{f}(x)}$ has an asymptote and $\mathrm{f}(x)$ has an asymptote $\Leftrightarrow \dfrac{1}{\mathrm{f}(x)} = 0$

$\mathrm{f}(x) = 1 \Leftrightarrow \dfrac{1}{\mathrm{f}(x)} = 1$ and $\mathrm{f}(x) = -1 \Leftrightarrow \dfrac{1}{\mathrm{f}(x)} = -1$

$|\,\mathrm{f}(x)\,| < 1 \Leftrightarrow \dfrac{1}{|\,\mathrm{f}(x)\,|} > 1$

Chapter 4

? (Page 63)

$\dfrac{\mathrm{d}V}{\mathrm{d}h}$ is the rate of change of the volume with respect to the height of the sand.

$\dfrac{\mathrm{d}h}{\mathrm{d}t}$ is the rate of change of the height of the sand with respect to time.

$\dfrac{\mathrm{d}V}{\mathrm{d}h} \times \dfrac{\mathrm{d}h}{\mathrm{d}t}$ is the rate of change of the volume with respect to time.

P (Page 65)

$$\begin{aligned} y &= (x^2 - 2)^4 \\ &= (x^2)^4 + 4(x^2)^3(-2) + 6(x^2)^2(-2)^2 + 4(x^2)(-2)^3 + (-2)^4 \\ &= x^8 - 8x^6 + 24x^4 - 32x^2 + 16 \end{aligned}$$

$$\begin{aligned} \frac{\mathrm{d}y}{\mathrm{d}x} &= 8x^7 - 48x^5 + 96x^3 - 64x \\ &= 8x(x^6 - 6x^4 + 12x^2 - 8) \\ &= 8x(x^2 - 2)(x^4 - 4x^2 + 4) \\ &= 8x(x^2 - 2)(x^2 - 2)^2 \\ &= 8x(x^2 - 2)^3 \end{aligned}$$

Exercise 4A (Page 67)

1 **(i)** $3(x+2)^2$

(ii) $8(2x+3)^3$

(iii) $6x(x^2-5)^2$

(iv) $15x^2(x^3+4)^4$

(v) $-3(3x+2)^{-2}$

(vi) $\dfrac{-6x}{(x^2-3)^4}$

(vii) $3x(x^2-1)^{\frac{1}{2}}$

(viii) $3\left(\dfrac{1}{x}+x\right)^2\left(1-\dfrac{1}{x^2}\right)$

(ix) $\dfrac{2}{\sqrt{x}}(\sqrt{x}-1)^3$

2 **(i)** $9(3x-5)^2$

(ii) $y = 9x - 17$

3 **(i)** $8(2x-1)^3$

(ii) $\left(\frac{1}{2}, 0\right)$, minimum

(iii)

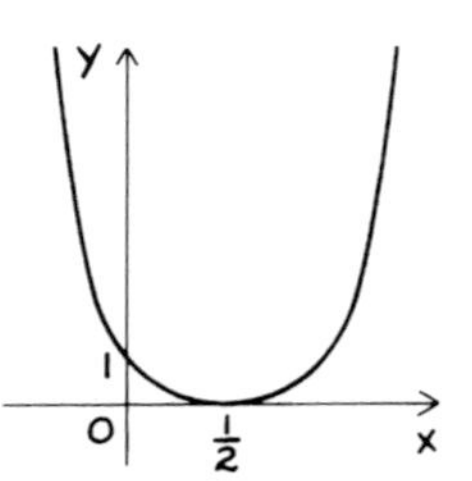

4 **(i)** $6x(x^2-4)^2$

(ii) $(0, -64)$, minimum;

$(-2, 0)$ point of inflection;

$(2, 0)$, point of inflection.

(iii)

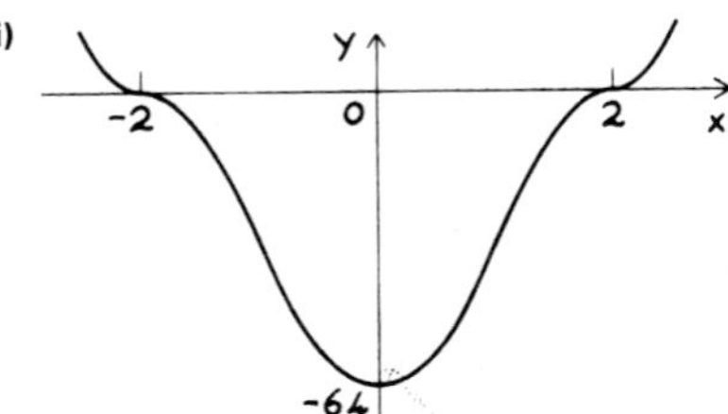

5 **(i)** $4(2x-1)(x^2-x-2)^3$

(ii) $(-1, 0)$, minimum;

$\left(\frac{1}{2}, \frac{6561}{256}\right)$, maximum;

$(2, 0)$, minimum

(iii)

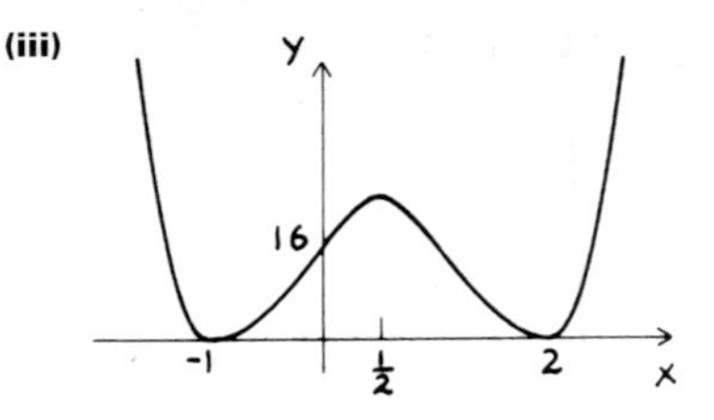

6 $4\ \text{cm}^2\,\text{s}^{-1}$

7 $-0.015\ \text{Ns}^{-1}$

8 $\frac{\pi}{10}\ \text{m}^2\,\text{day}^{-1}$ ($= 0.314\ \text{m}^2\,\text{day}^{-1}$ to 3 s.f.)

9 **(i)** $3x(3x-2)(x^3-x^2+2)^2$

(ii) $\dfrac{dy}{dx} = 0$ when $x = -1$ and when $x = 0$.

When $x < -1$ (e.g. -1.1) $\dfrac{dy}{dx} > 0$;

when $-1 < x < 0$ (e.g. -0.5) $\dfrac{dy}{dx} > 0$

$\Rightarrow$ point of inflection at $x = -1$.

When x is just greater than 0 (e.g. 0.1)

$\dfrac{dy}{dx} < 0 \Rightarrow$ maximum point at $x = 0$.

(iii) $a = \frac{2}{3}$

(iv) Gradient at $(1, 8)$ is 12; $y = 12x - 4$.

10 $\frac{1}{8}$ km

Activity 4.1 (Page 72)

$y = \dfrac{u}{v}$ where $u = x^{10}$ and $v = x^7$

gives $\dfrac{du}{dx} = 10x^9$ and $\dfrac{dv}{dx} = 7x^6$.

Using the quotient rule,

$$\frac{dy}{dx} = \frac{v\frac{du}{dx} - u\frac{dv}{dx}}{v^2}$$

$$= \frac{x^7 \times 10x^9 - x^{10} \times 7x^6}{x^{14}}$$

$$= \frac{10x^{16} - 7x^{16}}{x^{14}} = 3x^2$$

$$y = \frac{u}{v} = \frac{x^{10}}{x^7} = x^3 \Rightarrow \frac{dy}{dx} = 3x^2.$$

Exercise 4B (Page 73)

1 **(i)** $x(5x^3 - 3x + 6)$

(ii) $x^4(21x^2 + 24x - 35)$

(iii) $2x(6x + 1)(2x + 1)^3$

(iv) $-\dfrac{2}{(3x-1)^2}$

(v) $\dfrac{x^2(x^2+3)}{(x^2+1)^2}$

(vi) $2(2x + 1)(12x^2 + 3x - 8)$

(vii) $\dfrac{2(1+6x-2x^2)}{(2x^2+1)^2}$

(viii) $\dfrac{7-x}{(x+3)^3}$

(ix) $\dfrac{3x-1}{2\sqrt{x-1}}$

2 **(i)** $-\dfrac{1}{(x-1)^2}$ **(ii)** -1; $y = -x$

(iii) -1; $y = -x + 4$

(iv) The two tangents are parallel.

3 **(i)** $3x(x - 2)$

(ii) $(0, 4)$, maximum; $(2, 0)$, minimum

(iii)

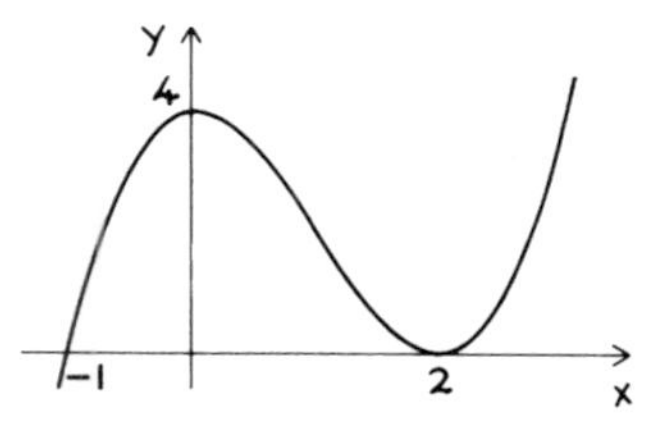

4 **(i)** $-\dfrac{1}{(x-4)^2}$ **(ii)** $4y + x = 12$

(iii) $y = x - 3$

(iv) $\dfrac{dy}{dx} \neq 0$ for any value of x

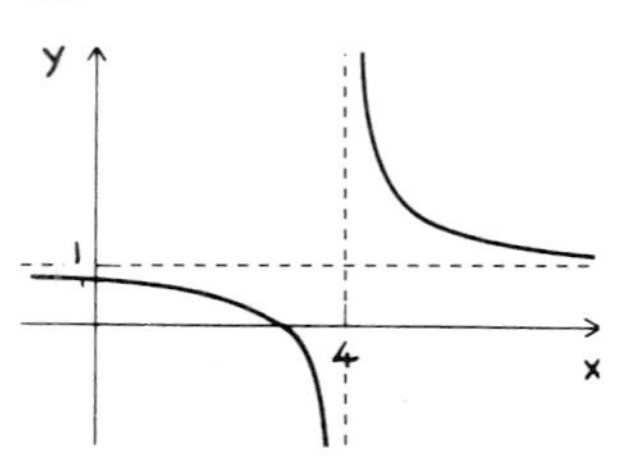

5 **(i)** $3(4x + 1)(x + 1)^2(2x - 1)^2$

(ii) $x = -1$, point of inflection;

$x = -\frac{1}{4}$, minimum;

$x = \frac{1}{2}$, point of inflection

(iii) $P(-1, 0)$; $Q\left(-\frac{1}{4}, -\frac{729}{512}\right)$; $R\left(\frac{1}{2}, 0\right)$

6 **(i)** $\dfrac{\sqrt{x}-2}{(\sqrt{x}-1)^2}$

(ii) $\frac{1}{4}$

(iii) $(4, 8)$

(iv) Tangent: $y = 8$; normal: $x = 4$

(v) **(a)** $Q\left(\frac{37}{4}, 8\right)$

(b) $R(4, 29)$

7 **(i)** $\dfrac{2(x+1)(x+2)}{(2x+3)^2}$

(ii) $(-1, -2)$; $(-2, -3)$

(iii) $(-1, -2)$, minimum; $(-2, -3)$, maximum

8 **(i)** $\dfrac{2x(x+1)}{(2x+1)^2}$; $(0, 0)$ and $(-1, -1)$

(ii) $(0, 0)$ minimum; $(-1, -1)$ maximum

9 **(i)** $\dfrac{dx}{dy} = 2y$

(ii) $y = \pm(x-4)^{\frac{1}{2}}$

(iii) $\dfrac{dy}{dx} = \pm\dfrac{1}{2(x-4)^{\frac{1}{2}}}$

(v) $x > 4$

10 **(i)** 0; 2; 1.6

(ii) $(1, 2)$

(iii) $f(x) \to 0$

(iv)

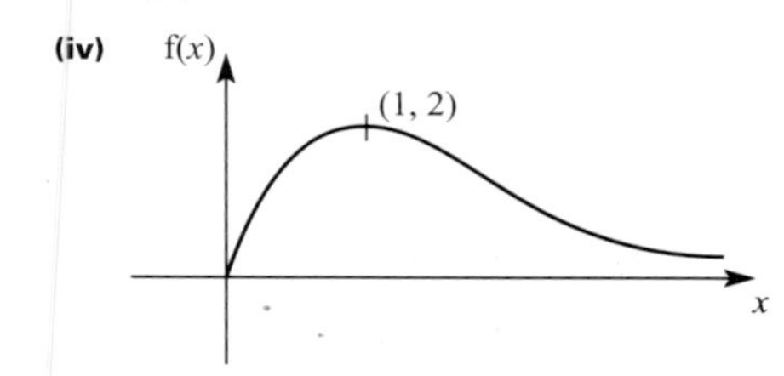

(v)

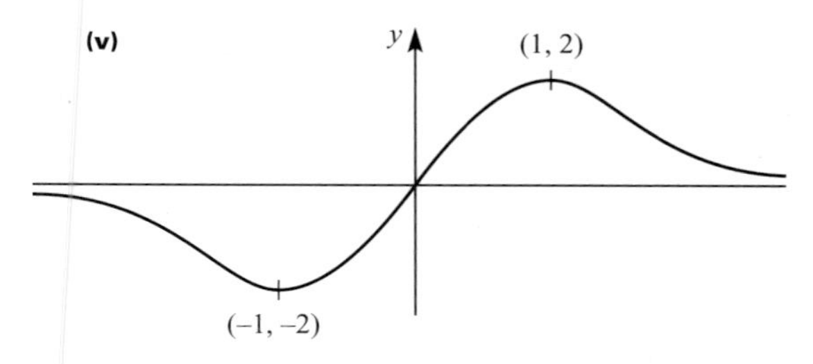

11 **(i)** $P(-1, 0)$; $Q(1, 0)$; $R(0, 1)$; $f(x) \to -1$

(ii) The y axis is the line of symmetry of the graph.

(iii) For any value a, $f'(a)$ and $f'(-a)$ have the same magnitude and opposite signs.

(iv) $\left(-\dfrac{1}{\sqrt{3}}, \dfrac{1}{2}\right)$; $\left(\dfrac{1}{\sqrt{3}}, \dfrac{1}{2}\right)$; points of inflection

12 **(i)** $\frac{3\sqrt{2}}{2}$

(iii) $\frac{3}{2}$; 3; gradient = ∞

Activity 4.2 (Page 77)

1 $\frac{dy}{dx} = 3x^2$

2 $x = \sqrt[3]{y} \Rightarrow \frac{dx}{dy} = \frac{1}{3}y^{-\frac{2}{3}} = \frac{1}{3y^{\frac{2}{3}}}$

3 $\frac{dx}{dy} = \frac{1}{3(x^3)^{\frac{2}{3}}} = \frac{1}{3x^2}$

4 $\frac{dy}{dx} \times \frac{dx}{dy} = 1$ or $\frac{dx}{dy} = \frac{1}{\frac{dy}{dx}}$

5 $y = 2x$: $\frac{dy}{dx} = 2$, $\frac{dx}{dy} = \frac{1}{2}$;

$y = x^2$: $\frac{dy}{dx} = 2x$, $\frac{dx}{dy} = \frac{1}{2x}$

$y = x^4$: $\frac{dy}{dx} = 4x^3$, $\frac{dx}{dy} = \frac{1}{4x^3}$

6 As for 4.

(P) (Page 78)

$\frac{dy}{dx} = \frac{1}{2}$ and $\frac{dx}{dy} = 2$; No

Exercise 4C (Page 80)

1 **(i)** 0.16 cm min^{-1}

2 **(i)**

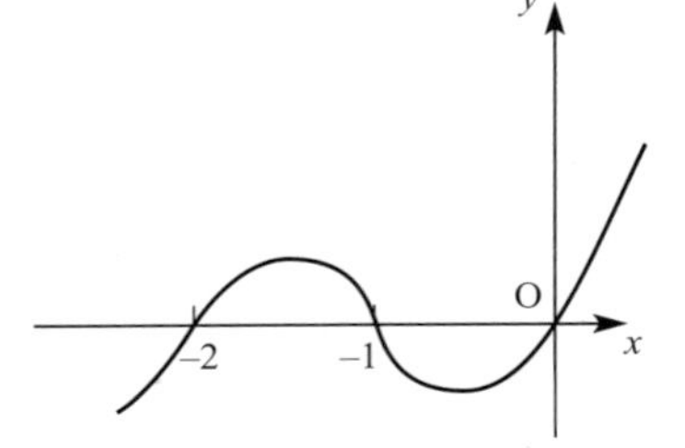

(ii)

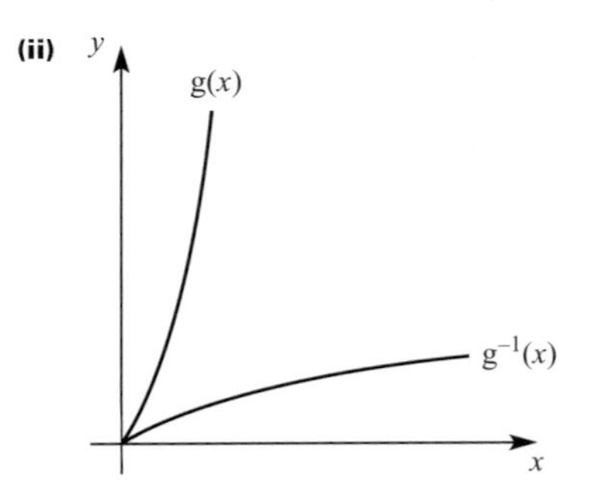

(iii) 26; $\frac{1}{26}$

3 $\frac{1}{3\pi}$ cm s^{-1}

4 **(i)** 3.2π (≈ 10.5) cm^3 s^{-1}

(ii) 0.8 cm s^{-1}

5 **(i)** $x = 0, 2\frac{2}{3}$

(iii)

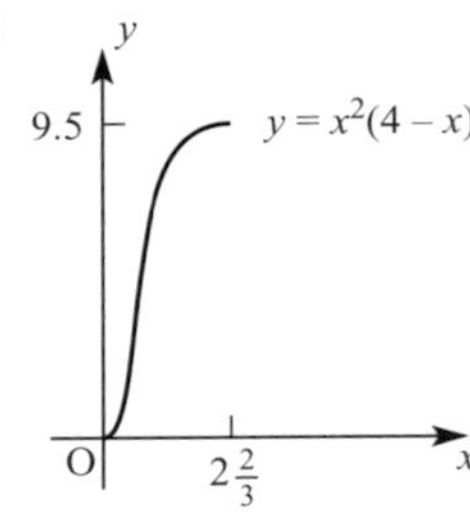

(iv) $\frac{4}{13}$

6 **(i)** **(a)**

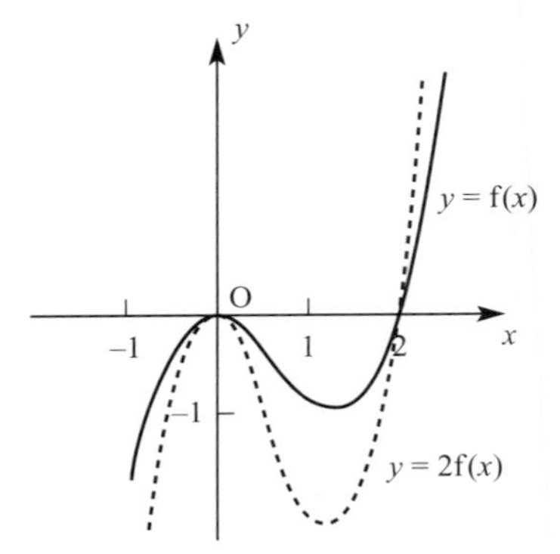

(b)

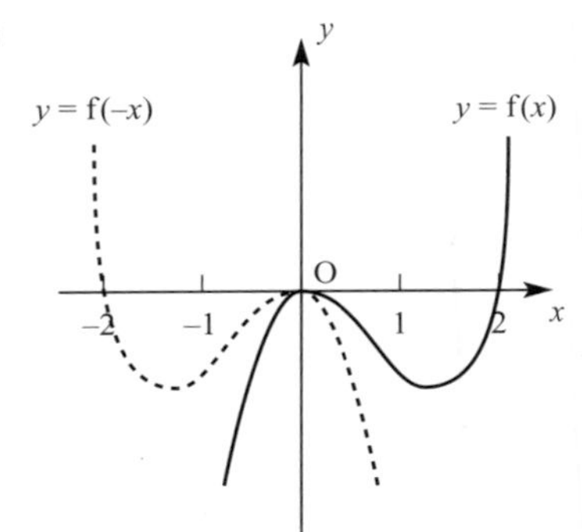

(c)

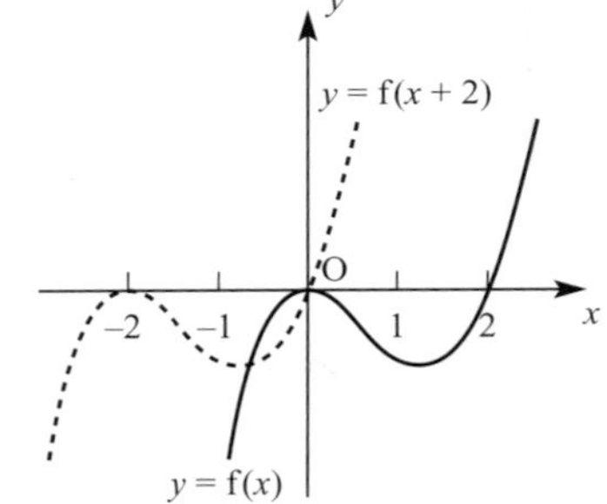

(ii) Not one-to-one

(iii)

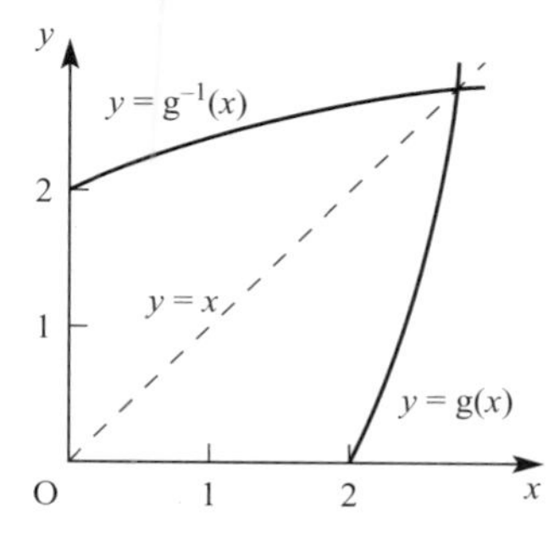

(iv) $15;\ \frac{1}{15}$

Activity 4.3 (Page 82)

(i) $z = x^p \Rightarrow \frac{\mathrm{d}z}{\mathrm{d}x} = px^{p-1}$

$z = y^q \Rightarrow \frac{\mathrm{d}z}{\mathrm{d}y} = qy^{q-1}$

(ii)
$$\frac{\mathrm{d}y}{\mathrm{d}x} = \frac{\mathrm{d}y}{\mathrm{d}z} \times \frac{\mathrm{d}z}{\mathrm{d}x}$$
$$= \frac{1}{qy^{q-1}} \times px^{p-1}$$
$$= \frac{1}{q\left(x^{\frac{p}{q}}\right)^{q-1}} \times px^{p-1}$$
$$= \frac{1}{qx^{p-\frac{p}{q}}} \times px^{p-1}$$
$$= \frac{p}{q}x^{p-1} \times x^{-p+\frac{p}{q}}$$
$$= \frac{p}{q}\,x^{\frac{p}{q}-1}$$

p (Page 82)

Direct argument

p (Page 83)

$\frac{\mathrm{d}}{\mathrm{d}x}(\mathrm{f}(x))$ is a polynomial of order $(n-1)$ so it has no term in x^n.

? (Page 85)

$y = \ln(3x)$ is a translation of $y = \ln(x)$ through $\begin{pmatrix}0\\3\end{pmatrix}$.

The curves have the same shape.

Exercise 4D (Page 86)

1 **(i)** $\frac{3}{x}$ **(ii)** $\frac{1}{x}$

(iii) $\frac{2}{x}$ **(iv)** $\frac{2x}{x^2+1}$

(v) $-\frac{1}{x}$

(vi) $1 + \ln x$

(vii) $x(1 + 2\ln(4x))$

(viii) $-\frac{1}{x(x+1)}$

(ix) $\frac{x}{x^2-1}$

(x) $\frac{1 - 2\ln x}{x^3}$

2 **(i)** $3\mathrm{e}^x$

(ii) $2\mathrm{e}^{2x}$

(iii) $2x\mathrm{e}^{x^2}$

(iv) $2(x+1)\mathrm{e}^{(x+1)^2}$

(v) $\mathrm{e}^{4x}(1 + 4x)$

(vi) $2x^2\mathrm{e}^{-x}(3 - x)$

(vii) $\frac{1-x}{\mathrm{e}^x}$

(viii) $6\mathrm{e}^{2x}(\mathrm{e}^{2x} + 1)^2$

3 **(i)** $0.108\mathrm{e}^{0.9t}$

(ii) $0.108\,\mathrm{m\,h^{-1}}$; $0.266\,\mathrm{m\,h^{-1}}$; $0.653\,\mathrm{m\,h^{-1}}$; $1.61\,\mathrm{m\,h^{-1}}$

4 **(i)** $\frac{\mathrm{d}y}{\mathrm{d}x} = (1 + x)\mathrm{e}^x$;

$\frac{\mathrm{d}^2y}{\mathrm{d}x^2} = (2 + x)\mathrm{e}^x$

(ii) $\left(-1, -\frac{1}{\mathrm{e}}\right)$

5 **(i)** Rotation symmetry, centre $(0, 0)$ of order 2. $\mathrm{f}(x)$ is an odd function since $\mathrm{f}(-x) = -\mathrm{f}(x)$.

(ii) $\mathrm{f}'(x) = 2 + \ln(x^2)$; $\mathrm{f}''(x) = \frac{2}{x}$

(iii) $\left(-\frac{1}{\mathrm{e}}, \frac{2}{\mathrm{e}}\right)$, maximum; $\left(\frac{1}{\mathrm{e}}, -\frac{2}{\mathrm{e}}\right)$, minimum.

6 **(i)** $\frac{\mathrm{e}^x(x-1)}{x^2}$

(ii) (l, e), minimum

(iii)

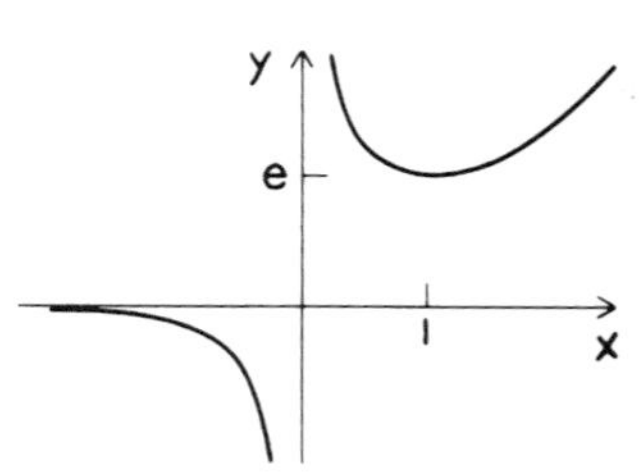

7 **(i)** $y = \ln x \Rightarrow \frac{\mathrm{d}y}{\mathrm{d}x} = \frac{1}{x}$;

$y = x\ln x \Rightarrow \frac{\mathrm{d}y}{\mathrm{d}x} = 1 + \ln x$

8 (i) $(1-x)e^{-x}$

(ii) $\left(1, \frac{1}{e}\right)$

9 (i) (a) $\frac{dP}{dt} = Ake^{kt}$; $A = 3$, $k = 2$

(b) $t = \ln 2$

(c) Increases without bound.

(ii) (a) $\frac{dP}{dt} = 3(a - 2bt)e^{(at - bt^2)}$; $a = 2$; $b = 0.1$

(b) Reduces to zero.

10 (i) $\ln m = -bt + \ln a$

(ii) $a = 20$; $b = 0.4$

(iii) $t = 19.0$

(iv) $-0.3pe^{-0.3t} - 0.2qe^{-0.2t}$

(v) $p = 6$, $q = 11$

11 (ii) $f'(x) = 1 - \ln x$; $f''(x) = -\frac{1}{x}$

(iii) (e, e)

(iv) $g(x) \leqslant e$

(v) $g(x)$ is a one-to-one function.

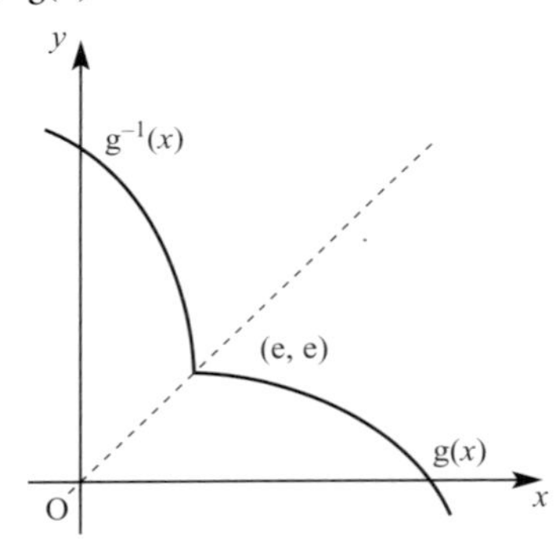

gradient = −0.5

12 (i) $(1, e^2)$

(ii) (a) Translation $\begin{pmatrix}1\\0\end{pmatrix}$; $(2, e^2)$

(b) Reflection in the y axis; $(-1, e^2)$

(c) Stretch, scale factor $\frac{1}{2}$ parallel to the x axis; $\left(\frac{1}{2}, e^2\right)$

(iii) $k = e^{-2}$

13 (i) 1

(ii) $f'(x) = \frac{1 - \ln x}{x^2}$; $f''(x) = \frac{2\ln x - 3}{x^3}$

(iii) $\frac{1}{e}$; $-\frac{1}{e^3}$

14 (i) $A(-\sqrt{3}, 0)$; $C(0, -3)$; $D(\sqrt{3}, 0)$

(iii) $B(-1, -2e)$; $E(3, 6e^{-3})$

(iv)

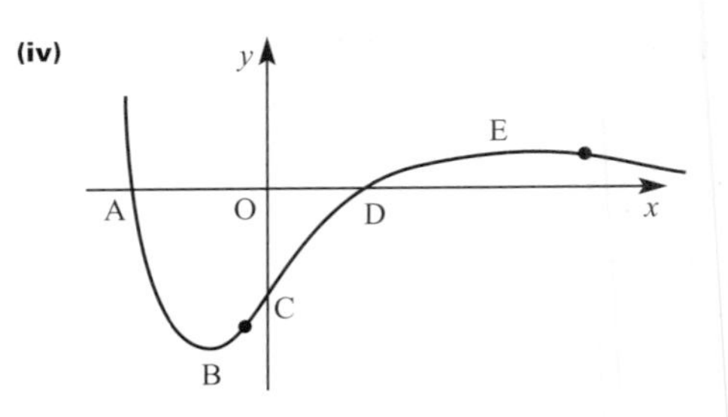

Activity 4.4 (Page 91)

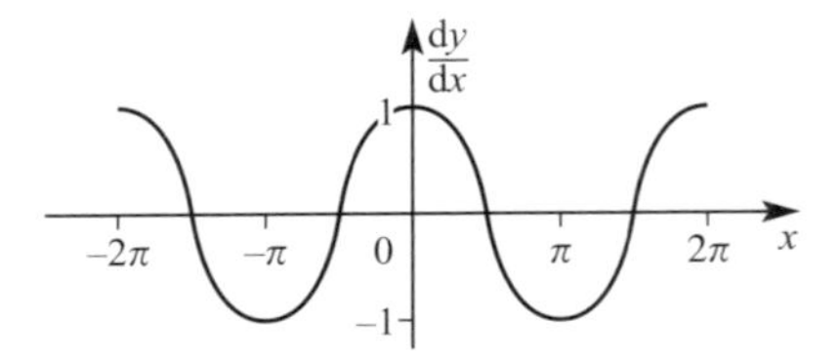

When $y = \sin x$ the graph of $\frac{dy}{dx}$ against x looks like the graph of $\cos x$.

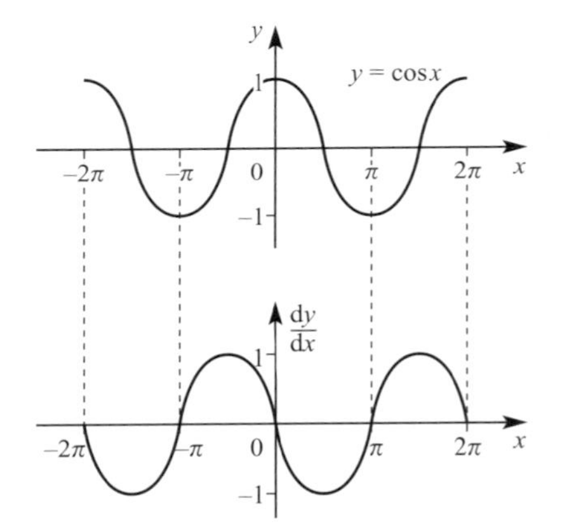

? (Page 92)

No. You can see this if you sketch both on a graphic calculator.

P (Page 92)

This is a demonstration but 'looking like' is not the same as proof.

Activity 4.5 (Page 93)

$$y = \tan x = \frac{\sin x}{\cos x}$$

$$\frac{dy}{dx} = \frac{\cos x(\cos x) - \sin x(-\sin x)}{\cos^2 x}$$

$$= \frac{\cos^2 x + \sin^2 x}{\cos^2 x} = \frac{1}{\cos^2 x}$$

Exercise 4E (Page 95)

1 **(i)** $-2\sin x + \cos x$

(ii) $\dfrac{1}{\cos^2 x}$

(iii) $\cos x + \sin x$

2 **(i)** $\dfrac{x}{\cos^2 x} + \tan x$

(ii) $\cos^2 x - \sin^2 x$

(iii) $e^x(\sin x + \cos x)$

3 **(i)** $\dfrac{x\cos x - \sin x}{x^2}$

(ii) $\dfrac{e^x(\cos x + \sin x)}{\cos^2 x}$

(iii) $\dfrac{\sin x(1 - \sin x) - \cos x(x + \cos x)}{\sin^2 x}$

4 **(i)** $\dfrac{2x}{\cos^2(x^2+1)}$

(ii) $-2\sin x\cos x$

(iii) $\dfrac{1}{\tan x}$

5 **(i)** $-\dfrac{\sin x}{2\sqrt{\cos x}}$

(ii) $e^x\left(\tan x + \dfrac{1}{\cos^2 x}\right)$

(iii) $8x\cos 4x^2$

(iv) $-2\sin 2x e^{\cos 2x}$

(v) $\dfrac{1}{1+\cos x}$

(vi) $\dfrac{1}{\sin x\cos x}$

6 **(i)** $\cos x - x\sin x$

(ii) -1

(iii) $y = -x$

(iv) $y = x - 2\pi$

7 **(i)** $3\cos x\sin^2 x$

(ii) $(-\pi, 0)$ point of inflection, $(-\frac{1}{2}\pi, -1)$ min,
$(0, 0)$ point of inflection, $(\frac{1}{2}\pi, 1)$ max,
$(\pi, 0)$ point of inflection

(iv)

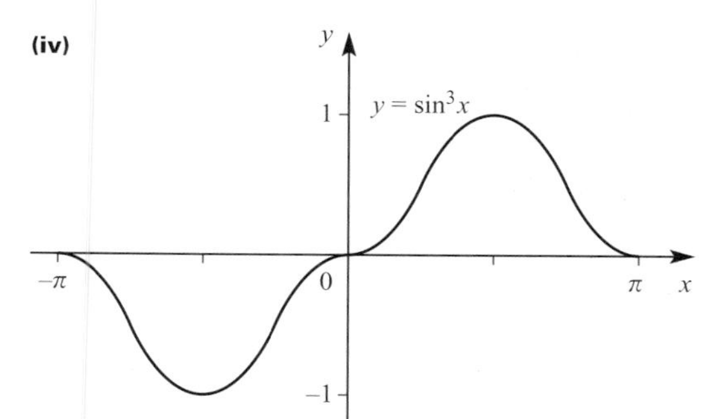

8 $\dfrac{dy}{dx} = e^x\cos 3x - 3e^x\sin 3x$

$\dfrac{d^2y}{dx^2} = -6e^x\sin 3x - 8e^x\cos 3x$

9 **(i)** $e^{-x}(\cos x - \sin x)$

(iii) $(0.79, 0.32)$, $(-2.4, -7.5)$

(iv) Differentiate with respect to x again and evaluate the second derivative at the stationary points.

? (Page 98)

(i) Interchange x and y to reflect in the line $y = x$.

(ii) The mapping is one-to-many.

Exercise 4F (Page 101)

1 **(i)** $4y^3\dfrac{dy}{dx}$

(ii) $2x + 3y^2\dfrac{dy}{dx}$

(iii) $x\dfrac{dy}{dx} + y + 1 + \dfrac{dy}{dx}$

(iv) $-\sin y\dfrac{dy}{dx}$

(v) $e^{(y+2)}\dfrac{dy}{dx}$

(vi) $y^3 + 3xy^2\dfrac{dy}{dx}$

(vii) $4xy^5 + 10x^2y^4\dfrac{dy}{dx}$

(viii) $1 + \dfrac{1}{y}\dfrac{dy}{dx}$

(ix) $xe^y\dfrac{dy}{dx} + e^y + \sin y\dfrac{dy}{dx}$

(x) $\dfrac{x^2}{y}\dfrac{dy}{dx} + 2x\ln y$

(xi) $e^{\sin y} + x\cos y e^{\sin y}\dfrac{dy}{dx}$

(xii) $\tan y + \dfrac{x}{\cos^2 y}\dfrac{dy}{dx} - (\tan x)\dfrac{dy}{dx} - \dfrac{y}{\cos^2 x}$

2 $\frac{1}{5}$

3 0

4 **(i)** 0

(ii) $y = -1$

5 $(1, -2)$ and $(-1, 2)$

6 **(i)** $\dfrac{y+4}{6-x}$

(ii) $x - 2y - 11 = 0$

(iii) $\left(2, -4\frac{1}{2}\right)$

(iv)

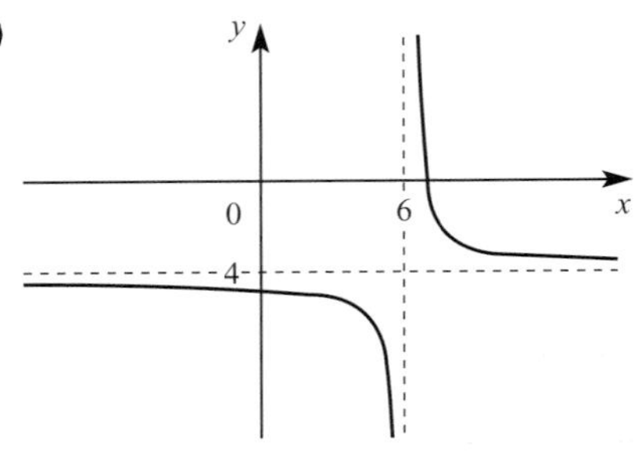

Asymptotes $x = 6$, $y = -4$

7 **(i)** $\ln y = x \ln x$

(ii) $\dfrac{1}{y}\dfrac{dy}{dx} = 1 + \ln x$

(iii) $(0.368, 0.692)$

(iv)

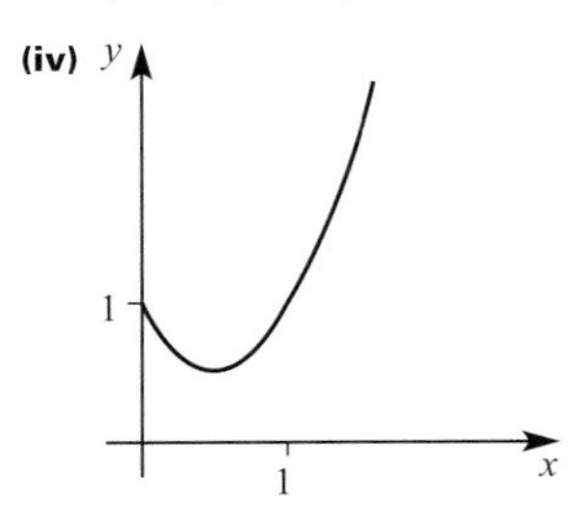

8 **(ii)** Max $(4, 8)$, min $(-4, -8)$

Chapter 5

? (Page 103)

It is the same as

$$\int_1^4 \sqrt{x}\,dx.$$

? (Page 105)

Yes: Using the chain rule

$$\frac{dy}{dx} = \frac{dy}{du} \times \frac{du}{dx}.$$

Integrating both sides with respect to x

$$y = \int\left(\frac{dy}{du} \times \frac{du}{dx}\right)dx = \int\left(\frac{dy}{du}\right)du.$$

Activity 5.1 (Page 107)

$$\tfrac{2}{5}(x-2)^{\frac{5}{2}} + \tfrac{4}{3}(x-2)^{\frac{3}{2}} + c$$

$$= \tfrac{2}{15}(x-2)^{\frac{3}{2}}\,[3(x-2) + 10] + c$$

$$= \tfrac{2}{15}(3x+4)(x-2)^{\frac{3}{2}} + c$$

Exercise 5A (Page 107)

1 **(i)** $\frac{1}{4}(x+1)^4 + c$

(ii) $\frac{2}{3}(2x-1)^{\frac{3}{2}} + c$

(iii) $\frac{1}{8}(x^3+1)^8 + c$

(iv) $\frac{1}{6}(x^2+1)^6 + c$

(v) $\frac{1}{5}(x^3-2)^5 + c$

(vi) $\frac{1}{6}(2x^2-5)^{\frac{3}{2}} + c$

(vii) $\frac{1}{15}(2x+1)^{\frac{3}{2}}(3x-1) + c$

(viii) $\frac{2}{3}(x+9)^{\frac{1}{2}}(x-18) + c$

2 **(i)** 205

(ii) 928 000

(iii) $5\frac{1}{3}$

(iv) 30

(v) 222 000

(vi) 586

(vii) 18.1

3 **(i)** 4

(ii) -4; the graph has rotational symmetry about $(2, 0)$.

4 **(i)** 5.2

(ii) 1.6

(iii) 6.8

(iv) Because region B is below the x axis, so the integral for this part is negative.

5 **(i)** 4

(ii) $2\frac{2}{3}$

(iii) $22\frac{1}{2}$

(iv) $1\frac{1}{9}$

6 **(i)** $A(-1, 0)$: $x \geqslant -1$

7 **(i)** **(a)** $\dfrac{(1+x)^4}{4} + c$

(b) $2\frac{2}{5}$

(ii) $\frac{1}{3}(2\sqrt{2} - 1) \approx 0.609$

8 Area $= 2(\sqrt{2} - 1) \approx 0.828$

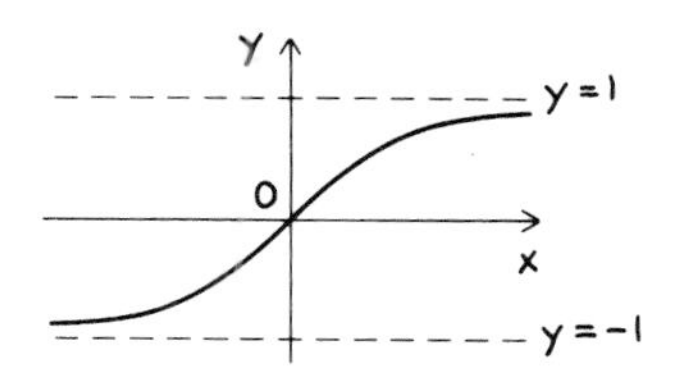

9 **(i)** $14(2x-1)^6$

(ii) $x = \frac{1}{16}$

(iii) $\frac{1}{72}$ square units

(iv) $\frac{1}{60}$

10 **(i)** **(a)** $8\sqrt{x} - \dfrac{3}{2x^2} + c$

(b) $2(1+x^2)^{\frac{3}{2}} + c$

(ii) $k = 2, a = 1, b = 2$; 32.5

Activity 5.2 (Page 113)

1 The areas of the two shaded regions are equal since $y = \dfrac{1}{x}$ is an odd function.

p (Page 114)

The denominator will contain a function of x that can take the value zero.

$x^2 - 2x + 3 = (x-1)^2 + 2$ so is defined for all values of x and is always greater than or equal to 2.

Exercise 5B (Page 114)

1 **(i)** $3\ln|x| + c$

(ii) $\frac{1}{4}\ln|x| + c$

(iii) $\ln|x-5| + c$

(iv) $\frac{1}{2}\ln|2x-9| + c$

(v) $\ln|x^2+1| + c$

(vi) $\frac{1}{3}\ln|3x^2+9x-1| + c$

2 **(i)** $\frac{1}{3}e^{3x} + c$ **(ii)** $-\frac{1}{4}e^{-4x} + c$

(iii) $-3e^{-\frac{x}{3}} + c$ **(iv)** $4e^{x^3} + c$

(v) $-\dfrac{2}{e^{5x}} + c$ **(vi)** $e^x - 2e^{-2x} + c$

3 **(i)** $2(e^8 - 1) = 5960$ **(ii)** $\ln\frac{49}{9} = 1.69$

(iii) 0.018 **(iv)** 4.70

(v) 0.906 **(vi)** $\frac{1}{2}\ln\frac{29}{9} = 0.585$

4 **(i)** $\frac{1}{2}(e - 1)$

(ii) $\frac{1}{2}(e^4 - 1)$

(iii) $\frac{1}{2}(e + e^4) - 1 = 27.7$ (to 3 s.f.)

5 **(i)** $(1 - 2x^2)e^{-x^2}$

(ii) $\dfrac{1}{\sqrt{2}}$

(iii) 0.294

6 0.490; 0.314

7 **(i)** P(2, 4); Q(–2, –4)

(ii) 8.77; 14.2 (to 3 s.f.)

8 **(i)** $\frac{1}{2}(1 - e^{-X^2})$

(ii) 0.3161; 0.4908; 0.4999; 0.5000

(iii) $\frac{1}{2}$

9 **(i)** $-(x+2)e^{-x}$

(ii) $(-2, e^2)$

(iii) $-e^2$; max. at $x = -2$

(v) $3 - \dfrac{4}{e}$

10 **(i)** $\frac{1}{5}(2x-3)^{\frac{5}{2}} + (2x-3)^{\frac{3}{2}} + c$

(ii) $\dfrac{\ln x + 2}{2\sqrt{x}}$; $2\sqrt{x}\ln x + c$

(iii) **(a)** $-2xe^{-x^2}$

(b) $3x^2e^{-x^6}$

11 **(i)** **(a)** $\frac{1}{2}\ln 3$

(b) $\sqrt{9+x^2} + c$

(ii) **(b)** $\left(\dfrac{1}{\sqrt{2}}, \dfrac{1}{\sqrt{2e}}\right)$ and $\left(-\dfrac{1}{\sqrt{2}}, -\dfrac{1}{\sqrt{2e}}\right)$

(c) 0.074

12 **(i)**

(ii) $\ln\left(\dfrac{e^2+1}{2}\right) \approx 1.434$

(iii) $\ln\left(\dfrac{e^2+1}{2}\right) \approx 1.434$

(iv) The same. The substitution $e^x = t^2$ transforms the integral in part **(ii)** into that in part **(iii)**.

13 **(ii)** $\frac{1}{2}\ln 2$

(iii) $-\frac{1}{2}\ln 2$

(iv) translation $\begin{pmatrix}-1\\0\end{pmatrix}$

(v) $-\frac{1}{2}\ln 2$

14 **(i)** **(a)** $-4xe^{-2x^2}$

(b) $e^{-2x^2} - 4x^2e^{-2x^2}$

(ii) $\frac{1}{4}(1 - e^{-2k^2})$

(iii) Max. at $(0.5, 0.303)$

15 **(i)** 4; $5\ln 5 - 4$

(ii) **(a)** Reflection in $y = x$

(b) Stretch scale factor 3 parallel to y axis

(iv) **(a)** $3(5\ln 5 - 4)$

(b) $4\ln 3 + 5\ln 5 - 4$

16 **(i)** 101 m

(ii) $\frac{dy}{dx} = -0.4e^{-0.08x}$; -0.4

(iii) 49.88 units^2

(iv) 40.24 units^2; 480 000 m^3(2 s.f.)

17 **(i)** $\frac{1 - x^2}{(x^2 + 1)^2}$

(ii) $\left(-1, -\frac{1}{2}\right)$ and $\left(1, \frac{1}{2}\right)$

(iii) $\frac{1}{2}\ln|x^2 + 1| + c$

(iv) 22 026

18 **(i)** $\left(0, \frac{1}{2}\right)$; $y = 1$

(ii) $\frac{e^x}{(1 + e^x)^2}$; $\frac{1}{4}$

(iii) $\ln\left(\frac{1 + e}{2}\right)$

(iv) Rotation symmetry, order 2, centre $\left(0, \frac{1}{2}\right)$

19 **(i)** Rotation symmetry, order 2, centre $(0, 0)$

(ii) $\left(1, \frac{1}{2}\right)$; $\left(-1, -\frac{1}{2}\right)$

(iii) $\frac{1}{2}\ln 2$

20 **(i)** $\frac{1}{2}$

(ii) $\left(-\frac{1}{2}, -\frac{1}{8}\right)$

Investigation (Page 122)

$a_0 = 1$

$a_1 = 1$

$a_2 = \frac{1}{2!}$

$a_3 = \frac{1}{3!}$

$a_4 = \frac{1}{4!}$

$e = 2.718\,281\,83$ (8 d.p.)

Investigation (Page 122)

Scheme B: $R = 2.594$

Scheme C: $R = 2.653$

1000 instalments: $R = 2.717$

10^4 instalments: $R = 2.718$

10^6 instalments: R agrees with the value of e to 5 d.p.

Exercise 5C (Page 125)

1 **(i)** $-\cos x - 2\sin x + c$

(ii) $3\sin x - 2\cos x + c$

(iii) $-5\cos x + 4\sin x + c$

2 **(i)** $\frac{1}{3}\sin 3x + c$

(ii) $\cos(1 - x) + c$

(iii) $-\frac{1}{4}\cos^4 x + c$

(iv) $\ln|2 - \cos x| + c$

(v) $-\ln|\cos x| + c$

(vi) $-\frac{1}{6}(\cos 2x + 1)^3 + c$

3 **(i)** $-\cos(x^2) + c$

(ii) $e^{\sin x} + c$

(iii) $\frac{1}{2}\tan^2 x + c$

(iv) $\frac{-1}{\sin x} + c$

4 **(i)** 1

(ii) $\frac{1}{16}$

(iii) 1

(iv) $e - 1$

(v) $\ln 2$

5 (i)

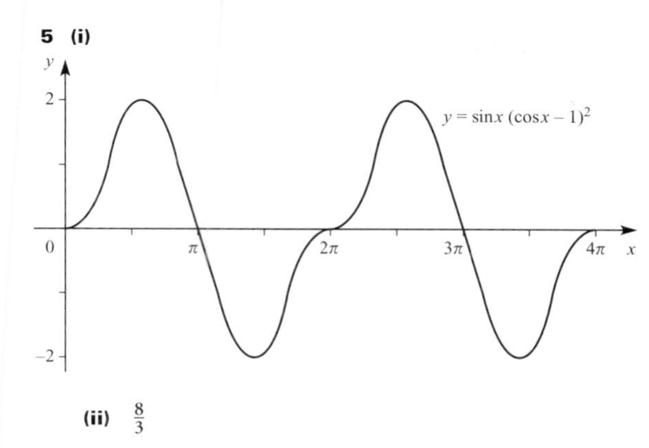

(ii) $\frac{8}{3}$

Activity 5.3 (Page 126)

(i) **(a)** $\dfrac{d}{dx}(x\cos x) = -x\sin x + \cos x$

(b) $\Rightarrow \quad x\cos x = \int -x\sin x\,dx + \int \cos x\,dx$

$\Rightarrow \quad \int x\sin x\,dx = -x\cos x + \int \cos x\,dx$

(c) $\Rightarrow \quad \int x\sin x\,dx = -x\cos x + \sin x + c$

(ii) **(a)** $\dfrac{d}{dx}(xe^{2x}) = x \times 2e^{2x} + e^{2x}$

(b) $\Rightarrow xe^{2x} = \int 2xe^{2x}\,dx + \int e^{2x}\,dx$

$\Rightarrow \int 2xe^{2x}\,dx = xe^{2x} - \int e^{2x}\,dx$

(c) $\Rightarrow \int 2xe^{2x}\,dx = xe^{2x} - \frac{1}{2}e^{2x} + c$

? (Page 126)

Each of the integrals in Activity 5.3 is of the form $\int x\dfrac{dv}{dx}\,dx$ and is found by starting with the product xv.

Exercise 5D (Page 130)

1 **(i)** **(a)** $u = x, \dfrac{dv}{dx} = e^x$

(b) $xe^x - e^x + c$

(ii) **(a)** $u = x, \dfrac{dv}{dx} = \cos 3x$

(b) $\frac{1}{3}x\sin 3x + \frac{1}{9}\cos 3x + c$

(iii) **(a)** $u = 2x + 1, \dfrac{dv}{dx} = \cos x$

(b) $(2x + 1)\sin x + 2\cos x + c$

(iv) **(a)** $u = x, \dfrac{dv}{dx} = e^{-2x}$

(b) $-\frac{1}{2}xe^{-2x} - \frac{1}{4}e^{-2x} + c$

(v) **(a)** $u = x, \dfrac{dv}{dx} = e^{-x}$

(b) $-xe^{-x} - e^{-x} + c$

(vi) **(a)** $u = x, \dfrac{dv}{dx} = \sin 2x$

(b) $-\frac{1}{2}x\cos 2x + \frac{1}{4}\sin 2x + c$

2 **(i)** $\frac{1}{4}x^4\ln x - \frac{1}{16}x^4 + c$

(ii) $xe^{3x} - \frac{1}{3}e^{3x} + c$

(iii) $x\sin 2x + \frac{1}{2}\cos 2x + c$

(iv) $\frac{1}{3}x^3\ln 2x - \frac{1}{9}x^3 + c$

3 $\frac{2}{15}(1 + x)^{\frac{3}{2}}(3x - 2) + c$

4 $\frac{1}{15}(x - 2)^5(5x + 2) + c$

5 **(i)** $x\ln x - x + c$

(ii) $x\ln 3x - x + c$

(iii) $x\ln px - x + c$

6 $x^2e^x - 2xe^x + 2e^x + c$

7 $(2 - x)^2\sin x - 2(2 - x)\cos x - 2\sin x + c$

Exercise 5E (Page 133)

1 **(i)** $\frac{2}{9}e^3 + \frac{1}{9}$

(ii) -2

(iii) $2e^2$

(iv) $3\ln 2 - 1$

(v) $\dfrac{\pi}{4}$

(vi) $\frac{64}{3}\ln 4 - 7$

2 **(i)** $(2, 0), (0, 2)$

(ii)

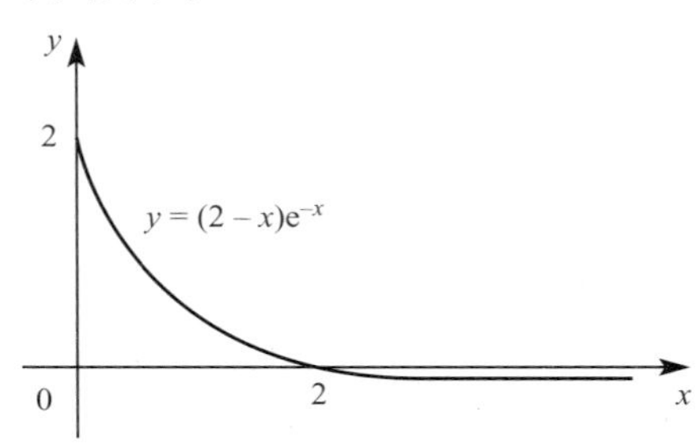

(iii) $e^{-2} + 1$

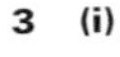

3 **(i)**

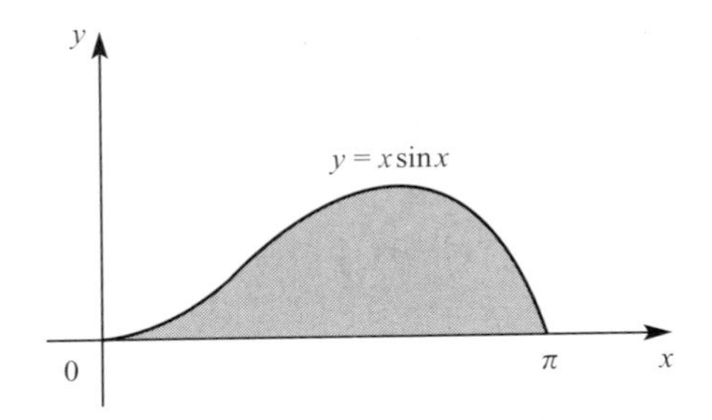

(ii) π

4 $5\ln 5 - 4$

5 1

6 $-\frac{4}{15}$ so area $= \frac{4}{15}$ square units

7 $x = 0.5$; area $= 0.134$ square units

8 The curve is below the trapezia.

9 $I_3 = 6 - 16e^{-1}$

Chapter 6

❓ (Page 135)

(i), **(ii)** and **(iv)** can be solved algebraically;

(iii) and **(v)** cannot.

❓ (Page 137)

0.012 takes 5 steps

0.385 takes 18 steps

0.989 takes 28 steps.

In general 0.abc takes (a + b + c + 2) steps.

Activity 6.1 (Page 138)

For 1 d.p., an interval length of < 0.05 is usually necessary, requiring $n = 5$. However, it depends on the position of the end points of the interval.

For example, the interval [0.25, 0.3125] obtained in 4 steps gives 0.3 (1 d.p.) but the interval [0.3125, 0.375] obtained in 4 steps is inconclusive. As are the interval [0.34375, 0.375] obtained in 5 steps, the interval [0.34375, 0.359375] obtained in 6 steps, the interval [0.34375, 0.3515625] obtained in 7 steps, etc.

In cases like this, 2 and 3 d.p. accuracy is obtained very quickly after 1 d.p.

The expected number of steps for 2 d.p., requiring an interval of length < 0.005, is 8 steps.

Activity 6.2 (Page 140)

Consider the case when $a < b$, $f(a) < 0$, $f(b) > 0$.

AB has gradient $\dfrac{f(b) - f(a)}{b - a}$

and equation

$$y - f(a) = \left(\frac{f(b) - f(a)}{b - a}\right)[x - a].$$

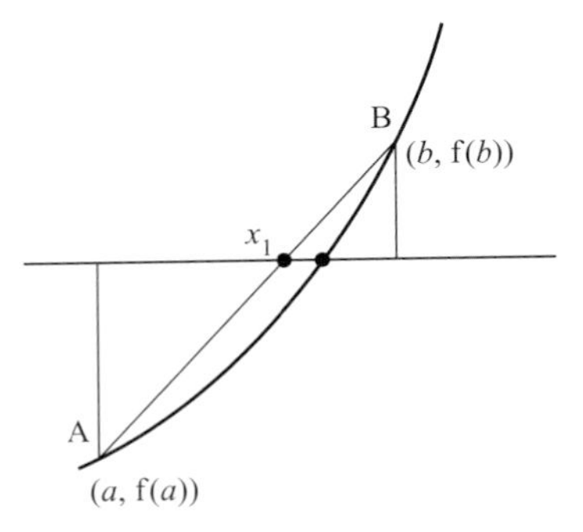

This crosses the x axis at $(x_1, 0)$

$$\Rightarrow\ -f(a) = \left(\frac{f(b) - f(a)}{b - a}\right)[x_1 - a]$$

$$\Rightarrow\ -bf(a) + af(a) = [f(b) - f(a)]x_1 - af(b) + af(a)$$

$$\Rightarrow\ af(b) - bf(a) = [f(b) - f(a)]x_1 \text{ or } x_1 = \frac{bf(a) - af(b)}{f(a) - f(b)}.$$

Exercise 6A (Page 142)

1 1.62, 1.28

2 **(i)** $[-2, -1]$; $[1, 2]$; $[4, 5]$

(ii)

(iii) -1.51, 1.24, 4.26

(iv) $a = -1.51171875$, $n = 8$

$a = 1.244384766$, $n = 12$

$a = 4.262695313$, $n = 10$

3 **(i)** $[1, 2]$; $[4, 5]$

(ii) 1.857, 4.536

4 **(ii)**

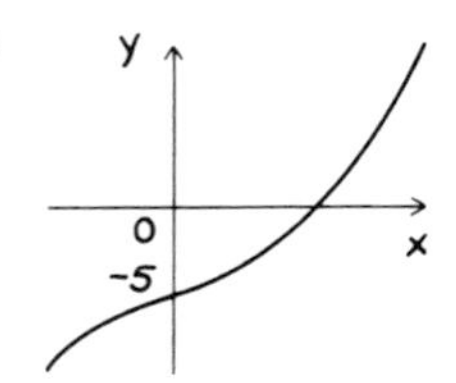

(iii) 1.154

5 **(i)** 2

(ii) [0, 1]; [1, 2]

(iii) 0.62, 1.51

6 **(i)**

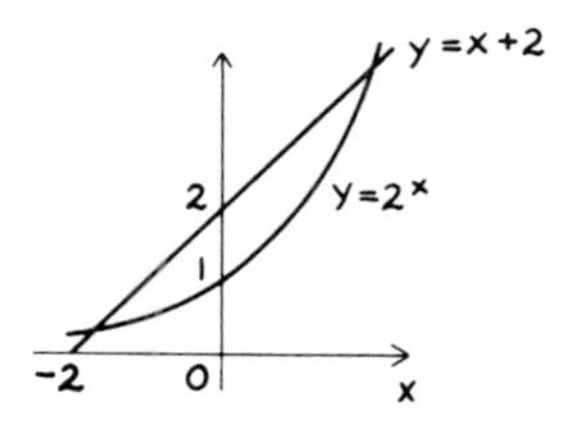

(ii) 2 roots

(iii) 2, −1.690

7 −1.88, 0.35, 1.53

8 **(i)** **(a)**

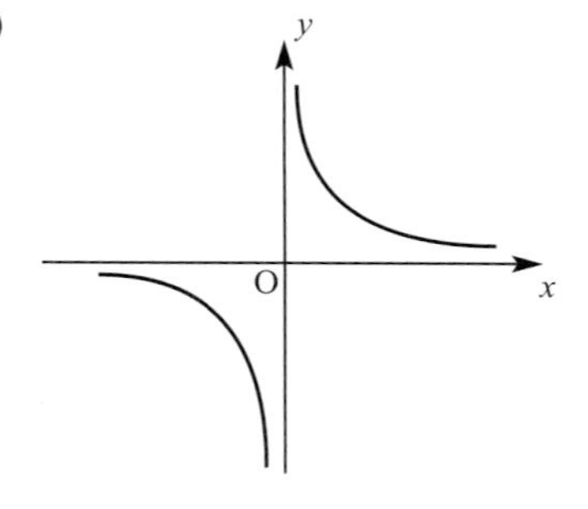

(b) No root

(c) Convergence to a non-existent root

(ii) **(a)**

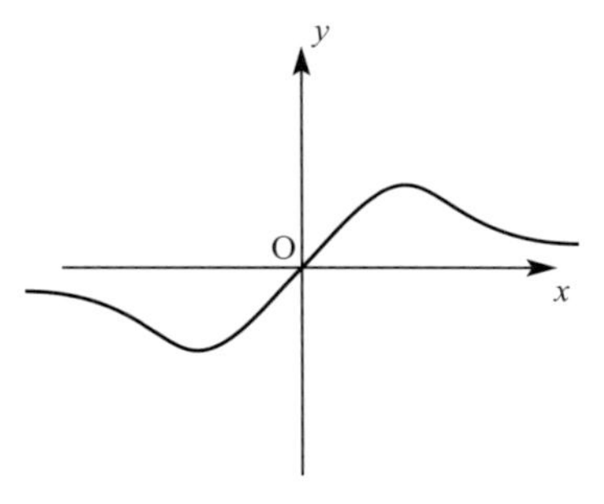

(b) $x = 0$

(c) Success

(iii) **(a)**

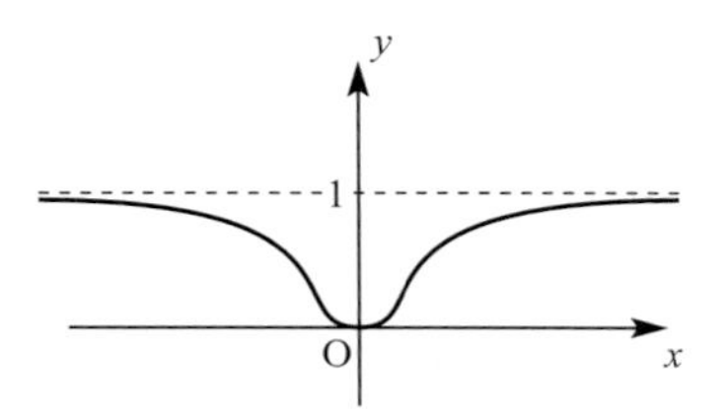

(b) $x = 0$

(c) Failure to find root

Investigation (Page 143)

(i) Converges to 0.7391 (to 4 d.p.)

since $\cos 0.7391 = 0.7391$ (to 4 d.p.).

(ii) Converges to 1.

$\sqrt{x} < x$ for $x > 1$, $\sqrt{x} > x$ for $x < 1$ and $\sqrt{1} = 1$

(iii) Converges to 1.6180 (to 4 d.p.) since this is the solution of $x = \sqrt{x+1}$ (i.e. the positive solution of $x^2 - x - 1 = 0$).

? (Page 145)

Writing $x^5 - 5x + 3 = 0$

as $x^5 - 4x + 3 = x$

gives $g(x) = x^5 - 4x + 3$

Generalising this to

$$x^5 + (n-5)x + 3 = nx$$

gives $g(x) = \dfrac{x^5 + (n-5)x + 3}{n}$

and indicates that infinitely many rearrangements are possible.

Activity 6.3 (Page 148)

$x_0 = -2$ gives divergence to $-\infty$

$x_0 = -1$ gives convergence to 0.618

$x_0 = 1$ gives convergence to 0.618

$x_0 = 2$ gives divergence to $+\infty$.

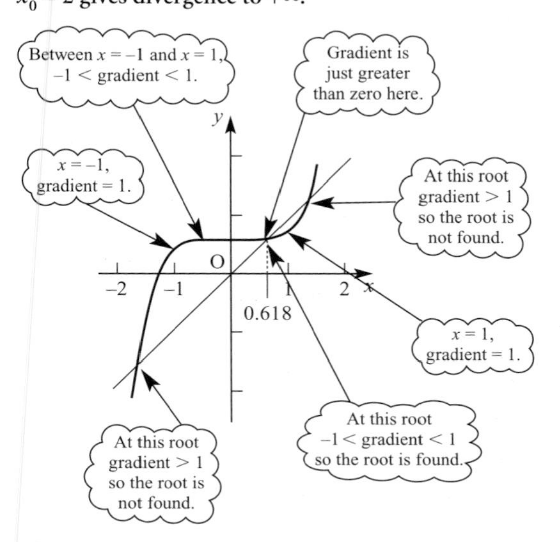

P (Page 148)

Bounds for the root have now been established.

Exercise 6B (Page 149)

1 **(ii)**

(iii) 1.521

2 **(iii)** 2.120

3 **(iii)** $x = \sqrt[3]{3 - x}$

(iv) 1.2134

4 **(ii)** 1.503

5 **(i)**

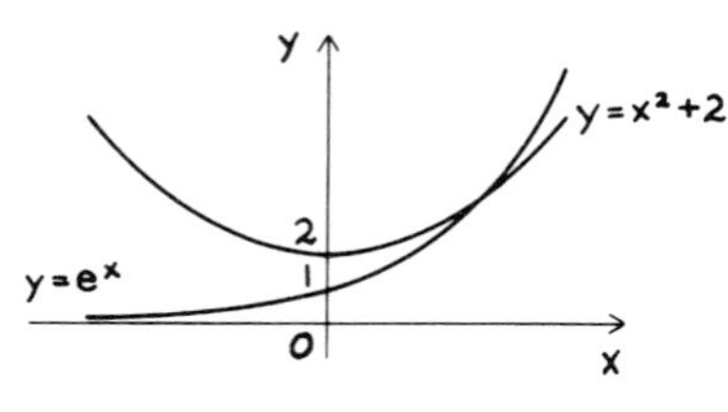

(ii) Only one point of intersection

(iii) $g(x) = \ln(x^2 + 2)$ is possible.

(iv) 1.319

6 **(i)**

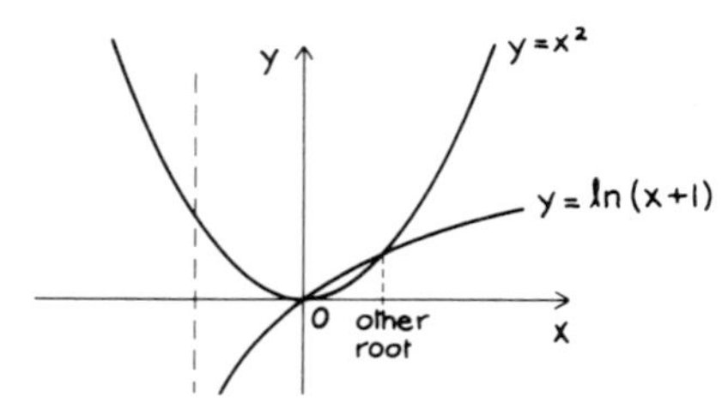

(ii) 0.747

7 **(i)**

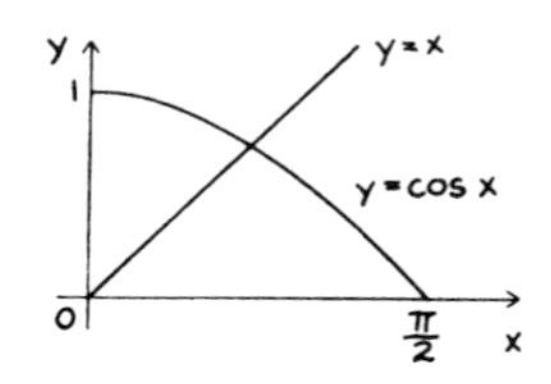

(ii) 0.739 09

Activity 6.4 (Page 150)

(i)

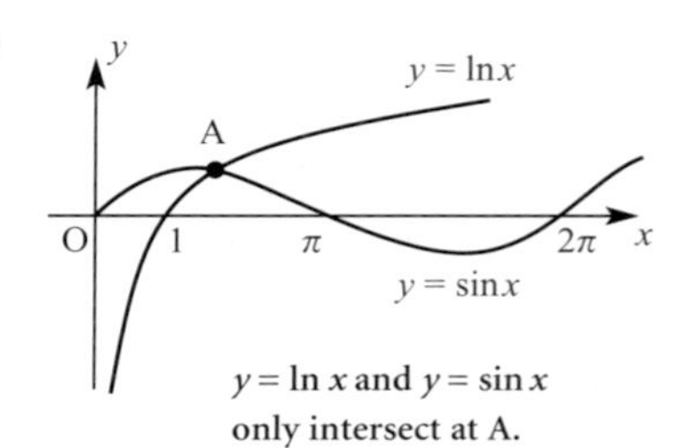

$y = \ln x$ and $y = \sin x$ only intersect at A.

$\ln x - \sin x = 0$

$x = 2$: $\ln 2 - \sin 2 < 0$

$x = 3$: $\ln 3 - \sin 3 > 0$

$\Rightarrow$ root in [2, 3]

Examples of rearrangements:

(a) **(ii)** Rearranging as $x = e^{\sin x}$

(iii) Gradient of $y = e^{\sin x}$ is < -1 near the root so the iteration diverges.

(b) **(ii)** Rearranging as $x = \arcsin(\ln x)$

(iii) Graph of $y = \arcsin(\ln x)$ does not intersect $y = x$

(c) **(ii)** Rearranging as $x = \ln x - \sin x + x$

(iii) Gradient of $y = \ln x - \sin x + x$ is > 1 near the root so the iteration diverges.

(d) **(ii)** Rearranging as $x = \sqrt{x(\sin x - \ln x + x)}$

(iii) Converges to $x = 2.219\,107\,149$.

Investigation (Page 151)

The first tangent is parallel to the x axis, so you cannot proceed.

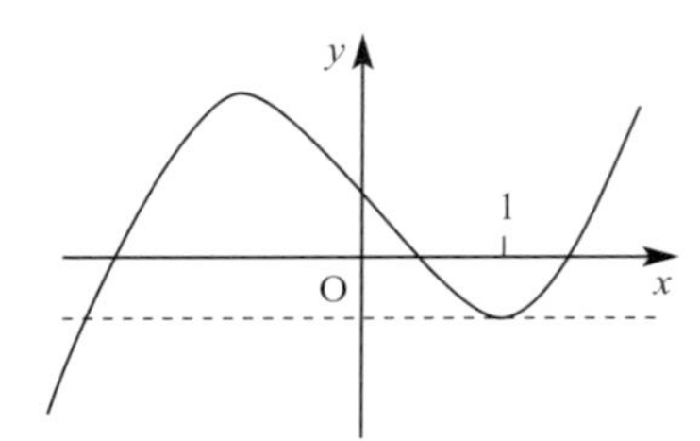

Exercise 6C (Page 152)

1 **(i)**

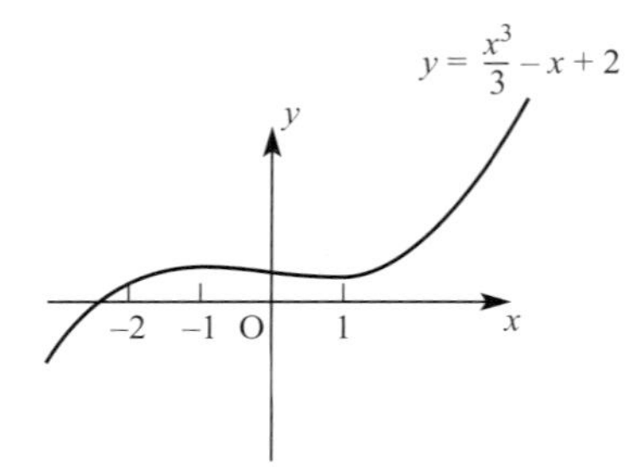

(ii) −2.355

(iii) Eventually converges to −2.355

2 **(i)** $f(0) = 1$; $f(1) = -5$

(ii) 0.54

(iii) The process involves division by zero.

3 **(i)** Sign changes in the intervals

$[-1, 0], [0, 1], [3, 4]$

(ii) -0.46; faster convergence with $x_0 = -1$

0.91; needs $x_0 = 1$ rather than $x_0 = 0$

3.73; faster convergence with $x_0 = 4$

(iii) $f(0) = 1$; $f'(0) = 1$

4 **(i)** Sign changes in $[1, 2]$ and $[4, 5]$

(ii) 1.86, 4.54

5 0.567

6 **(i)** Sign changes in $[-2, -1]$, $[0, 1]$ and $[1, 2]$

(ii) 1.8019, 0.4450, -1.2470

(iii) No, e.g. $-0.5 \to 1.8019$

7 **(i)** Sign changes in $[-1, 0]$, $[0, 1]$ and $[2, 3]$

(ii) -0.532, 0.653

(iii) 2.879 385 241 57

(iv) After a slow start (7 steps to give 1 d.p. accuracy) convergence is suddenly very rapid.

8 **(i)** 1

(ii)

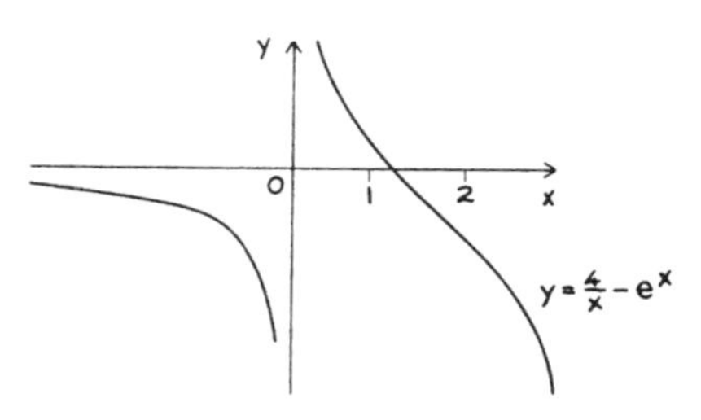

(iii) 1.202

(iv) 1.202 achieved in 3 steps.

Investigation (Page 153)

1 $x_1 = -1$; $f'(x_1) = 0$ so the iterations cannot proceed.

$x_1 = -1.5$; $x_2 < -2$ which is outside the domain of $f(x)$ so the iterations cannot proceed.

$x_1 = -1.8$ is a suitable starting point.

2 $x_1 = 1$; divergent

$x_1 = 1.2$; divergent

$x_1 = 1.4$; divergent

$x_1 = 1.6$; converges to 2.105 (the larger root)

$x_1 = 1.8$; converges to 1.895 (the root required)

$x_1 = 2$; $f'(x_1) = 0$ so the iterations cannot proceed.

So $x_1 = 1.8$ is a suitable starting point.

Chapter 7

Investigation (Page 156)

1.01, 1.02, 1.03

$\sqrt{1+x} \approx 1 + \frac{1}{2}x$ or $\sqrt{x} \approx \frac{1}{2}(1 + x)$

$k = \frac{1}{2}$

0.20

P (Page 158)

$(1 + x)^{\frac{1}{2}} = 3$ but substituting $x = 8$ into the expansion gives successive approximations of 1, 5, -3, 29, -131, … and these are getting further from 3 rather than closer to it.

Investigation (Page 159)

$-0.19 < x < 0.60$

$-0.08 < x < 0.07$

Activity 7.1 (Page 160)

For $|x| < 1$ the sum of the geometric series is $\frac{1}{1+x}$ which is the same as $(1 + x)^{-1}$.

Investigation (Page 161)

$(1 - x)^{-3} = 1 + 3x + 6x^2 + 10x^3 \dots$

The coefficients of x are the triangular numbers.

? (Page 162)

$$\begin{aligned}\sqrt{101} &= \sqrt{100 \times 1.01} \\ &= 10\sqrt{1.01} \\ &= 10(1 + 0.01)^{\frac{1}{2}} \\ &= 10[1 + \tfrac{1}{2}(0.01) + \frac{(\frac{1}{2})(-\frac{1}{2})}{2!}(0.01)^2 + \dots] \\ &= 10.050 \text{ (3 d.p.)}\end{aligned}$$

? (Page 164)

$\sqrt{x-1}$ is only defined for $x > 1$.

A possible rearrangement is $\sqrt{x\left(1 - \frac{1}{x}\right)} = \sqrt{x}\left(1 - \frac{1}{x}\right)^{\frac{1}{2}}$.

Since $x > 1 \Rightarrow 0 < \frac{1}{x} < 1$ the binomial expansion could be used but the resulting expansion would not be a series of positive powers of x.

Exercise 7A (Page 164)

1 **(i)** **(a)** $1 - 2x + 3x^2$

(b) $|x| < 1$

(c) 0.43%

(ii) **(a)** $1 - 2x + 4x^2$

(b) $|x| < \frac{1}{2}$

(c) 0.8%

(iii) **(a)** $1 - \frac{x^2}{2} - \frac{x^4}{8}$

(b) $|x| < 1$

(c) 0.000 006 3%

(iv) **(a)** $1 + 4x + 8x^2$

(b) $|x| < \frac{1}{2}$

(c) 1.3%

(v) **(a)** $\frac{1}{3} - \frac{x}{9} + \frac{x^2}{27}$

(b) $|x| < 3$

(c) 0.0037%

(vi) **(a)** $2 - \frac{7x}{4} - \frac{17x^2}{64}$

(b) $|x| < 4$

(c) 0.000 95%

(vii) **(a)** $-\frac{2}{3} - \frac{5x}{9} - \frac{5x^2}{27}$

(b) $|x| < 3$

(c) 0.0088%

(viii) **(a)** $\frac{1}{2} - \frac{3x}{16} + \frac{27x^2}{256}$

(b) $|x| < \frac{4}{3}$

(c) 0.013%

(ix) **(a)** $1 + 6x + 20x^2$

(b) $|x| < \frac{1}{2}$

(c) 4%

(x) **(a)** $1 + 2x^2 + 2x^4$

(b) $|x| < 1$

(c) 0.000 20%

(xi) **(a)** $1 + \frac{2x^2}{3} - \frac{4x^4}{9}$

(b) $|x| < \frac{1}{\sqrt{2}}$

(c) 0.000 048%

(xii) **(a)** $1 - 3x + 7x^2$

(b) $|x| < \frac{1}{2}$

(c) 1.64%

2 **(i)** $1 + 3x + 3x^2 + x^3$

(ii) $1 + 4x + 10x^2 + 20x^3$ for $|x| < 1$

(iii) $a = 25, b = 63$

3 **(i)** $16 - 32x + 24x^2 - 8x^3 + x^4$

(ii) $1 - 6x + 24x^2 - 80x^3$ for $|x| < \frac{1}{2}$

(iii) $a = -128, b = 600$

4 **(i)** $1 + x + x^2 + x^3$ for $|x| < 1$

(ii) $1 - 4x + 12x^2 - 32x^3$ for $|x| < \frac{1}{2}$

(iii) $1 - 3x + 9x^2 - 23x^3$ for $|x| < \frac{1}{2}$

5 **(ii)** $1 + \frac{x}{8} + \frac{3x^2}{128}$ for $|x| < 4$

(iii) $1 + \frac{9x}{8} + \frac{19x^2}{128}$

6 **(i)** $1 - y + y^2 - y^3 \ldots$

(ii) $1 - \frac{2}{x} + \frac{4}{x^2} - \frac{8}{x^3}$

(iv) $\frac{x}{2} - \frac{x^2}{4} + \frac{x^3}{8} - \frac{x^4}{16}$

(v) $x < -2$ or $x > 2$; $-2 < x < 2$; no overlap in range of validity.

7 **(ii)** $1 + x + \frac{3x^2}{2} + \frac{5x^3}{2}$ for $|x| < \frac{1}{2}$

(iii) 0.005 16

Exercise 7B (Page 168)

1 $\frac{2a^2}{3b^3}$

2 $\frac{1}{9y}$

3 $\frac{x+3}{x-6}$

4 $\frac{x+3}{x+1}$

5 $\frac{2x-5}{2x+5}$

6 $\frac{3(a+4)}{20}$

7 $\frac{x(2x+3)}{(x+1)}$

8 $\frac{2}{5(p-2)}$

9 $\frac{a-b}{2a-b}$

10 $\frac{(x+4)(x-1)}{x(x+3)}$

11 $\frac{9}{20x}$

12 $\frac{x-3}{12}$

13 $\frac{a^2+1}{a^2-1}$

14 $\frac{5x-13}{(x-3)(x-2)}$

15 $\frac{2}{(x+2)(x-2)}$

16 $\frac{2p^2}{(p^2-1)(p^2+1)}$

17 $\frac{a^2-a+2}{(a+1)(a^2+1)}$

18 $\frac{-2(y^2+4y+8)}{(y+2)^2(y+4)}$

19 $\frac{x^2+x+1}{x+1}$

20 $-\frac{(3b+1)}{(b+1)^2}$

21 $\frac{13x-5}{6(x-1)(x+1)}$

22 $\frac{4(3-x)}{5(x+2)^2}$

23 $\frac{3a-4}{(a+2)(2a-3)}$

24 $\frac{3x^2-4}{x(x-2)(x+2)}$

Exercise 7C (Page 171)

1 **(i)** 84

(ii) 4

(iii) −2

(iv) 5.24 or 0.76

(v) 3 or $\frac{1}{3}$

(vi) 0 or 3

(vii) 1.71 or 0.29

(viii) $-\frac{1}{9}$

(ix) −1.25 or 4

(x) −1.52 or 0.57

2 $\frac{6}{11}$

3 **(i)** $\frac{210}{n+1} - \frac{156}{n} = 4$

(ii) $n = 6$

4 **(i)** $\frac{600}{x}$

(ii) $\frac{600}{x-1}$

(iii) $x^2 - x - 600 = 0,\ x = 25$

5 **(i)** $\frac{270}{x}, \frac{270}{x-10}$

(ii) $x^2 - 10x - 9000 = 0,\ x = 100$

(iii) Arrive 1 pm

6 **(i)** True for all values of x

(ii) $x = \frac{1}{2}$

(iii) $x = -\frac{1}{5}$ or $x = 5$

7 Cost = £16, 16 staff left

8 12 thick slices

9 **(i)** 1.714 ohms

(ii) 4 ohms

(iii) Equivalent to half

P (Page 173)

This is an example of proof by contradiction. Assuming that the equation can be solved leads to the contradiction 1 = 0.

? (Page 175)

The identity is true for all values of x. Once a particular value of x is substituted you have an equation. Equating constant terms is equivalent to substituting $x = 0$.

Exercise 7D (Page 176)

1 **(i)** $\frac{1}{(x-2)} - \frac{1}{(x+3)}$

(ii) $\frac{1}{x} - \frac{1}{(x+1)}$

(iii) $\frac{2}{(x-4)} - \frac{2}{(x-1)}$

(iv) $\frac{2}{(x-1)} - \frac{1}{(x+2)}$

(v) $\frac{1}{(x+1)} + \frac{1}{(2x-1)}$

(vi) $\frac{2}{(x-2)} - \frac{2}{x}$

(vii) $\frac{1}{(x-1)} - \frac{3}{(3x-1)}$

(viii) $\frac{3}{5(x-4)} + \frac{2}{5(x+1)}$

(ix) $\frac{5}{(2x-1)} - \frac{2}{x}$

(x) $\dfrac{2}{(2x-3)} - \dfrac{1}{(x+2)}$

(xi) $\dfrac{8}{13(2x-5)} + \dfrac{9}{13(x+4)}$

(xii) $\dfrac{19}{24(3x-2)} - \dfrac{11}{24(3x+2)}$

Exercise 7E (Page 178)

1 (i) $\dfrac{9}{(1-3x)} - \dfrac{3}{(1-x)} - \dfrac{2}{(1-x)^2}$

(ii) $\dfrac{4}{(2x-1)} - \dfrac{2x}{(x^2+1)}$

(iii) $\dfrac{1}{(x-1)^2} - \dfrac{1}{(x-1)} + \dfrac{1}{(x+2)}$

(iv) $\dfrac{5}{8(x-2)} + \dfrac{6-5x}{8(x^2+4)}$

(v) $\dfrac{5-2x}{(2x^2-3)} + \dfrac{2}{x+2}$

Can be taken further using surds.

(vi) $\dfrac{2}{x} - \dfrac{1}{x^2} - \dfrac{3}{(2x+1)}$

(vii) $\dfrac{10x}{(3x^2-1)} - \dfrac{3}{x}$

Can be taken further using surds.

(viii) $\dfrac{1}{(2x^2+1)} + \dfrac{1}{(x+1)}$

(ix) $\dfrac{8}{(2x-1)} - \dfrac{4}{(2x-1)^2} - \dfrac{3}{x}$

2 $A = 1, \quad B = 0, \quad C = 1$

3 $A = 1, \quad B = 0, \quad C = -4$

Investigation (Page 180)

The binomial expansion is

$1 - x + 3x^2$.

The expansion is valid when $|x| < \frac{1}{2}$.

Which method is preferred is a matter of personal preference for **(a)** and **(b)** but for **(c)** must be **(iii)**.

Exercise 7F (Page 180)

1 (i) $4 + 20x + 72x^2$

(ii) $-4 - 10x - 16x^2$

(iii) $\dfrac{5}{2} + \dfrac{11x}{4} + \dfrac{33x^2}{8}$

(iv) $-\dfrac{1}{8} - \dfrac{5x}{16} - \dfrac{x^2}{8}$

2 (i) $\dfrac{2}{(2x-1)} - \dfrac{3}{(x+2)}$

(ii) $1 + 2x + 4x^2 \ldots a = 1, b = 2, c = 4$, for $|x| < \frac{1}{2}$

(iii) $\dfrac{1}{2} - \dfrac{x}{4} + \dfrac{x^2}{8}$ for $|x| < 2$

(iv) $-\dfrac{7}{2} - \dfrac{13x}{4} - \dfrac{67x^2}{8}$; 0.505%

3 (i) $2 + x - x^2$

$\dfrac{2}{(2-x)} - \dfrac{1}{(1+x)}$

(ii) $|x| < 1$

4 (i) $\dfrac{1}{(1-x)} - \dfrac{9}{(3-x)}$

(ii) $0, 1\frac{1}{2}$

(iii) $\dfrac{4x}{3} + \dfrac{8x^2}{3}$

Chapter 8

? (Page 183)

Possible answers are:

Bridge: wavelength 50–100 m; amplitude 15–30 m

Ripple: wavelength 0.02–0.05 m; amplitude 0.005–0.01 m

Bridge: $a = 15$–30; $b = \frac{\pi}{50}$–$\frac{\pi}{25}$ (about 0.06–0.13)

Ripple: $a = 0.005$–0.01; $b = 125$–300

Exercise 8A (Page 186)

1 (i) 90°

(ii) 60°, 300°

(iii) 14.0°, 194.0°

(iv) 109.5°, 250.5°

(v) 135°, 315°

(vi) 210°, 330°

2 (i) -1

(ii) $\dfrac{-2}{\sqrt{3}}$

(iii) $\dfrac{-2}{\sqrt{3}}$

(iv) $\dfrac{-2}{\sqrt{3}}$

(v) 0

(vi) $-\sqrt{2}$

3 (i) $B = 60°, C = 30°$

(ii) $\sqrt{3}$

4 (i) $L = 45°, N = 45°$

(ii) $\sqrt{2}, \sqrt{2}, 1$

5 (ii) 14.0°

6 (i) $0 \leqslant a \leqslant 90°$

(ii) No, for each of the second, third and fourth quadrants a different function is positive.

(iii) No, the graphs of all three of the functions do not intersect at a single point.

7 (i) 0°, 180°, 360°

(ii) 45°, 225°

(iii) 60°, 300°

(iv) 54.7, 125.3°, 234.7°, 305.3°

(v) 18.4°, 71.6°, 198.4°, 251.6°

(vi) 45°, 135°, 225°, 315°

Activity 8.1 (Page 187)

$y = \sin(\theta + 60°)$ is obtained from $y = \sin\theta$ by a translation $\begin{pmatrix} -60° \\ 0 \end{pmatrix}$.

$y = \cos(\theta - 60°)$ is obtained from $y = \sin\theta$ by a translation $\begin{pmatrix} 60° \\ 0 \end{pmatrix}$.

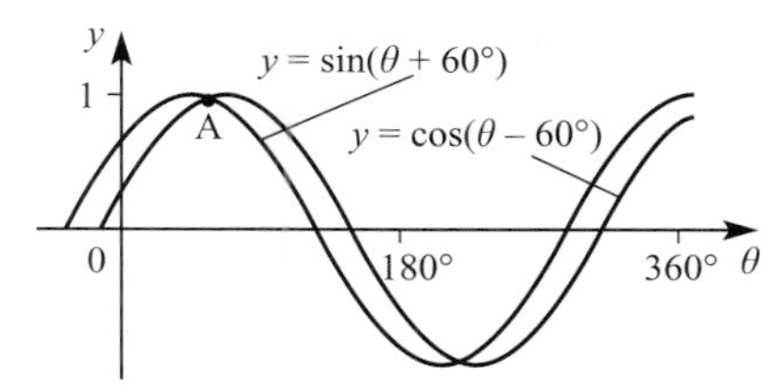

It appears that the θ co-ordinate of A is midway between the two maxima (30°, 1) and (60°, 1).

Checking: $\theta = 45° \rightarrow \sin(\theta + 60°) = 0.966$
$\cos(\theta - 60°) = 0.966.$

If 60° is replaced by 35°, using the trace function on a graphic calculator would enable the solutions to be found.

(Page 187)

Area of a triangle $= \frac{1}{2}$ base $\times$ height. The definitons of sine and cosine in a right-angled triangle.

Activity 8.2 (Page 188)

(i) $\sin(\theta + \phi) = \sin\theta\cos\phi + \cos\theta\sin\phi$

$\Rightarrow \sin[(90° - \theta) + \phi] = \sin(90° - \theta)\cos\phi + \cos(90° - \theta)\sin\phi$

$\Rightarrow \sin[90° - (\theta - \phi)] = \cos\theta\cos\phi + \sin\theta\sin\phi$

$\Rightarrow \cos(\theta - \phi) = \cos\theta\cos\phi + \sin\theta\sin\phi$

(ii) $\Rightarrow \cos[\theta - (-\phi)] = \cos\theta\cos(-\phi) + \sin\theta\sin(-\phi)$

$\cos(\theta + \phi) = \cos\theta\cos\phi - \sin\theta\sin\phi$

(iii) $\tan(\theta + \phi) = \dfrac{\sin(\theta + \phi)}{\cos(\theta + \phi)}$

$$= \frac{\sin\theta\cos\phi + \cos\theta\sin\phi}{\cos\theta\cos\phi - \sin\theta\sin\phi}$$

$$= \frac{\dfrac{\sin\theta\cos\phi}{\cos\theta\cos\phi} + \dfrac{\cos\theta\sin\phi}{\cos\theta\cos\phi}}{\dfrac{\cos\theta\cos\phi}{\cos\theta\cos\phi} - \dfrac{\sin\theta\sin\phi}{\cos\theta\cos\phi}}$$

$$= \frac{\tan\theta + \tan\phi}{1 - \tan\theta\tan\phi}$$

(iv) $\tan[\theta + (-\phi)] = \dfrac{\tan\theta + \tan(-\phi)}{1 - \tan\theta\tan(-\phi)}$

$\tan(\theta - \phi) = \dfrac{\tan\theta - \tan\phi}{1 + \tan\theta\tan\phi}$

(Page 189)

No. In part (iii) you get $\tan 90° = \dfrac{\sqrt{3} + \frac{1}{\sqrt{3}}}{1 - \sqrt{3} \times \frac{1}{\sqrt{3}}}$.

Neither tan 90° nor $\dfrac{1}{1-1}$ is defined. For the result to be valid you must exclude the case when $\theta + \phi = 90°$ (or 270°, 450°, ...).

Similarly in part (iv) you must exclude $\theta - \phi = 90°$, 270°, etc.

Exercise 8B (Page 190)

1 (i) $\dfrac{\sqrt{3}}{2\sqrt{2}} + \dfrac{1}{2\sqrt{2}}$

(ii) $-\dfrac{1}{\sqrt{2}}$

(iii) $\dfrac{\sqrt{3} - 1}{\sqrt{3} + 1}$

(iv) $\dfrac{\sqrt{3} + 1}{\sqrt{3} - 1}$

2 (i) $\dfrac{1}{\sqrt{2}}(\sin\theta + \cos\theta)$

(ii) $\frac{1}{2}(\sqrt{3}\cos\theta + \sin\theta)$

(iii) $\frac{1}{2}(\sqrt{3}\cos\theta - \sin\theta)$

(iv) $\dfrac{1}{\sqrt{2}}(\cos 2\theta - \sin 2\theta)$

(v) $\dfrac{\tan\theta + 1}{1 - \tan\theta}$

(vi) $\dfrac{\tan\theta - 1}{1 + \tan\theta}$

3 (i) $\sin\theta$

(ii) $\cos 4\phi$

(iii) 0

(iv) $\cos 2\theta$

4 (i) 15°

(ii) 157.5°

(iii) 0° or 180°

(iv) 111.7°

(v) 165°

5 (i) $\frac{\pi}{8}$

(ii) 2.79 radians

6 (i) $\frac{1}{\sqrt{5}}$

(ii) $\sin\beta = \frac{3}{5}, \cos\beta = \frac{4}{5}$

7 (i) $\frac{1}{k}x\sin kx + \frac{1}{k^2}\cos kx + c$

(ii) $\cos 2x - \cos 8x$

8 (ii) $\alpha = \frac{5\pi}{12}$

(iii) $p = \frac{1}{2}, q = \frac{\sqrt{3}}{2}$

$A \approx 0.058\,66$ (5 d.p.)

$A = 0.058\,30$ (5 d.p.)

(Page 192)

For $\sin 2\theta$ and $\cos 2\theta$, substituting $\theta = 45°$ is helpful.

You know that $\sin 45° = \cos 45° = \frac{1}{\sqrt{2}}$ and that $\sin 90° = 1$ and $\cos 90° = 0$.

For $\tan 2\theta$ you cannot use $\theta = 45°$. Take $\theta = 30°$ instead; $\tan 30° = \frac{1}{\sqrt{3}}$ and $\tan 60° = \sqrt{3}$.

No, checking like this is not the same as proof.

Exercise 8C (Page 196)

1 (i) 14.5°, 90°, 165.5°, 270°

(ii) 0°, 35.3°, 144.7°, 180°, 215.3°, 324.7°, 360°

(iii) 90°, 210°, 330°

(iv) 30°, 150°, 210°, 330°

(v) 0°, 138.6°, 221.4°, 360°

2 (i) $-\pi, 0, \pi$

(ii) $-\pi, 0, \pi$

(iii) $\frac{-2\pi}{3}, 0, \frac{2\pi}{3}$

(iv) $\frac{-3\pi}{4}, \frac{-\pi}{4}, \frac{\pi}{4}, \frac{3\pi}{4}$

(v) $\frac{-11\pi}{12}, \frac{-3\pi}{4}, \frac{-7\pi}{12}, \frac{-\pi}{4}, \frac{\pi}{12}, \frac{\pi}{4}, \frac{5\pi}{12}, \frac{3\pi}{4}$

3 $3\sin\theta - 4\sin^3\theta, \theta = 0, \frac{\pi}{4}, \frac{3\pi}{4}, \pi, \frac{5\pi}{4}, \frac{7\pi}{4}, 2\pi$

4 51°, 309°

5 $\cot\theta$

6 $\frac{\tan\theta(3 - \tan^2\theta)}{1 - 3\tan^2\theta}$

8 (ii) 63.4°

9 (i)

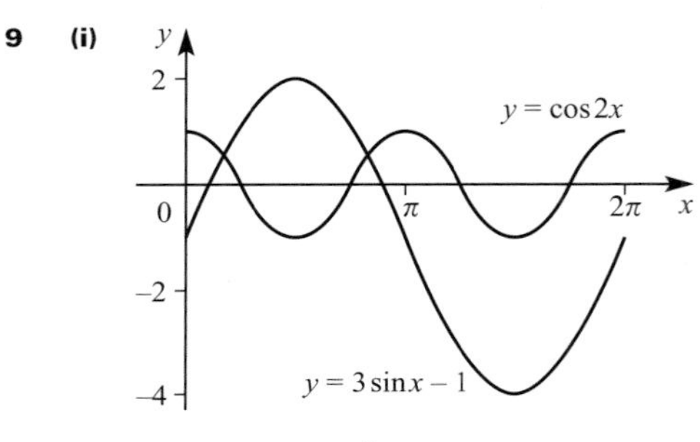

(iii) $x = \frac{\pi}{6}$ or $x = \frac{5\pi}{6}$

(Page 197)

Either give a counter-example, for example $\alpha = \beta = 45°$ so $\sin\alpha + \sin\beta = \frac{2}{\sqrt{2}}$ but $\sin(\alpha + \beta) = \sin 90° = 1$ and $\frac{2}{\sqrt{2}} \neq 1$.

Or deduce the correct result, as given in the working that follows in the text. Notice that you would have to prove that the correct result is not the same as $\sin(\alpha + \beta)$.

Activity 8.3 (Page 198)

$\cos(\theta + \phi) = \cos\theta\cos\phi - \sin\theta\sin\phi$ ①

$\cos(\theta - \phi) = \cos\theta\cos\phi + \sin\theta\sin\phi$. ②

Adding ① and ②

$\cos(\theta + \phi) + \cos(\theta - \phi) = 2\cos\theta\cos\phi$

Let $\theta + \phi = \alpha$; $\theta - \phi = \beta$;

$\Rightarrow \cos\alpha + \cos\beta = 2\cos\left(\frac{\alpha + \beta}{2}\right)\cos\left(\frac{\alpha - \beta}{2}\right)$

Similarly, subtracting ② from ①

$\Rightarrow \cos(\theta + \phi) - \cos(\theta - \phi) = -2\sin\theta\sin\phi$

$\Rightarrow \cos\alpha - \cos\beta = -2\sin\left(\frac{\alpha+\beta}{2}\right)\sin\left(\frac{\alpha-\beta}{2}\right)$

Investigation (Page 198)

In tune:

$x_1 + x_2 = 2a\sin\left(\omega t + \frac{\varepsilon}{2}\right)\cos\frac{\varepsilon}{2}$

$= a'\sin\left(\omega t + \frac{\varepsilon}{2}\right)$

which is a single wave.

Out of tune:

$x_1 + x_2 = 2a\sin\left(\omega + \frac{\delta}{2}\right)t\cos\frac{\delta t}{2}$

Most piano tuners use a tuning fork to give them a perfect note. They compare the note from the piano with it. If the piano note is nearly right but not exactly, you can hear beats. When the piano note is exactly right there are no beats.

Exercise 8D (Page 200)

1 **(i)** $2\cos 3\theta\sin\theta$

(ii) $2\cos 3\theta\cos 2\theta$

(iii) $-2\sin 5\theta\sin 2\theta$

(iv) $\cos\theta$

(v) $\sqrt{2}\sin 3\theta$

2 $2\cos 3\theta\cos\theta$

$20°, 90°, 100°, 140°$

3 $\dfrac{\tan 4\theta}{\tan\theta}$

4 $0, \frac{\pi}{4}, \frac{3\pi}{4}, \pi, \frac{5\pi}{4}, \frac{7\pi}{4}, 2\pi$

5 $\cos(\theta + 43°)$

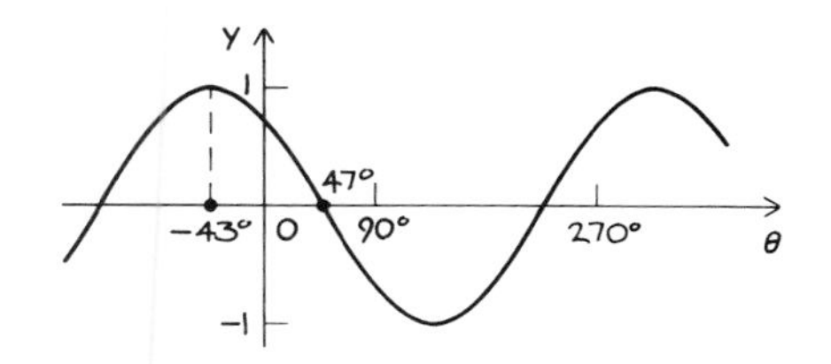

Exercise 8E (Page 204)

1 **(i)** $\sqrt{2}\cos(\theta - 45°)$

(ii) $5\cos(\theta - 53.1°)$

(iii) $2\cos(\theta - 60°)$

(iv) $3\cos(\theta - 41.8°)$

2 **(i)** $\sqrt{2}\cos\left(\theta + \frac{\pi}{4}\right)$

(ii) $2\cos\left(\theta + \frac{\pi}{6}\right)$

3 **(i)** $\sqrt{5}\sin(\theta + 63.4°)$

(ii) $5\sin(\theta + 53.1°)$

4 **(i)** $\sqrt{2}\sin\left(\theta - \frac{\pi}{4}\right)$

(ii) $2\sin\left(\theta - \frac{\pi}{6}\right)$

5 **(i)** $2\cos(\theta - (-60°))$

(ii) $4\cos(\theta - (-45°))$

(iii) $2\cos(\theta - 30°)$

(iv) $13\cos(\theta - 22.6°)$

(v) $2\cos(\theta - 150°)$

(vi) $2\cos(\theta - 135°)$

6 **(i)** $13\cos(\theta + 67.4°)$

(ii) Max 13, min −13

(iii)

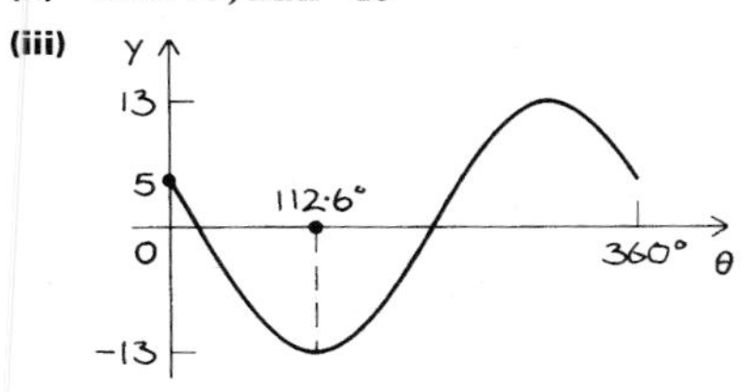

(iv) 4.7°, 220.5°

7 **(i)** $2\sqrt{3}\sin\left(\theta - \frac{\pi}{6}\right)$

(ii) Max $2\sqrt{3}$, $\theta = \frac{2\pi}{3}$; min $-2\sqrt{3}$, $\theta = \frac{5\pi}{3}$

(iii)

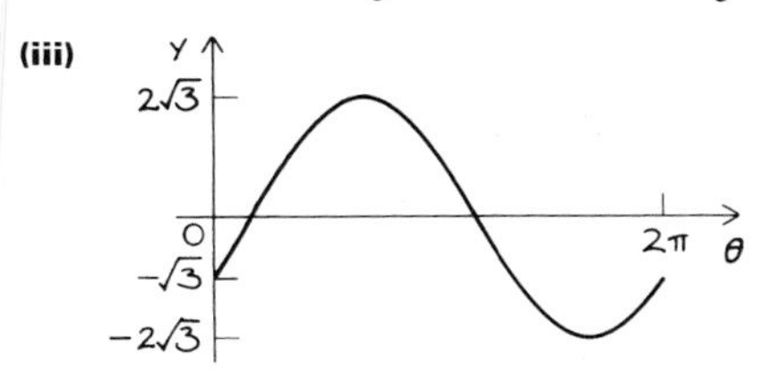

(iv) $\frac{\pi}{3}, \pi$

8 **(i)** $\sqrt{13}\sin(2\theta + 56.3°)$

(ii) Max $\sqrt{13}$, $\theta = 16.8°$; min $-\sqrt{13}$, $\theta = 106.8°$

(iii)

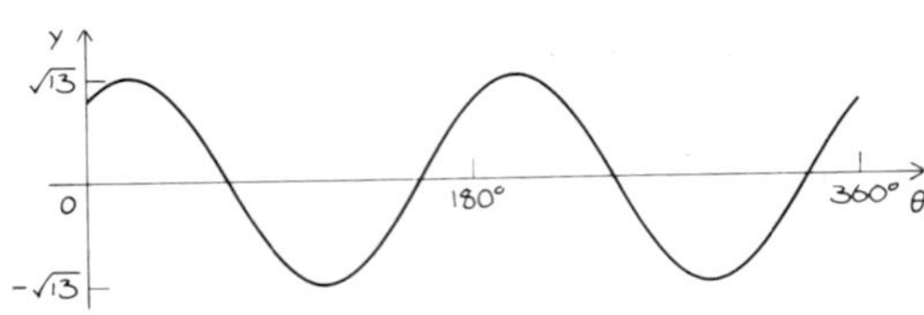

(iv) 53.8°, 159.9°, 233.8°, 339.9°

9 **(i)** $\sqrt{3}\cos(\theta - 54.7°)$

(ii) Max $\sqrt{3}$, $\theta = 54.7°$; min $-\sqrt{3}$, $\theta = 234.7°$

(iii)

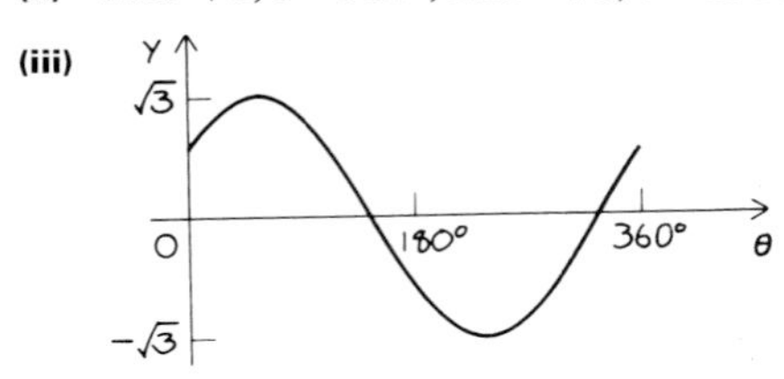

(iv) Max $\dfrac{1}{3 - \sqrt{3}}$, $\theta = 234.7°$; min $\dfrac{1}{3 + \sqrt{3}}$, $\theta = 54.7°$

10 **(ii)** 30.6° or 82.0°

11 **(i)** $\cos x \cos \alpha - \sin x \sin \alpha$

(ii) $r = \sqrt{29}$, $\alpha = 68.2°$

(iii) Max $\sqrt{29}$ when $x = 291.8°$,

min $-\sqrt{29}$ when $x = 111.8°$

(iv) $x = 235.7°$ or $347.9°$

12 **(i)** $\sqrt{34}\cos(x + 30.96°)$

(ii) $x = 15.7°$ or $282.4°$

(iii) $x = 7.9°$ or $141.2°$ or $187.9°$ or $321.2°$

13 **(i)** $R = 10$, $\alpha = 53.13°$

(ii)

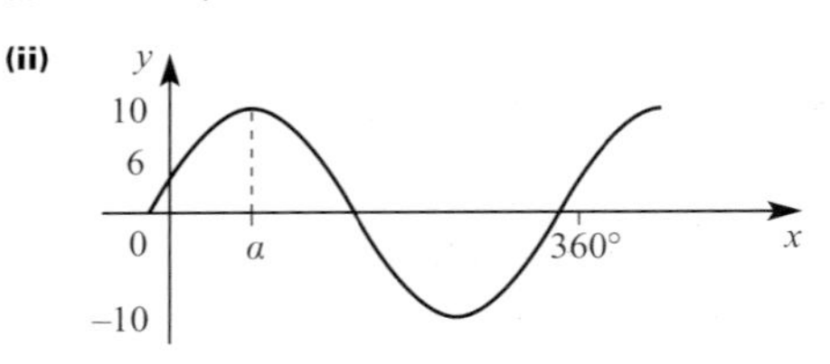

(iii) $x = 119.55°$ or $346.71°$

(iv) $\theta = 103.29°$ or $330.45°$

14 **(i)** $c = \sqrt{a^2 + b^2}$

(ii) $\tan \alpha = \dfrac{b}{a}$

(iii) $\alpha = 36.87°$

(iv) $\theta = 103.29°$ or $330.45°$

15 **(i)** $\dfrac{2}{\sqrt{5}}$

(ii) $a = 2$, $b = 1$

(iii) $R = \sqrt{5}$

$-\sqrt{5} - 1 \leqslant \text{f}(x) \leqslant \sqrt{5} - 1$

16 **(i)** $R = \sqrt{10}$, $\alpha = 18.43°$

(ii) $x = 90°$ or $306.9°$

(iii) $x = 90°$, $233.1°$ or $306.9°$

(iv) Part **(iii)** also contains solutions to

$-3\cos x = 1 - \sin x$

17 **(ii)** $\theta = -40.9°$

(iii) $\sqrt{7}\sin(\theta + 40.9°)$, $h = \sqrt{7}$, $\theta = 30°$

Investigation (Page 209)

The total current is

$$I = A_1 \sin \omega t + A_2 \sin(\omega t + \alpha) \qquad (\text{where } \omega = 2\pi f).$$

$$I = A_1 \sin \omega t + A_2 \sin \omega t \cos \alpha + A_2 \cos \omega t \sin \alpha$$

$$= (A_1 + A_2 \cos \alpha)\sin \omega t + (A_2 \sin \alpha)\cos \omega t$$

Let $A_1 + A_2 \cos \alpha = P$ and $A_2 \sin \alpha = Q$

so $I = P \sin \omega t + Q \cos \omega t$

$$= \sqrt{P^2 + Q^2}\sin(\omega t + \varepsilon)$$

where $\varepsilon = \arctan\left(\dfrac{Q}{P}\right)$.

This is a sine wave with the same frequency but a greater amplitude. The phase angle ε is between 0 and α.

Exercise 8F (Page 209)

1 **(i)** $\sin 6\theta$

(ii) $\cos 6\theta$

(iii) 1

(iv) $\cos \theta$

(v) $\sin \theta$

(vi) $\frac{3}{2}\sin 2\theta$

(vii) $\cos \theta$

(viii) -1

2 **(i)** $1 - \sin 2x$

(ii) $\cos 2x$

(iii) $\frac{1}{2}(5\cos 2x - 1)$

4 **(i)** 4.4°, 95.6°

(ii) 199.5°, 340.5°

(iii) $\dfrac{-\pi}{6}, \dfrac{\pi}{2}$

(iv) $-15.9°$, $164.1°$

(v) $\frac{\pi}{6}, \frac{\pi}{2}, \frac{5\pi}{6}$

(vi) $20.8°$, $122.3°$

(vii) $76.0°$, $135°$

P (Page 211)

Because the formula Area of a sector $= \frac{1}{2}r^2\theta$ assumes θ is in radians.

? (Page 212)

By the shape and symmetry of the graphs, in each case the maximum percentage error will occur for $\theta = 0.1$ radians.

$y = \sin\theta$: $\theta = 0.1$ rad

true value = 0.099 833

approximate value = 0.1

% error = 0.167%

$y = \tan\theta$: $\theta = 0.1$ rad

true value = 0.100 335

approximate value = 0.1

% error = 0.334%

$y = \cos\theta$: $\theta = 0.1$ rad

true value = 0.995 004

approximate value = 0.995

% error = 0.000 419%

Activity 8.4 (Page 212)

(i) When $\theta = 0$, $\frac{\cos\theta - \cos 2\theta}{\theta^2} = \frac{1-1}{0} = \frac{0}{0}$ (undefined)

(ii)

θ	$\frac{\cos\theta - \cos 2\theta}{\theta^2}$
0.20	1.475
0.18	1.480
0.16	1.484
0.14	1.488
0.12	1.491
0.10	1.494
0.08	1.496
0.06	1.498
0.04	1.499
0.02	1.500

P (Page 214)

The formula $\sin(\theta + \phi) = \sin\theta\cos\phi + \cos\theta\sin\phi$. This is used with $\theta = x$ and $\phi = \delta x$.

The small angle approximations for sin and cos.

Exercise 8G (Page 215)

1 (i) 2

(ii) $1 - \sqrt{3}\theta - \frac{\theta^2}{2}$

(iii) $1 - \frac{5\theta^2}{2}$

(iv) $\frac{1}{2}$

(v) -3θ

(vi) $\theta\sin\alpha + \theta^2\cos\alpha$

2 (i) 5θ

(ii) 5

3 (i) $\frac{\theta^2}{2}$

(ii) $\frac{1}{8}$

4 (i) $\frac{\sqrt{3}\theta^2}{2}$

(ii) $2\theta^2$

(iii) $\frac{\sqrt{3}}{4}$

5 (i) $8\theta^2$

(ii) $4\theta^2$

(iii) 2

6 (i) $\frac{1}{1+\theta}$

(ii) $1 - \theta + \theta^2$

(iii) 0.03% and 0.13%

7 (i) $\sqrt{1+\theta}$

(ii) $1 + \frac{1}{2}\theta - \frac{1}{8}\theta^2$

(iii) $\sqrt{1+\theta}$ since this has only used one approximation.

(iv) $\sqrt{1+\theta} = 1.048\,81$, $1 + \frac{1}{2}\theta - \frac{1}{8}\theta^2 = 1.048\,75$, true value 1.048 73.

Errors due to the double approximation appear to have cancelled out to some extent, rather than compounding.

8 (i) $\frac{1}{1 - \frac{1}{2}\theta^2}$

(ii) $1 + \frac{1}{2}\theta^2$

(iii) 0.47 radians

(iv) It is a good appoximation since 0.47 rad $\approx 27°$.

9 **(ii)** $\angle BAE = 90° - \angle OAB$

10 **(i)** $x = -\frac{\pi}{8}$ or $\frac{3\pi}{8}$

(ii) $2x$

(iii) $2x + 1 - 2x^2$

(iv) $x = -0.366$ or 1.366

(v) The angles in **(i)** are not 'small'.

11 **(i)** $\frac{2}{1-x} - \frac{2}{2-x}$; $k = \frac{3}{2}$

(iii) $\theta = \pm 0.2$

12 **(i)** $\sin x \cos(\delta x) + \cos x \sin(\delta x)$

(ii) $\sin x + (\delta x)\cos x - \frac{(\delta x)^2}{2}\sin x$

(iii) $\cos x - \frac{(\delta x)}{2}\sin x$

(iv) $\cos x$

(v) Derivative of $\sin x$

13 **(i)** $\frac{1}{2}\theta\sin 2\theta + \frac{1}{4}\cos 2\theta + c$

(ii) $1 - 6x + 24x^2 - 80x^3$ for $|x| < \frac{1}{2}$

(iii) $a = 1, b = 6$; $0.005\,15$

14 **(i)** **(a)** $-\frac{1}{2}$

(ii) **(b)** $a = \frac{1}{2}, b = -\frac{1}{16}$

Investigation (Page 218)

$$\tan 89° = \frac{1}{\tan 1°} = \frac{1}{\tan\frac{\pi}{180}} \approx \frac{1}{\frac{\pi}{180}}$$

$$\Rightarrow \tan 89° \approx \frac{180}{\pi}$$

Activity 8.5 (Page 220)

General solution is $\theta = 2n\pi + \arcsin c$

or $\theta = (2n + 1)\pi - \arcsin c$

i.e. even multiples of π are followed by $+ \arcsin c$

odd multiples of π are followed by $- \arcsin c$.

Now $(-1)^n = +1$ when n is even and

$(-1)^n = -1$ when n is odd

so $\theta = n\pi + (-1)^n \arcsin c$.

Chapter 9

? (Page 225)

At points where the rate of change of gradient is greatest.

p (Page 233)

$\frac{x}{a} = \cos\theta$, $\frac{y}{b} = \sin\theta$

$$\therefore \left(\frac{x}{a}\right)^2 + \left(\frac{y}{b}\right)^2 = \cos^2\theta + \sin^2\theta = 1$$

$$\Rightarrow \frac{x^2}{a^2} + \frac{y^2}{b^2} = 1$$

Exercise 9A (Page 234)

1 **(i)** **(a)**

t	−2	−1.5	−1	−0.5	0	0.5	1	1.5	2
x	−4	−3	−2	−1	0	1	2	3	4
y	4	2.25	1	0.25	0	0.25	1	2.25	4

(b)

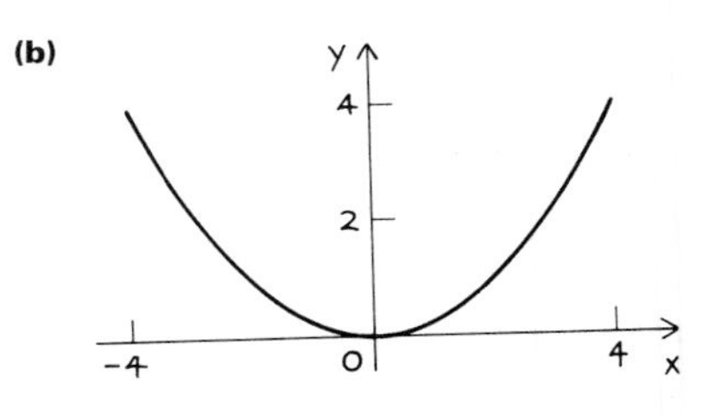

(c) $y = \frac{x^2}{4}$

(ii) **(a)**

θ	0°	30°	60°	90°	120°	150°	180°	210°	240°	270°	300°	330°	360°
x	1	0.5	−0.5	−1	−0.5	0.5	1	0.5	−0.5	−1	−0.5	0.5	1
y	0	0.25	0.75	1	0.75	0.25	0	0.25	0.75	1	0.75	0.25	0

(b)

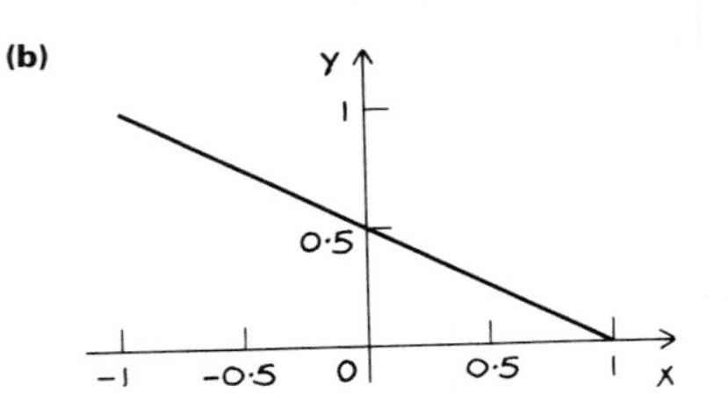

(c) A segment of $y = \frac{1-x}{2}$,
where $-1 \leqslant x \leqslant 1$ and $0 \leqslant y \leqslant 1$

(iii) **(a)**

t	−2	−1.5	−1	−0.5	0	0.5	1	1.5	2
x	4	2.25	1	0.25	0	0.25	1	2.25	4
y	−8	−3.375	−1	−0.125	0	0.125	1	3.375	8

(b)

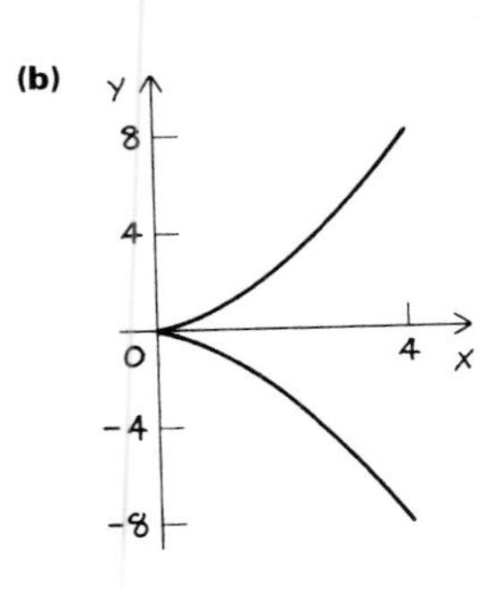

(c) $y^2 = x^3$

(iv) (a)

θ	0°	30°	60°	90°	120°	150°	180°	210°	240°	270°	300°	330°	360°
x	0	0.25	0.75	1	0.75	0.25	0	0.25	0.75	1	0.75	0.25	0
y	1	2	2.73	3	2.73	2	1	0	–0.73	–1	–0.73	0	1

(b)

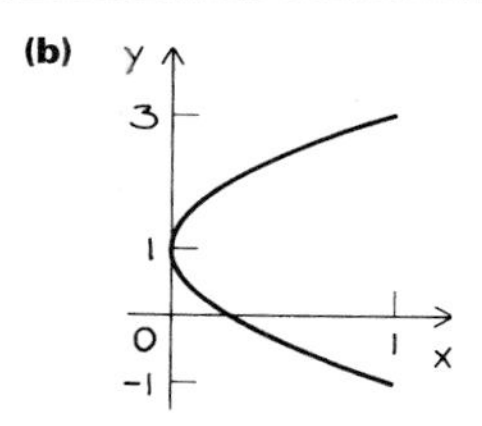

(c) Part of $(y-1)^2 = 4x$,

where $0 \leqslant x \leqslant 1$ and $-1 \leqslant y \leqslant 3$

(v) (a)

θ	0°	30°	60°	90°	120°	150°	180°	210°	240°	270°	300°	330°	360°
x	∞	4	2.3	2	2.3	4	∞	–4	–2.3	–2	–2.3	–4	∞
y	∞	3.5	1.2	0	–1.2	–3.5	∞	3.5	1.2	0	–1.2	–3.5	∞

(b)

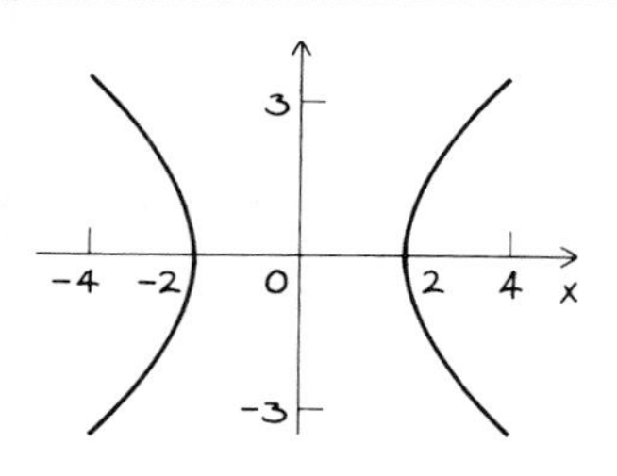

(c) $x^2 - y^2 = 4$

(vi) (a)

θ	0°	30°	60°	90°	120°	150°	180°	210°	240°	270°	300°	330°	360°
x	0	0.5	1.5	2	1.5	0.5	0	0.5	1.5	2	1.5	0.5	0
y	3	2.6	1.5	0	–1.5	–2.6	–3	–2.6	–1.5	0	1.5	2.6	3

(b)

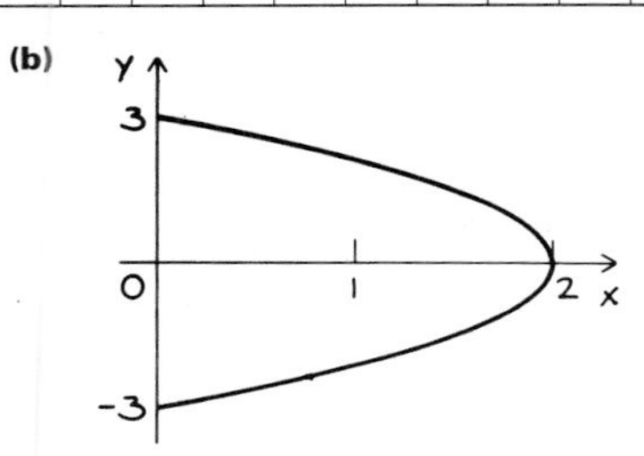

(c) Part of $y^2 = \frac{9}{2}(2 - x)$,

where $0 \leqslant x \leqslant 2$ and $-3 \leqslant y \leqslant 3$

(vii) (a)

θ	0°	30°	60°	90°	120°	150°	180°	210°	240°	270°	300°	330°	360°
x	0	0.6	1.7	∞	–1.7	–0.6	0	0.6	1.7	∞	–1.7	–0.6	0
y	0	1.7	–1.7	0	1.7	–1.7	0	1.7	–1.7	0	1.7	–1.7	0

(b)

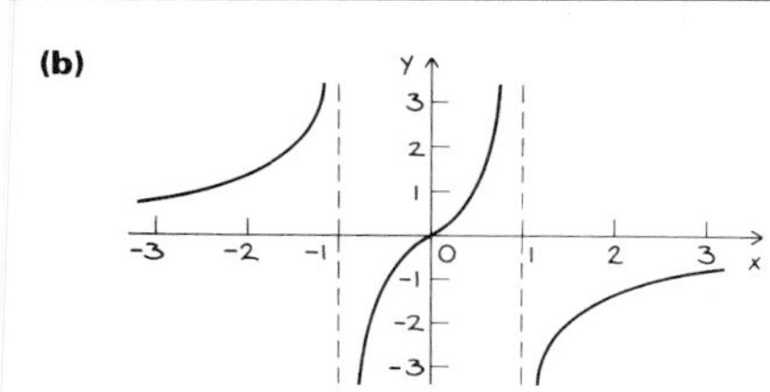

(c) $y = \dfrac{2x}{1 - x^2}$

(viii) (a)

t	–2	–1.5	–1	–0.5	0	0.5	1	1.5	2
x	4	2.25	1	0.25	0	0.25	1	2.25	4
y	6	3.75	2	0.75	0	–0.25	0	0.75	2

(b)

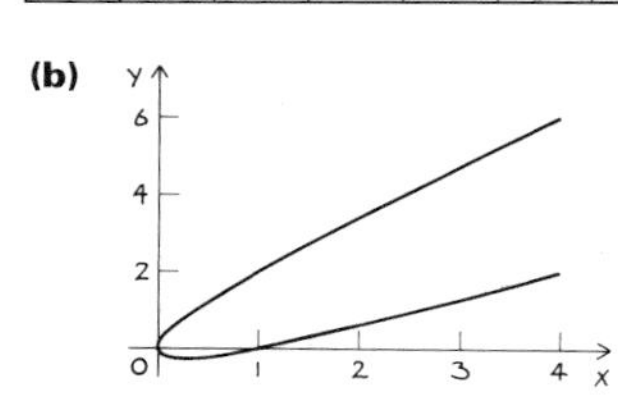

(c) $y = x \pm \sqrt{x}$

(ix) (a)

t	–2	–1.5	–1	–0.5	0	0.5	1	1.5	2
x	2	3	∞	–1	0	0.33	0.5	0.6	0.7
y	–0.7	–0.6	–0.5	–0.33	0	1	∞	–3	–2

(b)

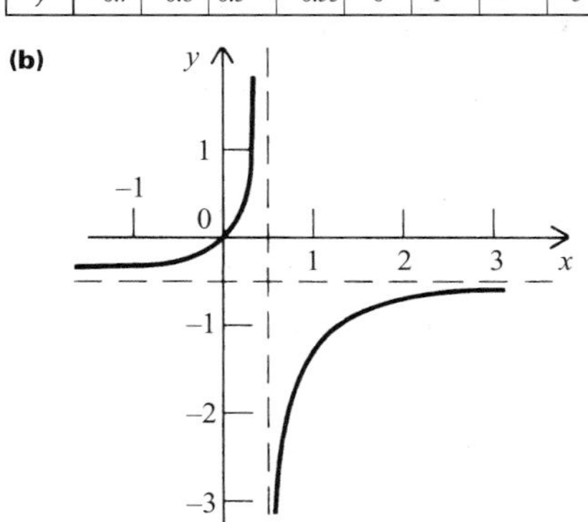

(c) $y = \dfrac{x}{1 - 2x}$

2 **(i)** $x^2 + y^2 = 25$

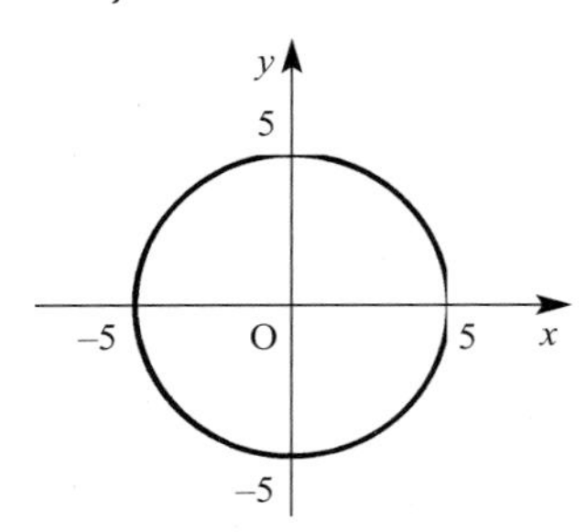

(ii) $x^2 + y^2 = 9$

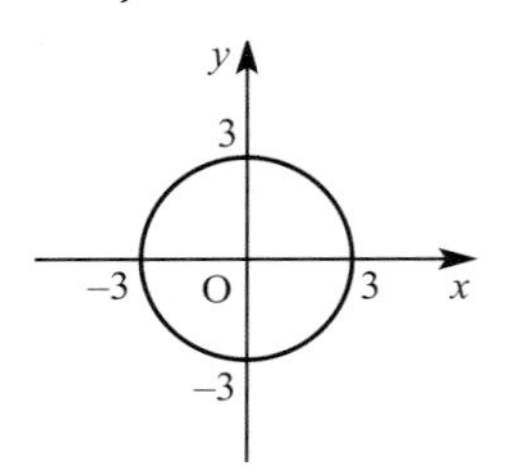

(iii) $(x-4)^2 + (y-1)^2 = 9$

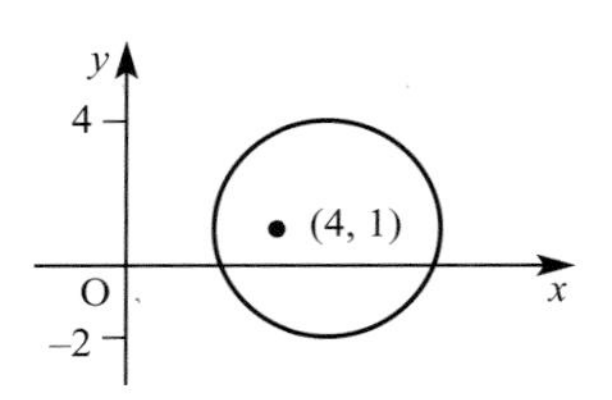

(iv) $(x+1)^2 + (y-3)^2 = 4$

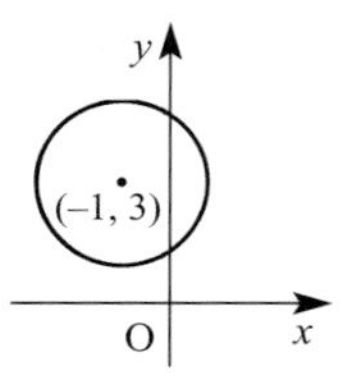

3 **(i)** **(a)** $xy = 1$ **(b)** $xy = 16$

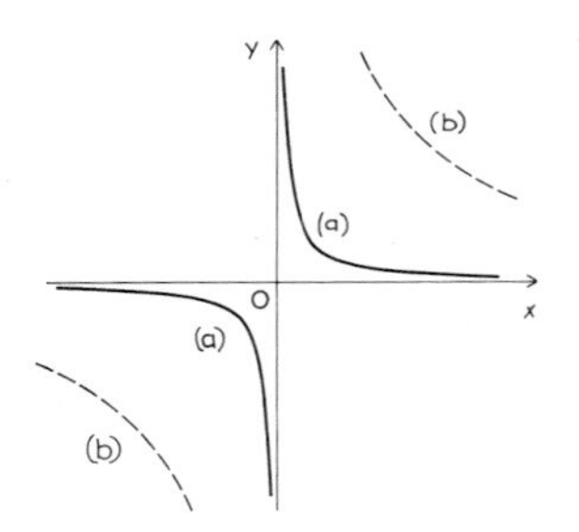

(ii) The curve in **(b)** is an enlargement of the one in **(a)**, centre the origin, s.f. 4.

4 **(i)**

t	–2	–1.5	–1	–0.5	0	0.5	1	1.5	2
x	4	2.25	1	0.25	0	0.25	1	2.25	4
y	16	5.0625	1	0.0625	0	0.0625	1	5.0625	16

(ii)

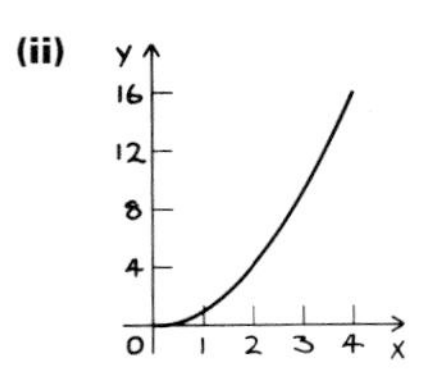

(iii) Because it should also state 'for $x \geqslant 0$'

5 **(i)** $y = \dfrac{x}{2} - \dfrac{x^2}{80}$

(ii)

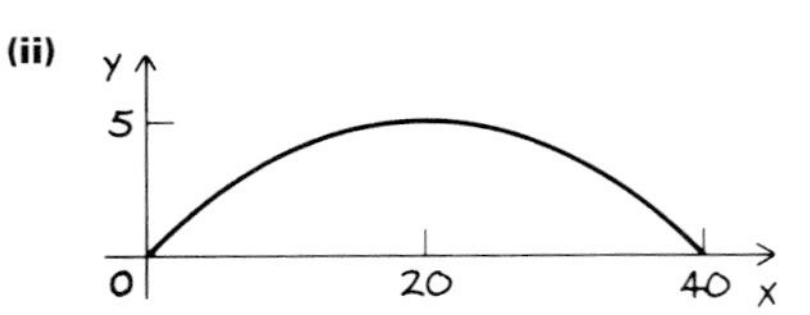

6 **(i)**

t	0	1	2	3	4	5	6
x	0	40	80	120	160	200	240
y	0	25	40	45	40	25	0

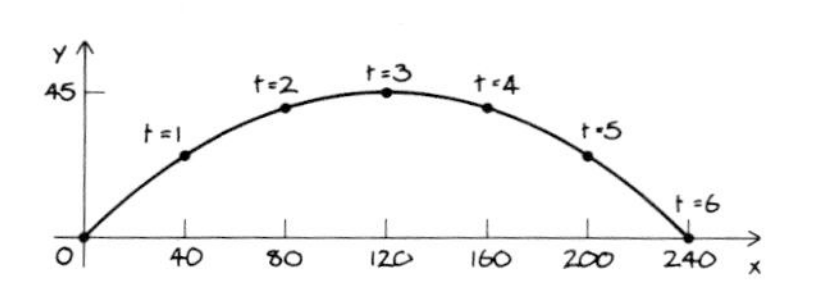

(ii) 240 m

(iii)

t	0	1	2	3	4	5	6
x	0	39	76	111	144	175	204
y	0	25	40	45	40	25	0

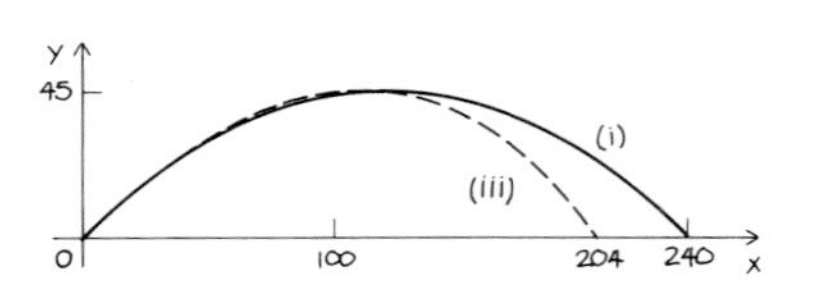

(iv) 36 m

7 **(i)**

t	–4	–3	–2	–1	0	1	2	3	4
x	9	4	1	0	1	4	9	16	25
y	–5	–4	–3	–2	–1	0	1	2	3

(ii)

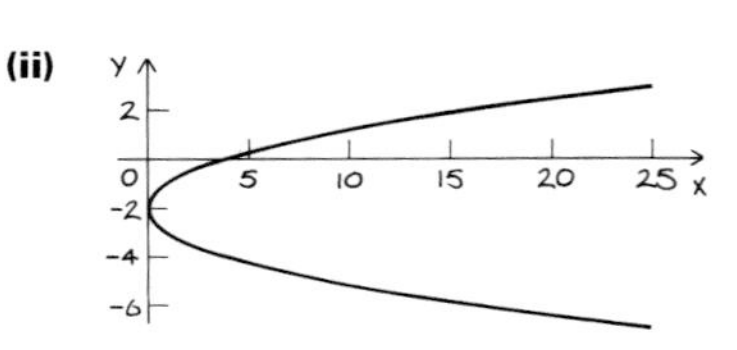

(iii) $y = -2$ **(iv)** $x = (y+2)^2$

8 (i)

t	–2	–1.5	–1	–0.5	0	0.5	1	1.5	2
x	0.14	0.22	0.37	0.61	1	1.65	2.72	4.48	7.39
y	–0.91	–1.00	–0.84	–0.48	0	0.48	0.84	1.00	0.91

(ii) $x > 0$

(iii)

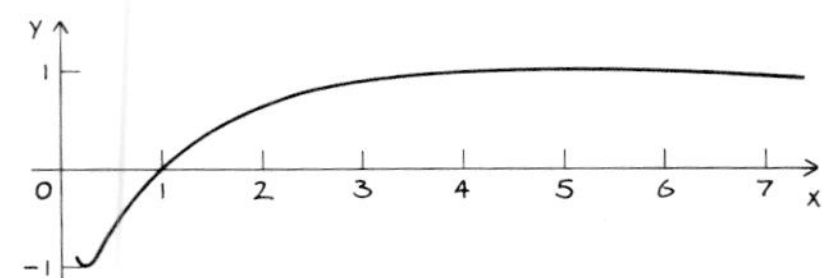

(iv) The graph oscillates infinitely many times from –1 to +1 for $t < -2$, i.e. where $0 < x < 0.14$.

For $t > 2$ the graph oscillates infinitely many times from –1 to +1, but successive distances between a maximum and a minimum become increasingly large.

9 (i)

θ	0	$\frac{\pi}{3}$	$\frac{2\pi}{3}$	π	$\frac{4\pi}{3}$	$\frac{5\pi}{3}$	2π	$\frac{7\pi}{3}$	$\frac{8\pi}{3}$	3π
x	0	$0.2a$	$1.2a$	$3.1a$	$5.1a$	$6.1a$	$6.3a$	$6.5a$	$7.5a$	$9.4a$
y	0	$0.5a$	$1.5a$	$2a$	$1.5a$	$0.5a$	0	$0.5a$	$1.5a$	$2a$

θ	$\frac{10\pi}{3}$	$\frac{11\pi}{3}$	4π	$\frac{13\pi}{3}$	$\frac{14\pi}{3}$	5π	$\frac{16\pi}{3}$	$\frac{17\pi}{3}$	6π
x	$11.3a$	$12.4a$	$12.6a$	$12.7a$	$13.8a$	$15.7a$	$17.6a$	$18.7a$	$18.8a$
y	$1.5a$	$0.5a$	0	$0.5a$	$1.5a$	$2a$	$1.5a$	$0.5a$	0

(ii)

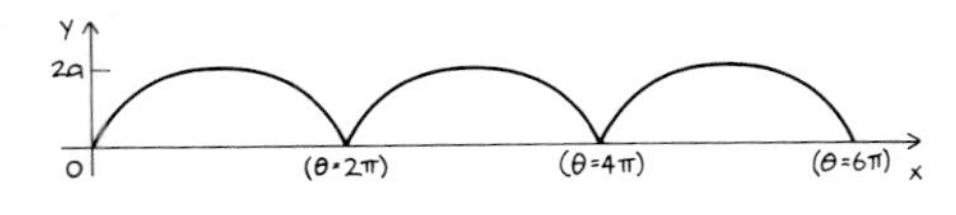

(iii) Periodic

10 (i)

θ	0	$\frac{\pi}{3}$	$\frac{\pi}{2}$	$\frac{2\pi}{3}$	π	$\frac{4\pi}{3}$	$\frac{3\pi}{2}$	$\frac{5\pi}{3}$	2π
x	a	$0.13a$	0	$-0.13a$	$-a$	$-0.13a$	0	$0.13a$	a
y	0	$0.65a$	a	$0.65a$	0	$-0.65a$	$-a$	$-0.65a$	0

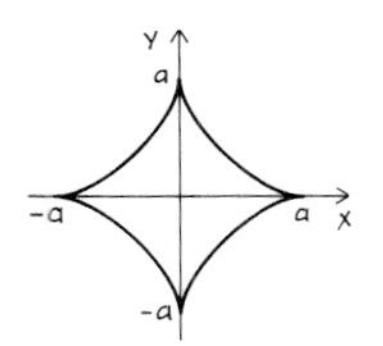

(ii)

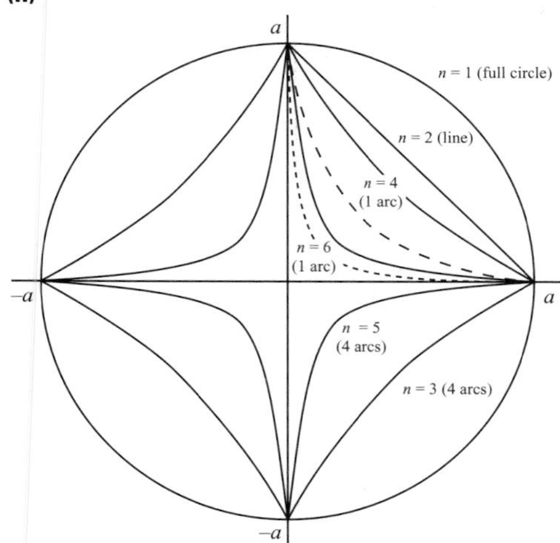

When $n = 0$ the curve becomes the single point (a, a).

(iii) (a) The larger the value of n, the closer the curve is to the axes. If the power is even, the curve is only in the first quadrant.

(b) If the power is odd, the curve is in all four quadrants.

Investigations (Page 237)

Cutting out patterns

The shape of each piece when laid on its side is as shown in the diagram.

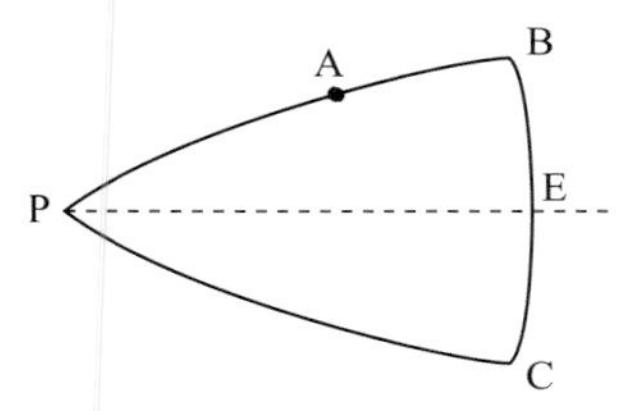

The question is 'What is the equation of the curve PAB?'

The arc BEC is $\frac{1}{8}$ of the equator of the ball and so has length $\frac{\pi r}{4}$ (r is the radius of the ball).

PE is the arc from the (North) pole to the equator and so has length $\frac{\pi r}{2}$.

The co-ordinates of a general point A on the arc PB are given by

$$x = r\theta \cos\left(\frac{\pi}{8} \times \frac{\sin\theta}{\theta}\right),\ y = r\theta \sin\theta\left(\frac{\pi}{8} \times \frac{\sin\theta}{\theta}\right)$$

with θ taking values between 0 (P) and $\frac{\pi}{2}$ (B).

The apparent motion of planets

Here are some pointers to get you started on this investgation.

For convenience, take the starting point as a time when the planets are in line.

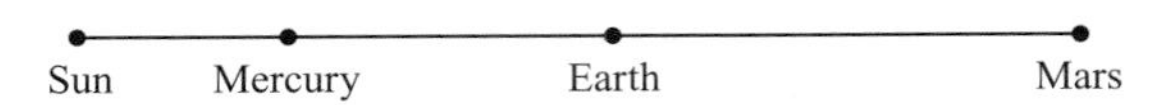

At a time d days later, Mercury has turned through $4d°$ relative to the Sun, Earth through $d°$ and Mars through $\frac{1}{2}d°$.

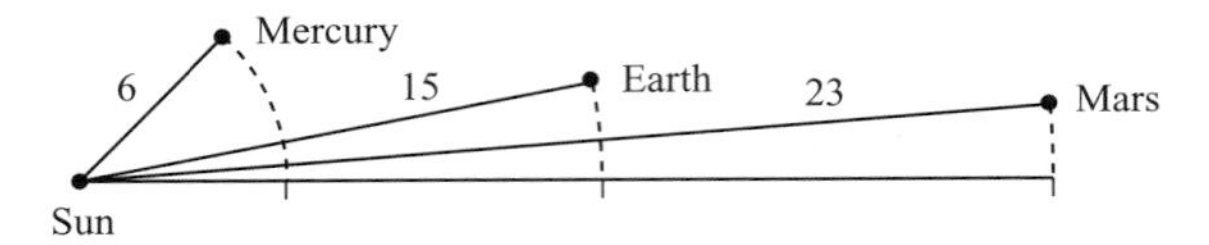

Taking the Sun as the origin, their positions are

Mercury $(6\cos 4d, 6\sin 4d)$

Earth $(15\cos d, 15\sin d)$

Mars $(23\cos \frac{1}{2}d, 23\sin \frac{1}{2}d)$.

So, relative to the Earth, the positions of the other two planets are

Mercury $(6\cos 4d - 15\cos d, 6\sin 4d - 15\sin d)$

Mars $(23\cos \frac{1}{2}d - 15\cos d, 23\sin \frac{1}{2}d - 15\sin d)$.

Plot these on your graphic calculator, using parametric mode.

Exercise 9B (Page 242)

1 **(i)** t

(ii) $\dfrac{1+\cos\theta}{1+\sin\theta}$

(iii) $\dfrac{t^2+1}{t^2-1}$

(iv) $-\frac{2}{3}\cot\theta$

(v) $\dfrac{t-1}{t+1}$

(vi) $-\tan\theta$

(vii) $\dfrac{1}{2e^t}$

(viii) $\dfrac{(1+t)^2}{(1-t)^2}$

2 **(i)** 6

(ii) $y = 6x - \sqrt{3}$

(iii) $3x + 18y - 19\sqrt{3} = 0$

3 **(i)** $\left(\frac{1}{4}, 0\right)$

(ii) 2

(iii) $y = 2x - \frac{1}{2}$

(iv) $\left(0, -\frac{1}{2}\right)$

4 **(i)** $x - ty + at^2 = 0$

(ii) $tx + y = at^3 + 2at$

(iii) $(at^2 + 2a, 0)$, $(0, at^3 + 2at)$

6 **(i)** $-\dfrac{b}{at^2}$

(ii) $at^2y + bx = 2abt$

(iii) $X(2at, 0)$, $Y\left(0, \dfrac{2b}{t}\right)$

(iv) Area $= 2ab$

7 **(ii)** $y = tx - 2t^2$

(iii) $[2(t_1 + t_2), 2t_1t_2]$

(iv) $x = 4$

8 **(i)** $t = 1$

(iii) $x + y = 3$

(v) $(-8, -5)$

9 **(i)** $t = -2$

(iii) $y = 2x - 6$

(iv) $(-5, 9)$

10 **(i)** $-\dfrac{3\cos t}{4\sin t}$

(ii) $3x\cos t + 4y\sin t = 12$

(iii) $t = 0.6435 + n\pi$

11 **(i)** $x\cos\theta + y\sin\theta = 3\sin\theta + 3\cos\theta + 2$

(iii) 2.85, 5.01 radians

(iv)

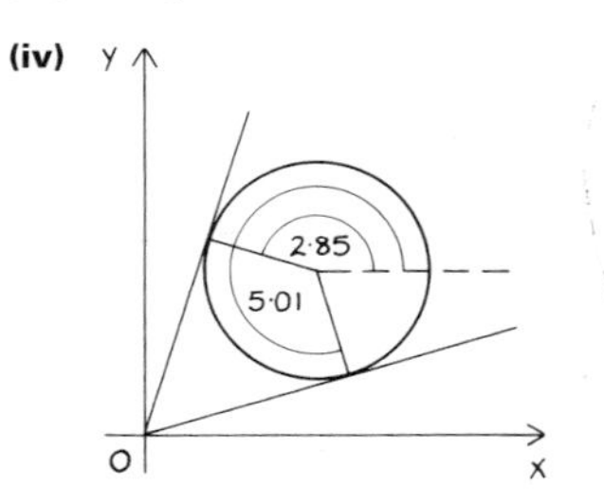

12 **(i)** $-\dfrac{\cos\theta}{\sin\theta}$

(ii) $y\cos\theta - x\sin\theta = 5\cos\theta - 2\sin\theta$

13 **(i)** $\dfrac{x^2}{9} + \dfrac{y^2}{4} = 1$

(ii)

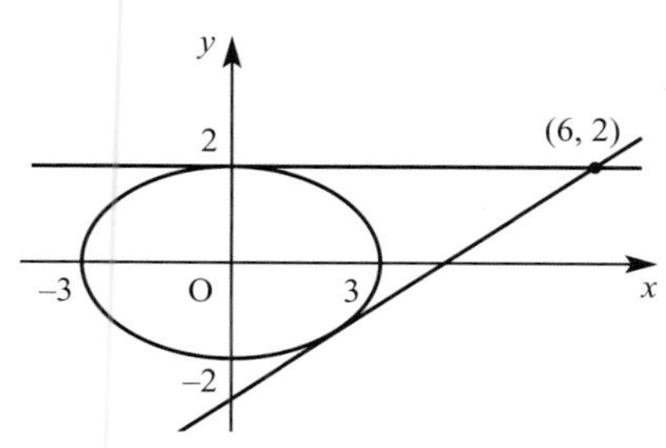

(iii) $-\dfrac{2\cos\theta}{3\sin\theta}$

(v) $\theta = 1.57$ or 5.64 (2 d.p.)

14 (i) (a) $\dfrac{x^2}{16} + \dfrac{y^2}{9} = 1$

(b) $20\sin(\theta + 0.9273)$

(c) max. $L = 20$ when $\theta = 0.6435$

(ii) (a) $-\dfrac{2}{\cos\theta}$

(b) $-\dfrac{3\cos\theta}{4\sin\theta}$

(c) $\theta = 0.34$

15 (i) $t = \dfrac{1-x}{x}$

(ii) $\dfrac{dy}{dt} = \dfrac{2t}{(1+t)^2(1-t)^2}$; $\dfrac{dx}{dt} = -\dfrac{1}{(1+t)^2}$

(iii) $y = \dfrac{1}{1-t}$

16 (i)

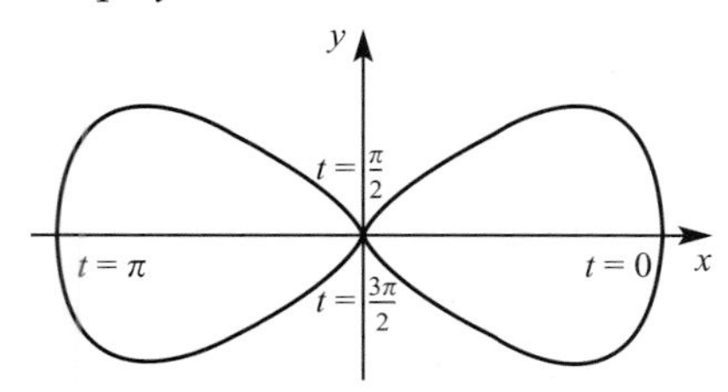

(ii) $\dfrac{dy}{dx} = -\dfrac{\cos 2t}{\sin t}$

(iv) $t = 0.253$ or 2.889 (3 d.p.)

17 (i) $x = \sqrt{5}\cos(\theta - 0.4636)$; $-\sqrt{5} \leqslant x \leqslant \sqrt{5}$

(ii) $\frac{1}{2}$

(iv) 3; 1

18 (i)

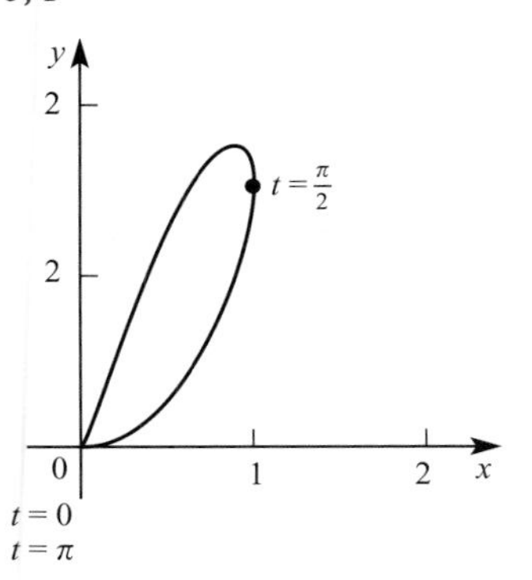

(ii) 0 and π

(iii) $-\dfrac{t}{2}\cos 2t + \frac{1}{4}\sin 2t + c$

(iv) $\dfrac{\pi}{4}$

19 (i) $\dfrac{2}{\sqrt{5}}, \dfrac{1}{\sqrt{5}}, \dfrac{4}{5}$

(ii) $-1, 2, 1$

(iii) $R = \sqrt{5}$, $C = (\sqrt{5}, \frac{4}{5})$

(iv) $\dfrac{2\cos 2t}{2\cos t - \sin t}$; -1

20 (i) $\dfrac{\sin\theta}{1-\cos\theta}$, $(\pi, 2)$

(ii) $\sqrt{5}\cos(\alpha - 1.107)$; $\alpha = 2.214$

(iii) 3π

21 (i) $(\frac{1}{2}, 0), (0, 1), (0, -1)$

(iii) $-3t$

22 (i) $A(2, 0), \theta = 0$; $B(0, 1), \theta = \dfrac{\pi}{2}$

(ii) $\dfrac{x^2}{4} + y^2 = 1$

(iii) $-\dfrac{\cos\theta}{2\sin\theta}$

(iv) $(-2\sin\alpha, \cos\alpha)$, $\dfrac{\sin\alpha - \cos\alpha}{2(\sin\alpha + \cos\alpha)}$

Chapter 10

? (Page 253)

You can either estimate it as a disc or as two cones.

? (Page 254)

1 (i) A cylinder

(ii) A sphere

(iii) A torus

2 $\dfrac{7\pi}{3}$

p (Page 257)

Follow the same procedure as that on page 255 but with the solid sliced into horizontal rather than vertical discs.

Exercise 10A (Page 258)

1 For example: ball, top (as in top & whip), roll of sellotape, pepper mill, bottle of wine/milk etc., tin of soup

2 **(i)**

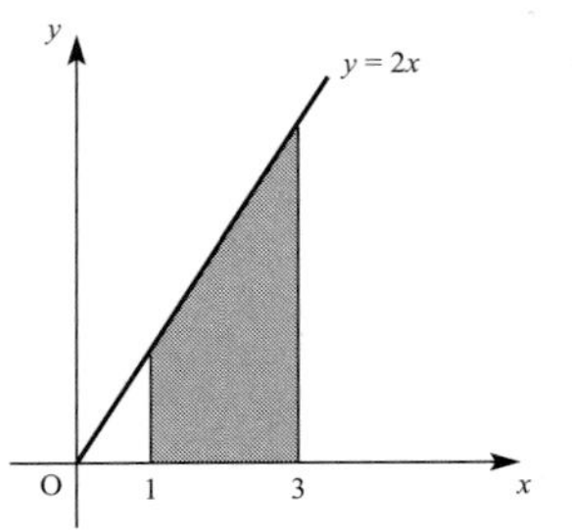

$\dfrac{104\pi}{3}$

(ii)

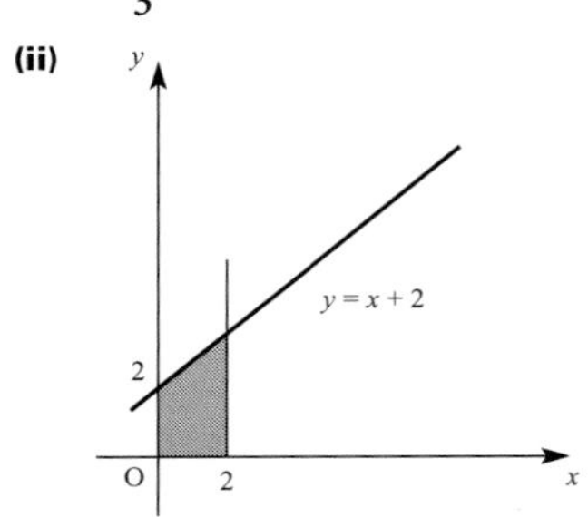

$\dfrac{56\pi}{3}$

(iii)

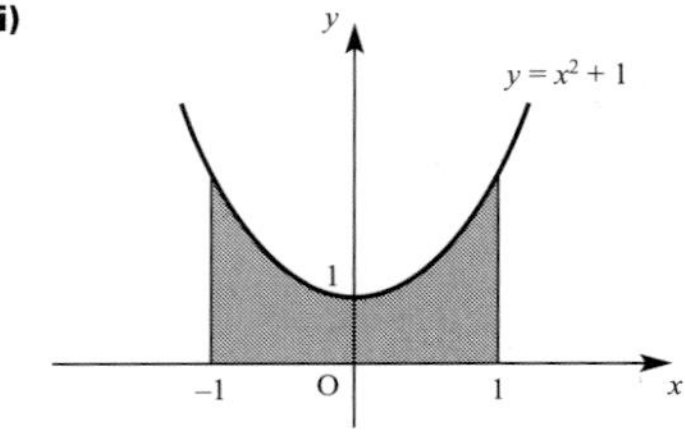

$\dfrac{56\pi}{15}$

(iv)

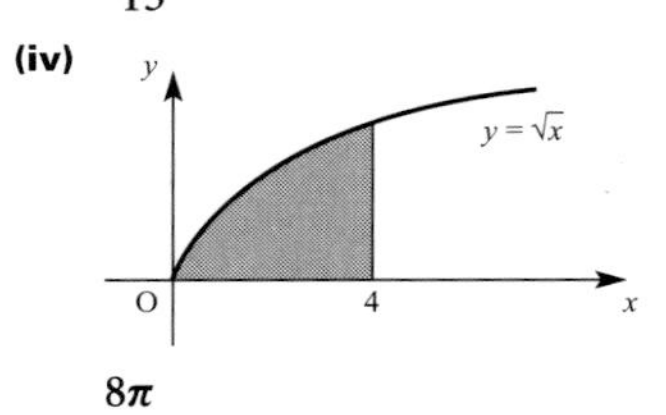

8π

3 **(i)** A(–3, 4); B(3, 4)

(ii) 36π units^3

4 **(i) (ii)**

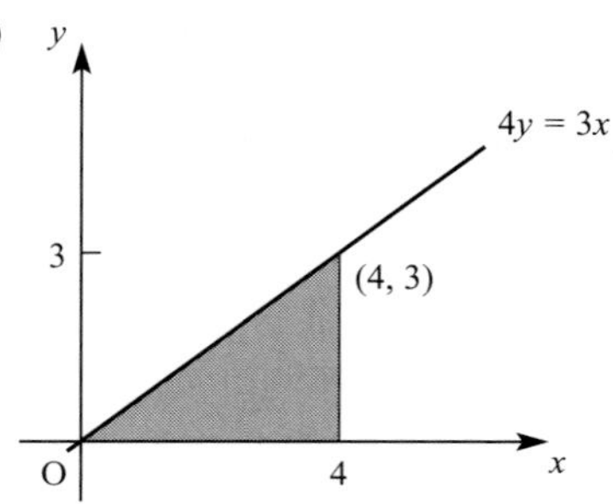

(iii) 12π units^3

5

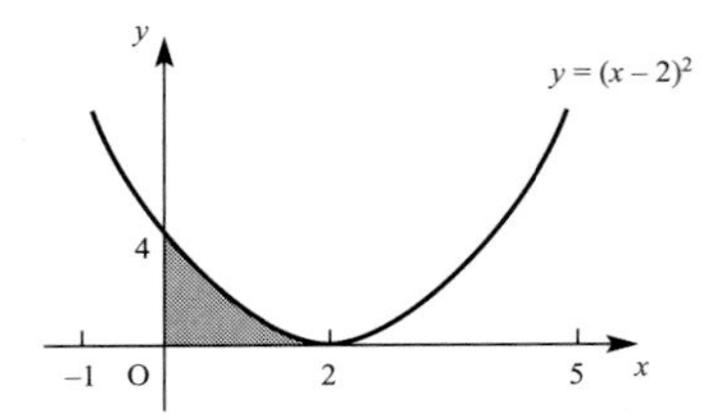

(ii) $2\frac{2}{3}$units^2 **(iv)** 6.4π units^3

6 **(i)**

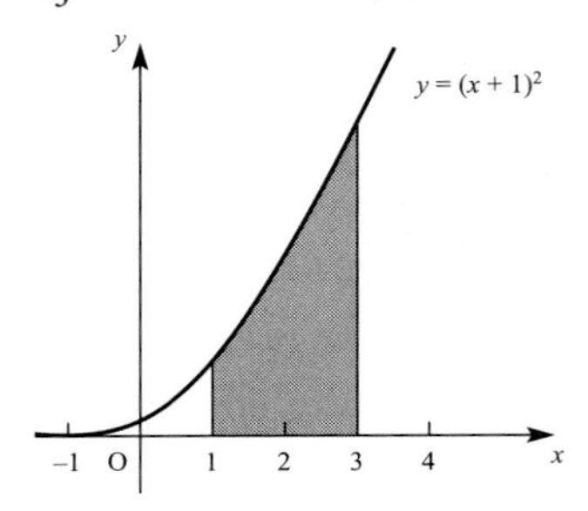

(ii) $18\frac{2}{3}$ units^2 **(iii)** $x^4 + 4x^3 + 6x^2 + 4x + 1$

(iv) $\dfrac{992\pi}{5}$

7 **(i)**

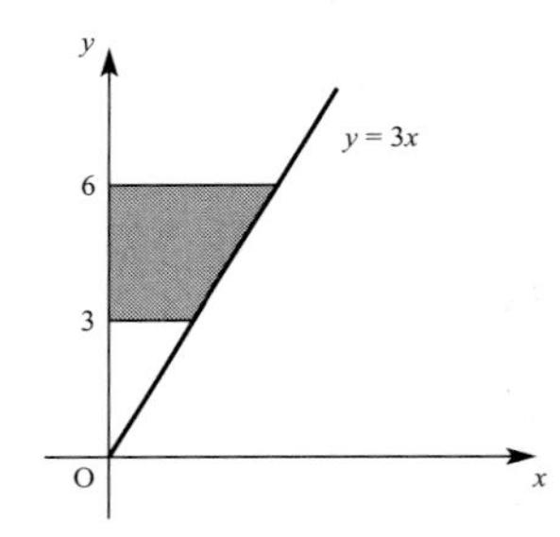

7π

(ii)

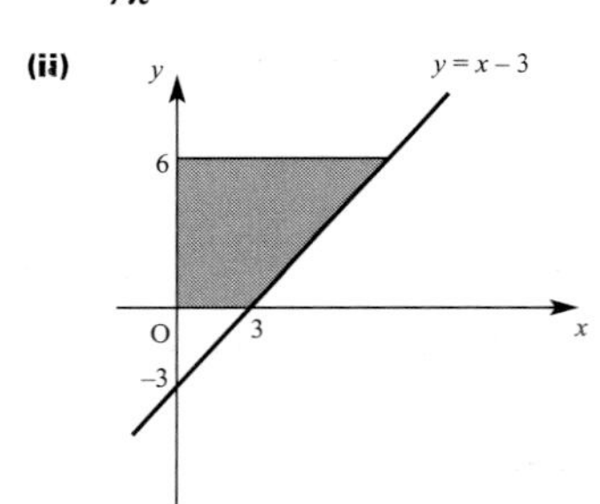

234π

(iii)

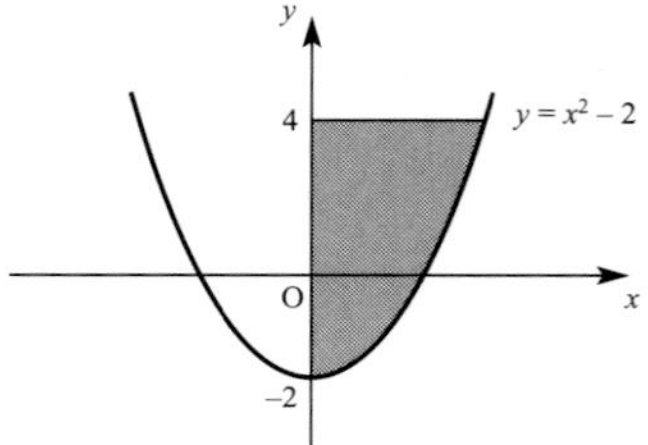

18π

8 **(i)** $\dfrac{2000\pi}{3}$

(ii) $\dfrac{1408\pi}{3}$

9 **(i)**

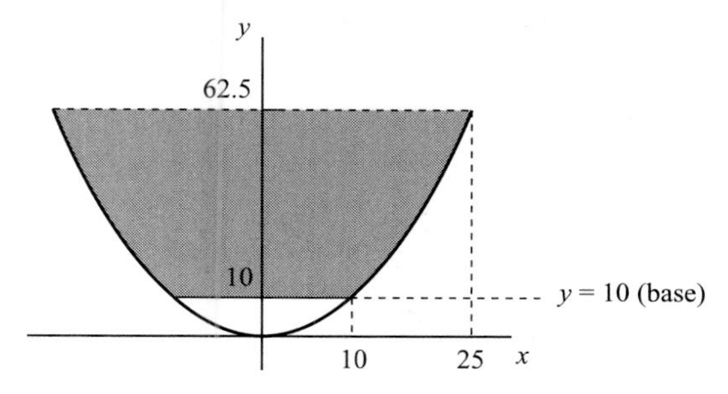

(ii) 45.9 litres

10 **(i)**

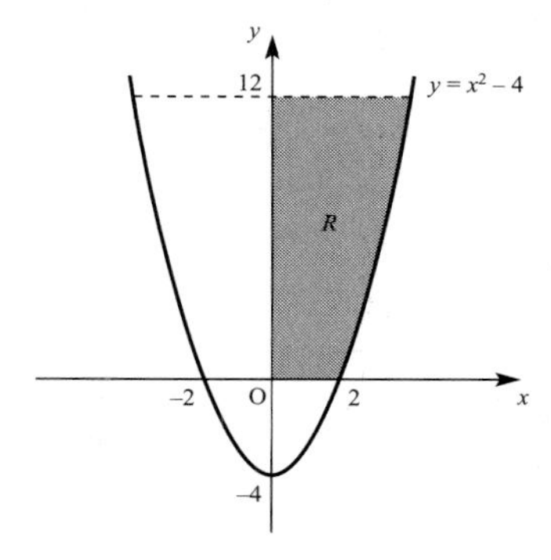

(ii) $\int_0^{12} \pi(y+4)\,dy$

(iii) 3 litres

(iv) $\int_0^{10} \pi(y+4)\,dy = 90\pi = \frac{3}{4}$ of 120π

❓ (Page 261)

Substitution using $u = x^2 - 1$ needs $2x$ in the numerator.

Not a product, not suitable for integration by parts.

Exercise 10B (Page 264)

1 **(i)** $\ln\left|\dfrac{3x-2}{1-x}\right| + c$

(ii) $\dfrac{1}{1-x} + \ln\left|\dfrac{x-1}{2x+3}\right| + c$

(iii) $\ln\left|\dfrac{x-1}{\sqrt{x^2+1}}\right| + c$

(iv) $\ln\left|\dfrac{(x-1)^2}{\sqrt{2x+1}}\right| + c$

(v) $\ln\left|\dfrac{x}{1-x}\right| - \dfrac{1}{x} + c$

(vi) $\frac{1}{2}\ln\left|\dfrac{x+1}{x+3}\right| + c$

(vii) $\ln\left|\dfrac{\sqrt{x^2+4}}{x+2}\right| + c$

(viii) $\ln\left|\dfrac{2x+1}{x+2}\right| + \dfrac{1}{2(2x+1)} + c$

2 $-\dfrac{x}{x^2+4} + \dfrac{1}{x-3}$, $\ln\left(\dfrac{\sqrt{2}}{6}\right)$

3 $\dfrac{1}{x^2} - \dfrac{2}{x} + \dfrac{4}{2x+1}$

4 **(i)** **(a)** $\dfrac{2}{1-2x} + \dfrac{1}{1+x}$

(b) $\ln\left(\frac{11}{8}\right) = 0.318\,45$

(ii) **(a)** $3 + 3x + 9x^2 + \ldots$

(b) 0.318 00

(c) 0.14%

5 **(i)** $A = 1, B = 3, C = -2$

(ii) $2 + \ln\left(\frac{125}{3}\right) = 5.73$

6 **(i)** $\frac{1}{2}xe^{2x} - \frac{1}{4}e^{2x} + c$

(ii) $\dfrac{9\pi - 2}{24}$

(iii) $A = 8, C = 1$

7 **(i)** $\dfrac{2}{1+2x} - \dfrac{(x+1)}{1+x^2}$

(ii) $|x| < \frac{1}{2}$

(iii) 0.078

8 **(i)** $B = 1, C = 16$

(ii) $\frac{33}{2}\ln 2$

(iii) $8 + 5x + 2x^2 + \dfrac{x^4}{2}$ for $|x| < 1$

9 **(i)** $2 + \dfrac{1}{u-1} - \dfrac{1}{u+1}$

? (Page 266)

You will return to these integrals in Activity 10.1.

Activity 10.1 (Page 267)

(i) This is a quotient. The derivative of the function on the bottom is not related to the function on the top, so you cannot use substitution. However, as the function on the bottom can be factorised, you can put it into partial fractions.

$$\int \frac{x-5}{x^2+2x-3}\,dx = \int \frac{2}{(x+3)}\,dx - \int \frac{1}{(x-1)}\,dx$$
$$= 2\ln|x+3| - \ln|x-1| + c$$

(ii) The derivative of the function on the bottom line is $2x + 2$, which is twice the function on the top line. So the integral is of the form

$$k\int \frac{f'(x)}{f(x)}\,dx = k\ln|f(x)| + c.$$

This integral can also be found using partial fractions, but using logarithms is quicker.

$$\int \frac{x+1}{x^2+2x-3}\,dx = \tfrac{1}{2}\int \frac{2x+2}{x^2+2x-3}\,dx$$
$$= \tfrac{1}{2}\ln|x^2+2x-3| + c$$

(iii) This is a product of x and e^x. There is no relationship between one function and the derivative of the other, so you cannot use substitution. As one of the functions is x, you can use integration by parts.

$$\int xe^x\,dx = xe^x - \int e^x\,dx$$
$$= xe^x - e^x + c$$

(iv) This is also a product, this time of x and e^{x^2}. e^{x^2} is a function of x^2, and $2x$ is the derivative of x^2, so you can use the substitution $u = x^2$.

$$\int xe^{x^2}\,dx = \int \tfrac{1}{2}e^u\,du \quad \text{where } u = x^2$$
$$= \tfrac{1}{2}e^u + c$$
$$= \tfrac{1}{2}e^{x^2} + c$$

(v) In this case the numerator is the differential of the denominator and so the integral is the natural logarithm of the modulus of the denominator.

$$\int \frac{2x+\cos x}{x^2+\sin x}\,dx$$

Since $\frac{d}{dx}(x^2+\sin x) = 2x + \cos x$ the integral is $\ln|x^2+\sin x| + c$.

(vi) This is a product: $\sin^2 x$ is a function of $\sin x$, and $\cos x$ is the derivative of $\sin x$, so you can use the substitution $u = \sin x$.

$$\int \cos x\sin^2 x\,dx = \int u^2\,du \quad \text{where } u = \sin x$$
$$= \tfrac{1}{3}u^3 + c$$
$$= \tfrac{1}{3}\sin^3 x + c$$

Exercise 10C (Page 268)

1 **(i)** $\tfrac{1}{3}\sin(3x-1) + c$

(ii) $\dfrac{-1}{(x^2+x-1)} + c$

(iii) $-e^{1-x} + c$

(iv) $\tfrac{1}{2}\sin 2x + c$

(v) $x\ln 2x - x + c$

(vi) $\dfrac{-1}{4(x^2-1)^2} + c$

(vii) $\tfrac{1}{3}(2x-3)^{\frac{3}{2}} + c$

(viii) $\ln\left|\dfrac{x-1}{x+2}\right| - \dfrac{1}{x-1} + c$

(ix) $\tfrac{1}{4}x^4\ln x - \tfrac{1}{16}x^4 + c$

(x) $\ln\left|\dfrac{x-3}{2x-1}\right| + c$

(xi) $\tfrac{1}{2}e^{x^2+2x} + c$

(xii) $-\ln(\sin x + \cos x) + c$

(xiii) $-\tfrac{1}{2}x^2\cos 2x + \tfrac{1}{2}x\sin 2x + \tfrac{1}{4}\cos 2x + c$

(xiv) $-\tfrac{1}{2}\cos 2x + \tfrac{1}{6}\cos^3 2x + c$

2 **(i)** $\tfrac{8}{3}$

(ii) $\tfrac{1}{3}\ln 4$

(iii) $48 + 8\ln 4 \quad 2$

(iv) $\tfrac{2}{3} - \tfrac{5}{6\sqrt{2}} \approx 0.0774$

(v) $\tfrac{8}{3}\ln 2 - \tfrac{7}{9}$

3 $\tfrac{4}{3}$

4 $\tfrac{1}{3}(2\sqrt{2} - 1)$

5 0.24

6 $\tfrac{1}{8}\pi - \tfrac{1}{4}$

7 **(i)** $-\frac{1}{2}xe^{-2x} - \frac{1}{4}e^{-2x} + c$

(ii) 0.112

8 **(i)** $-\frac{1}{2}\cos(2x-3) + c$

(ii) $\frac{3}{4}e^4 + \frac{1}{4}$

(iii) $\frac{1}{2}\ln|x^2 - 9| + c$

9 **(i)** $\frac{38}{9}$

(ii) $\frac{1}{4} - \frac{3}{4e^2}$

10 $\frac{1}{4}, \frac{1}{4} - \frac{3}{4e^2}$

? (Page 269)

There are any number of functions that cannot be integrated algebraically, for example fractions involving different sorts of elements, like $\frac{x^3 + \cos x}{x^4 + e^x}$.

By contrast, all functions of x can be differentiated with respect to x, usually using the standard rules. However for the differentiation to be valid, their curves must be smooth. Some functions, like $\frac{1}{(x-2)(x-5)}$ and $|x-4|$ can be differentiated apart from at certain points, in these cases $x = 2$ and 5 and $x = 4$ respectively.

? (Page 270)

(i) **(a)** Underestimate

(b) Yes, would improve

(ii) **(a)** Cannot tell

(b) Cannot tell because of the point of inflection in the graph

(iii) **(a)** Overestimate

(b) Yes, would improve

Activity 10.2 (Page 270)

1

n	h	Approximation to I
1	4	0.454 054 054
2	2	0.344 674 085
4	1	0.310 798 581
8	0.5	0.301 630 068
16	0.25	0.299 285 378

2 It is clearly going to be 0.2… and the next digit will probably be 9. After that nothing can be said.

? (Page 271)

You may be able to judge the sign of the error, that is whether the answer is an overestimate or an underestimate. You can say nothing about the size of the error.

Activity 10.3 (Page 271)

1 0.298 498 931

2

n	h	Approximation to I	ε	$\frac{\varepsilon}{h^2}$
1	4	0.454 054 054	0.155 555 123	0.0097
2	2	0.344 674 085	0.046 175 154	0.0115
4	1	0.310 798 581	0.012 299 650	0.0123
8	0.5	0.301 630 068	0.003 131 137	0.0125
16	0.25	0.299 285 378	0.000 786 447	0.0126

The greater the number of strips, the more accurate the answer. The error is approximately proportional to h^2. Since the value of h halves each time, the error is one quarter of its previous value.

P (Page 272)

Line 1 uses the fact that the error is proportional to h^2.
Line 2 follows from subtraction.
Line 3 follows from dividing by $(h_1^2 - h_2^2)$.
Line 4 is a rearrangement of the second statement in line 1.
In line 5, k is substituted in line 4.

Exercise 10D (Page 273)

1 **(i)**

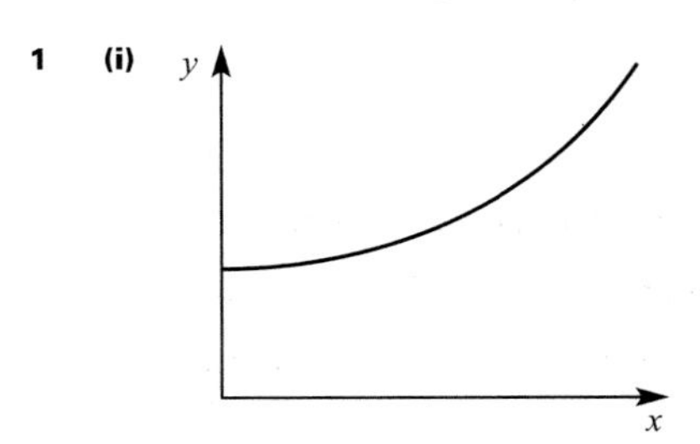

(ii) 2.179 218, 2.145 242, 2.136 756, 2.134 635

(iii) 2.13

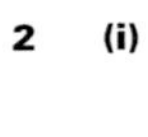

2 **(i)**

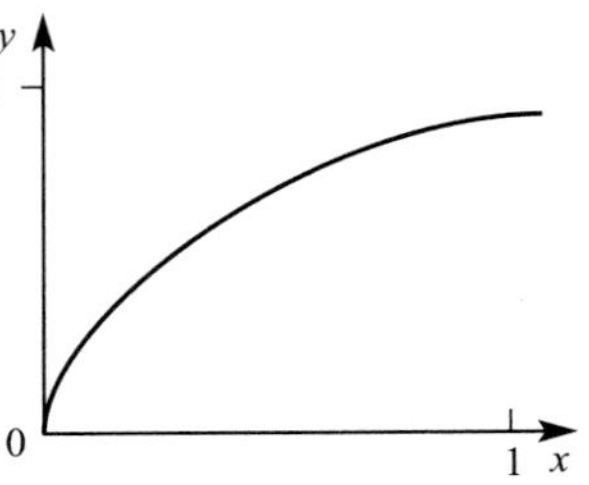

(ii) 0.458 658, 0.575 532, 0.618 518, 0.634 173, 0.639 825

(iii) 0.64

3 **(i)**

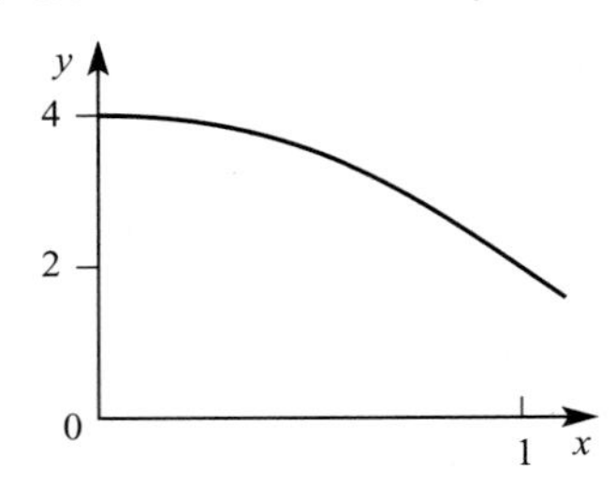

(ii) **(a)** 3

(b) 3.1

(c) 3.131 176

(d) 3.138 988

(iii) 3.14 (This actually converges to π.)

4 **(i)** 2, 2, 4, 4

(ii)

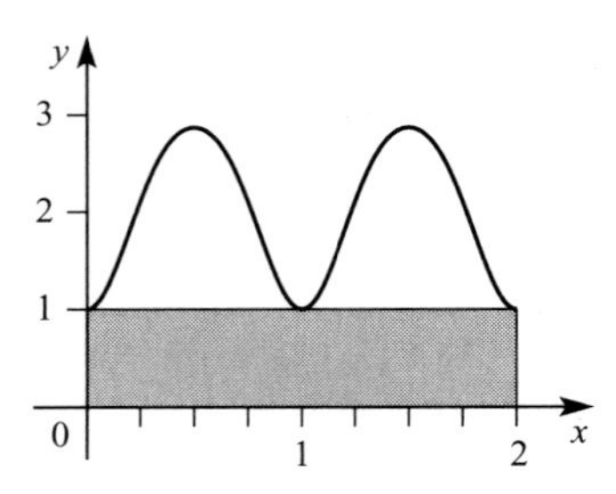

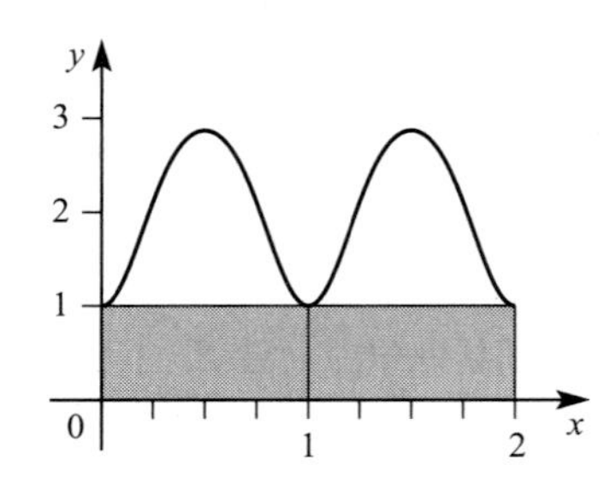

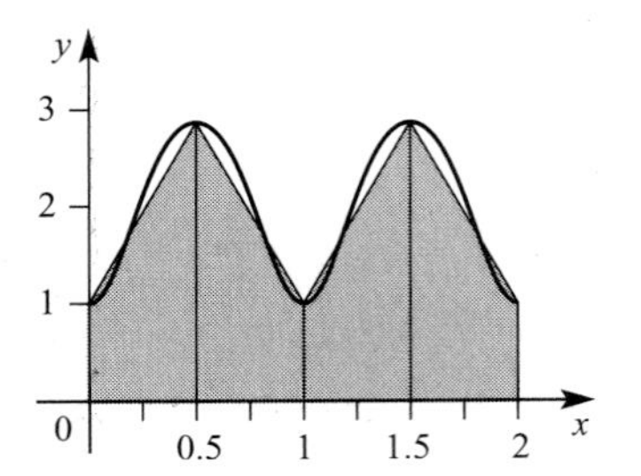

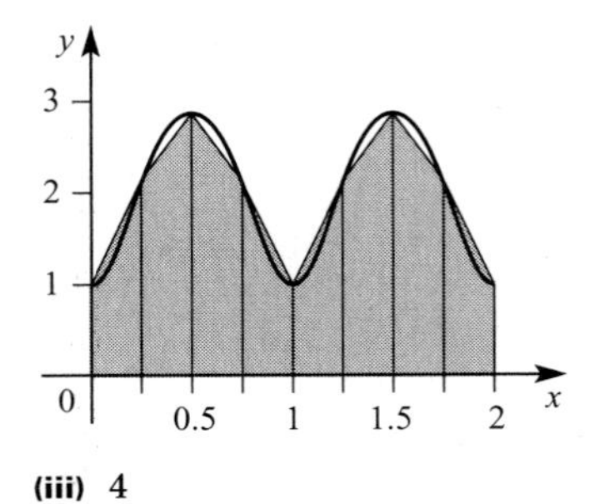

(iii) 4

5 0.34

Investigation (Page 273)

(i)

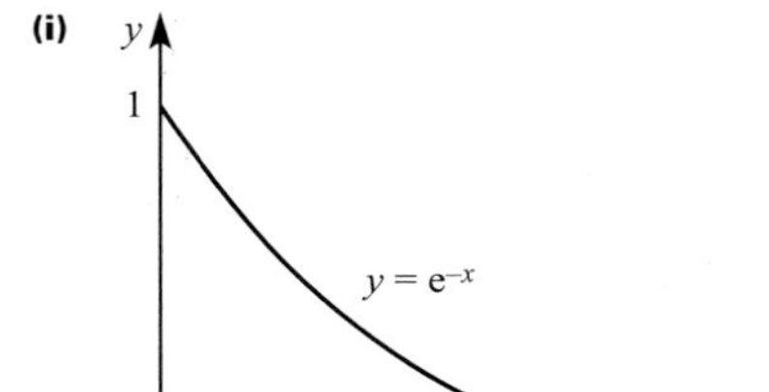

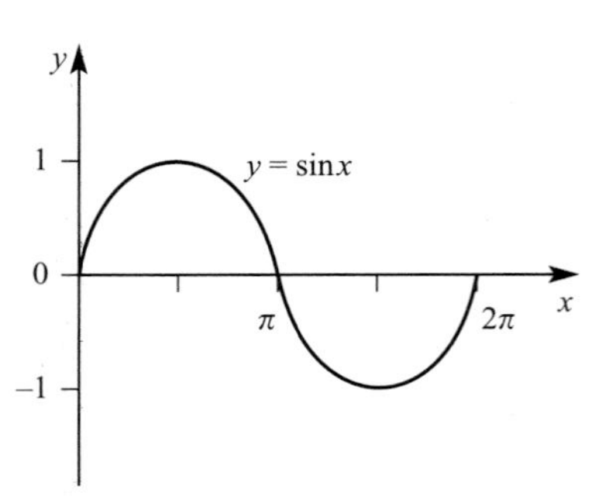

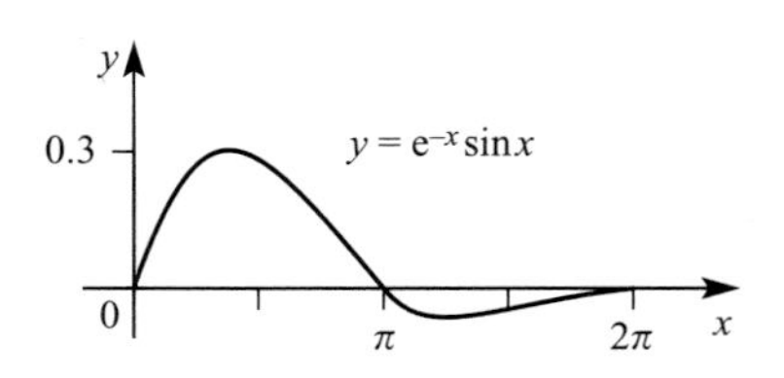

(ii) 0.469 115, 0.508 270

(iii) 0.521 321

Chapter 11

❓ (Page 275)

To find the distance between the two vapour trails you need two pieces of information for each of them: either two points that it goes through, or else one point and its direction. All of these need to be in three dimensions. However, if you want to find the closest approach of the two aircraft you also need to know, for each of them, the time at which it was at a given point on its trail and the speed at which it was travelling. (This answer assumes constant speeds and directions.)

Exercise 11A (Page 281)

1 **(i)** $3\mathbf{i} + 2\mathbf{j}$

(ii) $5\mathbf{i} - 4\mathbf{j}$

(iii) $3\mathbf{i}$

(iv) $-3\mathbf{i} - \mathbf{j}$

(v) $2\mathbf{j}$

2 **(i)**

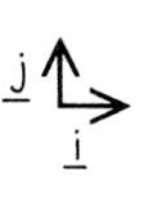

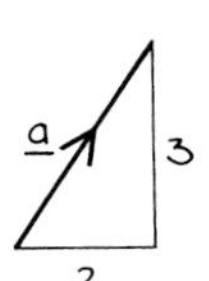

$(\sqrt{13}, 56.3°)$

(ii)

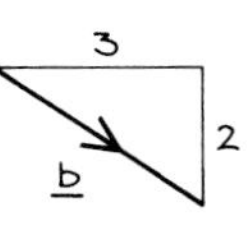

$(\sqrt{13}, -33.7°)$

(iii)

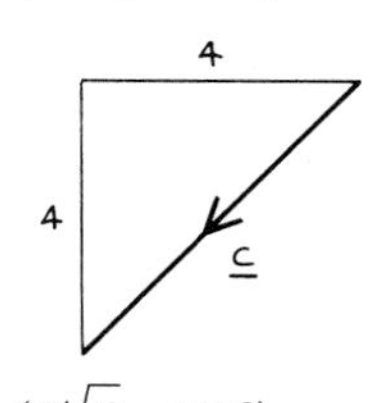

$(4\sqrt{2}, -135°)$

(iv)

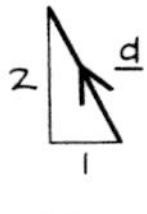

$(\sqrt{5}, 116.6°)$

(v)

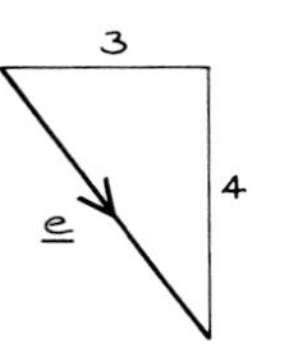

$(5, -53.1°)$

3 **(i)**

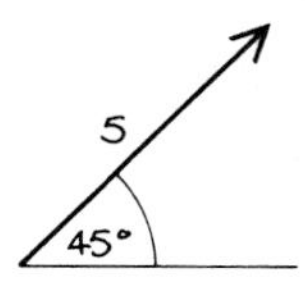

$3.54\mathbf{i} + 3.54\mathbf{j}$

(ii)

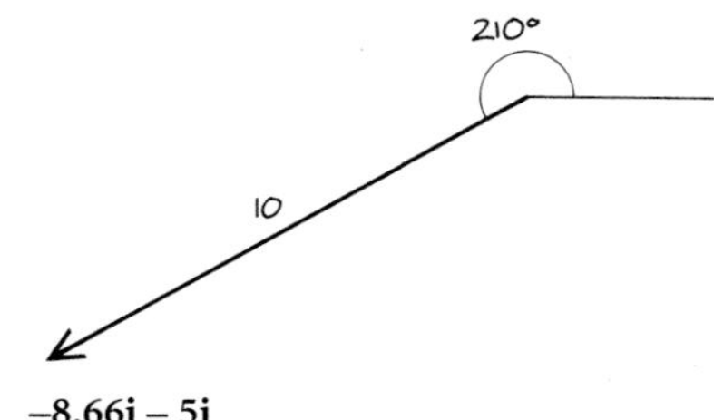

$-8.66\mathbf{i} - 5\mathbf{j}$

(iii)

$4\mathbf{j}$

(iv)

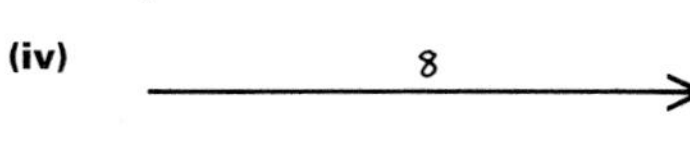

$8\mathbf{i}$

(v)

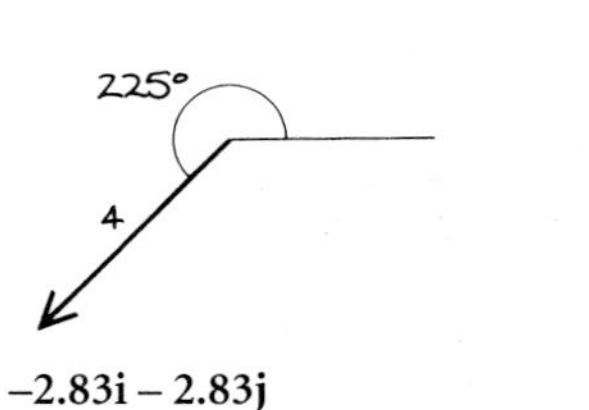

$-2.83\mathbf{i} - 2.83\mathbf{j}$

4 **(i)** $2\mathbf{i} - 2\mathbf{j}$

(ii) $2\mathbf{i}$

(iii) $-4\mathbf{j}$

(iv) $4\mathbf{j}$

(v) $-\mathbf{i} + \mathbf{j}$

(vi) $\mathbf{i} - \mathbf{j}$

(vii) $8\mathbf{i}$

(viii) $-8\mathbf{i}$

(ix) $2\mathbf{i} - 4\mathbf{j}$

(x) $4\mathbf{i} + 4\mathbf{j}$

5 **(i)** A: 2i + 3j, C: –2i + j

(ii) $\overrightarrow{AB} = -2i + j$, $\overrightarrow{CB} = 2i + 3j$

(iii) **(a)** $\overrightarrow{AB} = \overrightarrow{OC}$

(b) $\overrightarrow{CB} = \overrightarrow{OA}$

(iv) A parallelogram

Exercise 11B (Page 287)

1 **(i)** $\begin{pmatrix} 6 \\ 8 \end{pmatrix}$

(ii) $\begin{pmatrix} 1 \\ 1 \end{pmatrix}$

(iii) $\begin{pmatrix} 0 \\ 0 \end{pmatrix}$

(iv) $\begin{pmatrix} 8 \\ -1 \end{pmatrix}$

(v) –3j

2 **(i)** 2i + 3j

(ii) i

(iii) j

(iv) 3i + 2j

(v) 0

3 **(i)** **(a)** b

(b) a + b

(c) –a + b

(ii) **(a)** $\frac{1}{2}(a + b)$

(b) $\frac{1}{2}(-a + b)$

(iii) PQRS is any parallelogram and $\overrightarrow{PM} = \frac{1}{2}\overrightarrow{PR}$, $\overrightarrow{QM} = \frac{1}{2}\overrightarrow{QS}$

4 **(i)** **(a)** i

(b) 2i

(c) i – j

(d) –i – 2j

(ii) $|\overrightarrow{AB}| = |\overrightarrow{BC}| = \sqrt{2}$, $|\overrightarrow{AD}| = |\overrightarrow{CD}| = \sqrt{5}$

5 **(i)** $-p + q$, $\frac{1}{2}p - \frac{1}{2}q$, $-\frac{1}{2}p$, $-\frac{1}{2}q$

(ii) $\overrightarrow{NM} = \frac{1}{2}\overrightarrow{BC}$, $\overrightarrow{NL} = \frac{1}{2}\overrightarrow{AC}$, $\overrightarrow{ML} = \frac{1}{2}\overrightarrow{AB}$

6 **(i)** $\begin{pmatrix} \frac{2}{\sqrt{13}} \\ \frac{3}{\sqrt{13}} \end{pmatrix}$

(ii) $\frac{3}{5}i + \frac{4}{5}j$

(ii) $\begin{pmatrix} \frac{-1}{\sqrt{2}} \\ \frac{-1}{\sqrt{2}} \end{pmatrix}$

(iv) $\frac{5}{13}i - \frac{12}{13}j$

(v) i

(vi) $\begin{pmatrix} \frac{-1}{\sqrt{5}} \\ \frac{2}{\sqrt{5}} \end{pmatrix}$

(vii) $\begin{pmatrix} \frac{-1}{\sqrt{5}} \\ \frac{2}{\sqrt{5}} \end{pmatrix}$

(viii) $\begin{pmatrix} \frac{1}{\sqrt{5}} \\ \frac{2}{\sqrt{5}} \end{pmatrix}$

(ix) $\begin{pmatrix} \cos\alpha \\ \sin\alpha \end{pmatrix}$

(x) $\begin{pmatrix} \cos\beta \\ \sin\beta \end{pmatrix}$

p (Page 291)

$$\overrightarrow{OP} = \overrightarrow{OA} + \lambda(\overrightarrow{OB} - \overrightarrow{OA})$$
$$= (1 - \lambda)\overrightarrow{OA} + \lambda\overrightarrow{OB}$$

Activity 11.1 (Page 291)

(ii) $\begin{pmatrix} -2 \\ -9 \end{pmatrix}$, $\begin{pmatrix} 0 \\ -5 \end{pmatrix}$, $\begin{pmatrix} 2 \\ -1 \end{pmatrix}$, $\begin{pmatrix} 3 \\ 1 \end{pmatrix}$, $\begin{pmatrix} 3\frac{1}{2} \\ 2 \end{pmatrix}$, $\begin{pmatrix} 4 \\ 3 \end{pmatrix}$, $\begin{pmatrix} 8 \\ 11 \end{pmatrix}$

(iv) 0, 1, $\frac{1}{2}$, $\frac{3}{4}$

(v) **(a)** It lies between A and B.

(b) It lies beyond B.

(c) It lies beyond A.

Activity 11.2 (Page 294)

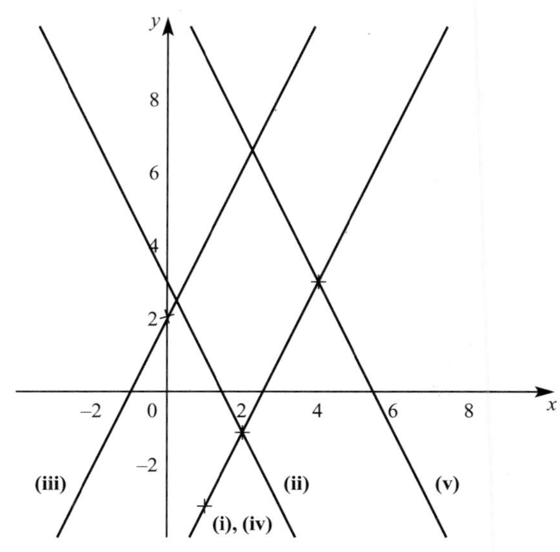

(i) and **(iv)** are the same since **(a)** putting $\lambda = -1$ in **(i)** gives $\begin{pmatrix} 1 \\ -3 \end{pmatrix}$ **(b)** $\begin{pmatrix} 1 \\ 2 \end{pmatrix}$ is parallel to $\begin{pmatrix} 3 \\ 6 \end{pmatrix}$.

(iii) is parallel to **(i)** since the direction vector is the same.

(iv) is parallel to **(ii)** since $\begin{pmatrix} -1 \\ 2 \end{pmatrix} = -\begin{pmatrix} 1 \\ -2 \end{pmatrix}$.

Exercise 11C (Page 297)

1 **(i)** **(a)** 2i + 8j

(b) $\sqrt{68}$

(c) 3i + 7j

(ii) **(a)** −4i − 3j

(b) 5

(c) 2i + 1.5j

(iii) **(a)** 6i + 8j

(b) 10

(c) i + 3j

(iv) **(a)** 6i − 8j

(b) 10

(c) 0

(v) **(a)** 5i + 12j

(b) 13

(c) −7.5i − 2j

2 *Note: These answers are not unique.*

(i) $\mathbf{r} = \begin{pmatrix} 2 \\ 1 \end{pmatrix} + \lambda\begin{pmatrix} 1 \\ 2 \end{pmatrix}$

(ii) $\mathbf{r} = \begin{pmatrix} 3 \\ 5 \end{pmatrix} + \lambda\begin{pmatrix} -1 \\ 1 \end{pmatrix}$

(iii) $\mathbf{r} = \begin{pmatrix} -6 \\ -6 \end{pmatrix} + \lambda\begin{pmatrix} 1 \\ 1 \end{pmatrix}$

(iv) $\mathbf{r} = \begin{pmatrix} 5 \\ 3 \end{pmatrix} + \lambda\begin{pmatrix} 1 \\ 1 \end{pmatrix}$

(v) $\mathbf{r} = \lambda\begin{pmatrix} 2 \\ 1 \end{pmatrix}$

(vi) $\mathbf{r} = \lambda\begin{pmatrix} -1 \\ 4 \end{pmatrix}$

(vii) $\mathbf{r} = \lambda\begin{pmatrix} -1 \\ 4 \end{pmatrix}$

(viii) $\mathbf{r} = \begin{pmatrix} 3 \\ -12 \end{pmatrix} + \lambda\begin{pmatrix} -1 \\ 4 \end{pmatrix}$

3 **(i)** $y = 3x - 1$

(ii) $y = \frac{1}{2}x + 1$

(iii) $y = x - 1$

(iv) $y = x - 1$

(v) $y = 5$ (x may take any value)

4 *Note: These answers are not unique.*

(i) $\mathbf{r} = \begin{pmatrix} 0 \\ 3 \end{pmatrix} + \lambda\begin{pmatrix} 1 \\ 2 \end{pmatrix}$

(ii) $\mathbf{r} = \begin{pmatrix} 0 \\ -4 \end{pmatrix} + \lambda\begin{pmatrix} 1 \\ 1 \end{pmatrix}$

(iii) $\mathbf{r} = \begin{pmatrix} 0 \\ -1 \end{pmatrix} + \lambda\begin{pmatrix} 2 \\ 1 \end{pmatrix}$

(iv) $\mathbf{r} = \lambda\begin{pmatrix} -4 \\ 1 \end{pmatrix}$

(v) $\mathbf{r} = \begin{pmatrix} 0 \\ 4 \end{pmatrix} + \lambda\begin{pmatrix} -2 \\ 1 \end{pmatrix}$

5 **(i)** $\begin{pmatrix} 4 \\ 1 \end{pmatrix}$

(ii) $\begin{pmatrix} 5 \\ 5 \end{pmatrix}$

(iii) $\begin{pmatrix} 12 \\ 17 \end{pmatrix}$

(iv) $\begin{pmatrix} -5 \\ 6 \end{pmatrix}$

(v) $\begin{pmatrix} 6 \\ 3 \end{pmatrix}$

6 **(i)** 12.8 km

(ii) $20\,\text{km h}^{-1}$, $5\,\text{km h}^{-1}$

(iii) After 40 minutes there is a collision.

7 **(i)** $\overrightarrow{OL} = \begin{pmatrix} 10 \\ 4.5 \end{pmatrix}$; $\overrightarrow{OM} = \begin{pmatrix} 7 \\ 3.5 \end{pmatrix}$; $\overrightarrow{ON} = \begin{pmatrix} 4 \\ 1 \end{pmatrix}$

(ii) AL: $\mathbf{r} = \begin{pmatrix} 1 \\ 0 \end{pmatrix} + \lambda\begin{pmatrix} 2 \\ 1 \end{pmatrix}$; BM: $\mathbf{r} = \begin{pmatrix} 7 \\ 2 \end{pmatrix} + \mu\begin{pmatrix} 0 \\ 1 \end{pmatrix}$;

CN: $\mathbf{r} = \begin{pmatrix} 13 \\ 7 \end{pmatrix} + \nu\begin{pmatrix} 3 \\ 2 \end{pmatrix}$

(iii) **(a)** (7, 3)

(b) (7, 3)

(iv) The lines AL, BM and CN are concurrent. (They are the medians of the triangle, and this result holds for the medians of any triangle.)

p (Page 299)

The cosine rule

Pythagoras' theorem

p (Page 301)

$$\begin{pmatrix} a_1 \\ a_2 \end{pmatrix} \cdot \begin{pmatrix} b_1 \\ b_2 \end{pmatrix} = a_1 b_1 + a_2 b_2$$

$$\begin{pmatrix} b_1 \\ b_2 \end{pmatrix} \cdot \begin{pmatrix} a_1 \\ a_2 \end{pmatrix} = b_1 a_1 + b_2 a_2$$

These are the same because ordinary multiplication is commutative.

Exercise 11D (Page 302)

1 **(i)** 42.3°

(ii) 90°

(iii) 18.4°

(iv) 31.0°

(v) 90°

(vi) 180°

2 **(i)** $\mathbf{r} = \begin{pmatrix} 1 \\ 0 \end{pmatrix} + \lambda \begin{pmatrix} 2 \\ 1 \end{pmatrix}$

(ii) $\mathbf{r} = \begin{pmatrix} 6 \\ 1 \end{pmatrix} + \mu \begin{pmatrix} 1 \\ 2 \end{pmatrix}$

(iii) $\begin{pmatrix} 7 \\ 3 \end{pmatrix}$

(iv) 36.9°

3 **(i)** Parallelogram: AB || CD, BC || DA

(ii) A(5, 2); B(1, 1); C(2, 4); D(6, 5)

(iii) 57.5°, 122.5°

4 **(i)** $\begin{pmatrix} 3 \\ 1 \end{pmatrix}, \begin{pmatrix} -1 \\ 3 \end{pmatrix}$

(ii) $\overrightarrow{BA} \cdot \overrightarrow{BC} = 0$

(iii) $|\overrightarrow{AB}| = |\overrightarrow{BC}| = \sqrt{10}$

(iv) (2, 5)

5 **(i)** $\overrightarrow{PQ} = -4\mathbf{i} + 2\mathbf{j}$; $\overrightarrow{RQ} = 4\mathbf{i} + 8\mathbf{j}$

(ii) 26.6°

(iii) $3\mathbf{i} + 7\mathbf{j}$

(iv) 53.1°

p (Page 304)

The length of a vector

The vector $a_1\mathbf{i} + a_2\mathbf{j} + a_3\mathbf{k}$ is shown in the diagram.

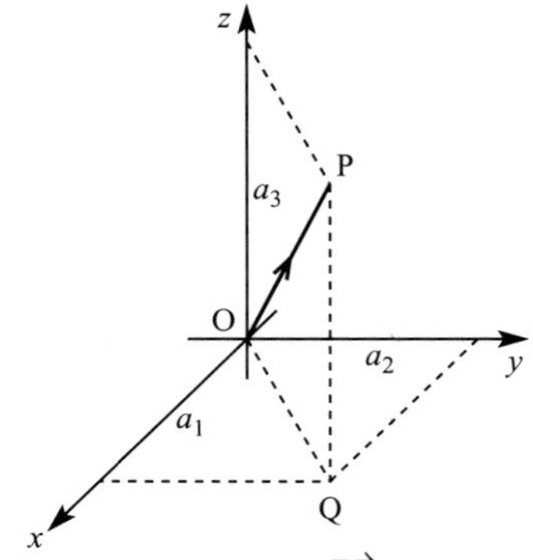

Start with the vector $\overrightarrow{OQ} = a_1\mathbf{i} + a_2\mathbf{j}$.

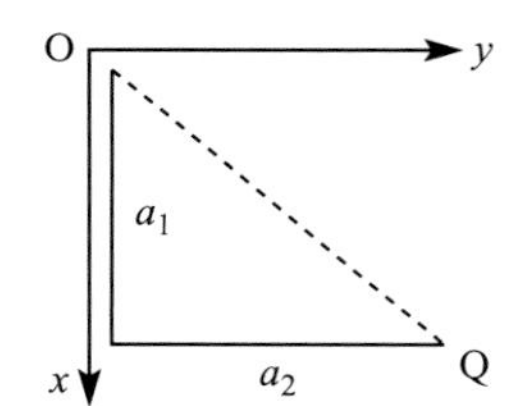

Length $= \sqrt{a_1^2 + a_1^2}$

Now look at the triangle OQP.

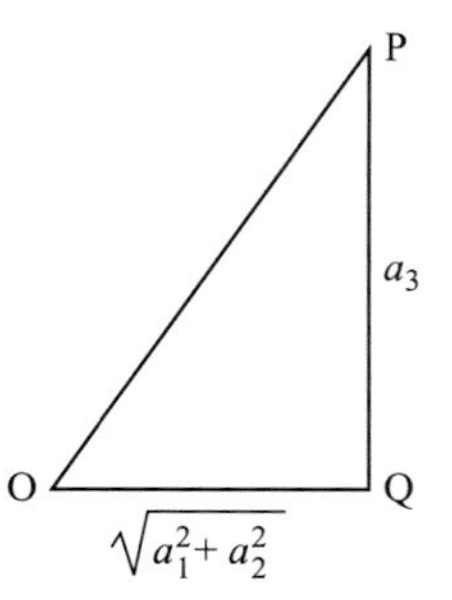

$$\begin{aligned} OP^2 &= OQ^2 + QP^2 \\ &= (a_1^2 + a_2^2) + a_3^2 \end{aligned}$$

$$\Rightarrow \quad OP = \sqrt{a_1^2 + a_2^2 + a_3^2}$$

P (Page 304)

The angle between two vectors

Consider the triangle OAB with angle AOB = θ, as shown in the diagram.

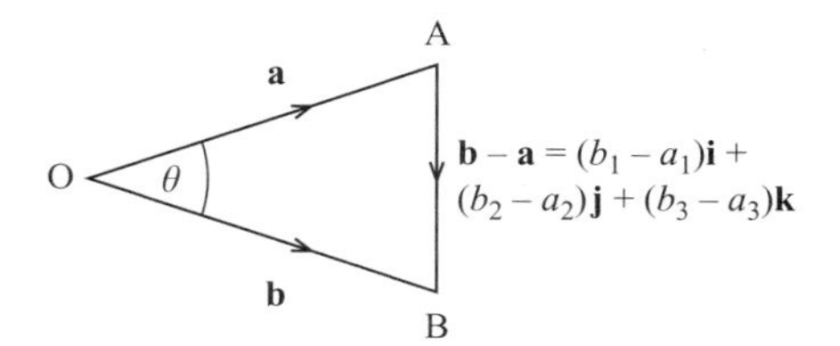

$$\cos\theta = \frac{OA^2 + OB^2 - AB^2}{2 \times OA \times OB}$$

$OA^2 = a_1^2 + a_2^2 + a_3^2$, $OB^2 = b_1^2 + b_2^2 + b_3^2$,

$AB^2 = (b_1 - a_1)^2 + (b_2 - a_2)^2 + (b_3 - a_3)^2$

$$\Rightarrow \quad \cos\theta = \frac{2(a_1b_1 + a_2b_2 + a_3b_3)}{2|\mathbf{a}||\mathbf{b}|}$$

$$= \frac{\mathbf{a}.\mathbf{b}}{|\mathbf{a}||\mathbf{b}|}$$

Exercise 11E (Page 311)

Note: Many of these answers are not unique.

1 **(i)** $\mathbf{r} = \begin{pmatrix} 2 \\ 4 \\ -1 \end{pmatrix} + \lambda\begin{pmatrix} 3 \\ 6 \\ 4 \end{pmatrix}$

(ii) $\mathbf{r} = \begin{pmatrix} 1 \\ 0 \\ -1 \end{pmatrix} + \lambda\begin{pmatrix} 1 \\ 0 \\ 0 \end{pmatrix}$

(iii) $\mathbf{r} = \begin{pmatrix} 1 \\ 0 \\ 4 \end{pmatrix} + \lambda\begin{pmatrix} 5 \\ 3 \\ -6 \end{pmatrix}$

(iv) $\mathbf{r} = \begin{pmatrix} 0 \\ 0 \\ 1 \end{pmatrix} + \lambda\begin{pmatrix} 2 \\ 1 \\ 3 \end{pmatrix}$

(v) $\mathbf{r} = \lambda\begin{pmatrix} 1 \\ 2 \\ 3 \end{pmatrix}$

2 **(i)** $\dfrac{x-2}{3} = \dfrac{y-4}{6} = \dfrac{z+1}{4}$

(ii) $x - 1 = \dfrac{y}{3} = \dfrac{z+1}{4}$

(iii) $x - 3 = \dfrac{z-4}{2}$ and $y = 0$

(iv) $\dfrac{x}{2} = \dfrac{z-1}{4}$ and $y = 4$

(v) $x = -2$ and $z = 3$

3 **(i)** $\mathbf{r} = \begin{pmatrix} 3 \\ -2 \\ 1 \end{pmatrix} + \lambda\begin{pmatrix} 5 \\ 3 \\ 4 \end{pmatrix}$

(ii) $\mathbf{r} = \begin{pmatrix} -6 \\ 0 \\ -4 \end{pmatrix} + \lambda\begin{pmatrix} 6 \\ 2 \\ 3 \end{pmatrix}$

(iii) $\mathbf{r} = \begin{pmatrix} 0 \\ 0 \\ -1 \end{pmatrix} + \lambda\begin{pmatrix} 1 \\ 2 \\ 3 \end{pmatrix}$

(iv) $\mathbf{r} = \lambda\begin{pmatrix} 1 \\ 1 \\ 1 \end{pmatrix}$

(v) $\mathbf{r} = \begin{pmatrix} 2 \\ 0 \\ 0 \end{pmatrix} + \lambda\begin{pmatrix} 0 \\ 1 \\ 1 \end{pmatrix}$

4 **(i)** 29.0°

(ii) 76.2°

(iii) 162.0°

5 **(i)** 53.6°

(ii) 81.8°

(iii) 8.7°

6 **(i)** (0, 4, 3)

(ii) $\begin{pmatrix} -5 \\ 4 \\ 3 \end{pmatrix}$, $\sqrt{50}$

(iii) $\mathbf{r} = \begin{pmatrix} 5 \\ 0 \\ 0 \end{pmatrix} + \lambda\begin{pmatrix} -5 \\ 4 \\ 3 \end{pmatrix}$

(iv) $\begin{pmatrix} 3\frac{3}{4} \\ 1 \\ \frac{3}{4} \end{pmatrix}$, 63.4°

(v) Spider is then at P(2.5, 2, 1.5) and $\overrightarrow{OP}.\overrightarrow{AG} = 0$, $|\overrightarrow{OP}| = 3.54$

7 **(i)** A(4, 0, 0), F(4, 0, 3)

(ii) 114.1°, 109.5°

(iii) They touch but are not perpendicular.

8 **(i)** $\begin{pmatrix} -0.25 \\ 0 \\ 0 \end{pmatrix}$

(ii) (0, 0.05, 1.1)

(iii) DE: $\mathbf{r} = \begin{pmatrix} 0 \\ 0 \\ 1 \end{pmatrix} + \lambda\begin{pmatrix} 1 \\ 0 \\ 0 \end{pmatrix}$

EF: $\mathbf{r} = \begin{pmatrix} 0.25 \\ 0 \\ 1 \end{pmatrix} + \lambda\begin{pmatrix} 0 \\ 1 \\ 2 \end{pmatrix}$

9 **(i)** (1, 0.5, 0)

(ii) 41.8°

(iii) 027°

(iv) (2, 2.5, 2)

(v) $t = 2$, $\sqrt{5}$ km

Answers

❓ (Page 315)

A three-legged stool is the more stable. Three points, such as the ends of the legs, define a plane but a fourth will not, in general, be in the same plane. So the ends of the legs of a three-legged stool lie in a plane but those of a four-legged stool need not. The four-legged stool will rest on three legs but could rock on to a different three.

❓ (Page 317)

(i) 90° with all lines.

(ii) No, so long as the pencil remains perpendicular to the table.

Activity 11.3 (Page 322)

Repeat the work in Example 11.22 replacing (7, 5, 3) by (α, β, γ), so 7 by α, 5 by β and 3 by γ; and (3, 2, 1) by (n_1, n_2, n_3) and 6 by $-d$.

Exercise 11F (Page 322)

1 **(i)** $\overrightarrow{AB} = \begin{pmatrix} -2 \\ -2 \\ -6 \end{pmatrix}$; $\overrightarrow{AC} = \begin{pmatrix} 1 \\ -2 \\ -1 \end{pmatrix}$

(ii) $\mathbf{r} = \begin{pmatrix} 0 \\ 1 \\ 1 \end{pmatrix} + \lambda\begin{pmatrix} -2 \\ -2 \\ -6 \end{pmatrix} + \mu\begin{pmatrix} 1 \\ -2 \\ -1 \end{pmatrix}$

(iv) The vector $\begin{pmatrix} 5 \\ 4 \\ -3 \end{pmatrix}$ is perpendicular to the plane ABC.

2 **(i)** $\overrightarrow{LM} = \begin{pmatrix} 2 \\ 2 \\ -2 \end{pmatrix}$; $\overrightarrow{LN} = \begin{pmatrix} 5 \\ 2 \\ -1 \end{pmatrix}$

(iii) $x - 4y - 3z = -2$

3 **(iii)** The plane is parallel to the yz plane and passes through (3, 0, 0).

4 **(iii)** B

5 **(iii)** Three points define a plane.

(iv) (1, 0, –1)

6 **(i)** (0, 1, 3)

(ii) (1, 1, 1)

(iii) (8, 4, 2)

(iv) (0, 0, 0)

(v) (11, 19, –10)

7 **(i)** **(a)** $\mathbf{r} = \begin{pmatrix} 2 \\ 2 \\ 3 \end{pmatrix} + \lambda\begin{pmatrix} 1 \\ -1 \\ 2 \end{pmatrix}$

(b) (1, 3, 1)

(c) $\sqrt{6}$

(ii) **(a)** $\mathbf{r} = \begin{pmatrix} 2 \\ 3 \\ 0 \end{pmatrix} + \lambda\begin{pmatrix} 2 \\ 5 \\ 3 \end{pmatrix}$

(b) (1, 0.5, –1.5)

(c) 3.08

(iii) **(a)** $\mathbf{r} = \begin{pmatrix} 3 \\ 1 \\ 3 \end{pmatrix} + \lambda\begin{pmatrix} 1 \\ 0 \\ 0 \end{pmatrix}$

(b) (0, 1, 3)

(c) 3

(iv) **(a)** $\mathbf{r} = \begin{pmatrix} 2 \\ 1 \\ 0 \end{pmatrix} + \lambda\begin{pmatrix} 3 \\ -4 \\ 1 \end{pmatrix}$

(b) (2, 1, 0): A is in the plane

(c) 0

(v) **(a)** $\mathbf{r} = \lambda\begin{pmatrix} 1 \\ 1 \\ 1 \end{pmatrix}$

(b) (2, 2, 2)

(c) $\sqrt{12}$

8 **(i)** $x + 2y + 3z = 25$

(ii) $206 = 150 + 56$

(iii) W is in the plane; $\overrightarrow{UW}.\overrightarrow{UV} = 0$

9 **(i)** $\mathbf{r} = \begin{pmatrix} 13 \\ 5 \\ 0 \end{pmatrix} + \lambda\begin{pmatrix} 3 \\ 1 \\ -2 \end{pmatrix}$

(ii) (4, 2, 6)

(iii) 11.2

10 **(ii)** $\overrightarrow{AB} = \begin{pmatrix} -1 \\ 2 \\ 1 \end{pmatrix}$; $\overrightarrow{AC} = \begin{pmatrix} 8 \\ -4 \\ 1 \end{pmatrix}$; in both cases the scalar product = 0

(iii) 132.9°

(iv) 8.08

11 **(i)** **(a)** 5

(b) $\sqrt{89}$

(ii) 62.2°

(iii) 20.9

(iv) (4, 6, –3)

12 **(i)** PQ: $\mathbf{r} = \begin{pmatrix} 2 \\ 2 \\ 4 \end{pmatrix} + \lambda \begin{pmatrix} -1 \\ 2 \\ 2 \end{pmatrix}$; XY: $\mathbf{r} = \begin{pmatrix} -2 \\ -2 \\ -3 \end{pmatrix} + \mu \begin{pmatrix} 1 \\ 2 \\ 3 \end{pmatrix}$

(iii) Yes

(iv) Yes, (1, 4, 6)

13 **(i)** $\mathbf{r} = \begin{pmatrix} 4 \\ 1 \\ 3 \end{pmatrix} + \lambda \begin{pmatrix} 2 \\ 3 \\ 5 \end{pmatrix}$

(ii) (0, –5, –7)

(iii) Q: (3, –1, 4) A_1: (2, –3, 5)

(iv) Both 78.5° (3 s.f.)

14 **(ii)** $\begin{pmatrix} 2 \\ -1 \\ 3 \end{pmatrix}$

(iii) (10, –5, 15)

(iv) OA: $\mathbf{r} = \lambda \begin{pmatrix} 5 \\ -12 \\ 16 \end{pmatrix}$; AB: $\mathbf{r} = \begin{pmatrix} 5 \\ -12 \\ 16 \end{pmatrix} + \mu \begin{pmatrix} 1 \\ 5 \\ 1 \end{pmatrix}$

(v) 69°

15 **(i)** $\mathbf{r} = \begin{pmatrix} 8 \\ 0 \\ -4 \end{pmatrix} + \lambda \begin{pmatrix} 2 \\ 1 \\ -1 \end{pmatrix}$

(ii) (2, –3, –1)

(iii) $\sqrt{150}$

(iv) 3 : 2

(v) 8.48° (2 d.p.)

16 **(i)** $\mathbf{r} = \begin{pmatrix} 2 \\ 0 \\ 15 \end{pmatrix} + \lambda \begin{pmatrix} 4 \\ 3 \\ -2 \end{pmatrix}$

(ii) $\begin{pmatrix} -1 + 4\lambda \\ 1 + 3\lambda \\ 14 - 2\lambda \end{pmatrix}$, (6, 3, 13)

(iii) 13

(iv) 1 : 2

17 **(i)** $\begin{pmatrix} 2 \\ -3 \\ 4 \end{pmatrix}$

(ii) $\mathbf{r} = \begin{pmatrix} 3 \\ -8 \\ 12 \end{pmatrix} + \lambda \begin{pmatrix} 2 \\ -3 \\ 4 \end{pmatrix}$; (–1, –2, 4)

(iii) (0, –3.5, 6)

(iv) 15.6° (1 d.p.)

18 **(i)** $\mathbf{r} = (2\mathbf{i} + 3\mathbf{j} + 5\mathbf{k}) + \lambda(3\mathbf{i} + \mathbf{j} - 2\mathbf{k})$

(ii) $\lambda = 1$; (5, 4, 3)

(iii) (9.5, 5.5, 0)

(iv) (6.5, 4.5, 2); 1.87 (3 s.f.)

(v) $\mathbf{i} + 2\mathbf{j} = 3\mathbf{k}$; 38.2° (1 d.p.)

19 **(i)** $2x - 3y + 7z = -5$

(ii) $\mathbf{r} = (130\mathbf{i} - 40\mathbf{j} + 20\mathbf{k}) + \lambda(8\mathbf{i} - 4\mathbf{j} + \mathbf{k})$

(iii) $10\mathbf{i} + 20\mathbf{j} + 5\mathbf{k}$

(iv) 135 m

20 **(i)** $\begin{pmatrix} a \\ b \\ 1 \end{pmatrix}$

(ii) $\overrightarrow{AB} = \begin{pmatrix} 2 \\ -3 \\ 0 \end{pmatrix}$; $\overrightarrow{AC} = \begin{pmatrix} 3 \\ -5 \\ 1 \end{pmatrix}$

(iii) $2a - 3b = 0$; $3a - 5b + 1 = 0$

(iv) $3x + 2y + z = 6$

(v) 36.7° (1 d.p.)

(vi) $(3\frac{2}{3}, -3\frac{2}{3}, 2\frac{1}{3})$

21 **(i)** $\overrightarrow{AB} = 14\mathbf{i} + 2\mathbf{j} + 5\mathbf{k}$; $\overrightarrow{AD} = -5\mathbf{i} + 10\mathbf{j} + 10\mathbf{k}$; (13, 14, 18)

(iii) $\lambda = \frac{1}{3}$, $\mu = \frac{2}{15}$. It contains the origin.

(iv) $2x + 11y - 10z = 0$

22 **(i)** (6, 4.5, 3)

(iii) $x - 2z = 0$

(iv) AOBC: $\begin{pmatrix} 0 \\ 2 \\ -3 \end{pmatrix}$; DOBE: $\begin{pmatrix} 1 \\ 0 \\ -2 \end{pmatrix}$; 41.9° (1 d.p.); 138.1°

23 **(i)** $\mathbf{r} = \begin{pmatrix} 2 \\ 3 \\ 5 \end{pmatrix} + \lambda \begin{pmatrix} 1 \\ 1 \\ -0.5 \end{pmatrix}$

(ii) (12, 13, 0)

(iii) 109.5° (1 d.p.)

(iv) 25 m

24 **(i)** $\mathbf{r} = \begin{pmatrix} 2 \\ -1 \\ 3 \end{pmatrix} + t \begin{pmatrix} -1 \\ 1 \\ 2 \end{pmatrix}$; (4, –3, –1)

(ii) $5x + 2y + z - 15 = 0$

(iv) 21°

25 **(i)** (3, 1, 0)

(ii) 63.4°

(iv) $\mathbf{r} = \begin{pmatrix} 1 \\ 1 \\ 1 \end{pmatrix} + \lambda \begin{pmatrix} 1 \\ 2 \\ 2 \end{pmatrix}$

(v) $\left(\frac{5}{3}, \frac{7}{3}, \frac{7}{3}\right)$ or $\left(\frac{1}{3}, -\frac{1}{3}, -\frac{1}{3}\right)$

26 **(i)** $\sqrt{26}$

(iii) $x + 4y + z = 12$

(iv) $\mathbf{r} = (\mathbf{i} + \mathbf{j} - 2\mathbf{k}) + \lambda(\mathbf{i} + 4\mathbf{j} + \mathbf{k})$; (1.5, 3, –1.5)

(v) 65.4°

27 **(i)** $\begin{pmatrix}-1\\-1\\-3\end{pmatrix}$; $\begin{pmatrix}-3\\-1\\-2\end{pmatrix}$; 36.3°

(ii) $x - y + 2z = 2$

(iii) $\mathbf{r} = \begin{pmatrix}3\\1\\3\end{pmatrix} + \lambda\begin{pmatrix}1\\-1\\2\end{pmatrix}$; (2, 2, 1), $\sqrt{6}$

28 **(ii)** $\lambda = \frac{1}{2}$, $\mu = -\frac{1}{2}$; They are coplanar.

(iii) $x - y + z = 4$

(iv) 79.1°

29 **(i)** $\sqrt{37}$ m

(ii) $12x - y + 6z = 6$

(iii) 126.2°, 53.8°

(iv) (1.30, 3.25, 0)

30 **(i)** A(–50, –50, 0); B(50, –50, 0); C(50, 50, 0); D(–50, 50, 0); E(0, 0, 100)

(ii) ECD: $2y + z = 100$; EDA: $-2x + z = 100$; EAB: $-2y + z = 100$

(iii) $\mathbf{r} = \begin{pmatrix}0\\0\\20\end{pmatrix} + \lambda\begin{pmatrix}2\\0\\1\end{pmatrix}$, 35.8 m

Investigation (Page 332)

You should see two interlocking hoops.

The two points should be at (–1.6, 2.4) and (3.2, 2.4).

Chapter 12

Exercise 12A (Page 339)

1 $\frac{dv}{dt}$ is the rate of change of velocity with respect to time, i.e. the acceleration.

The differential equation tells you that the acceleration is proportional to the square of the velocity.

2 $\frac{ds}{dt} = \frac{k}{s^2}$

3 $\frac{dh}{dt} = k\ln(H - h)$

4 $\frac{dm}{dt} = \frac{k}{m}$

5 $\frac{dP}{dt} = k\sqrt{P}$

6 $\frac{de}{d\theta} = k\theta$

7 $\frac{d\theta}{dt} = -\frac{(\theta - 15)}{160}$

8 $\frac{dN}{dt} = \frac{N}{20}$

9 $\frac{dv}{dt} = \frac{4}{\sqrt{v}}$

10 $\frac{dA}{dt} = \frac{2k\sqrt{\pi}}{\sqrt{A}} = \frac{k'}{\sqrt{A}}$

11 $\frac{d\theta}{ds} = -\frac{s}{4}$

12 $\frac{dh}{dt} = -\frac{1}{8\pi h^2}$

13 $\frac{dV}{dt} = -\frac{2V}{1125\pi}$

14 $\frac{dh}{dt} = \frac{(2 - k\sqrt{h})}{100}$

Investigation (Page 341)

H is about (70° N, 35° W) and L is about (62° N, 5° W) so they are separated by 30° in longitude at a mean latitude of 66°. Reference to the scale shows this to be about 900 nautical miles.

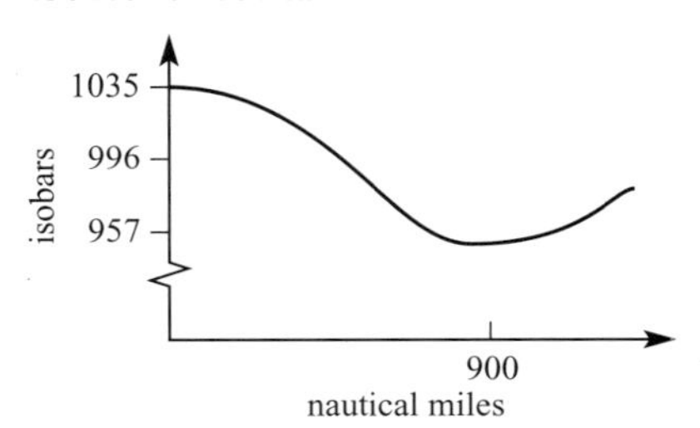

The mean level is 996 and the amplitude 39 so a model is

$$p = 996 + 39\cos\left(\frac{\pi x}{900}\right) \text{ and}$$

$$\frac{dp}{dx} = \frac{-39\pi}{900}\sin\left(\frac{\pi x}{900}\right)$$

or $\frac{dp}{dx} = -a\sin bx$ with $a = 0.136$ and $b = 0.0035$.

? (Page 343)

$\ln|y| + c_1 = \frac{1}{2}x^2 + c_2$ can be rewritten as

$\ln|y| = \frac{1}{2}x^2 + (c_2 - c_1)$.

Exercise 12B (Page 344)

1 **(i)** $y = \frac{1}{3}x^3 + c$

(ii) $y = \sin x + c$

(iii) $y = e^x + c$

(iv) $y = \frac{2}{3}x^{\frac{3}{2}} + c$

2 **(i)** $y = -\dfrac{2}{(x^2 + c)}$

(ii) $y^2 = \frac{2}{3}x^3 + c$

(iii) $y = Ae^x$

(iv) $y = \ln|e^x + c|$

(v) $y = Ax$

(vi) $y = (\frac{1}{4}x^2 + c)^2$

(vii) $y = -\dfrac{1}{(\sin x + c)}$

(viii) $y^2 = A(x^2 + 1) - 1$

(ix) $y = -\ln(c - \frac{1}{2}x^2)$

(x) $y^3 = \frac{3}{2}x^2 \ln x - \frac{3}{4}x^2 + c$

Exercise 12C (Page 348)

1 **(i)** $y = \frac{1}{3}x^3 - x - 4$

(ii) $y = e^{x^3/3}$

(iii) $y = \ln(\frac{1}{2}x^2 + 1)$

(iv) $y = \dfrac{1}{(2 - x)}$

(v) $y = e^{(x^2-1)/2} - 1$

(vi) $y = \sec x$

2 **(i)** $\theta = 20 - Ae^{-2t}$

(ii) $\theta = 20 - 15e^{-2t}$

(iii) $t = 1.01$ hours

3 **(i)** $N = Ae^t$

(ii) $N = 10e^t$

(iii) N tends to ∞, which would never be realised because of the combined effects of food shortage, predators and human controls.

4 $\dfrac{ds}{dt} = \dfrac{2}{s}$; $s = \sqrt{4t + c}$

5 **(i)** $\dfrac{1}{3y} + \dfrac{1}{3(3 - y)}$

(ii) $\frac{1}{3}\ln\left|\dfrac{y}{3 - y}\right| + c$ or $\frac{1}{3}\ln\left|\dfrac{Ay}{3 - y}\right|$

(iii) $y = \dfrac{3x^3}{(4 + x^3)}$

6 $y = 2 + e^{-kt}$

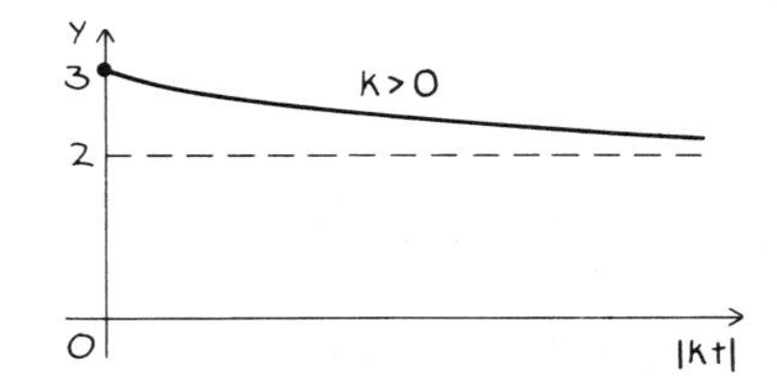

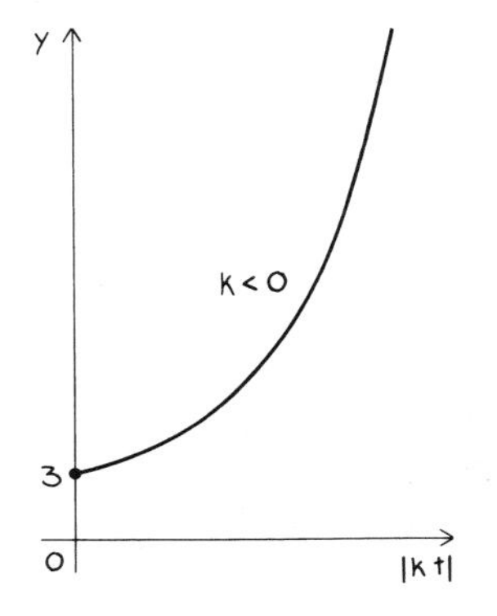

7 **(i)** $N = 1500e^{0.0347t} = 1500 \times 2^{t/20}$

(ii) $N = 24\,000$

(iii) 11 hours 42 minutes

8 **(ii)** $\dfrac{1}{x - 1} - \dfrac{1}{x + 1}$

(iii) $y = \dfrac{(x + 1)}{2(x - 1)} e^{3-x}$

10 $\dfrac{dx}{dt} = \dfrac{(2 - 3x)}{100}$, $x = \frac{1}{3}(2 - 2e^{-3t/100})$,

time taken = 40.8 seconds

11 **(i)** $P = 600e^{kt}$

(iii) $P = 600e^{(0.005t - 0.4\sin(0.02t))}$; very good fit

(iv) 549

12 **(i)** $\dfrac{dr}{dt} = \dfrac{k}{r^2}$

(ii) $k = 5000$; 141 m (3 s.f.)

(iii) $\dfrac{dr}{dt} = \dfrac{k_1}{r^2(2 + t)}$; $k_1 = 10\,000$

(iv) 104 m (3 s.f.)

13 **(i)** $\dfrac{1}{3(2 - x)} + \dfrac{1}{3(1 + x)}$

(ii) $\frac{1}{3}$

(iv) 1.18 hours (2 d.p.)

(v) 0.728 kg

14 **(i)** $2x\sin 2x + \cos 2x + c$

(iii) $y^2 = 4x^2 + 4x\sin 2x + 2\cos 2x + 1$

15 (i) $y^2 = 4x$

(ii) $\frac{dy}{dx} = \frac{1}{t}$

(iv) $y^2 = -2x^2 + c$; $y^2 + 2x^2 = 4$

(v)

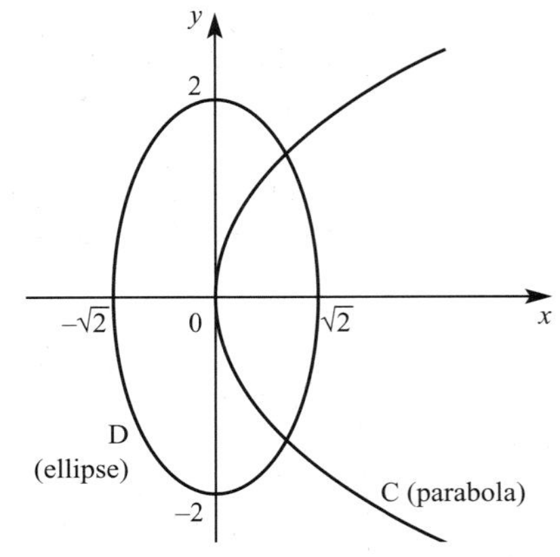

16 (i) $\frac{3}{(3x-1)} - \frac{1}{x}$

(iii) $t = 1.967$ (3 d.p.)

(iv) 500 and 3550

17 (ii) $\cot x$; $\ln(\sin x) + c$

(iii) $y = 0.185$ (3 s.f.); minimum

18 (i) $b = 25$, $a = 0.2$

(ii) (a) 20

(b) 60, $\frac{1}{2}\ln 2$

(iii) $f(t) = \cos t$, $c = 1000$

19 (ii) $\frac{\sin\theta - 2\cos\theta}{2\sin\theta + \cos\theta}$

(iii) $\frac{y^2}{2} + y = -\frac{x^2}{2} + 2x$; a circle with centre $(2, -1)$, radius $\sqrt{5}$

(iv) $\sqrt{5}\cos(\theta + \arctan\frac{1}{2})$

20 (i) (a) 0.215

(b) It predicts that $P \to \infty$.

(ii) (a) $\frac{2}{P} + \frac{2}{2-P}$

(c) $\frac{2e^{\frac{t}{2}}}{1 + e^{\frac{t}{2}}}$

(d) Population $\to$ 2 million.

21 (i) $\frac{1}{1+x} - \frac{x}{1+x^2}$

(iii) $1 - \frac{x^2}{2} + \frac{3x^4}{8}$; $1 + x - \frac{x^2}{2} - \frac{x^3}{2} + \frac{3x^4}{8} + \frac{3x^5}{8}$

22 (i) (a) $\frac{dh}{ds} = ks$, $h = \frac{1}{2}ks^2$

(b)

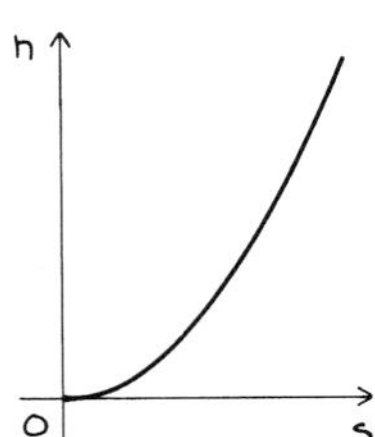

(c) Unrealistic as wave height increases without limit, ever faster

(ii) (a) $\frac{dh}{ds} = \frac{k}{s+5}$, $h = k\ln\left(\frac{s+5}{5}\right)$

(b)

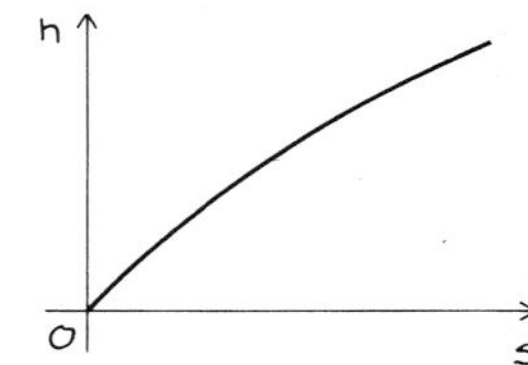

(c) More realistic but still no limit to wave height

(iii) (a) $\frac{dh}{ds} = ke^{-cs}$, $h = A(1 - e^{-cs})$

(b)

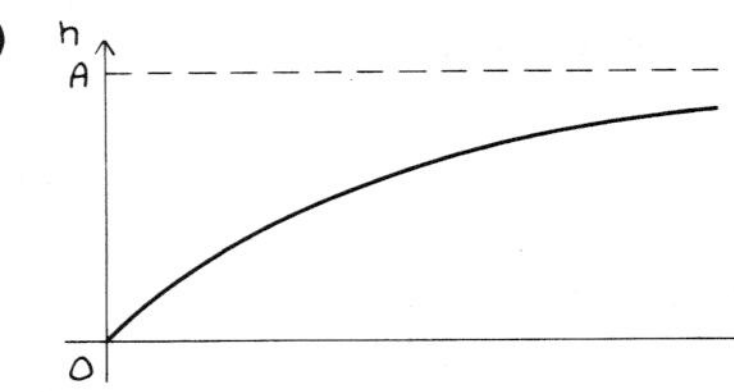

(c) The most realistic

Investigation (Page 357)

Using the assumptions in Exercise 12A, question 7: the rate of cooling is proportional to the temperature of the tea above the surrounding air. The initial temperature is 95°C and the cooling rate is 0.5°Cs^{-1}. So

$$\theta = 15 + 80e^{-t/160}.$$

Adding 10% milk at 5°C gives

$$\theta = 15 + 71e^{-t/160}.$$

The final temperature is lower if the milk is added at the end.